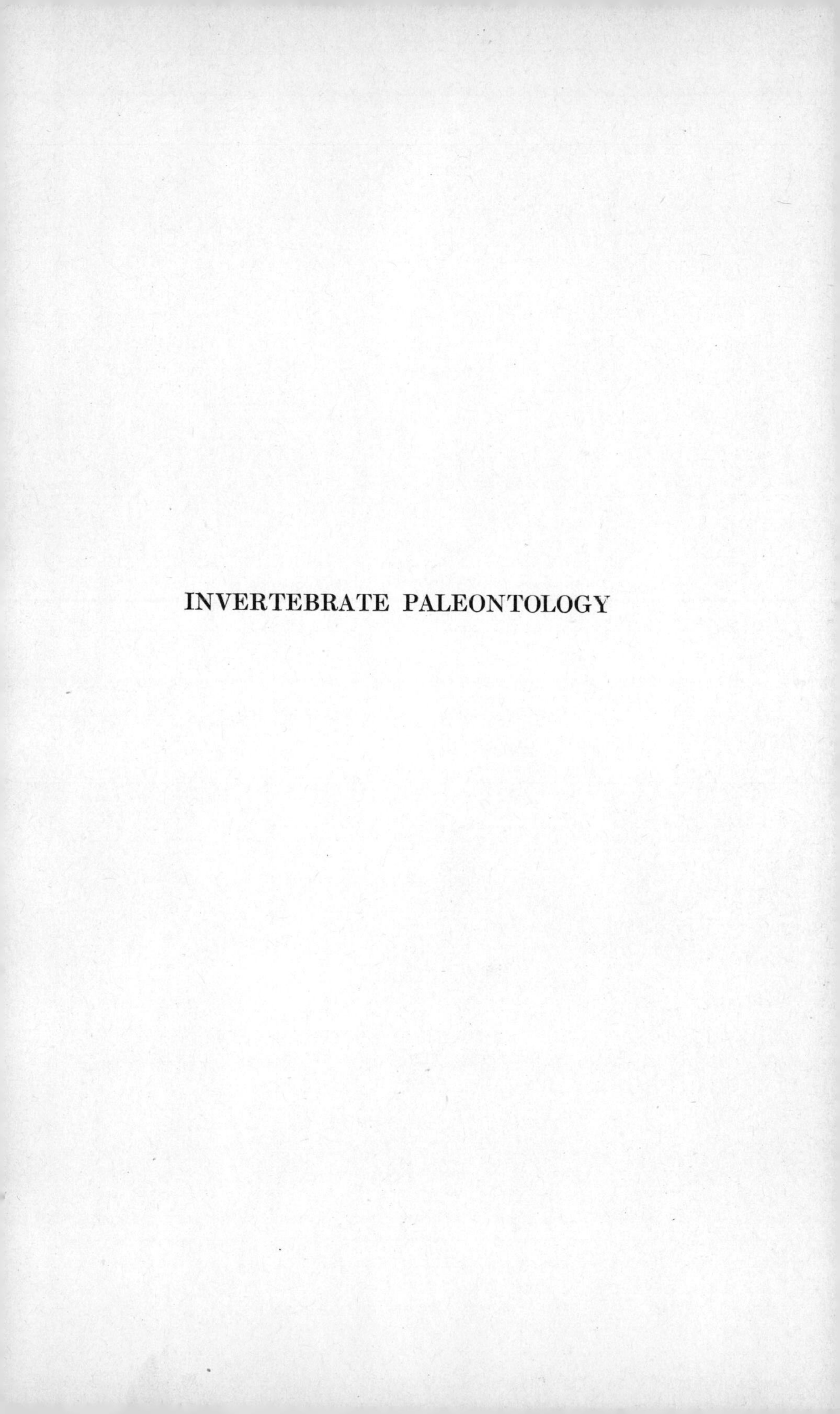

INVERTEBRATE PALEONTOLOGY

INVERTEBRATE PALEONTOLOGY

BY

WILLIAM H. TWENHOFEL

Professor of Geology and Paleontology
University of Wisconsin

AND

ROBERT R. SHROCK

Assistant Professor of Geology
Massachusetts Institute of Technology

First Edition
Third Impression

McGRAW-HILL BOOK COMPANY, Inc.
NEW YORK AND LONDON
1935

PRINTED IN THE UNITED STATES OF AMERICA

THE MAPLE PRESS COMPANY, YORK, PA.

PREFACE

Paleontology deals with the life of the past. That life is now represented by fossils, which are mainly the preserved hard or skeletal parts of the original organisms. Any serious study of paleontology should be accompanied by careful study of the relations existing between the skeletal parts and soft tissues of living organisms so that restoration and interpretation of the fleshy parts of extinct organisms may be made from their skeletal remains. The present environmental organic relations, frequently extremely involved, should likewise be studied so that some understanding of the environmental relations among the fossil organisms themselves and between them and their physical environment may be acquired.

Approaching the study of fossils from these points of view, they are no longer mere lifeless stones but become entities of a one-time living world; they represent adaptations to and products of the environments in which they and their ancestors lived; they appear as living organisms in harmony with, but also in competition with, their plant and animal associates; and finally they evolve, in which evolution they take their proper place in the intricately interwoven fabric of organic development and become at the same time beacons along the road of geologic time, marking off successive stages in earth history.

With these various aspects in mind, and always with a studied effort to adapt the subject matter to the needs of the beginning student, the authors have attempted to treat each invertebrate phylum with about the same completeness, irrespective of the importance of the phylum at the present time, the importance and abundance of the fossil remains, or the extent to which either fossil or living representatives have been studied.

In a general way the discussion of successive phyla follows the same outline, but there are some exceptions where deviation seems to be warranted. The introductory part of the chapter sets forth the salient features of the phylum as a primary subdivision of the animal kingdom and attempts a general description of the phylum as a whole. Since, in any discussion of fossil organisms, it is of paramount importance to know the relations of preservable hard parts to the fleshy parts of the organism, typical representatives of each phylum are treated fully from this zoological point of view. This part of the chapter is followed by a detailed consideration of the composition, extent, architecture, and structure of the hard parts capable of preservation. A discussion of classification is next in order. Subdivisions down to or below orders in rank are described, illustrated, and traced in geologic history. Present environmental relations are next compared with those of the past, and finally a short discussion is devoted to the geologic history and stratigraphic importance of the several subdivisions of the phylum. After much consideration it seemed best to limit the bibliography to only a very few of the more recent and significant works, and to avoid as much as possible introducing references in the body of the text. Since the text is written for the American student of paleontology, it naturally follows that the majority of references, as well as illustrations, are of American origin.

No attempt has been made to limit the use of technical terms, but these are almost always defined the first time they appear. The index will indicate the page or pages on which the term is defined or described and, if illustrated, the page on which the illustration appears. The student of fossil invertebrates must ultimately acquire a technical vocabulary, for precise definitions and accurate descriptions are impossible without it, and little or nothing is gained by postponing its acquisition or avoiding its use.

The text was prepared jointly without any definite division of labor, hence we assume responsibility both jointly and severally. The illustrations were prepared by the junior author. The senior author assisted in and approved the selection of the materials to be illustrated and accepts responsibility for them. The illustrations are designed to show certain definite structures and features rather than to illustrate an entire specimen. In some instances it seemed advisable to sacrifice absolute accuracy for clarity and effectiveness; hence this fact should be considered in studying the numerous drawings.

Parts or all of Figs. 62, 72, 75, 114, 116–117, 126–128, 131–132, 137, 145, 159–161, 165 and 168–169 were prepared under the junior author's supervision by Miss Carol Haugh, whose assistance is hereby gratefully acknowledged. The authors are further deeply indebted to the following authors and publishers for kind permission to reproduce certain illustrations: Blackwood and Sons for numerous figures from "Manual of Paleontology" by Nicholson and Lydekker; Macmillan & Company, Ltd., for illustrations from "Text-book of Zoology" by Parker and Haswell; D. Appleton-Century Company for several figures from "Outlines of Zoology" by Thomson; A. & C. Black, Ltd., for certain illustrations from "A Treatise on Zoology" by Lankester and collaborators; and McGraw-Hill Book Company, Inc., for three figures from "Paleontology" by Berry. Many figures have been taken from American and English periodicals and geological reports for which acknowledgments to the authors are made in appropriate connections. Finally, parts of the manuscript were read by Mr. E. F. Bean, State Geologist of Wisconsin, whose criticism and suggestions are hereby acknowledged.

W. H. Twenhofel.
R. R. Shrock.

Madison, Wisconsin,
October, 1935.

CONTENTS

	Page
Preface	v

CHAPTER I

Introduction	1
Definition of Paleontology	1
The Organic World	2
The Animal Kingdom	5
Classification of Animals	7
Habitats and Habits of Animals	10
Definition of Fossil	13
Nature of Fossil Record	15
Unaltered Remains	15
Altered Remains	15
Impressions (Molds) and Casts	18
Burrows, Borings, and Tubes	19
Coprolites or Castings	19
Miscellaneous Markings	20
Uses of Fossils	20
Use of Fossils for Correlation	22
Fossils as Indices of Ancient Geography	23
Fossils as Indices of Ancient Climates	23
Fossils as Evidence of Evolution	23
The Geologic Time Scale	26

CHAPTER II

Protozoa	27
Introduction	27
Class Mastigophora (Flagellata)	32
Class Sarcodina	34
Foraminifera	35
Nature of the Organism	35
Relation of Organism to Test	37
The Foraminiferal Test	38
Classification of Foraminifera	45
Ecology of Foraminifera	45
Geologic History	46
Amoebaea	47
Testacea (Thecamoeba)	47
Heliozoa	48
Radiolaria	48

PAGE
Class Sporozoa 50
Class Infusoria 50
References 50

CHAPTER III

PORIFERA 52
Introduction 52
Character of the Animal 52
Shape of Animal 53
The Body Wall 53
The Canal System 55
Reproduction 56
The Skeleton 56
General Skeletal Structure 57
Fossilization of Skeletal Material 58
Form and Character of Spicules and Skeleton 58
Classification 61
Class Calcarea 61
Class Hexactinellida 65
Class Desmospongia 65
Forms of Unknown Affinities 66
Ecology 68
Geologic History 69
References 70

CHAPTER IV

COELENTERATA 72
Introduction 72
The Organism 73
The Polyp 73
The Medusa 75
Reproduction 76
The Exoskeleton 77
Development of the Exoskeleton 78
Classification 79
Class Hydrozoa 80
The Organism 80
Habitat and Geologic History 81
Classification 81
Group Stromatoporoidea 83
Character of the Exoskeleton 84
Geologic History 85
Group Graptozoa 87
The Exoskeleton 87
Habitat 89
Geologic History 89
Biologic Affinities 90

PAGE
Classification . . . 90
Order Dendroidea . . . 90
Order Graptoloidea . . . 92
Axonolipa . . . 92
Axonophora . . . 92
Class Scyphozoa . . . 94
Class Anthozoa (Actinozoa) . . . 95
The Organism . . . 95
Relation of the Animal and Skeleton . . . 97
Reproduction and Ontogeny . . . 99
Habitat . . . 100
Classification . . . 100
Subclass Tetracoralla (Rugosa) . . . 100
Subclass Hexacoralla . . . 108
Order Madreporaria . . . 109
Order Antipitharia . . . 112
Subclass Alcyonaria (Octocoralla) . . . 112
Subclass Tabulata . . . 116
Class Ctenophora . . . 121
Appendix to the Coelenterata . . . 122
Archaeocyathinae . . . 122
Evolution of the Coelenterata . . . 124
Coelenterata as Rock Builders . . . 125
References . . . 127

CHAPTER V

WORMS . . . 129
Introduction . . . 129
The Organism . . . 129
Character of the Fossil Record . . . 131
Classification . . . 137
Phylum Platyhelminthes . . . 139
Phylum Nemathelminthes . . . 139
Phylum Trochelminthes . . . 140
Phylum Annelida (Annulata) . . . 141
Class Chaetopoda . . . 142
Subclass Polychaeta . . . 142
Order Phanerocephala (Errantia) . . . 143
Order Cryptocephala (Sedentaria, Tubicola) . . . 143
Order Miskoa . . . 144
Subclass Oligochaeta . . . 145
Subclass Myzostomida . . . 145
Subclass Echiurida . . . 145
Class Sipunculoidea (Gephyrea) . . . 146
Class Archiannelida . . . 146
Class Hirudinea (Leeches) . . . 146
Geologic History of the Worms . . . 146
Geologic Work of the Worms . . . 147

PAGE

CHAPTER VI

ECHINODERMA . . . 149
Introduction . . . 149
The Animal and its Habits . . . 150
General Considerations . . . 150
Symmetry of the Body . . . 150
The Water-vascular System . . . 151
Ambulacra and Food Grooves . . . 151
Attachment . . . 153
Habitat and Habits . . . 153
Ancestry . . . 155
The Test . . . 155
Stratigraphic Range . . . 157
Classification . . . 157
Subphylum Pelmatozoa . . . 158
Class Cystoidea . . . 159
The Calyx . . . 160
Ambulacral Areas and Arms . . . 161
Attachment . . . 163
Classification . . . 163
Order Amphoridea . . . 164
Order Rhombifera . . . 164
Order Diploporita . . . 165
Order Aporita . . . 165
Class Edrioasteroidea . . . 166
Class Blastoidea . . . 167
The Calyx . . . 168
The Ambulacra . . . 168
Brachioles and Stem . . . 171
Geologic History . . . 171
Classification . . . 172
Class Crinoidea . . . 172
General Considerations . . . 172
The Animal . . . 173
The Skeleton . . . 176
Evolution and Ontogeny . . . 180
Stratigraphic Range . . . 182
Classification . . . 184
Order Camerata . . . 185
Order Flexibilia . . . 185
Order Inadunata . . . 185
Order Articulata . . . 188
Subphylum Eleutherozoa . . . 188
Class Stelleroidea . . . 190
Classification . . . 191
Subclass Asteroidea . . . 192
Subclass Auluroidea . . . 193
Subclass Ophiuroidea . . . 194

PAGE
Class Echinoidea 197
General Considerations 197
The Animal 197
The Test 198
Ontogeny 206
Ecology 206
Stratigraphic Range 206
Classification 208
Order Bothriocidaroida 208
Order Cidaroida 208
Order Centrechinoida 209
Order Exocycloida 209
Order Plesiocidaroida 209
Order Echinocystoida 211
Order Perischoechinoida 211
Class Holothuroidea 213
Phylogeny of the Echinoderma 215
Echinoderma as Geologic Agents 217
References 219

CHAPTER VII

BRYOZOA 220
Introduction 220
The Animal 223
The Skeleton 224
Classification 229
Order Ctenostomata 230
Order Cyclostomata 231
Order Trepostomata 235
Order Cryptostomata 239
Order Cheilostomata 243
Geologic Importance and Ecology 245
Evolution of the Bryozoa 247
Geologic History 247
References 249

CHAPTER VIII

BRACHIOPODA 250
Introduction 250
The Animal 252
Relation of Animal to Shell 252
The Visceral Cavity 254
The Muscular System 255
The Brachial Cavity 258
Attachment 259
The Shell 261
General Considerations 261
Shape and Size of Shell 263

PAGE
Composition and Structure of Shell Material . . . 265
Surface Characteristics . . . 267
Structures on the Cardinal Margin . . . 271
The Pedicle Opening . . . 274
Internal Skeletal Structures . . . 276
Brachial Supports . . . 277
Pallial Markings . . . 280
Muscles and Muscle Scars . . . 280
Classification . . . 281
Order Palaeotremata . . . 284
Order Atremata . . . 284
Order Neotremata . . . 286
Order Protremata . . . 287
Order Telotremata . . . 292
Ontogeny and Evolution . . . 295
Ecology . . . 296
Geologic History . . . 297
Nature of Fossils . . . 299
References . . . 299

CHAPTER IX

MOLLUSCA . . . 301
General Considerations . . . 301
The Animal . . . 301
The Shell . . . 304
Classification . . . 304
Class Amphineura . . . 306
Class Pelecypoda (Lamellibranchia) . . . 309
General Considerations . . . 309
The Animal . . . 310
The Shell . . . 318
Classification . . . 330
Order Prionodesmacea . . . 333
Order Anomalodesmacea . . . 333
Order Teleodesmacea . . . 334
Geologic History . . . 334
Class Gastropoda . . . 341
General Considerations . . . 341
The Animal . . . 342
The Shell . . . 345
Classification . . . 350
Subclass Streptoneura . . . 351
Order Aspidobranchia . . . 351
Order Ctenobranchia . . . 351
Subclass Euthyneura . . . 355
Order Opisthobranchia . . . 355
Order Pulmonata . . . 355
Geologic History . . . 357

	Page
Class Scaphopoda	360
Class Cephalopoda	363
General Considerations	363
The Animal	364
The Shell	365
Classification	382
Subclass Nautiloidea	382
The Living Nautilus	383
Order Holochoanites	385
Order Mixochoanites	385
Order Schistochoanites	385
Order Orthochoanites	386
Order Cyrtochoanites	386
Subclass Ammonoidea	386
Order Intrasiphonata	388
Order Extrasiphonata	388
Subclass Coleoidea (Dibranchia)	388
Order Belemnoidea	388
Order Sepioidea	389
Order Octopoda	391
Geologic History	391
Geologic History of the Mollusca	400
Evolution of the Phylum	400
Ecology	401
Stratigraphic Range	403
References	404

CHAPTER X

ARTHROPODA	406
Introduction	406
The Animal and Its Exoskeleton	407
Classification	409
Class Crustacea	410
The Animal	410
The Exoskeleton	412
Subclass Trilobita	413
General Considerations	413
The Exoskeleton	414
Classification	423
Order Opisthoparia	426
Order Proparia	426
Ecology	429
Stratigraphic Range	431
Nature of the Fossil Record	432
Subclass Branchiopoda	433
General Considerations	433
Classification	433
Order Anostraca	434

PAGE
Order Notostraca . . . 435
Order Conchostraca . . . 435
Order Cladocera . . . 436
Subclass Ostracoda . . . 436
General Considerations . . . 436
The Carapace or Shell . . . 437
Stratigraphic Range . . . 439
Subclass Copepoda . . . 440
Subclass Cirripedia . . . 440
General Considerations . . . 440
Geologic History . . . 441
Subclass Malacostraca . . . 443
General Considerations . . . 443
Geologic History and Classification . . . 443
Class Onychophora . . . 446
General Considerations . . . 446
Classification . . . 447
Class Myriapoda . . . 447
General Considerations . . . 447
Classification . . . 448
Class Insecta . . . 449
General Considerations . . . 449
Classification . . . 452
Geologic History . . . 456
Class Arachnida . . . 459
General Considerations . . . 459
The Exoskeleton . . . 460
Classification . . . 462
Subclass Merostomata . . . 462
General Considerations . . . 462
Order Xiphosura . . . 463
Order Synxiphosura . . . 465
Order Eurypterida . . . 466
Order Limulava . . . 469
Subclass Embolobranchiata . . . 469
General Considerations . . . 469
Geologic History of the Arthropoda . . . 471
Evolution . . . 471
Ecology . . . 474
Stratigraphic Range . . . 475
Nature of the Fossil Record . . . 476
References . . . 477

INDEX . . . 479

INVERTEBRATE PALEONTOLOGY

CHAPTER I

INTRODUCTION

DEFINITION OF PALEONTOLOGY

Paleontology may be defined as the science which deals with the life of past geological ages, as shown by the fossilized remains of ancient plants and animals. *Biology*, the science which deals with life, is divisible into *botany*, the science of plants, and *zoology*, the science of animals. Paleontology, a subdivision of biology, may be divided into *paleobotany*, treating of fossil plants, and *paleozoology*, treating of fossil animals. Among students of the latter science, however, it has long been general practice to employ the term paleontology, instead of paleozoology, for the science of fossil animals; hence the title of the present work—"Invertebrate Paleontology," or that branch of paleontology which deals with fossil invertebrates.

Major J. W. Powell, the second director of the U. S. Geological Survey, clearly outlined the scope of paleontology as follows:

> Paleontology, the science of fossils, is the geologist's clock, by which he determines the times in earth history when the beds containing the fossils were deposited. Geological time is divided into periods which are characterized by the existence of certain plants and animals. Without paleontology the geologic classification of formations, their correlation, and the determination of their mutual relations would be impossible. In fact, real and symmetrical progress in geology would be impossible without corresponding interrelated development and refinement in its handmaid, paleontology. The study of the economic geology of any region of complicated structure is blind and inconsequent unless the time relations are known. These relations are indicated by the fossils which the strata contain.

THE ORGANIC WORLD

The *organic world* comprises all living things and has two large subdivisions—the *animal kingdom* and the *plant kingdom*. The

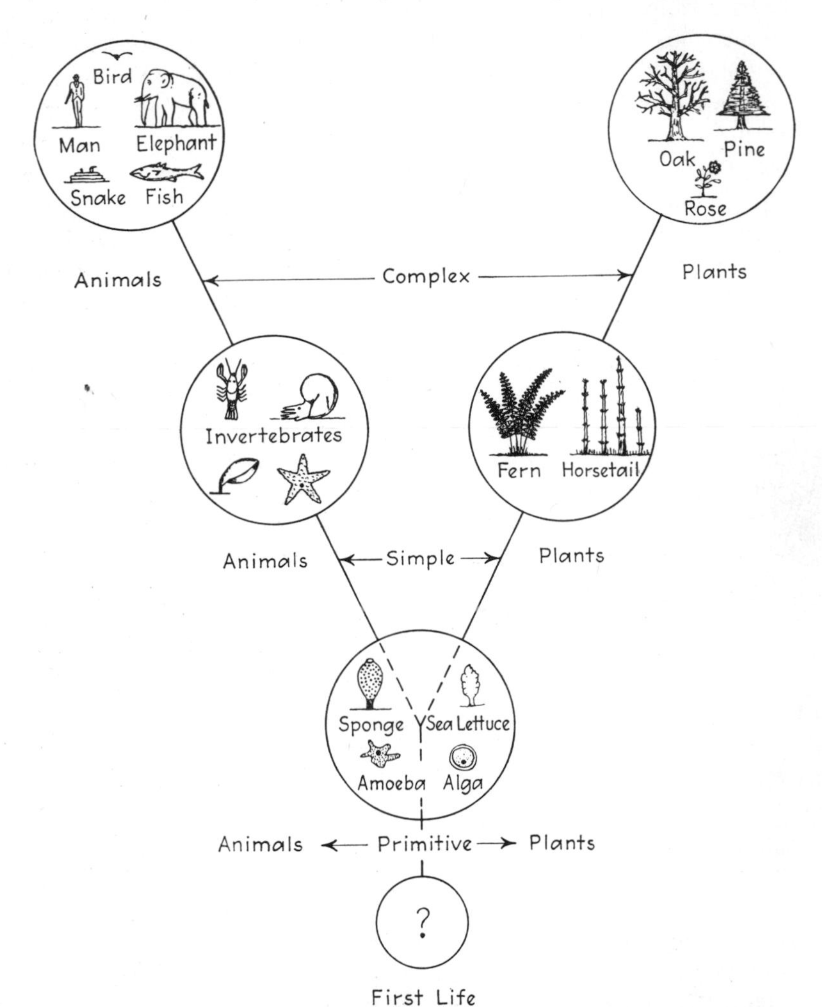

Fig. 1.—Generalized diagram showing the relations of animals and plants.

relation of these two kingdoms is shown diagrammatically in Fig. 1 in the form of the letter Y. At the upper ends of this Y may be placed such complex animals as man, bird, elephant, snake, and fish and such advanced plants as the oak, the pine, and the rose. In intermediate positions are simple animals as the crayfish, mollusk, brachiopod, etc., and simple plants as the fern and horsetail. At the base of the two branches belong simple and primitive animals, well represented by sponges and the protozoan *Amoeba,* and similar lowly plants, represented by algae. To complete the diagram, the primitive plants and animals should merge downward into some common ancestral form from which both may be considered to have evolved. Some investigators think that this ancestral form was an extremely simple plant, thus presupposing plants to have been in existence longer than animals, but others believe that the first organisms possessed characteristics common to both plants and animals. Whatever the case, some of these early one-celled organisms adopted sessile habits, acquired food from the immediate surroundings, and ultimately developed the plant kingdom. Others evolved the ability to search for food, acquired the power of locomotion, and developed the animal kingdom. However the above changes took place and whatever the characteristics of the common ancestor of animals and plants, it remains reasonably certain that the first form of life to appear on earth was a single-celled organism. And, further, this hypothetical organism was invested with the potentialities from which the processes of organic development, acting throughout past geologic ages, have created the dynasties of plants and animals that have moved across the stage of geologic time. The only record of that grand procession is found in the fossils—evidences of ancient life preserved in the materials and rocks of the earth's crust.

The great abundance and variety of life impress every student who carries his observations beyond the larger forms. A count of the animals and plants in a forest soil and a meadow soil, respectively, over an area of 4 sq. ft. and to a depth to which a bird may easily scratch (about ½ in.), showed a total of 112 animal items and 194 seeds and fruits in the former and 1,254 animal items and 3,113 seeds in the latter. These totals indicate 1,216,880 animals and 2,107,810 seeds and fruits per acre of forest land and 13,654,810 animals and 33,822,745 seeds and fruits per acre of meadow land. The counts were made near Washington, D.C. Microscopic animals and seeds were not counted.[1] Had the investigation been carried to greater depths, it naturally follows that the totals would have been much larger. Similar investigations of life in fresh and salt waters, and on and in the bottom sediments of water bodies, would almost certainly show an equal abundance of plants and animals.

The number of known living species of animals was estimated in 1912 to be 522,400.[2] The work of the past two decades has greatly increased this number; nevertheless, many thousands of organisms are still unknown and undescribed. It has been estimated that there are 3,500,000 to 4,000,000 species of insects alone, but such an estimate may be based on a very nice definition of *species*. Beebe's recent descent to half a mile below sea level has shown that there exists in the great oceanic depths an unknown and almost unbelievably fantastic assemblage of organisms.

Prior to 1800, fossil organisms had received little critical attention. Only 127 species of fossil plants and 2,100 species of fossil animals were known in 1820. By 1847 the former had increased to 2,050 and the latter to 24,300. Since that time these numbers have multiplied tremendously.

It seems safe to state that, if all living organisms are considered, not more than 1 out of 10,000 will ever leave a fossil record. The ratio will vary with the species, habitat, and the place of death and burial. Under some conditions nearly every organism with hard parts will become fossilized, but under other conditions the same organisms will have nothing preserved. Countless millions of the American bison have roamed the western prairies, yet only an occasional bone of one of these may now be found. It is probable that after the lapse of a thousand years not one in a million of these animals will have left a bone, or any other indication, of its former presence. Insects live in most lands in numbers reaching astronomic proportions, yet probably not more than one in many millions will leave any fossil evidence of its existence.

It may be assumed that similar conditions of preservation have always prevailed and that the fossil record, therefore, gives

[1] McAtee, W. L., Census of four square feet, *Science*, vol. 26, pp. 447–449, 1907.

[2] Pratt, H. S., On the number of known species of animals, *Science*, n. s., vol. 35, pp. 467–468, 1912.

an incomplete picture of the abundance and character of ancient life. Furthermore, man certainly has seen only a small percentage of the many hundreds of millions of fossils present in the earth's crust and knows and has described only a part of the many species. It becomes apparent then that man's knowledge of fossil organisms is of about the same relative magnitude as his knowledge of existing life. Even when all of the fossil species have been found and described, and in spite of the great increase in knowledge of the life of past ages accruing from those discoveries, the record will still be fragmentary because millions of ancient organisms almost certainly left no fossil record of their existence. Nevertheless, the known fossils are believed to portray correctly in its broader outlines the life of ancient times, and it is thought that more extensive knowledge will do little more than add detail to the grander picture already outlined. Paleontologists have long recognized in this picture the doctrine of evolution—descent with accumulative modifications—and new knowledge, they feel, will only strengthen the foundation on which the doctrine rests.

THE ANIMAL KINGDOM

The animal kingdom, which comprises the left arm of the Y in Fig. 1, may be compared to a great tree, the *animal tree,* with many branches and branchlets (Fig. 2). In this work attention will be directed only to the invertebrate division of the tree.

The tips of the branches and branchlets of the animal tree represent modern life. By following the branchlets back to the larger branches and then along the latter to their place of junction with the trunk, it is seen that the nearer one approaches the trunk, and also the base of the tree, the simpler and less numerous become the groups of animals. The diagram clearly indicates that related forms of life evolved from common parent stocks and also that the latter branched from the main trunk of the animal tree at various times in its geologic history. Going back still farther into geologic time, the trunk of the animal tree finally merges with that of the plant tree, indicating that both diverged from a common ancestral stock. The history and development of this stock fade into the impenetrable beginnings of the planet.

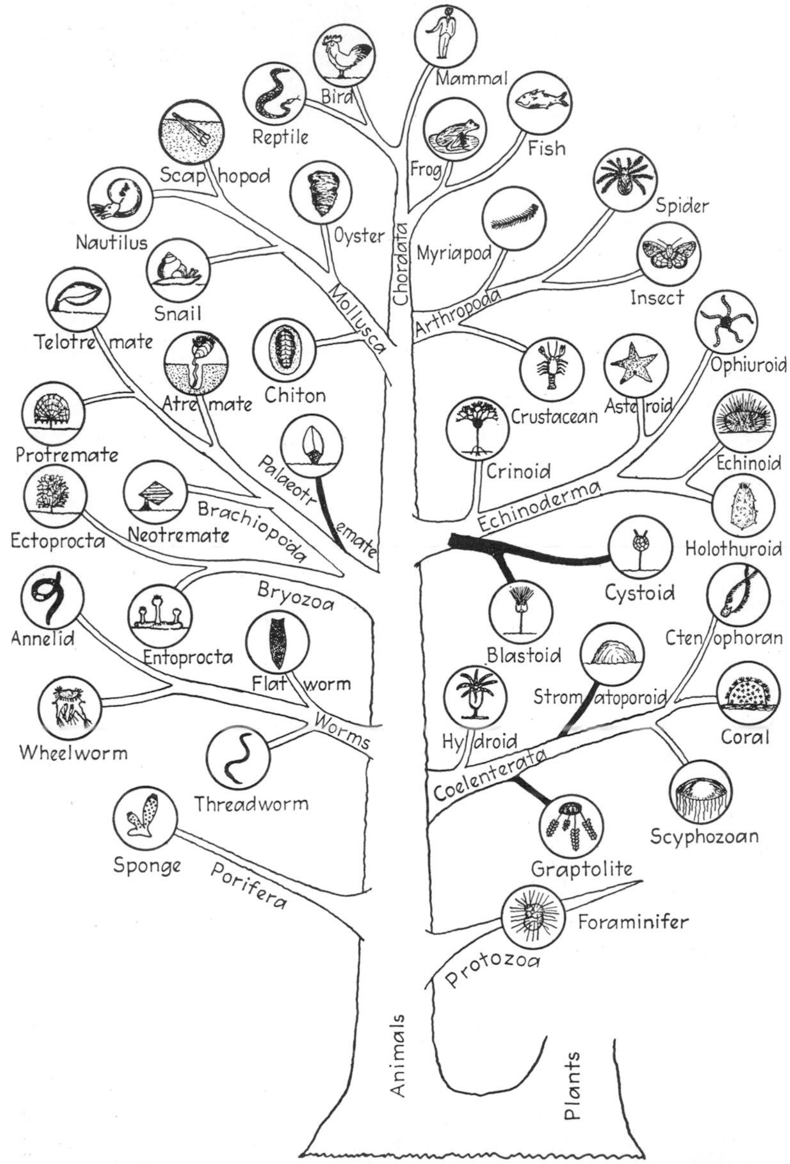

FIG. 2.—Diagrammatic and generalized tree of animal life. The various phyla and their subdivisions are shown by distinct branches and branchlets respectively. All branches are shown springing from the general animal stock, but their position on the tree does not necessarily indicate either the time when the phylum split away from the main trunk or the relative organic complexity of the members of the phylum. Extinct branchlets are shown in solid black.

If one imagines the tree just described as becoming covered with drifting sands, so that only the tips of the branchlets and branches are exposed, the relations between modern and ancient animals are not apparent. The exposed tips represent modern life, but ancient life is concealed beneath the sands of the dune. It is the task of the paleontologist to exhume the buried tree, by working downward into the rocks of the earth's crust and backward into geologic time, and to demonstrate the relations that exist between the living species of animals and those that have become extinct.

CLASSIFICATION OF ANIMALS

Not only are organisms classified into two great kingdoms, but these in turn are subdivided into successively smaller and more restricted groups, ending finally with the individual, the only real biologic entity. The bases for the classification of animals are the relations among the organisms, but the grouping is purely artificial and is largely for convenience.

The smallest taxonomic division usually employed is the *species.* This term has been applied to a group of closely related organisms which possess in common one or more distinctive characteristics and do or may interbreed and reproduce their characters in fertile young. Other definitions of species have been proposed, and estimates of the number of known species vary greatly depending upon the way that the investigator defines the term. Fertile interbreeding seems to be necessary among individuals of the same species. In general, it appears that the fertility of animals depends upon the length of time that has elapsed since separation from the parent stock. A group of closely related species comprise a genus, a group of genera constitute a family, related families are grouped into orders, related orders into classes, and classes into phyla—the primary divisions of the animal and plant kingdoms. The animal kingdom may be divided into 13 phyla (singular, phylum; Gr. *phylon,* race). which from the simplest to the most complex are:

1. Protozoa...................... One-celled organisms such as *Amoeba.*
2. Porifera...................... Sponges.
3. Coelenterata.................. Hydrozoans and corals.
4. Platyhelminthes............... Flatworms.
5. Nemathelminthes............. Threadworms.

6. Trochelminthes	Wheelworms or wheel animalcules.
7. Annelida (Annulata)	Annulated or segmented worms.
8. Echinoderma	Sea lilies, starfishes, sand dollars, and sea urchins.
9. Bryozoa	Sea moss or moss animals.
10. Brachiopoda	Lamp shells.
11. Mollusca	Clams, snails, cuttlefish, octopuses.
12. Arthropoda	Crayfish, centipedes, spiders, and insects.
13. Chordata	Animals with backbones: fish, amphibians, reptiles, birds, and mammals.

This classification is based, to a large extent, on the skeletal structures of the organisms, but the soft parts in many groups are also of taxonomic importance. Since the soft parts of organisms can be studied only in living species, it becomes extremely difficult to assign several important extinct fossil groups to their proper taxonomic positions, for little or nothing is known respecting soft parts except as revealed in the structural features of the skeletal remains. Among these extinct groups are the coral-like fossils known as "stromatoporoids"; the "graptolites," which closely resemble living hydroid coelenterates but also show characters suggesting affinities with the Bryozoa; and the "trilobites," which appear to be related to living Crustacea. The geologic range and relative abundance of the phyla are indicated in Fig. 3.

The subdivision of a phylum is illustrated by the complete classification of the domestic dog and of man:

Kingdom	Animalia	Animalia
Phylum	Chordata	Chordata
Class	Mammalia	Mammalia
Order	Carnivora	Primate
Family	Canidae	Hominidae
Genus	*Canis*	*Homo*
Species	*familiaris*	*sapiens*
Individual	Carlo	John Brown

Most fossils are designated by a double name, of which the first refers to the genus and the second to the species. In rare cases a third name is added to indicate a subspecies or variety. The first or generic name is always capitalized. The second or specific name, which usually refers to some distinctive feature of the fossil, and the varietal name, which is also generally descriptive, are never capitalized. Both should always agree in gender with the generic name. The complete name of the fossil is usually followed by the name or names of the writer or writers who first described it. The fossil *Pentamerus oblongus*

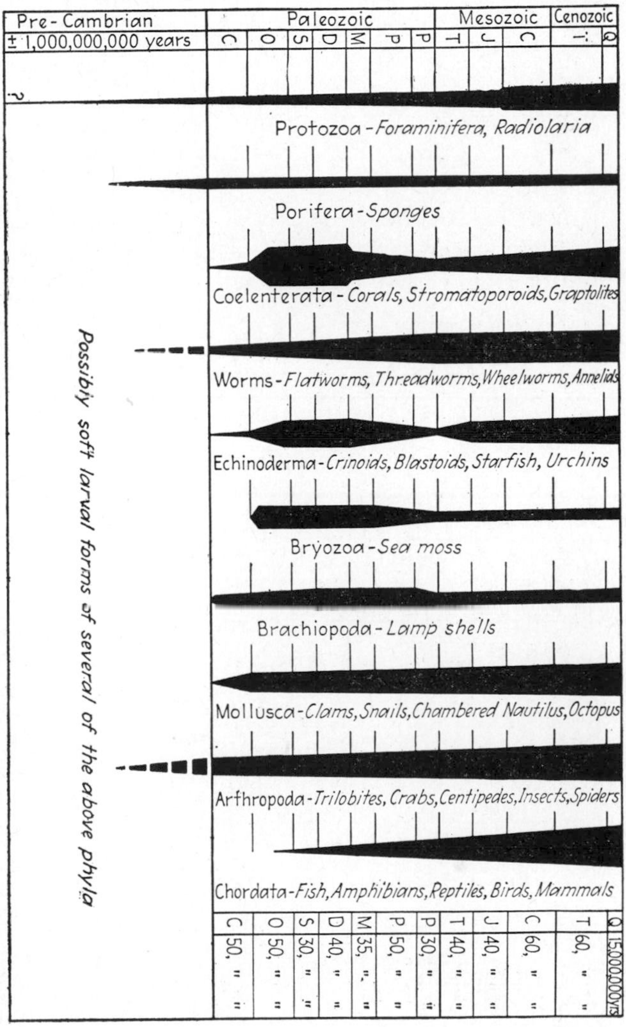

FIG. 3.—Diagram showing the geologic range and relative abundance of the phyla of the animal kingdom, based on the fossil record. The time relations are indicated on the right side of the diagram. The width of each phylum indicates the approximate abundance, and the length shows the geologic range; both are based on the known or inferred fossil record. The diagrams of the phyla are not comparable with each other. The Arthropoda and worms certainly arose and underwent considerable evolution in the Pre-Cambrian, though their fossil record is obscure. Protozoa and Porifera have been reported from the Pre-Cambrian by several investigators, but some paleontologists question either the occurrence, identification, or age of the so-called fossils.

cylindricus Hall and Whitfield may be taken as an example to illustrate the significance of the different words in the name of a fossil.

Pentamerus	Generic name, referring to the five compartments into which the hollow shell is divided by certain internal partitions.
oblongus	Specific name, referring to the oblong shape of the shell and agreeing in gender with the generic name.
cylindricus	Subspecific or varietal name, referring to the cylindrical nature of the oblong shell and agreeing in gender with the generic name.
Hall and Whitfield	Hall (James) and Whitfield (R. P.), the first writers to describe the subspecies.

Although the names of genera and species should call attention to those features which were responsible for the original differentiation from closely related forms, it has become general practice also to use the names of localities of collection. Much less commendable is the rather common practice of naming genera and species after persons. This should be seriously criticized, for such names carry little significance and cast doubtful honor on the person concerned.

HABITATS AND HABITS OF ANIMALS

There are numerous habitats or environments possible of occupancy by the manifold variety of existing animal and plant life, and at the present time all habitats contain a population of animals and plants which are adapted to conditions there. Similar habitats and adaptations appear to have existed since the advent of life upon the earth.

There are three fundamental life habitats—*air*, *land*, and *water*. The life of the extensive air habitat can have the remains of its inhabitants preserved only in the environments of the other two, for aerial organisms must fall to earth or into water when they die. The environments of the land are varied, including the treeless summits of mountains, moss-covered tundra, heavily forested slopes of uplands and moist flatlands, treeless grass-covered prairies, barren deserts, dune areas of many coasts, lush forest growths of temperate and tropical rain-belt regions, and swamps of regions of immature topography and about bodies of water (Fig. 4). Each of these environments may in turn be subdivided. In some of them organic remains may be preserved; in others this is virtually impossible.

The aqueous habitat is equally as varied as that of the land and consists of rivers, lakes, swamps, seas, and oceans. In the bottom materials of these water bodies is an environment which is probably the most favorable of all for the preservation of organic remains, provided there are not enough scavengers to destroy the materials and sufficiently rapid burial to prevent decay and solution of the delicate organic structures. Rivers frequently receive contributions of organic matter from bordering

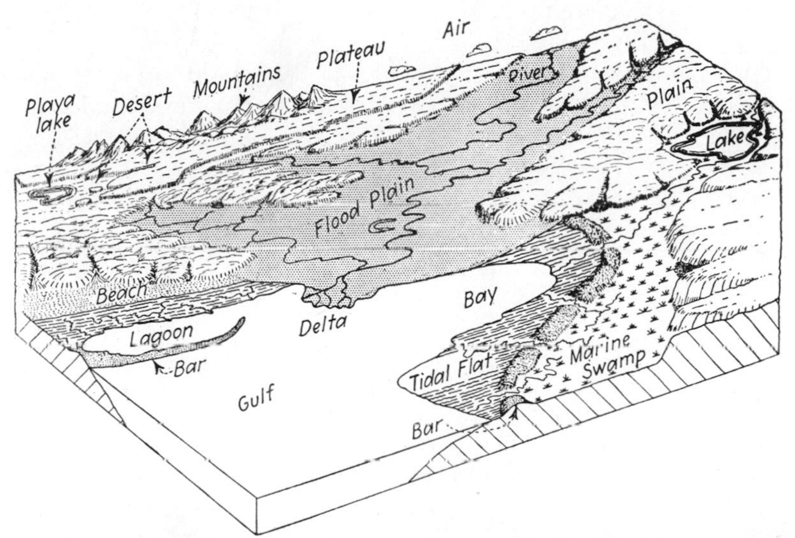

FIG. 4.—Continental environments adjacent to and far from the ocean, and marine environments along the coast.

lands and in times of flood themselves reach out to grasp some of the organisms of the flood plains through which they flow. The lake is somewhat like the river in that there are large opportunities for it to obtain the remains of air and land organisms. The seas and oceans, however, are the great receptacles wherein organic development has been and continues to be enacted and into which come large contributions of organic materials from the air, land, and rivers. As a consequence, the larger proportion of fossils are found in marine formations, and it may be expected that the fossil remains of the geologic future will be found in similar strata.

The bottom of a sea or ocean may be divided into four great life zones: *littoral*, *neritic*, *bathyal*, and *abyssal* (Fig. 5). The *littoral* or *tidal life zone* comprises the narrow strip of shore between highest and lowest tides. Under conditions of unusually high waters the outer part of the beach may become a part of the littoral zone, and with unusually low water the inner portion of the neritic zone may become a part of the littoral. Living conditions are extremely difficult because of the diurnal ebb and flow of the tide with the resultant alternate covering and exposure of the bottom materials and organisms. Obviously conditions of preservation are poor.

The *neritic life zone* is that of the continental shelf. It comprises the bottom and overlying waters between lowest tide and

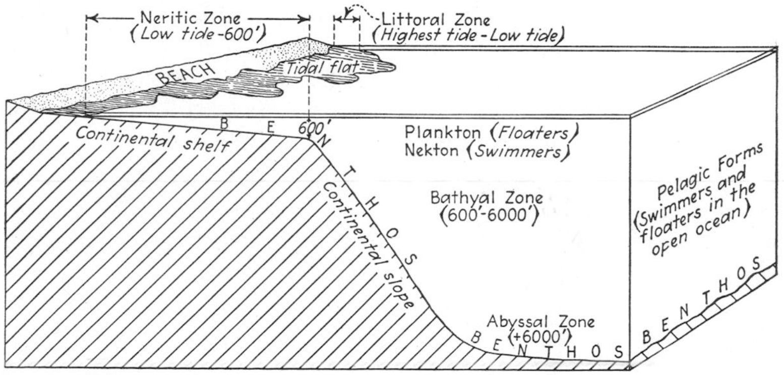

FIG. 5.—Diagram showing the different types of life and the life zones in the ocean.

the 100-fathom (600-ft.) line. This is the zone of lighted and agitated waters, of abundant plant life, and of abundant food for the prolific assemblage of animals which make their home on the bottom or in the superjacent water. The bottom especially is usually densely populated, and conditions of preservation may range from very poor to excellent depending largely upon the rate of deposition and the character and abundance of scavengers. The majority of invertebrate fossil assemblages of the geologic column appear to have flourished upon the bottoms of the neritic zone, and much of invertebrate evolution is thought to have taken place upon the continental shelves of ancient seas.

The *bathyal life zone* includes the bottom and superjacent water between the 100- and 1,000-fathom (600- and 6,000-ft.) lines. It merges on the landward side into the lighted waters of the neritic zone and on the seaward side into the dark abyss. Only the very top of the zone has any light at all, and the amount is negligible; hence there is little or no plant life. Because of the depth there is practically no motion of the water. On rare occasions unusually high storm waves may agitate the upper part of the zone for a short period of time. Deposition is slow in the bathyal zone, and the possibility of preservation does not seem good. Life conditions, however, are such that there is a large and varied assemblage of organisms in the zone.

The *abyssal life zone* of the oceans includes the bottom and overlying waters below a depth of 1,000 fathoms (6,000 ft.). Here the waters are dark and cold, the pressures are very great, and there is no green plant life and little animal life. Deposition is slow, but how much organic material is preserved cannot be stated, though it seems likely that the quantity is relatively small.

The *pelagic life zone* comprises the vast stretches of open ocean beyond the outer limits of the littoral zone and down to abyssal depths. The population consists of swimmers and floaters which, in numerous genera and species, are adapted to the different depths and to the character of the underlying bottoms as to both the composing sediments and the life.

Each of the aqueous environments just described has an assemblage of organisms which may be divided into three groups depending upon their habits of life. Bottom-dwelling forms are included in the *benthos.* These may be fixed, in which case they are designated *sessile benthos;* or they may wander about on the bottom from place to place and comprise the *vagrant benthos.* The *nekton* are the organisms which are provided with effective organs or structures of locomotion and which make their homes in the waters above the bottoms. Some nektonic forms travel long distances during life and frequently die far from the places of birth. The *plankton* include floating organisms without organs of locomotion or with those organs so feebly developed as to be ineffective. Planktonic forms float about subject to the currents and waves of the body of water in which they dwell and are often carried thousands of miles in this manner.

DEFINITION OF FOSSIL

In spite of the fact that the term *fossil* (L. *fossilis*, fr. *fodere*, to dig, something dug up) has been defined in a great many ways by different authors, there is as yet little consensus of opinion on a precise definition, though there are certain requirements common to most if not all of the definitions. Rather than attempt still another, it seems more advisable to point out the important characteristics of the objects which paleontologists have been calling fossils for several centuries.

Certainly a fossil must be *some evidence of the existence of an animal or plant that once lived.* Rocks composed of mineral substances precipitated as a result of organic activity are not fossils, though certain restricted parts of a stratum may be referred to as fossils, if they exhibit specific structures such as laminations, etc. (*e.g.*, algal colonies). The innumerable products of human ingenuity, whether they be the crudest of eoliths, carvings, paintings, buildings, or manufactured articles, are not usually considered fossils because they give little or no indication of the physical nature of the organism which made them.

If, however, a footprint or handprint is inadvertently or purposely impressed in soft mud, wet concrete, or cooling lava, it may one day become a true fossil. Hence, the mold of the mother and child found in the cindery cover of Pompeii is potentially a true fossil. From the examples just given it becomes clear that not only must a fossil give evidence of the existence of an organism, but *it must also furnish some idea of the character* (*size, shape, form, structure, ornamentation,* etc.) *of part or all of the organism.*

The skeletons of many kinds of animals trapped long ago in the tar pits of California are regarded as fossils, yet one would hesitate to apply that term to a dead shepherd dog were it to meet death in the same pit in the same manner tomorrow. Likewise, most anthropologists do not hesitate to apply the term fossil to the bones of Cro-Magnon man found buried in the caves of Europe, yet they would not think of applying the same term to the skeleton of John Smith buried a few years ago in the Crown Point cemetery. It becomes, obvious, therefore, that *a fossil must have age*, but this particular requirement is so intangible and indeterminable that it cannot be defined. In the majority of cases the organisms represented by the fossils lived prior to the present time unit. They need not be extinct, however.

Some authors insist that *fossils must have been preserved in the materials of the earth's crust by natural agencies and processes.* Immediately the question arises as to whether man, or for that matter any living organism, is a natural agent. The authors are of the opinion that any organism, regardless of the way in which it was buried, may become a fossil.

NATURE OF FOSSIL RECORD

Every organism has the possibility of leaving two general types of fossil records. One consists of structures external to the body of the organism but caused by part or all of the body; and the other includes the body itself, preserved in its entirety, in part, or in fragments which have been detached from the body. Such remains cannot be regarded as fossils, however, until they have been preserved in the materials of the earth's crust for posterity and have acquired that indefinite age quality which human sentiment demands.

Unaltered Remains.—In rare cases ancient animals may be preserved *in toto* with little or no alteration from the original state. One of the most striking examples is that of the extinct mammoths of Siberia which have been preserved in cold storage in the frozen tundra for over 25,000 years. Some of the animals are so perfectly preserved that the eyes, skin, blood, flesh, and even partly digested vegetation in the stomach remain much as they were when the animals died. In fact these animals were first discovered by dogs, which fed on their flesh and ultimately led men to the exposed bodies.[1]

More common, but much less spectacular than the preceding cases, are the thousands of mammalian bones in the Cenozoic rocks of western United States, the many molluscan shells from Tertiary strata in different parts of the world, and the countless atremate and neotremate brachiopod shells in the Upper Cambrian strata of the Upper Mississippi Valley. Many of these have suffered little alteration since burial.

Altered Remains.—The vast majority of fossils have undergone more or less alteration since the death of the organism responsible

[1] Tolmachoff, I. P., The carcasses of the Mammoth and Rhinoceros found in the frozen ground of Siberia, *Trans. Amer. Philosophical Soc.*, n. s., vol. 23, pt. 1, art. 1, 74 pp., 1929.

for them. These altered remains may be classified into a number of groups, depending upon the degree to which original material, shape, size, and structure have been retained.

In certain fossils solution or other chemical action has removed parts of the constituent material without adding anything. This frequently results in a simpler chemical composition. This type of alteration is illustrated by many Cenozoic molluscan shells, of which the original periostracum or outer chitinous covering has either completely disappeared or is represented by a carbonaceous film, and the calcareous shell matter often shows evidence of solution. In more ancient rocks originally chitinous structures, such as the skeletal parts of graptolites and the exoskeletons of arthropods, are now represented by thin films of carbon. The nitrogen, oxygen, and hydrogen of the original chitin have long since escaped as a result of decay. This action has been referred to recently as *distillation*.

Shells and skeletal structures of a porous nature are often altered by the addition of mineral substances of various kinds. Percolating ground waters invade the pores and deposit minerals there without in any way altering the original shell or skeletal matter. In this way the fossils are made much heavier, in many cases are somewhat enlarged, and nearly always are made less susceptible to future destruction. Fossilized bones and recent molluscan shells illustrate this common type of alteration, which is often referred to as *permineralization*.

Under favorable conditions ground waters often dissolve part or all of the original shell or skeletal matter of a buried organism and deposit in its place some other substance. This *replacement*, as it is designated, may result in complete destruction of the microscopic structure of the original matter, or it may faithfully preserve it (Fig. 6). The myriads of silicified specimens of *Pentamerus oblongus*, so common in the Niagaran of Wisconsin and elsewhere, illustrate the former, whereas the silicified woods of several petrified forests of western United States exhibit the latter condition. The common replacing substances are calcite, dolomite, cryptocrystalline quartz, chalcedony, and iron sulphide in the form of marcasite or pyrite. Most shells which were originally of aragonite have been changed to calcite or dolomite; many calcareous shells have become silicified (especially true of coelenterates and brachiopods); and in pyritiferous shales

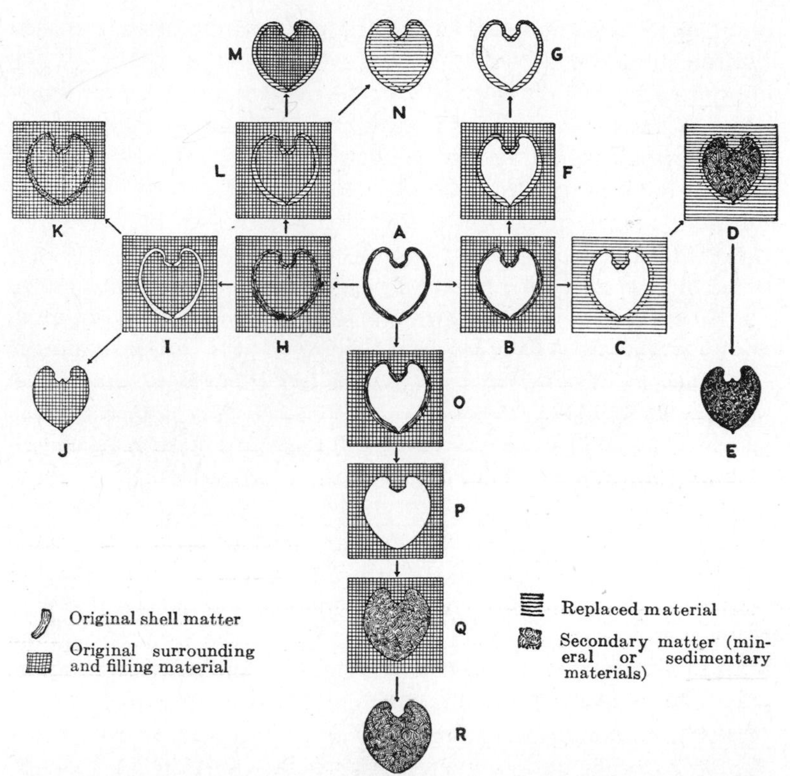

FIG. 6.—Diagram showing the different ways in which a hollow shell such as *Arca* can leave a fossil record of its former presence. The arrows indicate the direction in which fossilization proceeds from the original shell (*A*). All shells are shown in cross section. A solid object of the same shape as the shell of *Arca* would show none of the forms which are dependent for their origin on the presence of an internal cavity.

A. Original shell. *B*. Shell buried without interior filled. *C*. Shell and surrounding material replaced. *D*. Original cavity filled with secondary material. *E*. Filling of internal cavity freed from containing rock. This filling is an *internal mold*. It has impressed on its surface the counterpart of the internal surface of the original shell. *F*. Only shell matter replaced, with cavity remaining. Crystals sometimes grow into the cavity. *G*. Replaced shell released from containing rock. *H*. Shell filled and then buried. *I*. Shell matter removed by solution, with the remaining cavity representing the position of the original shell. *J*. Original filling released from rock. This is an *internal mold* exactly like *E* except in the manner of formation. *K*. Cavity left after solution of original shell filled with secondary material to form a *natural cast*. *L*. Shell alone replaced; filling and surrounding material unaffected. *M*. Replaced shell, with unaltered filling, freed from surrounding rock. *N*. Shell and filling replaced and then released from surrounding rock. *O*. Shell buried without interior filled. *P*. Shell matter dissolved leaving an *external mold*. The surface of the cavity bears an impression which is the counterpart of the exterior surface of the original shell. *Q*. Cavity left after solution of shell filled with secondary matter. *R*. Filling of cavity released from surrounding rock. This filling is a *replica* of the original surface of the shell.

brachiopod and mollusk shells are often completely replaced by iron sulphide.

Impressions (Molds) and Casts.—Any organic structure may leave an impression if it is pressed into a soft material capable of receiving and retaining the imprint (Fig. 6). Hollow shells or other organic structures buried in a rock and later removed by solution leave a cavity, on the wall of which is an impression of the exterior. This *external impression* has usually been designated an *external mold* or *natural mold*. If some plastic substance like gutta percha be pressed into such a cavity, there is obtained a filling known as an *artificial replica* of the original object. Percolating ground waters sometimes deposit mineral substances in external molds to form *natural replicas* of the original exterior of the shell. The surface of this filling is an exact duplicate of the original surface, and the size and shape are those of the original body. If a pelecypod shell is filled with mud or sand and then buried and later dissolved away by ground water, there will remain in the rock as a record of the shell an external mold upon which is impressed the counterpart of the external surface of the original shell and an *internal mold* in the form of a *filling* or *core* upon the surface of which there is an impression of the internal surface of the shell. The empty space between the wall of the external mold and the surface of the filling represents the cavity originally occupied by the shell. If this cavity should now become filled with some mineral substance, the filling would be a *natural cast*. Other modes of preservation are illustrated in Fig. 6.

Solid objects may leave an external mold but never an internal one. Thin objects like leaves are often responsible for molds which are generally referred to as *imprints* or *impressions*. Often the opposite walls of the small cavity left after the decomposition of the leaf may be pressed together so closely that one will be impressed on the other.

Many animals, during their travels over mud and sand bottoms, leave impressions of certain parts of their bodies such as *tracks*, *footprints*, and *trails*. While these are more often curiosities than significant fossils, they at least indicate something of the character of the appendages and other locomotory structures possessed by the animal. Fossil structures of this sort have been attributed to such different organisms as worms, mollusks, arthropods, and vertebrates. In each case the marking represents a single impression or a series of such impressions made in a fairly soft sediment by the basal part of an appendage or a continuous, variously formed groove or a series of such grooves left by the passage of some miniature ploughlike structure of the animal. Such markings as these may or may not tell something concerning the animals which made them. Often they record tragedies of the past, such as that found near the German city of Nierstein on the Rhine. Here in the sandstone, which was once a desert sand, are the small tracks of an insect. Death stalks the unwary insect in the form of lizard tracks which converge upon the insect tracks. Soon the two trails come together—and, beyond, the lizard walks alone.

Under very unusual conditions soft-bodied animals, such as the jellyfish which is over 90 per cent water, may be compressed by the weight of overlying muds into thin films, which in some cases leave partial or complete impressions of the exterior of the body without furnishing much information concerning the shape of the original organism.

Burrows, Borings, and Tubes.—Certain animals excavate burrows in the sand, bore holes into solid rock, gather granular bottom materials about their bodies, or secrete calcareous tubes in which they live. If the shells of the organism are left in the burrows, etc., as is sometimes the case with urchins and pelecypods, it is possible to determine the origin of the cavity. More often, however, the origin must be conjectured by comparison with similar features that are constructed or produced by living organisms, and in many cases any statement about the way in which some particular fossil was formed is little more than a guess.

Coprolites or Castings.—The term *coprolite* or *casting* has been applied to fossil excreta; hence the composing material has passed through the alimentary tract of some individual. In many cases the excreted matter has undergone physical and chemical changes and for these reasons stands out conspicuously on weathered surfaces. Coprolites may be in the form of straplike markings, discrete pellets, or an alternating series of markings and pellets. Fish coprolites found in the Devonian of New York contained ganoid scales, showing that the animal fed on that particular kind of fish.

Miscellaneous Markings.—Almost every serious collector of fossils has cached away in his cabinets peculiar markings or structures of one sort or another, which may have been made by some ancient animal that has either not yet been discovered or with which the fossils have not yet been associated. While these are always intriguing because of their unknown origin, they are of little practical value to the paleontologist.

USES OF FOSSILS

The organisms now represented as fossils lived at definite times during the geologic past and hence have *chronological significance* and value. William Smith, the great English stratigrapher, long ago discovered that his stratigraphic units had distinct assemblages of fossil organisms, and one of the great results of the study of the geologic column during the past century has been the demonstration that each important geologic time period is characterized by a distinctive group of animals and plants. The fossilized remains of these assemblages, therefore, have great value for determining *stratigraphic position* in the geologic column.

The forms and structures of animals, to a greater or lesser degree, bear the impress of the environment in which they lived, and the characteristics and arrangement of the fossilized remains reflect conditions of burial. Hence fossils may be of great use in determining *ancient environments*. They may also indicate something of the nature of *ancient climates*.

It has often been possible to determine the relations of ancient lands and seas through the study of the distribution of certain fossils, and the same studies have frequently shown the paths of migration of ancient organisms and the directions of currents. Fossils have always been of great importance, therefore, in the study of ancient geography or *paleogeography*.

Living organisms exhibit a great variety of interrelations in the various environments—commensalism, parasitism, etc. Fossil organisms very frequently furnish interesting insights into the relations of ancient organisms on coral reefs, shell banks, lagoons, etc. It has even been possible in some cases to determine what the animal ate, where and how it died, and what happened to it after death. Hence fossils may tell much concerning *paleoecology*, or the relations of ancient organisms.

Fossils comprise one of the foundation stones of the doctrine of *organic evolution*. Each fossil represents a biologic entity, and as the geologic column of the earth took form, it became clear to investigators that the plants and animals of each division had been derived by evolution from those of the preceding time and were in turn ancestral to those that followed.

Important as they are, fossils must always be used with certain limitations. As an example, one of the Tertiary formations of Kansas contains an assemblage of Pennsylvanian fossils derived by erosion from a previous stratigraphic sequence. Obviously these fossils are of no value for correlation and if taken at face value would yield extremely erroneous ideas with respect to the environment of deposition of the fossil-bearing strata and rather curious ideas with respect to evolution.

Fossils are not always found in the places where the living organisms made their homes. Shells are frequently carried elsewhere before or after death and entombed in sediments of environments in which the living organisms could not have dwelt. The sediments containing fossils are also consequences of ancient environments, and the impress of the environment on these sediments may be so marked as to preclude the possibility of incorrect interpretation. On the other hand, the impress of the environment of life on the organisms represented by the fossils may have been slight, and one may be led to consider the environment of deposition as that of life. It should be obvious, therefore, that great caution is essential. Agassiz found leaves of land plants, pieces of bamboo, stalks of sugar cane, and land shells in the Caribbean Sea at a depth of over 1,000 fathoms and at a distance of from 10 to 15 miles from land, in association with the shells of the bottom-dwelling organisms of deep water. Shells of echinoids and mollusks and bones of fishes occur in the swamps of the lands bordering the Gulf of St. Lawrence. These examples illustrate the problems confronting the paleontologist. Floating forms of the extinct graptolites attained world-wide distribution, yet the remains of the group are found in greatest abundance and with finest preservation at occasional levels in black shales which do not contain a normal bottom-dwelling assemblage of other fossils. The indications are that the environment in which the black shales were deposited probably was not one to which the graptolites were normally adapted, and hence it seems likely that the graptolite assemblage, and perhaps the other fossils as well, is one of death rather than of life. An assemblage thus brought together after death has been designated a *thanatocoenose*. Little or nothing of the life environment of the organisms of a thanatocoenose can be told from the containing sediments. A natural assemblage of living organisms or fossils is a *biocoenose*, and in the case of the fossils both they and the containing sediments have a community of characters that reflect the nature of the environment of deposition.

Use of Fossils for Correlation.—The value of any fossil, no matter what the objective of the study, depends upon its position in the geologic column and the geographic location. A fossil without this information is little more than a curiosity. It may tell of geography, but it is the geography of no known place or time. It represents some place in the geologic column, but that position is unknown. It represents a stage of evolution, but that stage is not determinate. Hence it is always of the utmost importance to know the location of a fossil both geographically and stratigraphically.

Students of sedimentary rocks since the days of William Smith in England and Cuvier, Lamarck, and Brogniart in France, about 125 years ago, have found that there is a very definite relation between the fossil contents of rocks and the position in the geologic column. It has been found that the more recently the rocks have been formed the more complex and varied the assemblage of the contained organisms; the earlier the simpler the organic content.

The relative ages of the units of the standard geologic column had first to be determined on the basis of superposition. The next step was to determine the fossil assemblage of each time unit. Thereafter the age of any isolated sequence of strata could be determined by the fossils present in it, and once the fossils were identified the sequence could then be assigned to the proper unit in the standard section.

The oldest sedimentary rocks, those of the Pre-Cambrian, are without definitely recognizable fossils, and for that reason cannot be identified or correlated by means of the organic content. Other criteria, therefore, must be sought. In all of the major divisions of the geologic column since the Pre-Cambrian, however, the organic assemblages have been determined, at least in the broader outlines, so that it is now comparatively easy to recognize the equivalents of each such division in any part of the world.

Fossils as Indices of Ancient Geography.—*Paleogeography* is the science which deals with ancient geography—with the former distribution of land and sea, with ancient rivers and lakes, former plains and mountains, and the positions of ancient shore lines. The adaptations of organisms are characteristic of particular environments; hence those shown by fossil forms may indicate the existence and position of ancient flood plains, deltas, prairies, mountains, deserts, lakes, rivers, shore lines, and the positions of the deep and shallow parts of the seas. Environments may be indicated, therefore, by the associations exhibited by fossil organisms. In the delta, as an example, there is a mingling in the deposits of both land and lacustrine or marine organisms. The distribution of fossil marine organisms may indicate former connections between bodies of water, and, similarly, occurrences of land animals may point to connections between lands now separated. Certain animals have always lived in the sea. Among these are the stony corals, the echinoderms, the brachiopods, and the cephalopods. Their presence in deposits, therefore, indicates the sea or proximity to the sea.

Fossils as Indices of Ancient Climates.—One of the great factors of most environments is the climate, and certain organisms are very narrowly adapted to climatic conditions. Among these are certain Foraminifera, corals, palms, magnolias, and others. The fossil palms from the Tertiary strata of Spitzbergen and the fossil magnolias from similar strata in Greenland; the great profusion of corals in the Devonian strata at Louisville, Ky., in the Ordovician and Silurian of Anticosti, in the Silurian of the Michigan Basin, and in the Silurian of the island of Gotland in the Baltic Sea; and the fossil ferns and primitive corals found on Antarctica all prove the existence of climates in these localities quite different from, and much warmer than, those of the present.

Fossils as Evidence of Evolution.—No line of evidence more forcefully and clearly supports the fundamental principle of evolution—"descent with accumulative modifications"—than that furnished by fossils. Through their study one sees dynasty after dynasty of organisms appear as simple, adaptable, and easily modified forms; witnesses their deployment into the many

TABLE 1.—TABLE OF GEOLOGIC TIME[1]

Era	Periods	Epochs, North America	Epochs, Europe	Organic characteristics
Cenozoic	Quaternary 3 per cent	Recent Pleistocene	Recent Pleistocene	Invertebrates of modern aspect. Mollusks very abundant. All other phyla except Brachiopoda well represented
Cenozoic	Tertiary 12 per cent	Pliocene Miocene Oligocene Eocene Paleocene	Pliocene Miocene Oligocene Eocene Paleocene	
Mesozoic	Cretaceous 12 per cent	Lance Montana Colorado Dakota Comanchian (Absent)	Danian Senonian Turonian Cenomanian Albian Aptian Barremian Neocomian	Extinction of ammonites. Abundant planktonic Foraminifera. General initiation of modern forms. Mollusks abundantly represented
Mesozoic	Jurassic 8 per cent	(Represented by continental and marine deposits. Epochal names not yet proposed)	Portlandian Kimmeridgian Lusitanian Oxfordian Callovian Bathonian Bajocian Lias	Great abundance of ammonites, culmination of belemnites, and appearance of oyster-like pelecypods
Mesozoic	Triassic 8 per cent	(Poorly represented in United States by marine deposits except on Pacific coast. Epochs undefined)	Rhaetic Keuper Muschelkalk Bunter	Appearance of true ammonites and disappearance of ceratites
Paleozoic	Permian 6 per cent	(Represented in United States by marine and continental lithological facies)	Zechstein Rotliegendes	Great extinction of ancient forms of life. Last of the trilobites. Many fusulinids
Paleozoic	Pennsylvanian 10 per cent	Monongahela-Virgil Conemaugh-Missouri Allegheny-Des Moines Pottsville Morrow	Stephanian Westphalian Namurian	Numerous fusulinids. Dominance of productid brachiopods

[1] Geologic time from the beginning of the Cambrian to the present has been estimated at 500,000,000 years. The time interval between the beginning of the Cambrian and the earliest earth history recorded in the rocks is placed at 1,000,000,000 years. The percentages indicated above express magnitude only and are to be regarded merely as estimates. European equivalents are not to be considered as exactly correlative with American epochal divisions. The correlations are only suggestive and approximate and are subject to change as additional facts accumulate.

TABLE 1.—TABLE OF GEOLOGIC TIME.[1]—(*Continued*)

	Periods	Epochs, North America	Epochs, Europe	Organic characteristics
Paleozoic	Mississippian 7 per cent	Chester Meramec Osage Kinderhook	Dinantian (Culm)	Climax of crinoids and blastoids. Numerous goniatites
	Devonian 8 per cent	Chautauquan Senecan Erian Ulsterian Oriskanian Helderbergian	Famennian Frasnian Givetian Eifelian Coblenzian Gedinnian	Great decline of trilobites and graptolites. Dominance of spiriferoid brachiopods and disappearance of pentameroid brachiopods. Sponges abundant locally
	Silurian 6 per cent	Cayugan Niagaran Anticostian-Medinan	Downtownian Ludlovian Wenlockian Llandoverian	Great extent of coral reefs, first abundance of spiriferoid brachiopods, culmination of pentameroid brachiopods. Many graptolites. Trilobites on decline
	Ordovician 10 per cent	Cincinnatian Mohawkian Chazyan Canadian	Ashgillian Caradocian Llandeilian Arenigian	Dominance of orthoid and strophomenoid brachiopods, abundance of graptolites, climax of ancient cephalopods, and many trilobites. First true coral reef
	Cambrian 10 per cent	Croixian Acadian Waucobian	Tremadocian Menevian Harlechian	Abundance and first appearance of trilobites and brachiopods. First appearance of most invertebrate phyla
Proterozoic				Fossil evidence consists of algal secretions, siliceous sponge spicules, and trails of various kinds which have been attributed to animals. Other evidence is questionable
Archeozoic				No direct evidence of life. Indirect evidence suggests the presence of the very simplest kinds of plants and animals

natural environments where they succeed or fail; sees the successful reach a zenith of abundance and complexity under optimum living conditions; and finally observes the races passing into old age with loss of racial vitality and ease of adaptability. Ultimately, their last futile attempts to overcome an environment to which they are no longer adapted results in degenerate or overspecialized forms which still continue for a short time into a future of organic development in which they are not destined to play a part. At last they disappear from the scene, these helpless stragglers, never to return, and from their decaying senile bodies arise no new races with vigor and strength. Senile races never seem to take the backward trail to simplicity and renewed vigor; rather, they must march on to the extinction that is inevitable. This is the panorama of organic development that the paleontologist may visualize from the study of organisms that have left a fossil record in the rocks.

THE GEOLOGIC TIME SCALE

The history of the earth has been divided into large time divisions known as *eras*. These have been subdivided, in descending rank, into *periods* and *epochs*. The ultimate basis for these divisions is diastrophism, but each unit, nevertheless, is characterized by a distinctive assemblage of fossils. The rock divisions corresponding to the different time divisions are as follows:

Time Units	Rock Units
Era	......[1]
Period	System
Epoch	Series

The names applied to the eras terminate in the suffix -zoic (Gr. *zoon*, animal), as Paleozoic, Mesozoic, etc. This practice in the beginning was based on the concept that there was progressive change in the life of the earth from the beginning to the present. Names of periods and epochs are commonly of geographic origin and terminate in the suffix -an, as Niagaran, unless some other ending is made desirable because of euphony. The geologic time scale shown in Table 1 is the one generally accepted at the present time.

[1] There is no generally accepted rock term for the strata belonging to an era. See Classification and nomenclature of rock units, *Bull. Geol. Soc. Amer.*, vol. 44, p. 429, 1933.

CHAPTER II

PROTOZOA

INTRODUCTION

The phylum Protozoa[1] includes the simplest and most primitive of animals. The individual protozoan consists of an irregular cell-like mass of protoplasm (*sarcode*), differentiated into at least one *nucleus* surrounded by more or less contractile *cytoplasm* (Fig. 7). The cytoplasm may be naked, or it may be surrounded by slightly denser protoplasm as a delicate covering. The entire cell acts as a single organism and performs all the functions necessary for life, such as acquisition and assimilation of food, excretion or rejection of waste products, reproduction, growth, and locomotion.

Although most of the Protozoa are solitary and composed of a single cell, there are a few forms in which a number of individuals are loosely fastened together to form aggregations. The latter individuals are sometimes referred to as *colonial Protozoa*. In the majority of such colonies the individuals are bound together by threads of cytoplasm or are embedded in a common matrix of protoplasm. Most of the cells, however, are similar in function and structure; hence, the colonial Protozoa are only cell aggregations, in which there is no differentiation of the cells into tissue or definite organs. The dividing line between these more complex forms of Protozoa and the most primitive forms of *Metazoa* (multicelled animals with cells differentiated into tissue and organs) can be drawn only with great difficulty.

Food, in some forms, is ingested on any part of the periphery of the body and, in others, through a special opening known as the *cytostome*. In the simpler forms the undigested portions and waste products are ejected from any part of the periphery; in somewhat more complex forms ejection of the waste takes place through a definite opening, designated the anal aperture or

[1] Protozoa—Gr. *protos*, first + *zoon*, animal; referring to the fact that members of the phylum are first among animals in simplicity.

cytopyge. Protozoans feed on small plants, other protozoans, and general organic debris. Some forms are also parasitic in the bodies of higher animals. These parasitic forms are of considerable importance to man because of association with certain diseases.

Locomotion is possible for the majority of protozoans and is accomplished by means of several different types of processes developed on the peripheral surface of the body. The simplest protozoans move very slowly by sending out finger-like extensions (*pseudopodia*, false feet) from any part of the cell. The

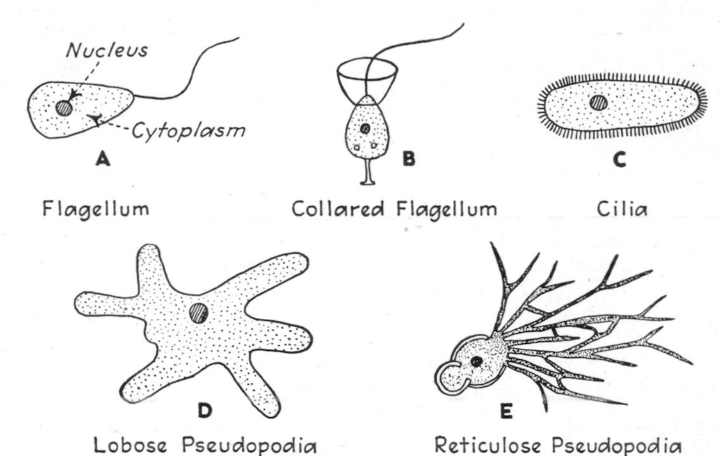

FIG. 7.—Diagrams illustrating the different locomotory-structures among the Protozoa.

other parts of the cell flow into these extensions. The protoplasm is contractile, and the pseudopodia, which can change shape and size readily, may be of lobose or reticulated character (Fig. 7 *D–E*). In the more complex protozoans locomotion is accomplished by means of minute hairlike processes (*cilia*) (Fig. 7 *C*), which cover the surface of the organism and drive it through the water with their wavelike rhythmic motion; or, as in the Flagellata, by one or more minute whiplike processes (*flagella*) on the anterior end of the body (Fig. 7 *A–B*). Parasitic forms, as the Sporozoa and also a few others, are without locomotory processes in the adult stages.

Reproduction among the Protozoa may be by one of two methods or by a combination of the two. In the first method the organism splits into two or more parts, with each part containing some of the original nucleus surrounded by some of the original cytoplasm. Each of these parts ultimately becomes a distinct and complete protozoan. This method of reproduction is known as *fission* or *vegetative reproduction.* In the second method two individual protozoans unite, the cytoplasms fuse, the two nuclei join to form a single nucleus, and a single organism results. This method is designated *conjugation* or *sexual reproduction,* and the union of the two cells is an intimation of sex, for it corresponds in a very general way to the union of ovum and spermatozoan in higher organisms. Some protozoans reproduce by successive alternations of fission and conjugation, giving rise to an *alternation of generations,* and the individuals of consecutive generations build shells which are different. Without this knowledge these two types of shells would very likely be considered as different species, whereas they were actually built by the same species.

A protozoan may be provided with a *shell* or *test,* or it may be naked. The test is generally completely surrounded by protoplasm, though at times part of the surface may be uncovered; hence, it may in most cases be referred to as an internal shell. The shell may be a single spheroidal chamber; a simple hollow tube open at one or both ends; a series of globular or ellipsoidal chambers connected by openings and arranged in a variety of ways; or a series of concentric, perforated shells separated from each other by delicate supporting structures. The walls of the test are either solid (*imperforate*) or porous (*perforate*). In perforate tests minute threads of protoplasm stream out through pores in the wall. In imperforate forms the protoplasm flows out through the main aperture or through many small apertures and may form a thin covering over the entire test (Fig. 8). The material of which the test is composed shows considerable diversity. If the test is secreted directly by the organism, the material is chitinous,[1] calcareous, or siliceous. It may, however, be formed of many minute grains or fragments of organic or inorganic matter selected by the organism from the bottom and cemented together into a variety of forms. Shells of calcareous or siliceous materials belonging to the first type are more complex

[1] Chitin is an amorphous organic compound composed of carbon, hydrogen, oxygen, and nitrogen.

in structure than those of the second type and are thought to have come into existence at a much later geological date.

Protozoa were generally unknown as such until after the discovery of the microscope, although forms larger than microscopic size are now known to exist and to have existed during the geologic past. The first shells found were referred to several different animal groups before their true identity and biologic relations were determined.

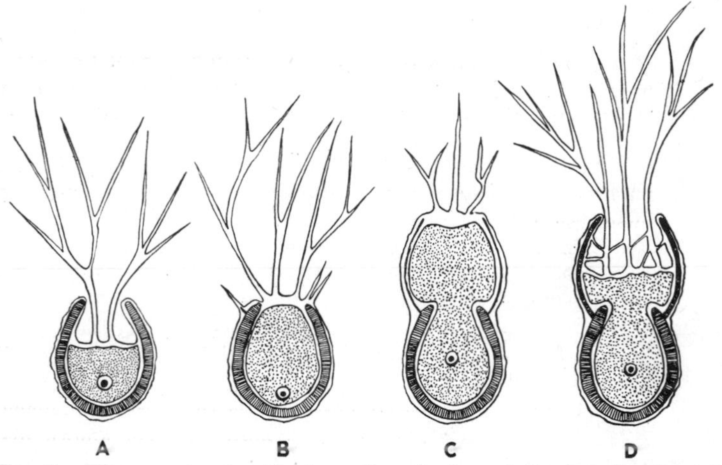

FIG. 8.—Diagram showing the formation of a foraminiferal shell. In *A* the single chamber of the shell is the proloculum; in *B–D* another chamber is added. Note the outflowing pseudopodia, the thin layer of protoplasm which encloses the shell, and the position of the nucleus. (*From Thomson, "Outlines of Zoology,"* [*D. Appleton-Century Company, Inc.*], *after Dreyer, with modifications.*)

Protozoans are now known to be present in almost every possible habitat or environment. They are the exciting agents concerned in a great many ailments or diseases such as malaria, sleeping sickness, amoebic dysentery, coastal fever of cattle in South Africa, etc.

In the present oceans the abandoned microscopic shells of Protozoa are raining down on the bottoms in prodigious numbers to form extensive deposits of "Globigerina" and "Radiolarian" oozes. Some of these ooze deposits formed in past geologic ages are now solidified into rock and are exposed above sea level. Such are some of the limestones and marls of the Gulf States in the southern part of the United States.

The following classification, representing a modified form of that given by Kudo and Galloway, shows the relations of the various subdivisions of the phylum:

Phylum 1. **Protozoa**—Single-celled, aquatic, parasitic, or terrestrial animals, without differentiation of cells for special functions. Most forms are solitary or single, but some are colonial.

Class 1. *Mastigophora* (*Flagellata*)—Cell wall fixed, shape permanent; equipped with one or more flagella; usually without a skeleton but having a siliceous skeleton in a few groups.

Order 1. Chrysomonadina—Fresh-water or marine, microscopic protozoans, having skeletons in some families. Skeleton may be a cyst with a siliceous wall or small disks composed of calcium carbonate. The *Silicoflagellidae* are known to have a fossil record.

Order 2. Cryptomonadina—Mainly marine, free-swimming or creeping forms with a spherical cyst composed of cellulose. (No known fossil record.)

Order 3. Dinoflagellida—Mainly marine, planktonic protozoans with body inclosed in an envelope of cellulose. Certain fossils have been referred to this order.

Order 4. Phytomonadina—Algal-like, free-living, biflagellate protozoans surrounded by a thick or thin cellulose membrane. (No known fossil record.)

Order 5. Euglenoidida—Large flagellates with plastic or definite body but without a preservable membrane. (No known fossil record.)

Order 6. Chloromonadina—Rare, one-celled, uninucleate flagellates. (No known fossil record.)

Order 7. Pantostomatida—Simple to complex, flagellated protozoans which may also have pseudopodia. (No known fossil record.)

Order 8. Protomonadina—Mainly parasitic flagellates with plastic or amoeboid bodies. (No known fossil record.)

Order 9. Polymastigidia—Unicellular, uni- or multinucleate, multiflagellate protozoans without a preservable membrane or skeleton. (No known fossil record.)

Class 2. *Sarcodina*—Protozoans with a changeable body form capable of sending out pseudopodia which function for both locomotion and food capture. Internal and external skeletal structures are developed in some groups. Solitary or colonial in habit. Reproduction by conjugation, by fission, or by a combination of both. Mastigophora and Sarcodina are thought by some to have descended from a common ancestral form.

Order 1. Proteomyxa—Mainly parasitic protozoans with threadlike pseudopodia which may branch or anastomose with each other. Without a skeleton. (No known fossil record.)

Order 2. Mycetozoa—Fungi-like protozoans which bear very close resemblance to certain very simple plants. (No known fossil record.)

Order 3. Foraminifera—Comparatively large, almost exclusively marine protozoans, with reticulose or rarely filose pseudopodia and always with a chitinous, calcareous, or agglutinated test which may be porous but not latticed. The fossil record is very extensive.

Order 4. Amoebaea—Protozoans with lobose or lamellose pseudopodia inhabiting a great variety of environments. May or may not have tests. The fossil record of this order is questionable.

Order 5. Testacea (Thecamoeba)—Amoeboid protozoans possessing a single-chambered test into which the entire body can be drawn. Tests composed of preservable material, but there is no known fossil record.

Order 6. Heliozoa—Spherical protozoans with radiating *axopodia* (pseudopodia that are more or less stiff and not inclined to reticulate or fuse) and without a central chitinous capsule. The body may be naked, surrounded by a chitinous mantle, or possess a latticed test which may or may not have spicules. Some of the skeletal elements are composed of preservable materials, but there is no known fossil record of the order.

Order 7. Radiolaria—Marine protozoans characterized by a central, perforated capsule composed of chitin. Skeletons are composed of chitin, siliceous material, and rarely of strontium sulphate. The fossil record of this order is a fairly sparse one but extends over a great part of geologic time.

Class 3. *Sporozoa*—Exclusively parasitic protozoans, usually incapable of movement, with fixed cell wall, with permanent shape, and without preservable skeletal material. They do not, therefore, in themselves leave any fossil record, but preservation seems possible in a fossilized host, such as insects preserved in amber.

Sporozoa may be divided into two subdivisions—*Telosporidia* (spores formed inside the cell) and *Neosporidia* (spores formed outside the cell).

Class 4. *Infusoria*—Protozoans having a ciliated exterior, a fixed wall, and a permanent shape but without skeletons. There is no known fossil record.

Infusoria may be divided into two subdivisions—*Ciliata* (ciliated throughout life) and *Suctoria* (ciliated only in very early stages of growth).

CLASS MASTIGOPHORA (FLAGELLATA)

The protozoans in this class comprise a very heterogeneous group but have the common characteristic of locomotive organs in the form of one or more flagella. A large number of Mastigophora (Fig. 9) bear chlorophyll, thus giving plant character-

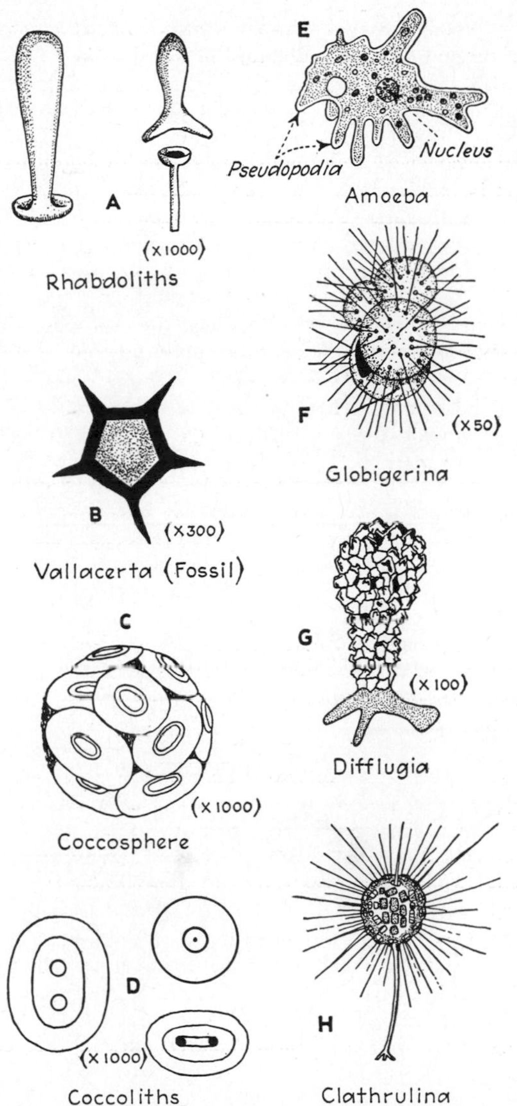

FIG. 9.—Protozoa. *A, C–D.* Minute calcareous bodies recovered from deep-sea ooze, attributed by some investigators to protozoans, by others to algae. *B. Vallacerta hortoni*, a fossil silicoflagellate from the Upper Cretaceous of California. *E. Amoeba*, a common, rather complex protozoan. *F. Globigerina*, a very common foraminifer of deep marine waters. *G. Difflugia*, a representative of the Testacea, with an agglutinated test. *H. Clathrulina*, a heliozoan with a siliceous test. (*A, C–D after Murray; B after Hanna; E from Parker and Haswell's "Text-book of Zoology," from Parker's "Biology," after Leidy, Gruber, and Howes; F after Brady; G from Parker and Haswell's "Text-book of Zoology," after Lang; H from Parker and Haswell's "Text-book of Zoology" and Bütschli's "Protozoa," after Schulze and Greeff.*)

istics to these forms. In fact many of the forms included in this class by zoologists have been classified as plants by some botanists. The Mastigophora include free-living and parasitic forms which are adapted to a wide range of aquatic habitats. Some are free swimmers, others are creepers, and still others are sessile. Supporting and skeletal structures are composed of material which usually leaves no fossil record. In a few cases, however, minute skeletal elements have been preserved.

In the planktonic *Chrysomonadina* the organism may have a cyst of which the wall is composed of siliceous material or of small disks of calcareous matter. The family *Silicoflagellidae* is known to have fossil representatives (Fig. 9 *B*), and very minute skeletons have been reported recently from the younger geological formations (Cretaceous to Recent) of California.[1]

The family *Coccolithophoridae* is characterized by skeletons which are composed of minute disks (discoliths) of calcium carbonate (Fig. 9 *A*, *C–D*). These minute bodies, which show considerable differences in shape, are common in some oozes but are not known as fossils. Some have referred them to plants. One other order, the *Dinoflagellida*, has been reported to have fossil representatives in the Cretaceous of Europe. The organism, which usually inhabits marine waters, is covered by an envelope of cellulose.

CLASS SARCODINA

The Sarcodina are represented at present by both fresh-water and marine forms. The body is capable of protruding finger-like or threadlike extensions designated pseudopodia. These may be retracted if necessary. The organism reproduces by either fission or conjugation and also by a combination of these. Tests or shells vary greatly in size, shape, and composition. Representatives of this class form almost all the known examples of fossil protozoans, and the Foraminifera and Radiolaria are by far the most important so far as fossils are concerned. Several other orders have preservable skeletal elements, but, so far as known, the fossil record is questionable. The first two orders,

[1] HANNA, G. D., Silicoflagellata from the Cretaceous of California, *Jour. Paleontology*, vol. 1, pp. 259–263, pl. 1, 1928; Silicoflagellates from the Cantua shale (abstract), *Pan-Amer. Geol.*, vol. 54, pp. 79–80, 1930; A new genus of Silicoflagellata from the Miocene of Lower California, *Jour. Paleontology*, vol. 4, pp. 415–416, pl. 1, 1930.

Proteomyxa and *Mycetozoa*, do not possess any preservable skeletal structures and hence have left no fossil record.

Foraminifera

This order of protozoans includes comparatively large forms, of which most live in marine waters. They occur abundantly in present oceans and have many fossil representatives. Most are benthonic and move about sluggishly on the bottom deposits by means of contractile pseudopodia. Some forms are sessile benthos, others are vagrant, and still others are pelagic. Over 35 per cent (48,000,000 sq. miles) of the present ocean bottom is covered by ooze composed of pelagic foraminiferal tests. Such ooze is generally absent in the deepest parts of the oceans because the empty calcareous tests are dissolved in the long journey toward the bottom.

The tests or shells of Foraminifera show a great range in size (0.01 mm. to 19 cm.), in shape (spherical, tubular, snail-like, etc.), and in composition (gelatinous, pseudochitinous, chitinous, "ferruginous," agglutinated, calcareous, and siliceous). The architecture of the shell may be simple (as in *Lagena*) or very complex (as in *Fusulina*). The walls of the test may be solid (imperforate) or perforated, and the exterior surfaces may be smooth or ornamented with spines, nodes, etc.

Great impetus has been given the study of Foraminifera during the past two or three decades. Microscopic forms, because they can often be secured rather easily from well cuttings, have become very important in the oil industry, where they are used to correlate oil-bearing and contiguous strata. Further, the rather extensive researches on the floras, faunas, and sediments of the oceanic waters and bottoms at many sites have produced a great mass of interesting information concerning the part in oceanic life played by the Protozoa. Thousands of new forms of Foraminifera have been described during the last decade, and nearly every issue of certain paleontological periodicals adds to the number. Some workers are of the opinion that perhaps not over half of the living and fossil Foraminifera have as yet been described.

Nature of the Organism.—The individual foraminifer consists of a cell composed of cytoplasm, which shows little or no differentiation, surrounding one or more nuclei. The cytoplasm streams out from the body, forming threadlike pseudopodia, which are often very long and may anastomose to present a characteristic tangled or knotted appearance (Fig. 8). In the imperforate shells these pseudopodia stream out through the aperture or apertural openings. In the perforated tests they also stream out through the minute pores in the wall.

Many Foraminifera exhibit two types of reproduction and two types of shells (*Dimorphism*)—a smaller shell (*megalospheric*) with a large initial chamber (*proloculum*), produced by budding or by vegetative reproduction; and a larger shell (*microspheric*) with a small proloculum, produced sexually. Megalospheric shells are usually the ones found, owing to greater abundance as compared with the microspheric forms. In fact, among many fossil species none of the latter is known, because they have not been discovered, because they have been described as other species, or because they were never preserved. Some writers have reported certain species to have three different forms of tests (*Trimorphism*).

In Fig. 10 the cycle of reproduction is illustrated diagrammatically. A megalospheric individual *A* is shown in the process of breaking up into many small bodies, composed of protoplasm and a nucleus, designated *zoospores* or *swarmers*. These swarmers develop flagella, leave the parent test, move about until they meet other swarmers from other megalospheric tests of the same species, and then fuse with these in pairs to produce a *zygote* (*B–E*). The zygote secretes a small shell around itself (*F*), the proloculum of the microspheric shell, and develops into a mature organism, building during its growth a large, many-chambered test (*G–H*) and becoming multinucleate. The many nuclei are scattered throughout the organism. As growth proceeds, these increase in number, and each gathers a small quantity of cytoplasm around itself. Finally, as uninucleate bodies, each leaves the parent test, develops minute pseudopodia (*I*), and secretes around itself a proloculum much larger than the one in the parent shell (*J*). This is the proloculum of the megalospheric test. As the animal grows (*K–L*), new chambers are added one by one, and the single nucleus changes its position so as to be almost always in the middle chamber of the test. As growth continues, the single nucleus finally splits up into a great many small nuclei, of which each gathers some cytoplasm about itself, becomes a swarmer, and leaves the test to repeat the cycle just outlined (*A'*). This life cycle, consisting of alternating sexual and asexual generations, is known as reproduction by *alternation of generations*.

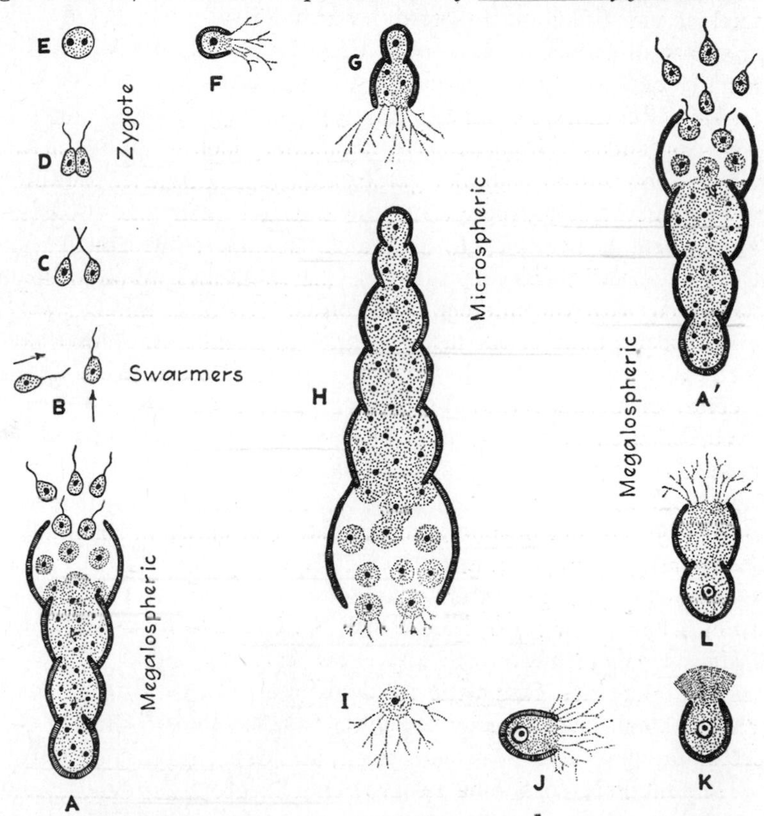

Fig. 10.—Diagram showing the cycle of reproduction in Foraminifera. *A, A'*. Megalospheric shells being deserted by swarmers. *B*. Swarmer from *A* being approached by swarmer from another megalospheric shell similar to *A*. *C–E*. Swarmers join to form a zygote. *F–G*. Zygote secretes the microspheric proloculum (*F*) and develops into the mature individual which secretes the remainder of the microspheric shell. *H*. Mature microspheric shell being deserted by numerous uninucleate bodies. *I–J*. Uninucleate body after leaving shell and later with megalospheric proloculum which it has secreted. *K–L*. Development of shell. *A'*. The beginning of another generation. (*Adapted from Kühn, with considerable modification.*)

Relation of Organism to Test.—The shell or test of the foraminifer is both external and internal, though most of the animal body lies inside the test wall. The shell begins as a small globular chamber called the *proloculum* (first little chamber) and takes a variety of shapes depending upon the manner in which subsequent chambers are added. The changes which take place during growth are shown diagrammatically in Fig. 8. The nucleus usually shifts its position so that it occupies the middle chamber of the test. It should be noted, also, that the test is usually completely surrounded by protoplasm, which adds new material to the surface of the exterior of the test wall, repairs fractures and other injuries, and builds the surface ornamentation where that is present. The wall of the test may be perforated with many minute openings or *foramina* (whence the name *Foraminifera*, bearing minute openings) through which tiny, threadlike pseudopodia protrude; or it may be imperforate, in which case the pseudopodia are given off from the outside surface of the protoplasmic mantle and through the aperture. Perforate forms also have the pseudopodia protruding through the aperture.

The Foraminiferal Test.—The size, composition, form, and architecture of the tests built by Foraminifera vary to such an extent that each of the various characters must be considered separately.

Size and Composition of Shells.—The smaller tests of Foraminifera range from 0.01 mm. to twice that dimension in diameter, as in some of the *Lagynidae*. The common forms range from 0.1 to 5 mm. in diameter with the common diameter of the order of magnitude of 0.5 mm. Some forms attain unusually large dimensions, as *Parafusulina*, which may be 70 mm. long, and *Neusina*, which may reach the surprisingly large size of 190 mm.

The shells of Foraminifera are composed of gelatinous, pseudochitinous (mucoid), chitinous, calcareous, siliceous (?), or "ferruginous" materials secreted by the organism or of particles of foreign matter selected from the bottom and cemented together by one of the substances just named. Tests thus made of foreign matter are said to be *agglutinated*.

Very few Foraminifera are without tests, and even the so-called naked forms have a slightly stiffened but flexible surface. The most primitive tests are probably those composed of gelatinous and chitinous substances. These have little chance of preservation. The next step in shell composition is shown by tests with organic or inorganic particles adhering to the outer surface of the chitin. It is but an added step from this type to the one in which the particles are actually cemented together by chitin. Replacement of the chitin by a calcareous cement gives a shell composed entirely of calcium carbonate without the foreign matter. A very few forms have tests partly or wholly composed of silica. It has been postulated that in some cases this silica is of organic secretion, but recent studies cast *grave doubt on this possibility*. The following table indicates the various combinations of materials in the different types of tests:

1. Organism with stiffened but flexible outer surface.
2. Test composed of gelatinous or chitinous matter.
3. Test of chitin with attached foreign particles.
4. Test of foreign particles cemented with chitin.
5. Test of foreign particles cemented by calcareous or siliceous material.
6. Test entirely of calcium carbonate.
7. Test partly or entirely of silica (doubtful).

It must be emphasized that this table does not necessarily represent a developmental or evolutionary series. There is still disagreement among leading students of the Foraminifera as to the succession of the different types of tests. It seems best, therefore, to give only the general features of each type mentioned above, to point out actual relations of the building materials, and to refrain from decision respecting order of development.

Gelatinous and Chitinous Tests.—Tests composed of these materials are very simple but do possess an aperture and have a definite shape. That chitin was one of the earliest substances used for tests is suggested by the fact that many Foraminifera, regardless of the material of the mature test, have a thin, chitinous, inner layer in the earliest portion of the shell. Purely chitinous tests are not common among living Foraminifera.

Agglutinated Tests.—Agglutinated tests are usually found among the more primitive groups of Foraminifera. The tests are composed of mica flakes, quartz grains, sponge spicules, shell fragments, and other foreign materials, either cemented to an inner chitinous layer or cemented together by ferruginous, chitinous, or calcareous matter. The actual materials which are used in the construction of the agglutinated tests are selected from the bottom deposits by the organisms, and they often exhibit a very great range in character. Some Foraminifera appear to have surprising selective ability. Others, however, show little if any discrimination in the selection of materials. *Astrorhiza* utilizes mud, sand, sponge spicules, shell fragments, etc., without discrimination. *Marsipella* uses mostly sponge spicules; *Psammosphaera fusca* selects nothing but sand grains, and these often of a single color; *P. parva* not only uses sand grains of a fairly uniform size but also frequently adds one large acerose sponge spicule which is built into the test wall in such a way that each end of the spicule protrudes (Fig. 11[7]). Other forms select only mica flakes, even though they are uncommon in the bottom deposits; and still others show a preference for sponge spicules, utilizing the large unbroken ones for constructing a framework and the smaller broken fragments for filling in the polygonal areas between the definitely arranged spicules in the main meshwork.

Calcareous and Siliceous Tests.—Cushman maintains that calcareous tests may develop directly from agglutinated forms by first having the calcium carbonate replace the "ferruginous" cement and then finally made to comprise the entire test, with complete exclusion of agglutinated foreign particles. He further holds that imperforate calcareous tests are more primitive than perforate ones. Galloway, on the other hand, considers that the agglutinated forms have never developed into any other type but represent rather the end products of several different lines of shell development. Calcareous tests are thought by him to have been formed directly from gelatinous forms.

Whatever their development, calcareous tests are very abundantly represented in present marine foraminiferal faunas and also are well represented among the more recent fossil species. Siliceous forms are uncommon among both living and fossil species and may or may not represent silica secreted by the organism.

FORM AND ARCHITECTURE. *Form.*—The typical foraminiferal test consists fundamentally of a series of chambers arranged more or less symmetrically with respect to the initial globular chamber or proloculum. A few shells have only one chamber, such as the flask-shaped *Lagena* (Fig. 11[2–3]), in which case the proloculum and test are the same. Such a test is said to be *monothalamous* or *unilocular*. The majority of the tests, however, are *polythalamous* or *multilocular*.

Formation of Test.—Probably the simplest of all tests is represented by *Lagena*, which is flask-shaped and unilocular, with the single opening or aperture at the end of the neck. Without the neck this test is exactly like the proloculum. Possibly more primitive, but not simpler, are the stellate tests of *Rhabdammina*, which are composed of a central body and radiating tubular arms made out of the material collected around the pseudopodia; or those of *Hyperammina*, in which the test is a tubular body (Fig. 11[10,11]). Next after the single-chambered test is that which consists of an elongated, tubular chamber usually coiled in some fashion about the proloculum (Fig. 11[6]).

In multilocular forms, after the first chamber has been constructed, further growth of the organism causes the protoplasm to overflow through the aperture to the outside where it collects and immediately begins to construct a new chamber, connected with the proloculum but not necessarily of the same shape or size (Fig. 8). If the protrusion of protoplasm is such that it surrounds the aperture in a symmetrical manner, the new chamber will surround the aperture of the proloculum in much the same manner as a collar. If the proloculum is entirely covered by the protruding protoplasm, then the new chamber will completely surround it. Collection of the protoplasm on only one side of the aperture will cause the new chamber to be formed in a corresponding position. It is obvious, therefore, that with growth many different arrangements of chambers may result, depending upon the relations between the protruding protoplasm and the aperture of the proloculum. The overflowing of the protoplasm is not a random matter but follows a very definite system for the individuals of each species, though the system is not always the same throughout the life of a given individual.

In *Nodosaria* successive chambers are arranged in a linear series with the base of one chamber surrounding the aperture of the preceding (Fig. 11[16]). Such a test may be referred to as *uniserial*. In a *biserial* form the chambers are arranged in two rows or series (Fig. 11[17]). This arrangement is illustrated in *Textularia* and has been designated *textularian* by some. *Triserial* forms have three chambers to a whorl, so that in such forms as *Verneuiliana* the chambers appear to be arranged in three series or rows (Fig. 11[18]). In *Lenticulina* the chambers are arranged about the proloculum in a planospiral fashion (Fig. 11[21]), and the test is said to be *planospiral*. If the chambers are arranged along a spiral line which does not lie in a plane, the test is *trochoid*. A

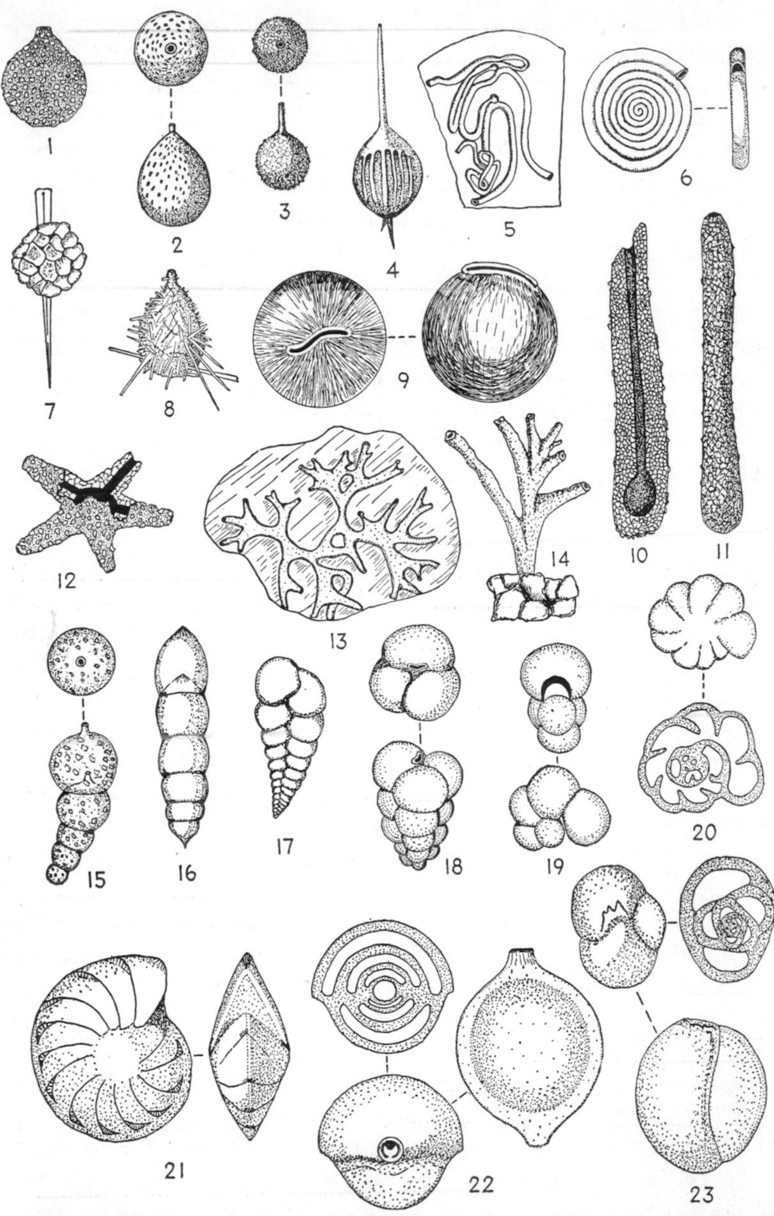

FIG. 11.—Foraminiferal tests showing shape, size, architecture, arrangement of chambers, nature of aperture, and character of test material. 1. *Saccammina* (agglutinated, ×7½). 2. *Lagena* (perforated, calcareous, ×37½). 3. *Lagena*

coiled test may be *evolute*, in which case all coils are visible; or completely *involute*, with only the last chamber, or the chambers of the last coil or whorl, visible. In a few shells the chambers may be so arranged that they have a definite angular relation with preceding chambers. In *Biloculina* (Fig. 11[22]) one chamber is 180 deg. from the preceding chamber; in *Triloculina* the difference is 120 deg., and in *Quinqueloculina* the angular relation between adjacent chambers is 72 deg. Some foraminiferal tests closely resemble small bushes and are designated *arborescent*. Depending upon the shape, tests may also be described by such terms as stellate (star shaped), discoid (disklike), flabelliform (fan shaped), pyriform (pear shaped), fistulose (having an abnormal opening into the test), etc. (see Fig. 11).

The arrangement of chambers often changes during the development of an individual, and the adult test may show several types of architecture. Development may be progressive or retrogressive. In certain forms, the chambers of the test are divided into smaller compartments (*chamberlets*) by a variety of dividing partitions, and the internal structure as a consequence becomes somewhat complicated (Fig. 12). Taking into account all of the different architectural types of tests, as well as the combinations of the materials of which they are composed, it is almost unbelievable that single-celled organisms could ever have constructed such tests as are known.

The order in which the various types of tests have developed is not yet completely known. Within the life cycle of certain species, definite architectural types follow each other. The succession, however, is not always the same in different species; hence, it is not possible to consider such successions as evolutionary series. Until more data are available, this moot question must be left in its present unsatisfactory condition.

(spinose, ×30). 4. *Lagena* (spinose, ×37½). 5. *Hyperammina* (×7½). 6. *Ammodiscus* (×5). 7. *Psammosphaera* (agglutinated, with single acerose sponge spicule, ×20). 8. *Reophax* (agglutinated with sponge spicules, ×25). 9. *Pilulina* (agglutinated, fine felted sponge spicules, ×6). 10, 11. *Hyperammina* (agglutinated, ×5). 12. *Rhabdammina* (agglutinated, ×5). 13. *Sagenella* (agglutinated, ×5). 14. *Dendrophrya* (arborescent, agglutinated, ×15). 15. *Hormosina* (agglutinated, ×7½). 16. *Nodosaria* (smooth, calcareous, ×15). 17. *Textularia* (biserial, calcareous, ×12½). 18. *Verneuiliana* (triserial, calcareous, ×12½). 19. *Globigerina* (planospiral, calcareous, ×25). 20. *Endothyra* (calcareous, ×12–15). 21. *Lenticulina* (involute, calcareous, ×6). 22. *Biloculina* (biloculine, calcareous, ×12½, ×20). 23. *Miliolina* (quinqueloculine, calcareous, ×8). (*All except* 20 *after Brady*.)

Aperture.—Each test has at least one opening or *aperture* through which the pseudopodia can protrude and the reproductive bodies escape. Complex forms, as *Fusulina* (Fig. 12), may show great variation in size, shape, and location of the aperture; and some possess numerous apertural openings instead of a single one. Apertures of several kinds are illustrated in Fig. 11.

Surface Ornamentation.—The exterior surfaces of calcareous Foraminifera are often highly ornamented with spines, nodes,

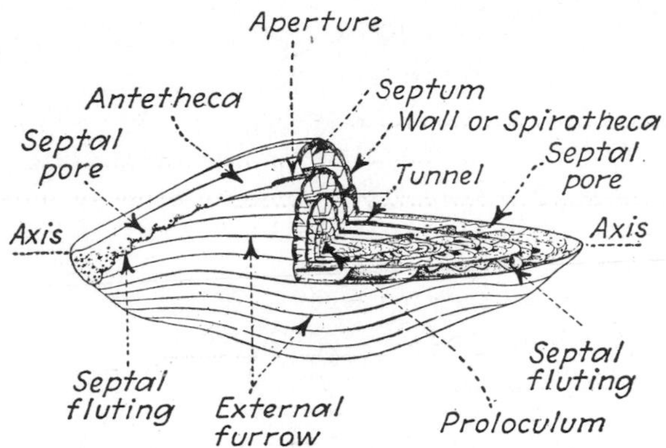

Fig. 12.—Diagram of a complex foraminiferal test (Fusulinid). (*After Dunbar and Condra.*)

knobs, costae, raised meshwork, etc. These features may be characteristic of the entire test, or they may be limited to certain chambers. They are often partly or entirely lost in the *gerontic* or old-age stage of growth.

Wall Structure.—In addition to the exterior ornamentation, the wall of the foraminiferal test may be thickened greatly by the addition of shell matter to the exterior of the chambers after they have been completed. This additional material often gives to the shell a much smoother appearance. The walls may also be perforated by small pores (*foramina*), in which case they are said to be *perforate*, or they may be solid (*imperforate*). The perforations when present may have either a regular or irregular disposition in the wall. In addition, the wall of the test may exhibit considerable range in microscopic structure, and in many groups this structure is of the greatest value in classifying the various forms.

Classification of Foraminifera.—The final classification of any group of organisms should rest on certain well-defined and generally accepted biological and paleontological principles among which are:

1. Every group of organisms has evolved through geologic time, undergoing accumulative modifications in the process.
2. The biogenetic law states that the life history of an individual recapitulates fairly completely or incompletely the developmental history of the race to which it belongs.
3. The order of development is: simple, complex, specialized, degenerate. Simple organisms do not seem to evolve from complex, specialized, or degenerate forms.

In addition to these general principles, certain features of the foraminiferal shells themselves are of use for marking out the minor subdivisions of the order. These in order of importance are:

1. Material of the wall; structure of the wall; character of the aperture; and number and arrangement of chambers.
2. Shapes of tests; structural features such as pores, septa, etc.
3. Ornamentation, size, etc.

Unfortunately the two leading American students of Foraminifera do not agree on the classification. Cushman has subdivided the order into 47 families, which are not in many cases the same as the 35 families proposed by Galloway. Until this discordance is eliminated, it seems best not to attempt any general grouping of the Foraminifera.

Ecology of Foraminifera.—The Foraminifera are either planktonic or benthonic. Large extinct forms, such as *Nummulites* and *Fusulina*, were benthonic, and most of the Paleozoic and early Mesozoic forms also appear to have had that habit of life. Planktonic forms first became numerous in the later Mesozoic and since that time have been abundant. The present calcareous deep-sea oozes owe their origin very largely to the planktonic *Biloculina* and *Globigerina*. Existing knowledge indicates that Foraminifera show a nice adjustment to temperature and depth, and because of this fact it has been possible to separate them into definite groups of species based on these relations. Hence, when these same groups of species are found as fossils in the later part of the geologic column, important inferences concerning ancient sea conditions may be drawn. Natland[1] has shown this relation in graphic form.

It seems likely that only a small percentage of the tests of Foraminifera are preserved. They are very fragile and hence very easily broken or dissolved. The calcareous tests of planktonic Foraminifera disappear by solution as they sink from the surface toward the bottom, and few or none attain depths as great as 15,000 feet. Siliceous tests may reach much greater depths. The planktonic Foraminifera constitute one of the components of the fundamental food supply of the ocean and are swallowed in large numbers by many marine animals. Myriads of tests are thus destroyed or reduced to fragments in the alimentary canals of the organisms. Burrowing animals also are responsible for the destruction of many tests.

Geologic History.—Foraminifera may have lived in the Pre-Cambrian seas, and fossil forms have been reported by Barrois from the Pre-Cambrian of Brittany, but doubt has been cast on the accuracy of the identification of the "fossils" and the age of the strata. True fossil Foraminifera have been found in the Cambrian and Ordovician, and by Silurian time they were fairly common.[2] Upward in the stratigraphic column they continue to increase in number. *Endothyra* is very abundant in Mississippian strata, and the various *Fusulinidae* characterize the Pennsylvanian and Permian strata throughout the world. In some cases entire beds of limestone are composed in large part of the spindle-shaped fusulinid tests. According to Cushman the tests of all Paleozoic foraminifera were arenaceous, but some workers are not of the same opinion.

It was not until the later Mesozoic that the planktonic foraminifers attained abundant representation—a condition which they have maintained to the present. Early in the era the fossil record is sparse, but during the Cretaceous there was a great increase in the number and variety of forms. Many families, still extant, started at that time. A gradual replacement of old

[1] NATLAND, M., The temperature- and depth-distribution of some recent and fossil foraminifera in the southern California region, *Bull. Scripps Inst. Oceanography, Univ. Calif., Tech. Ser.*, vol. 3, pp. 225–230, 1 table, 1933.

[2] Very recent work in Oklahoma, Indiana, Illinois, and Wisconsin indicates that "siliceous" foraminifera are not only present but also abundant in certain strata.

forms by modern types ensued during the Tertiary and has continued down to the present time. Large benthonic forms, known as *Nummulites*, flourished in profusion during the early part of the Tertiary in the great Tethys sea, lying at that time between Europe and Africa and over parts of southern Asia, and formed thick beds of limestone now exposed in the Alps, elsewhere in southern Europe and Asia, and in northern Africa. The blocks of the great pyramids of Gizeh, near Cairo, are composed of this "nummulitic limestone." Cretaceous and Tertiary strata exposed along the coastal plain in eastern and southern United States contain an abundance of calcareous foraminifera; and, finally, on the sea bottoms of the present, where conditions are favorable, "foraminiferal" limestones of future geologic periods are being formed.

Amoebaea

The protozoans comprising this order are not known as fossils, but peculiar minute calcareous bodies resembling "coccoliths" have been considered by some writers to have come from organisms included in the Amoebaea. It is possible that these small fossils should be referred to the Mastigophora (see page 34).

Testacea (Thecamoeba)

This order is composed of amoeboid protozoans which are surrounded by a single-chambered test into which the organism can draw its entire body. Usually there is only one aperture through which the pseudopodia may be extruded.

The test, which varies somewhat in form and structure, has, as a base, a chitinous or pseudochitinous (mucoid) membrane to which may be cemented foreign bodies acquired by the organism from the sea bottom or siliceous (rarely calcareous) platelets possibly secreted by the organism. The foreign bodies are sand grains (usually quartz) or diatom shells (Fig. 9 *G*). The platelets, which may be denticulated, are in the form of round, oval, elliptical, or quadrangular scales or disks, in some forms are disposed in imbricating fashion, and generally have a definite arrangement.

There does not seem to be any fossil record of the platelets described, but it is altogether possible that future work may show their presence in sedimentary rocks.

Heliozoa

Heliozoans are generally spherical organisms with radiating axopodia. They resemble the radiolarians but differ in lacking the central capsule. The body may be naked, covered by a gelatinous mantle, or provided with a lattice-like test which may or may not have spinelike spicules (Fig. 9 *H*). Foreign bodies, as sand grains and diatom shells, are sometimes found attached to the exterior surface of the organism. Siliceous scales and spines are found on a few forms.

The elements of the tests of heliozoans are not known as fossils. Since most of the forms having preservable test material are inhabitants of fresh-water pools and ponds, the chance of leaving a fossil record is remote.

Radiolaria

Radiolarians are exclusively marine, planktonic organisms characterized by a radiating arrangement of the filamentous pseudopodia (whence the name *Radiolaria*, radiating). They live mostly in tropical waters at or near the surface. When the siliceous tests are abandoned they slowly sink to the bottom where they may form important deposits if other substances are not present in sufficient quantity to mask them. These deposits are known as "radiolarian" ooze and cover some 2 to 3 per cent (2,000,000 sq. miles) of the present ocean bottoms. Radiolarian ooze may form on any bottom, but it is usually masked by other sediments on bottoms of depths less than 12,000 ft. On bottoms of greater depth foraminiferal and other soluble shells go into solution before reaching the bottom so that the tests of Radiolaria constitute much or most of the deposits. Radiolarian ooze closely resembles the ooze formed by minute plants (*diatoms*) and known as diatomaceous ooze. The former is exclusively marine, whereas the latter may be formed in either fresh or salt water. In both deposits the shells are always microscopic in size.

The body of the radiolarian is ordinarily spherical or spheroidal in form. It is divided into an *intracapsular* portion, composed of tough protoplasm with one or more nuclei, and an *extracapsular* portion, composed of one or more layers of jelly-like protoplasm. These are separated by a variously perforated membranous structure designated the *central capsule.* Radially directed rodlike or threadlike pseudopodia are given off from either of the fleshy portions of the animal.

The radiolarian skeleton is partly external but mainly internal. It is composed of *acanthin* (an organic compound similar to

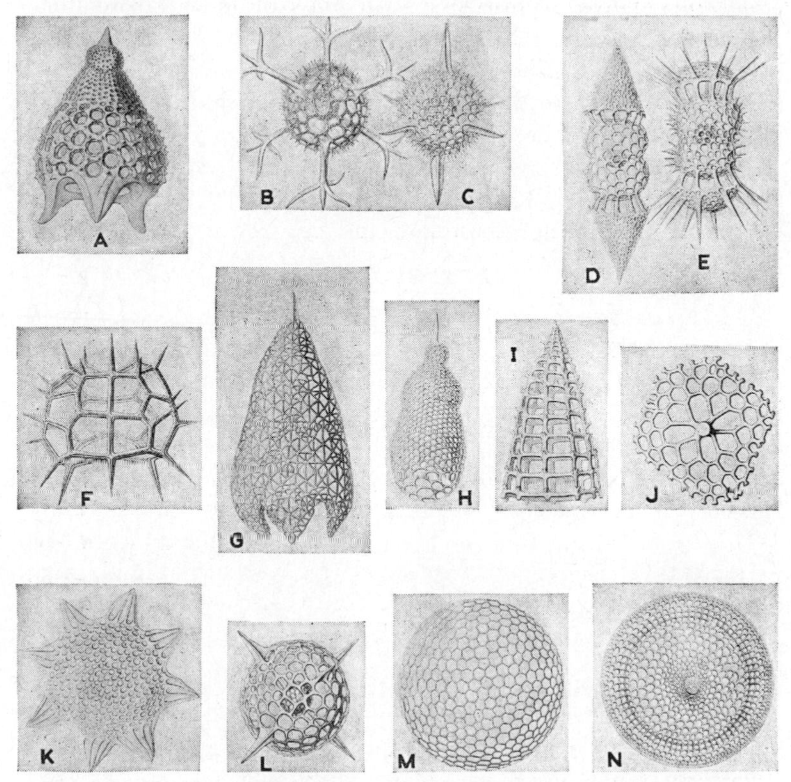

FIG. 13.—Tests of Radiolaria. *A. Podocyrtis* (×250). *B. Hexancistra* (×150). *C, L. Hexalonche* (×200, ×280). *D. Panartus* (×185). *E. Panicium* (×185). *F. Ceratospyris* (×320). *G. Tridictyopus* (×170). *H. Theocapsa* (×200). *I. Bathropyramis* (×160+). *J. Icosaspis* (×280). *K. Heliosestrum* (×165). *M. Aulonia* (×15). *N. Cecryphalium* (×210). (*After Haeckel.*)

chitin) in one group, strontium sulphate in a second small group, and silica in the majority of forms. In every case the skeletal material is secreted by the organism. The skeletal matter may consist of (1) loosely woven rods, spicules, and spines either unattached or fused together; (2) a firm meshwork of globular, conical, stellate, or discoidal shape, with the peripheral parts in some cases produced into simple or branching spines; or (3) a series of concentrically arranged perforated shells of various shapes, held together by minute supporting rods and spines. The skeletons may be symmetrical about a point, a line, or a plane; or they may be without apparent symmetry. They are always small, often have the surfaces exquisitely ornamented by spines and other similar structures, and exhibit great variety in form and architecture (Fig. 13).

The geologic record of Radiolaria, although extending over a great length of time, is a rather meager one. Tests are stated to have been found in rocks of supposed Pre-Cambrian age, and they are known in Paleozoic, Mesozoic, and Cenozoic strata, though rarely in great abundance.

CLASS SPOROZOA

The Sporozoa are exclusively parasitic and reproduce by means of *spores.* They possess neither cilia nor flagella and, except for a few forms which are able to move about by means of pseudopodia, lack the power of locomotion. Since the organism does not possess any preservable skeleton or test, a fossil record is not probable. Should the host of a sporozoan be perfectly preserved, however, as is the case with the hairy mammoths so perfectly preserved in the frozen tundra of Siberia, it is conceivable that they, as inhabitants of the fossilized animal, might also be preserved.

CLASS INFUSORIA

This class includes ciliated protozoans having a fixed wall and permanent shape but almost invariably without a test of any sort (one genus, *Coleps,* however, does have a test of platelets); hence, a fossil record is not likely. The class is usually divided into two orders—*Ciliata,* with cilia throughout life; and *Suctoria,* with cilia only in the very early growth stages.

References[1]

Brady, B. H.: Report on the Foraminifera dredged by *H. M. S. Challenger.* during the years 1873 to 1876. *Rep. Voy. Challenger Zool.,* vol. 9, 1884.

[1] No attempt has been made to list a complete bibliography on the different phyla. Only the most recent and comprehensive works, and special articles which are of such character as to be significant in the present discussion, are listed.

CUSHMAN, J. A.: Foraminifera, their classification and economic use (2d ed.), accompanied by an illustrated key to the genera of the Foraminifera. *Cushman Laboratory for Foraminiferal Res., Special Pubs.* 4 and 5, respectively, 1933.

GALLOWAY, J. J.: "A Manual of Foraminifera." The Principia Press, Bloomington, Ind., 1933.

HAECKEL, E.: "Die Radiolaren." *Eine Monographie* I, II, 1887. Report on the Radiolaria collected by *H. M. S. Challenger*. *Rep. Voy. Challenger Zool.*, vol. 18, 1862–1887.

KUDO, R. R.: "Handbook of Protozoology." Charles C. Thomas, Springfield, Ill., and Baltimore, Md., 1931.

CHAPTER III

PORIFERA

INTRODUCTION

The phylum Porifera[1] includes a restricted group of simple animals, the most familiar, but by no means the most typical, of which are the several sponges of commerce. The Porifera constitute the earliest and simplest group of the Metazoa, animals composed of many cells which are differentiated into definite tissues and organs, and represent the first advance above the Protozoa. They are typically sessile, aquatic, colonial organisms, living mainly in marine environments, but a few forms dwell in fresh water. In mature life they form a part of the benthos. Because of close resemblance to plants they were once referred to that kingdom; but the possession of a digestive system and other typical animal characteristics and the lack of either chlorophyll or cellulose stamp them as animals. They were once also referred to the Coelenterata.

CHARACTER OF THE ANIMAL

The body of a simple sponge may be compared to a vase, attached at the base, open at the top, and with the wall perforated by numerous canals (Fig. 14 *A*). The canals open into a central cavity known as the *cloaca* or *paragastric cavity*, which leads to the opening in the top of the organism, known as the *osculum*. Water enters the organism through the canals, passes into the cloaca, and is expelled through the osculum. The osculum may thus be thought of as a primitive anal opening. In some forms the cloaca has considerable depth, whereas in others it is very shallow and may be little more than a depression or flat space on the upper surface. All sponges have some parts of the inner surface lined with collared flagellate cells. In simple

[1] Porifera—L. *porus*, passage or pore + *ferre*, to bear; referring to the fact that the wall of the sponge is perforated by simple pores or complicated passages.

forms these are confined to the cloaca. In the more complex sponges the wall is thick, the structure is less simple, the canal system is considerably more complicated, the collared flagellate cells line parts of the canals, and there may be numerous oscula (Fig. 14).

Shape of Animal.—The shape of a sponge varies greatly. It may be cylindrical, spherical, globose, pyriform, foliate or leaf-like, explanate, or discoidal. Some species have long or short stems by which they are attached to objects on the bottom; others are stemless and are attached by their undersurfaces; and still others are anchored by root tufts of spicules, as illustrated by the living *Euplectella* (Fig. 18 *B–C*). Occasional forms are encrusting, and a few are more or less dendritic with the branches separated or united to form a more or less complex network. Body form may be constant for a given species, but since it commonly varies with the environment regardless of the species, shape may indicate little with respect to taxonomic relationships. The dimensions of sponges range from less than a millimeter to as much as 2 m.

The Body Wall.—The wall of the sponge consists of two well-defined layers of cells separated by an irregular layer of protoplasm (Fig. 14 *A*). The outer or external layer is known as the *ectoderm* and is composed of a single layer of pavement cells. These cells extend into the canals that perforate the body wall. The main function of the ectoderm seems to be that of protection. The inner layer, known as the *endoderm*, lines the cloaca and chambers and parts or the whole of the canals in the wall. The endoderm consists either of flagellated columnar cells tightly packed together or of thin pavement cells. The flagellate cells have a collar surrounding the *flagellum* and closely resemble an individual of the *Choanoflagellata* of the Protozoa (Fig. 7 *B*). These cells are designated *choanocytes*. The motions of the flagella draw currents of water into the wall of the sponge whence it is expelled through the osculum or through oscula. The endodermal cells absorb food from the passing water and yield waste products thereto. Between the endoderm and ectoderm are numerous spaces filled by a third or intermediate layer known as the *mesogloea*. This is composed of clear gelatinous protoplasm containing nucleated cells of various kinds. Certain of these, originating in the ectoderm, secrete the skeletal elements;

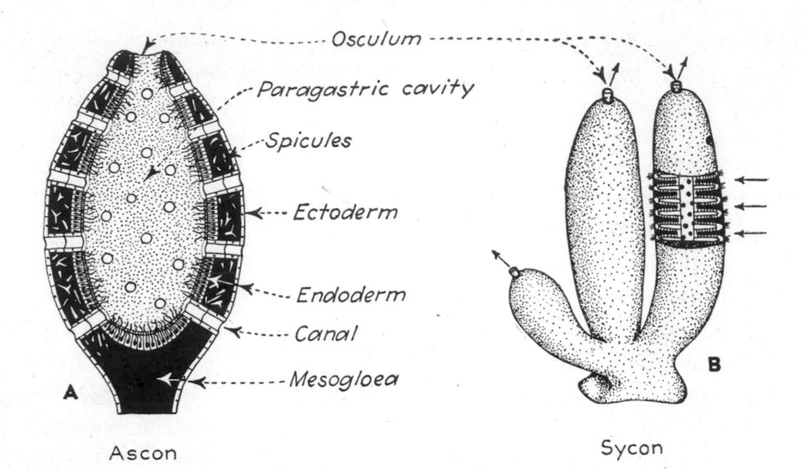

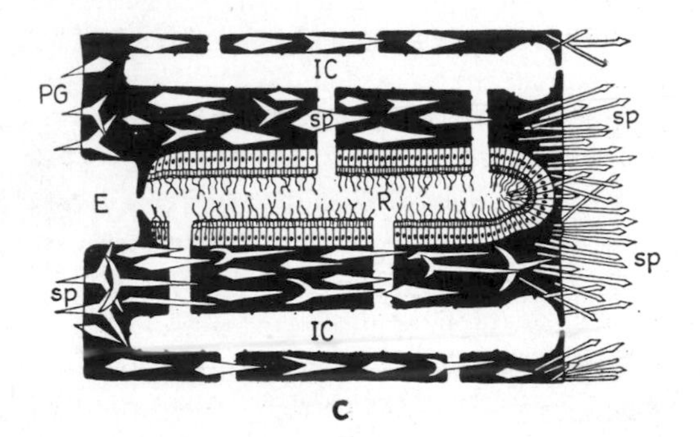

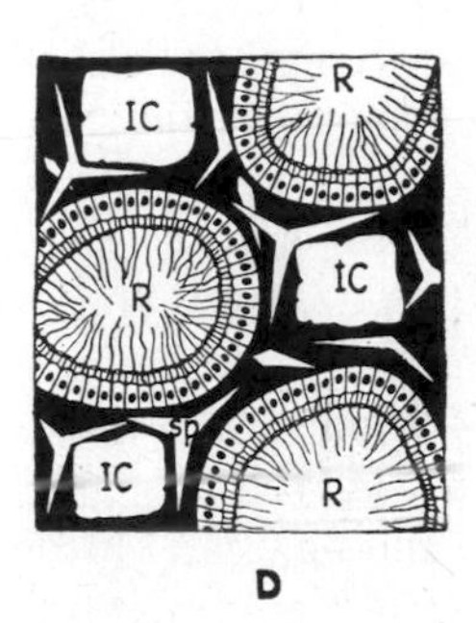

C – *Ciliated chambers*
DP – *Dermal pores*
E – *Excurrent passage*
Ex – *Excurrent canals*
IC – *Incurrent canals*
O – *Osculum*
PG – *Paragastric cavity*
R – *Radial canal*
SD – *Subdermal cavities*
sp – *Spicules*

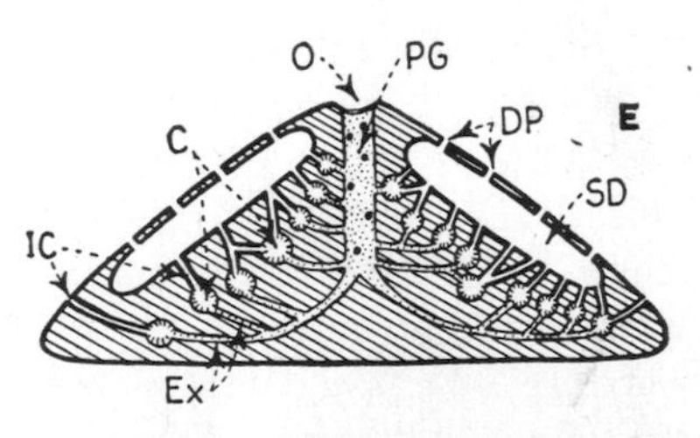

FIG. 14.—Modern sponges. Diagrams showing the three types of canal systems, shape and general structure of the entire body, and relation of the skeletal elements to the body wall. *A*. Diagrammatic. *B–D*. *Sycon gelatinosum: B*, view of a colony, with a small part of one branch cut away to show the internal structure; *C*, longitudinal section of several of the canals in the wall; *D*, transverse section of several canals. *E*. *Spongilla*, a fresh-water sponge. The spicules lie in the cross-lined portion which is the mesogloea. (*B–E modified after Parker and Haswell.*)

others—the wandering amoeboid cells—move about from one part of the sponge to another, and some develop into reproductive cells. Some cells of the mesogloea function as very crude muscular fibers.

The Canal System.—Most of the body wall of a sponge is ramified by some system of canals through which the currents of water produced by the choanocytes move. These canals begin on the exterior surface in *dermal* or *inhalant pores* and traverse the wall in various ways in different species to terminate finally in *exhalant pores* in the wall of the cloaca or in numerous oscula on the exterior surface of the sponge. In simple sponges, designated the *Ascon* type, the wall of the organism is perforated by numerous canals which extend directly from the exterior to the central cavity or cloaca. In these forms the cloaca is always lined with choanocytes, and similar cells may line parts of the canals. Water is drawn in through the canals and expelled through the osculum at the top (Fig. 14 *A*).

In somewhat more complex sponges, included in the *Sycon* type, the wall is thickened and is traversed by numerous straight radial passages which are generally arranged in a regular fashion (Fig. 14 *B–D*). Of these there are two kinds—the *incurrent canals*, which open to the exterior; and the *radial chambers*, which communicate with the cloaca through *excurrent passages*. The radial chambers and incurrent canals are disposed in parallel positions and are separated by fairly thin layers of fleshy substance which is perforated at numerous points by small pores, thus permitting communication between the two passages. Each radial chamber connects with an excurrent passage through a single pore, and the passage communicates directly with the cloaca (Fig. 14 *C*). The incurrent canal is lined with ectodermal cells, the radial chamber with choanocytes, and both the excurrent passages and the cloaca with flattened nonflagellate endodermal cells. In this form of sponge the radial chambers act as pumping stations. By the motion of the flagella water is drawn into the chamber through the incurrent canals and expelled into the cloaca through the excurrent passages. It then passes out of the cloaca through the osculum. Lying between the ectodermal and endodermal layers is the mesogloea in which the spicules of the skeleton are embedded (Fig. 14 *D*).

Figure 14 *E* illustrates an arrangement of canals known as the *Rhagon* type. This arrangement is characteristic of the siliceous sponges and represents a more complicated system than either of the two already described. The water enters a large vestibular cavity through dermal pores; flows through tiny canals into small spherical "ciliated chambers"; from which it moves into other tiny canals that lead inward into the cloaca; and finally flows out of the sponge through the osculum at the top. The skeletal elements lie embedded in the mesogloea between the ectoderm and endoderm.

Reproduction.—Two types of reproduction are exhibited by the Porifera—one sexual, the other asexual. In the sexual the embryo is formed in the mesogloea from the union of male and female sexual cells developed there from wandering amoeboid cells. This embryo is released into the cloaca from which it escapes to the outside through the osculum. After a period of free life as a ciliated larva, it settles to the bottom, attaches itself to some object, and develops into a mature individual. The asexual method, designated *vegetative reproduction* and sometimes referred to as *budding*, is by far the more common method of reproduction among the Porifera. The adult gives off budlike extensions from the body wall. These develop directly into new organisms which are internally connected with the parent (Fig. 14 *B*). The buds may remain attached to the parent throughout life, or they may be set adrift to settle down ultimately as separate individuals. So-called "colonies" are built when the buds remain with the parents, though it is questionable if the new buds should any more be considered new individuals than the twigs of a tree should be considered new trees. Fission is rare among the sponges, but if a piece of sponge is detached from the living individual it may develop into a mature form.

THE SKELETON

The skeleton or skeletal elements of the Porifera are the only parts ever fossilized, except for the rare cases in which the body, flattened and crushed, leaves an impression. The skeleton, which is not always developed, may consist of two types of material: (1) a leathery substance known as *spongin;* and (2) small skeletal elements, designated *spicules*, composed of silica or calcium carbonate (Fig. 15). The familiar bath sponge illustrates the first type of skeleton, and the beautiful glass sponge is representative of the second. The spicules of the second type may be scattered loosely throughout the mesogloea, or they may be united to form some kind of rigid meshwork. In either case the skeleton lies embedded in the mesogloea, where it is secreted, and is a true internal supporting structure. The skeletal material is almost always secreted by special cells (*scleroblasts*) which first form in the ectoderm and later migrate inward to the mesogloea. Fleshy spicules, however, may be formed by any one of the layers of the body wall, and, in a few sponges, foreign bodies, such as sand grains, sponge spicules, and siliceous shells of various types, may be utilized.

General Skeletal Structure.—In certain groups of sponges (including those commonly used for washing) there are no stony spicules. The skeleton consists entirely of silklike spongin fiber. This material, which is an almost insoluble nitrogenous organic substance containing iodine, is composed of exceedingly fine threads which branch and anastomose or are woven and felted together into a firm but elastic supporting structure. Spongin rarely assumes the form of spicules.

Some species of sponges, entirely devoid of spicules, have the skeletal structure composed of spongin strengthened by foreign bodies of various sorts, which serve the same purpose as the spicules. Such bodies are obtained from the bottom deposits by the sponge and include radiolarian and foraminiferal shells, sponge spicules, and sand grains.

Many sponges have the skeletal structures composed of spongin fibers and various kinds of siliceous spicules, and many of the latter may lie unattached in the mesogloea. On the death of the organism the siliceous spicules are released and become a part of the bottom deposits.

In some of the more complex sponges, such as the living *Euplectella* and the fossil *Hydnoceras*, the siliceous spicules may be arranged regularly, especially in relation to the canals of the sponge body, and may be interwoven, matted, cemented, or fused together to form a firm, rigid framework. Such skeletons stand a good chance of becoming fossilized, and the fossils *Protospongia*, *Hydnoceras*, and *Prismodictya* are typical examples (Fig. 19 *A–D*).

The calcareous sponges have spicules of various kinds composed of calcium carbonate in the form of calcite or aragonite. Each ray of the spicule is formed by the secretory activity of one cell. The individual spicules show variable forms, with a triradiate one the most common (Fig. 15^{24-27}). They may lie loose in the mesogloea or may be fused together to form a firm, rigid skeleton.

Fossilization of Skeletal Material.—The environment created by decomposition of the flesh of a dead sponge is one in which the extremely delicate spicules may be dissolved very easily. This is especially true of the readily soluble calcareous spicules and to a lesser degree of the opalized siliceous ones. It often happens, therefore, that much of the skeletal matter of a sponge is destroyed soon after death. Horny and spongin skeletal materials have little or no chance of being preserved.

Even if the spicules escape destruction in the situation just outlined and become a part of the bottom deposits, they may still be subjected to several modifying processes. Changes may take place during lithification of the deposits or after they have been elevated above sea level. Siliceous spicules may be dissolved by percolating ground waters, may be changed to a cryptocrystalline condition, or may be replaced in whole or in part by calcareous or other material. In the same way calcareous spicules may be dissolved or replaced by silica and other substances. It is clear, therefore, that the present condition of a fossil sponge is not necessarily its original one; hence the classification of fossil sponges must rest on the form of the skeleton and spicules as well as on the composition of the material of which they are made. A case in point is *Astraeospongia*, which almost always has the outer portion of the skeleton of calcite, but the inner core is still composed of silica, which appears to have been the original skeletal substance.

Form and Character of Spicules and Skeleton.—Sponge spicules have a wide range of shapes. They are often beautiful in form and exhibit great variety of detail in structure (Fig. 15). They fall rather conveniently into five architectural types.

The first and simplest of these consists typically of a single straight or slightly curved needle-like rod, which is solid if calcareous but possesses a tiny axial canal if siliceous. Such a spicule is said to be *one rayed* or *uniaxial* and is known as a *monaxon* (Fig. 15^{1-15}). Spicules of this type may be smooth, prickly, or knobby. They are very abundant in bottom sediments of present seas and fresh-water bodies, and siliceous

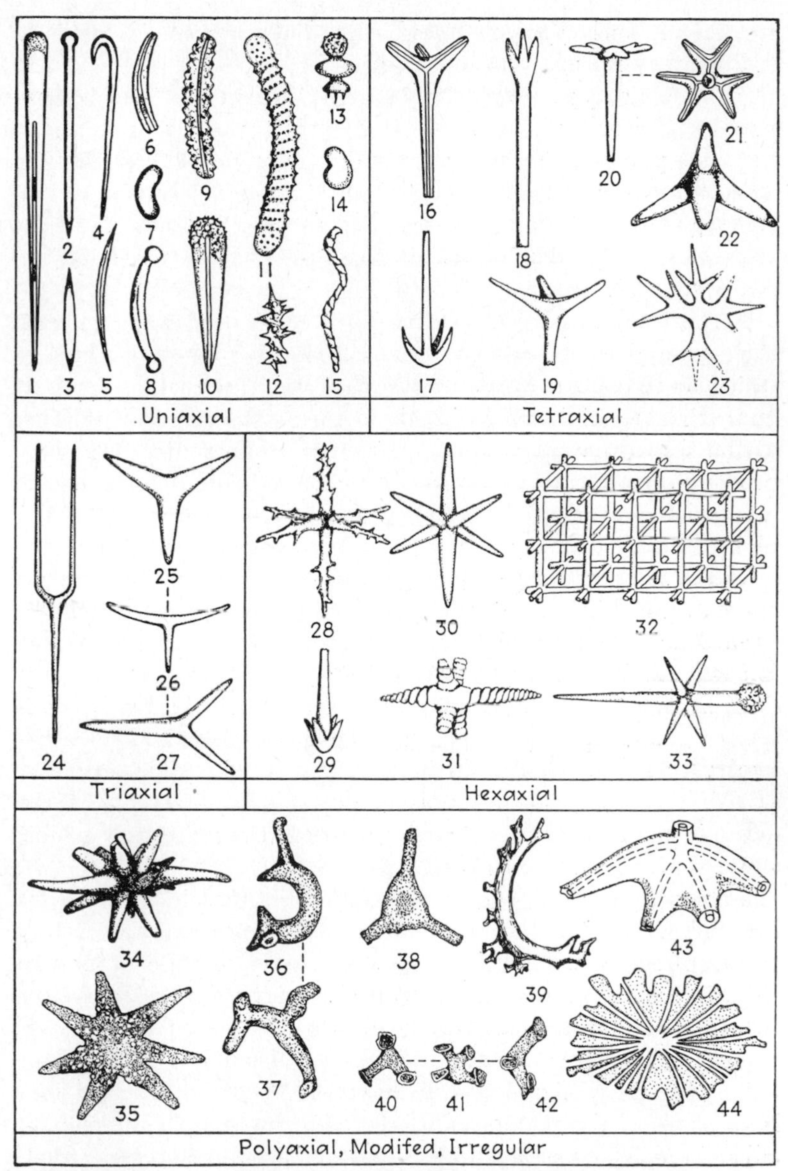

FIG. 15.—Sponge spicules highly magnified. All figures except 32, which is diagrammatic, and 33, which is a spicule from bottom sediments of the Pacific, are fossil forms. (1, 4, 15, 17, 19–22, *and* 39 *after Zittel;* 2–3, 5–14, 16, 18, 23–31, 34–38, *and* 40–44 *after Hinde.*)

spicules of this type are found commonly in certain kinds of sedimentary rocks.

The second type of spicule is *triradiate* or *triaxial* and is composed of calcareous material. It has three rays lying in about the same plane and radiating from a common point (Fig. 15^{24-27}). This type of spicule is not known among siliceous sponges, although certain modified types of four-rayed spicules may bear very close similarity to it. Triradiate spicules may also be designated *triaxons*.

A third type of spicule (*tetraxial*, *tetraxon*), common in both siliceous and calcareous sponges, consists of four rays, three of which lie in a plane at about 120 deg. apart, with the fourth at approximately right angles to the plane at the point of junction of the three rays. Modification of this fundamental form may produce a great variety of spicules. Lengthening of the fourth ray and fusion of the other three produce a form resembling a tack or nail. Curving of the three rays and lengthening of the fourth give a form resembling an anchor. Other peculiar forms are shown in Fig. 15^{16-23}. Three-rayed siliceous spicules may be formed if one of the rays is undeveloped, but these can always be differentiated from true triaxial ones by the composition. Two or more tetraxial spicules may be fused together, as in *Astraeospongia*, in such a way that six rays lie in one plane and the other two, very poorly developed if apparent at all, occur on either side of the plane at the point of junction of the six. In the example cited the rays are 60 deg. apart in the plane and exhibit a stellate structure (Fig. 19 *G*).

A fourth plan of architecture exhibited is that in which three rods are fused together near their mid-points in such a way that any rod is at right angles to the plane of the other two (Fig. 15^{28-33}). The six rays thus produced may or may not have the same lengths. These spicules are designated *hexaxial* or *hexactinellid* (also *hexaxons*). Such spicules serve as excellent building units with which to construct a rigid, durable skeleton. If the ends of the rays of one spicule are fused with the ends of adjacent spicules of a similar character, the result is a rigid meshwork with cubical interspaces (Fig. 15^{32}). The beautiful siliceous skeletons of the so-called "glass sponges," both fossil and living, are composed of hexaxial spicules bound together in one fashion or another. Hexaxial spicules are unknown in living calcareous sponges.

One large group of sponges, known as the *Lithistida*, is characterized by spicules which do not fall in any of the types just described, though they have often been regarded as modified tetraxons and monaxons. These spicules are known as *desmons* or *polyaxons* and are conspicuous because of terminal rootlike protuberances or processes by which adjacent spicules become interlocked and fused to form a massive, stony skeleton, which can be easily fossilized (Fig. 15[34-44]). Skeletons of fossil sponges of this type are common and are known from the Cambrian to the Present.

CLASSIFICATION

Sponges, except for the internal skeleton and the differentiation of the body wall into two definite layers, are quite similar to the colonial forms of the Protozoa, and it is thought by some investigators that the Porifera evolved from some ancestral stock like the Mastigophora of the Protozoa, because of the presence of the choanocytes in the endoderm of the body. In the typical sponge there are no localized nerve cells, no blood or circulatory system, and no organized muscular tissue, though certain cells in the mesogloea may perform functions suggesting some of these. The differentiation of cells into ectoderm, endoderm, and mesogloea, in spite of the simplicity of the sponge body, marks that animal as a metazoan, though a very primitive one.

On the basis of character and composition of the skeleton, the Porifera may be divided into three classes—Calcarea, Hexactinellida, and Desmospongia. In addition there may be added a fourth group to include spongelike fossil forms of unknown affinities.

Class Calcarea

This class is so named because the skeletal elements are composed entirely of calcareous matter (calcite or aragonite). The spicules may be monaxons, triaxons, or tetraxons, and they may be loose or united to form rigid skeletons. Living calcareous sponges are mainly inhabitants of shallow water and are found in greatest abundance in those portions of the sea bordering coasts.

Fossil representatives, known from the Devonian to Recent, appear to have had a similar habitat.

The Calcarea have been divided into two orders as follows:

Order 1. **Homocoela**—Calcareous sponges in which the lining of the cloaca consists throughout of collared flagellate cells. The two suborders *Ascones* and *Leucones* do not have much in the way of a preservable skeleton and have left only a very fragmentary fossil record.

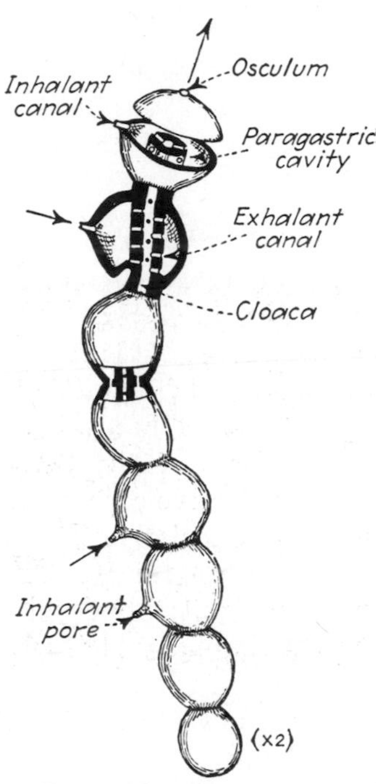

Fig. 16.—*Amblysiphonella*, a calcareous sycon sponge from the Pennsylvanian of Kansas. The specimen is variously sectioned to show the perforated walls of the paragastric cavity, the perforated partitions between adjacent chambers, and the internal structure. The walls of both cloaca and paragastric cavity are considerably thicker in the specimen than they probably were in life.

Order 2. **Heterocoela**—Calcareous sponges in which the cloaca is lined with flattened endodermal cells, with the collared flagellate cells limited to the canals or chambers. The two suborders are *Sycones* and *Pharetrones*. Both have left a fossil record of some importance.

Sycones are small, shallow-water, calcareous sponges with thin walls perforated by radially disposed canals. The skeletal elements are regularly arranged and are mainly triaxons and monaxons. Typical fossil representatives are *Amblysiphonella* from the Carboniferous and *Barroisia* from the Cretaceous (Figs. 16, 17). (Carboniferous to Present.)

The Pharetrones are thick-walled calcareous sponges with an intricate canal system and anastomosing spicules which form a rigid skeleton of

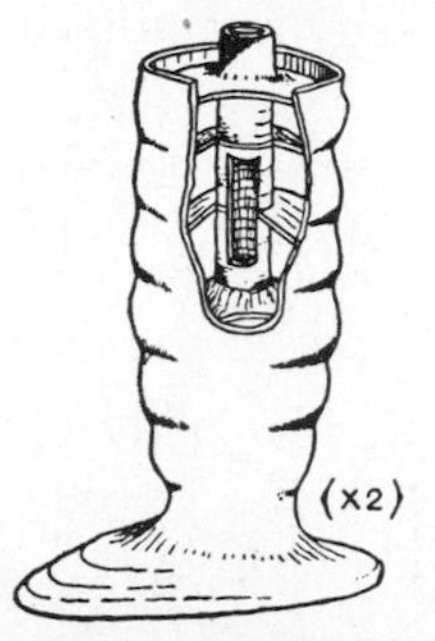

FIG. 17.—*Barroisia*, a calcareous sycon sponge from the Cretaceous. (*After Taylor.*)

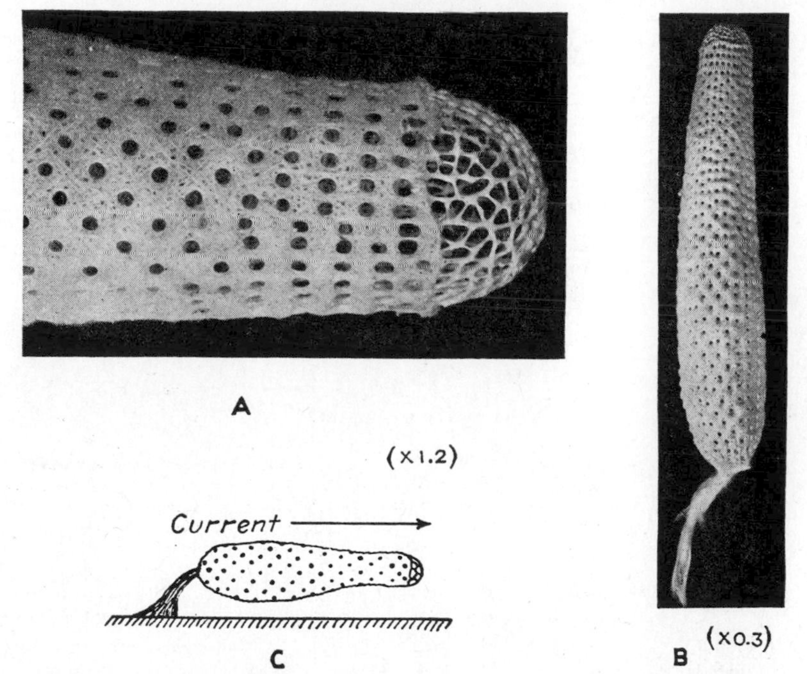

FIG. 18.—Modern sponges. *A–C*. A modern glass sponge, *Euplectella: A*, distal end of skeleton showing the nature and distribution of the pores, the character of the skeletal material, and the large osculum covered by a convex sieve plate; *B*, complete skeleton, with tuft of silken threads used for attachment; *C*, probable living position on the sea bottom.

variable shape. A typical fossil representative is *Eudea* (Fig. 19 *N–O*) from the Triassic and Jurassic. (Devonian to Cretaceous.)

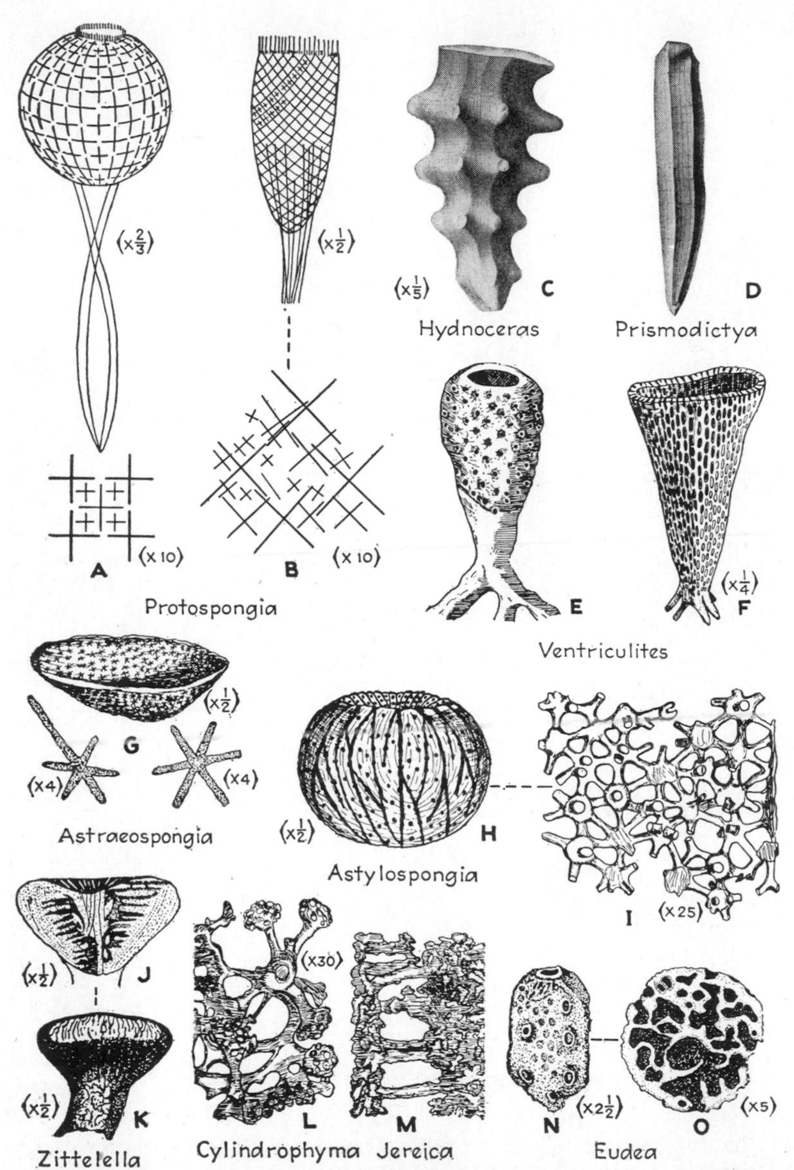

FIG. 19.—Fossil sponges. *A–B. Protospongia* from the Upper Cambrian. *C, Hydnoceras*, and *D, Prismodictya*, from the Devonian of New York. *E–F. Ventriculites* from the Cretaceous. *G. Astraeospongia* from the Silurian of Tennessee. *H–I. Astylospongia* from the Silurian of Gotland. *J–K. Zittelella* from the Ordovician. *L. Cylindrophyma*, a magnified portion of the skeleton, from the Jurassic. *M. Jereica*, a magnified portion of the skeleton, from the

Class Hexactinellida

The hexactinellid sponges are characterized by detached or fused siliceous hexaxial spicules (whence the name—Gr. *hektos*, six, + *aktis*, a ray, + L. dim. *ella*). The canal system is simple and consists of branched and unbranched flagellate chambers. The skeleton is entirely siliceous, and the spicules are united into a rigid framework through the addition of secondary silica, never of spongin. Many fossil species belong to this class. Two orders have been erected:

Order 1. **Lyssacina**—Siliceous sponges in which the spicules are either detached or but slightly fused. The fossil *Protospongia* of the Cambrian and *Hydnoceras* of the Devonian and the living *Euplectella* are typical of this order (Figs. 18 *A–C*, 19 *A–C*). (Cambrian to Present.)

Order 2. **Dictyonina**—Siliceous sponges in which the hexaxial spicules are so joined as to form a rigid meshwork with cubical interspaces. *Ventriculites* (Fig. 19 *E–F*) from the Cretaceous is a typical fossil representative of this order. (Triassic to Present.)

Class Desmospongia

This assemblage of sponges includes forms inhabiting both fresh and salt water and with or without skeletal structure. If present, the skeleton consists of spongin fibers alone, siliceous spicules alone (never hexaxial), or a combination of the two. Most living sponges belong in this group, and there is also a very good fossil representation. The class has been divided into the following five orders:

Order 1. **Tetractinellida**—The sponges in this group have four-rayed, siliceous spicules (Gr. *tetra*, four, + *aktis*, ray, + L. dim. *ella*), which are loose in the mesogloea or united by spongin. There is, therefore, no rigid skeleton. Fossil spicules belonging to this order are known from the Jurassic to the Present.

Order 2. **Lithistida**—In this order modified tetraxons and monaxons of siliceous material fuse to form massive skeletons which have often been fossilized. These are the most abundant of all fossil sponges and are divided into five suborders. *Jerea* from the Cretaceous is typical of the suborder Tetracladina; *Astylospongia* from the Silurian represents the Eutaxicladina; *Cylindrophyma* from the Jurassic typifies the

---

Jurassic. *N–O*. *Eudea*, complete specimen and transverse section showing cloaca and fibers. (*A—B after Dawson; C–D after Hall and Clarke; E–F after Nicholson and Lydekker; I after Zittel; J–K after Ulrich and Everett; L–M after Zittel; N–O after Hinde.*)

Anomocladina; *Doryderma* from the Cretaceous illustrates the Megamorina; and *Jereica* from the Cretaceous is representative of the Rhizomorina (Fig. 19). The order ranges from the Cambrian to the Present, with the most abundant development apparently beginning with the Jurassic.

Order 3. **Monactinellida**—In this order the skeleton is composed of one-rayed, siliceous monaxons (Gr. *mona*, one, + *aktis*, a ray, + L. dim. *ella*), which may be connected by spongin. The spicules are scattered through the mesogloea, and when the animal dies they become a part of the bottom deposits. Since most living marine siliceous sponges belong to this order, their spicules are characteristic constituents of existing marine sediments. Living species inhabit the more moderate depths.

The few fresh-water sponges (*Spongilla, et al.*) (Fig. 14 *E*) are also included in this order. These are not likely to leave a fossil record.

Fossil spicules of this order are found in marine strata ranging in age from the lower Paleozoic to the Present.

Order 4. **Ceratospongida** (**Ceratosa**)—Skeletons of horny spongin fibers (Gr. *keras*, horn, + *spongia*, sponge) characterize this order. The common bath sponge, *Euspongia*, is an abundant living representative, but there does not seem to be any known fossil record, although impressions of crushed specimens may be expected.

Order 5. **Myxospongida** (Gr. *myxa*, mucus, + *spongia*, sponge)—Individuals of this order have no skeleton and hence have left no fossil record.

Forms of Unknown Affinities

In this heterogeneous group are included a number of important fossil species of uncertain biologic affinities. Some are very likely sponges, though not closely related to any of the three classes described above; some *may* be sponges but may be referred to other phyla; whereas still others, referred to the Porifera by some investigators, very likely belong to other organic groups.

Receptaculites, the so-called "sunflower coral," and *Ischadites*, both characteristic of the lower and middle Paleozoic, seem to belong to the Porifera but cannot be placed in any of the divisions given above. The shape, internal structure, and arrangement and character of the canals suggest affinity with the Porifera. Both seem to have been calcareous (Fig. 20).

The *Archaeocyathinae* of the Cambrian may be calcareous sponges, as has been urged by Raymond,[1] or they may be

[1] The systematic position of the Archaeocyathinae, *Bull. Mus. Comp. Zool.* (Harvard), vol. 55, No. 6, pp. 172–177, 1931.

calcareous corals, as has been suggested by other investigators (see page 122). Taylor[1] considers the group ancestral to both the calcareous sponges and the Rugosa or Tetracoralla of the Coelenterata. The calcareous skeleton is horn shaped or

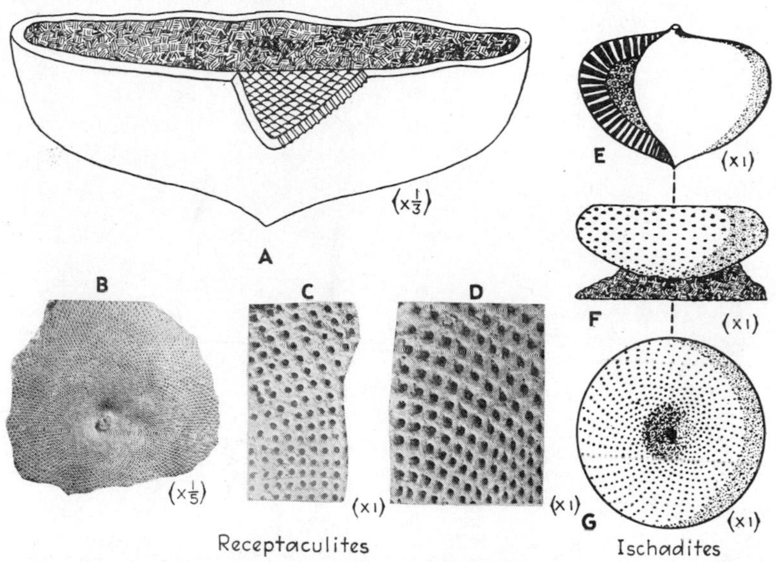

FIG. 20.—*A–D. Receptaculites oweni* from the Middle Ordovician at Freeport, Ill. *A*, restoration of a complete specimen, based on a mud filling of the hollow bowl. The surface of this filling bears an impression of the inner surface of the bowl. The wall is shown without the pores except in one small area. *B*, basal portion of a deformed specimen showing the characteristic arrangement of the pores. *C*, *D*, external and internal views, respectively, of small portions of the wall. *E–G. Ischadites iowensis* from the Middle Ordovician (Prosser) at Elkader, Iowa. *E*, restoration of a complete skeleton, based on well-preserved but slightly deformed specimens. The radial spicules are indicated as white rods, and the central opening on the upper surface is shown. In fossilized specimens the slightly pointed upper part has collapsed to form a central shallow depression. *F*, lateral view of a somewhat deformed specimen, with the base still buried in the matrix. *G*, top view of same specimen showing the characteristic arrangement of the radial spicules and pores. The shallow collapse depression around the opening is also shown.

cylindrical, with a hollow interior surrounded by a perforated double wall (Fig. 21). The two porous walls are separated by a distance ranging from several millimeters to as much as a centimeter. In this space are porous, septa-like partitions

[1] Archaeocyathinae, from the Cambrian of South Australia, with an account of the morphology and affinities of the whole class, *Mem. Roy. Soc. South Australia*, vol. II, pt. 2, 1910.

with radial arrangement. Hence the fossil has characteristics suggestive of both Porifera and Coelenterata.

It is possible that the Paleozoic *Cyclocrinites*, *Nidulites*, and *Pasceolus*, all organic structures of the same general character, are sponges, but the preponderance of evidence seems to indicate affinities with the algae.

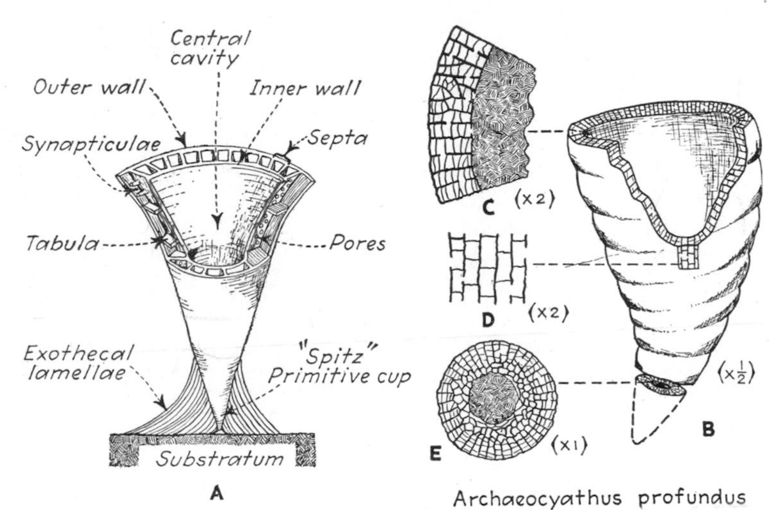

Fig. 21.—Archaeocyathinae. *A*. Generalized diagram of an archaeocyathid, showing the more important structural features. *B*. *Archaeocyathus profundus* from the Lower Cambrian of Labrador. In the actual specimen, on which the drawing is based, the central cavity is filled with stone.. *C*. Transverse section of a portion of the wall at the top of the calyx showing the prominent perforated septa and the numerous dissepiments. *D*. Tangential section showing the perforated septa and the dissepiments. *E*. Transverse section of the skeleton near the base showing the outer septal region and the inner vesiculose region. (*A after Taylor*.)

ECOLOGY

The Porifera exhibit very interesting adaptations to habitats and relations to other animals. All but one group are marine. The fresh-water forms (*Spongillidae*) live in rivers, canals, ponds, and lakes. The marine sponges are found in all seas and at all depths from the strand line to the deepest abysses of the ocean. The calcareous sponges (Calcarea) and the true horny ones (Ceratosa) are most abundant in shallow waters (less than 450 fathoms), whereas the siliceous sponges appear to live at all depths.

Living sponges in many cases are veritable aquariums. The interior of the organism may be found teeming with a great variety of life, consisting of crustaceans, worms, molluscs, and other invertebrates. In a recent investigation[1] a sponge about as large as a washtub was found to contain 17,128 individual animals—approximately two for every cubic inch of the sponge's bulk.

Highest in zoological rank were five little inch-long fishes, very slenderly built so that they could get about in the sponge canals. There were many worms and a number of barnacles. Most numerous, however, were shrimp of a strange species with one claw much larger than the other, and in some specimens almost as large as its body. There were 16,352 of these shrimp.

A different kind of exploitation of a growing sponge for protection is described by Dr. W. H. Longley, in charge of the laboratory at Tortugas. A crab that lives in the waters there tears off bits of living sponge and holds them to its shell until they take hold and continue their growth. Thereafter the crab has the benefit of concealment, enhanced by the inedibility of the sponge, which is full of disagreeable prickles and in addition has a most noxious odor.

The sulphur sponge *Cliona* bores into oyster shells and other bivalves for protection rather than for food. Sponges often live in intimate association with other animals or with plants in such a way that both are mutually benefited by the double life (*commensalism*).

The Porifera appear always to have been gregarious animals, and fossilized remains, where found in any abundance, are usually of local distribution.

GEOLOGIC HISTORY

Sponges are of great antiquity, ranging from the Pre-Cambrian to the Present. They appear to have originated in the Pre-Cambrian from an ancestral stock similar to the Choanoflagellata and to have come down through geologic time without much change. So far as known at the present time, they never gave rise to any other group of animals. They may well be said to have traveled a byroad of metazoan evolution (Fig. 3).

The fossil record of the Porifera is not an abundant one except in a few scattered localities, but it is of long duration. The

[1] Pearse, A. S., *Science News Letter*, May 27, 1933, p. 331.

earliest record is of siliceous spicules, reported from Pre-Cambrian rocks of Brittany and from the upper part of the Grand Canyon system of America. The fossil *Atikokania lawsoni* from the Seine River series at Steeprock Lake in Ontario possibly may be a siliceous sponge, and, if so, it represents the only fossil animal known from the first great time division of the Pre-Cambrian.

Protospongia from the Cambrian, and also *Archaeocyathus*, if it be a true sponge; *Receptaculites* and *Ischadites* from the Ordovician and later strata; *Astylospongia* and *Astraeospongia* from the Silurian; *Hydnoceras, Prismodictya*, and the numerous other forms from the famous "glass-sponge" assemblages in the Devonian of New York; and *Amblysiphonella* from the Pennsylvanian are important index fossils of the Paleozoic. Some have world-wide distribution, whereas others are limited to restricted localities.

Sponge remains are well represented in Mesozoic rocks and are especially abundant in Jurassic strata of Europe. In the Swabian Alps the lower part of a great reef or bioherm in the upper Jurassic limestone is composed largely of sponge remains, some of which are exceptionally well preserved. Cretaceous sponges, among which lithistids, hexactinellids, and calcareous sponges are the common kinds, are well represented in the Lower Greensand and in the Chalk of England.

Tertiary sponges are represented mainly by detached and isolated spicules. Few whole specimens have been found. Isolated sponge spicules have very wide distribution in present marine and fresh-water deposits and are frequently encountered in residues from the acid digestion of ancient calcareous rocks. Certain types of flint and chert nodules sometimes contain great numbers of siliceous sponge spicules, and it has been suggested that some of these rocks owe their origin to the solution of spicules and the subsequent deposition of the dissolved silica.

References

BEECHER, C. E.: Brachiospongidae; a memoir on a group of Silurian sponges. *Yale Univ., Peabody Mus. Mem.* 2, pt. 1, 28 pp., 1889.

CLARKE, J. M.: The great glass-sponge colonies of the Devonian; their origin, rise, and disappearance. *Jour. Geol.*, vol. 28, pp. 25–37, 1920.

HALL, J., and CLARKE, J. M.: A memoir on the Paleozoic reticulate sponges constituting the family Dictyospongidae. *N. Y. State Geol., Ann.*

Rept. 15, pt. 2, pp. 741–984; 16, pp. 341–448; *N. Y. State Mus. Mem.* 2, 350 pp., 1898.

TAYLOR, T. G.: Archaeocyathinae, from the Cambrian of South Australia, with an account of the morphology and affinities of the whole class. *Mems. Roy. Soc. South Australia*, vol. 2, pt. 2, 1910.

WALCOTT, C. D.: Cambrian geology and paleontology, IV, No. 6, Middle Cambrian Spongiae. *Smith. Misc. Coll.*, vol. 67, No. 6, pp. 261–364, 31 pls., 1920.

CHAPTER IV

COELENTERATA[1]

INTRODUCTION

The phylum Coelenterata comprises a large group of living and extinct organisms which show an advance over the sponges in the following ways: (1) They possess a definite "mouth" or oral opening; (2) they have a *coelenteron* (whence the name of the phylum) or "stomach"; (3) they exhibit considerable development of muscular tissue and have more or less prehensile organs for obtaining food; (4) they lack both a canal system and collared flagellate cells—two of the distinctive structures of the Porifera—(5) except in one group, all are characterized by the possession of stinging cells; and, finally, (6) because of greater advancement, they show more range in individuality.

Typical living coelenterates are the fresh-water *Hydra,* sea anemones, stony corals, and jellyfish or medusae. There is also included in the phylum a great host of fossil forms which have left no living descendants.

Throughout their history the Coelenterata have been aquatic in habitat. Most have been and still are marine, but a few now live in fresh or brackish waters, and some may have done so throughout geologic history. All of the fossil stony corals, the extinct stromatoporoids and graptolites, and the few fossil hydrozoans were apparently marine.

The phylum has left one of the most complete of fossil records and includes a large number of fossil forms which are of great stratigraphic importance. This completeness of record and abundance of material have encouraged extensive study of fossil coelenterates.

[1] Coelenterata—Gr. *koilos,* hollow + *enteron,* intestine; referring to the hollow internal cavity of the individual coelenterate.

THE ORGANISM

The individual coelenterate has one of two definite forms: a hollow, saclike body designated a *polyp;* or an umbrella-shaped structure known as a *jellyfish* or *medusa* (Fig. 22). Polyps are almost invariably attached (sessile), whereas medusae are free swimming (nektonic or nektonic-planktonic).

The Polyp.—A typical polyp may be cylindrical, spheroidal, or discoidal in shape, with a hollow central cavity (coelenteron) opening to the exterior through a "mouth" at the top (Fig. 22 *A*). The basal part is loosely attached to some object on the bottom and is known as the *pedal disk.* The upper part, connected to the pedal disk by the *body wall,* is designated the *oral disk.* In the central part of the oral disk (sometimes referred to as the *peristome*) is a more or less elongated opening—the "mouth" or *oral opening*—which may communicate directly with the coelenteron or indirectly through a short invagination of the body wall known as the *esophagus* or *gullet.* Rising from the oral disk, as either solid or hollow outgrowths of the body wall, are one or more rows or circlets of *tentacles* (Fig. 22 *A*). The number of tentacles may be closely related to the internal structure of the polyp, as found in one group of coelenterates, or there may be no relation. When the animal is feeding the tentacles are extended, but when it is disturbed they are retracted and folded over the mouth.

The tentacles and body wall of the polyp are composed of two well-defined layers of tissue, known as ectoderm and endoderm, separated by an irregular, unorganized mass of protoplasm, the mesogloea. The *ectoderm* forms the outer layer of the organism and secretes the horny or calcareous "exoskeleton." It also contains simply organized muscular and nerve tissues. Most individual coelenterates, whether polyp or medusa, have the ectodermal surface partly or completely covered with minute stinging cells, the *cnidoblasts.* Similar cells are found on the endodermal layer of certain forms. Each cell contains a small vesicle (*nematocyst*) filled with an irritating or poisonous fluid and is equipped with a spirally coiled filament which, when released, shoots out like an uncoiling spring. Small organisms struck or penetrated by the filament are stunned or paralyzed. The cell has a sensory projection on the exterior which when

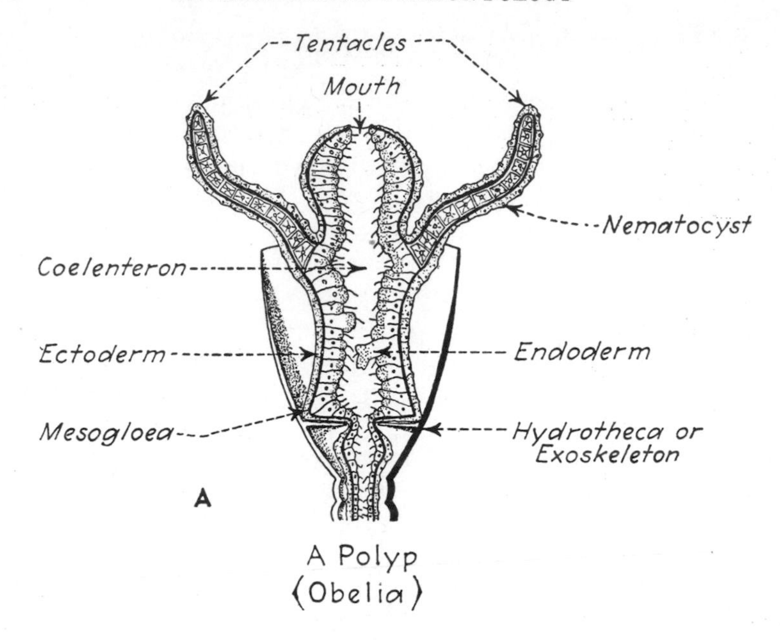

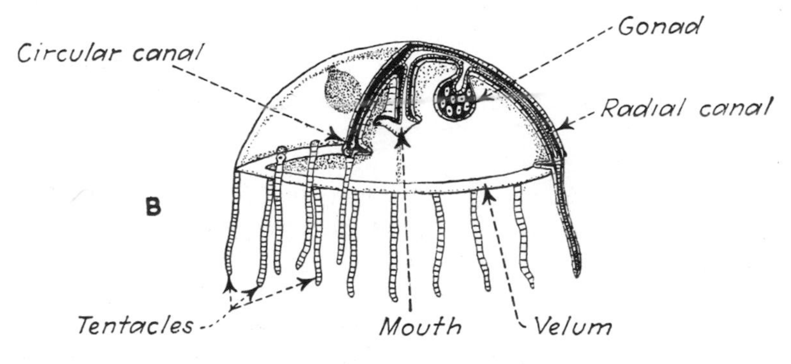

FIG. 22.—The two types of individual Coelenterata. *A.* A *polyp* (*Obelia,*) sectioned vertically to show the numerous structures of the body and relation to the exoskeleton. *B.* A *medusa*, sectioned to show the important external and internal structures. (*After Parker and Haswell, with slight modifications.*)

disturbed causes the release of the filament and the poisonous fluid.

The inside of the coelenteron, and of those tentacles that are hollow, is lined with *endoderm*. The cells which comprise this layer are not collared as in the Porifera, though they may have flagella and may possess cnidoblasts. They acquire and assimilate the food, discharge waste products into the coelenteron, and in some forms produce the sexual organs. Sexual and waste products and fertilized ova leave the organism through the oral opening. Both food and foreign sexual products are brought into the coelenteron through the same opening. The entrance and expulsion of water and contained materials are brought about by contractions of the body wall.

The *mesogloea*, between the endoderm and the ectoderm, is a poorly developed, unorganized mass of protoplasm. It may or may not be present, and except for aiding in circulation of fluids it usually does not perform any important functions. In a few instances it is known to secrete minute spicular skeletal elements.

The polyp almost always exhibits well-developed radial or bilateral symmetry. The latter is thought to be more fundamental and primitive. The walls may be smooth or wrinkled. The wall of the coelenteron may possess prominent inward folds known as *mesenteries*. These have radial arrangement and greatly increase the absorptive surface of the digestive cavity. The mesenteries are covered with muscular fibers on both sides. These are transversely striated on one side of the mesenteries and longitudinally striated on the other and show in their arrangement the fundamental bilateral symmetry of the polyp. The arrangement of muscles in the extinct groups of corals (Tetracoralla, Heliolitidae, etc.) is unknown, but the presence of distinct bilateral symmetry in the exoskeletons of many species shows that such symmetry must have existed in the soft parts of the polyp and not unlikely, therefore, in the muscles. The mesenteries have exoskeletal counterparts in the form of radially directed partitions known as *septa*.

The Medusa.—The second form exhibited by certain coelenterates is the jellyfish or medusa. This resembles an umbrella with small tentacles along the rim and a mouth in the central part on the underside. There is considerable variety, and in some forms a difference of function, in the different tentacles of the umbrella. Except in the *Ctenophora*, medusae are plentifully supplied with stinging cells. Some medusae have a shelflike structure, known as the *velum*, on the underside of the margin (Fig. 22 *B*).

In some forms of Coelenterata a medusoid stage alternates with a polyp stage, in a cycle of reproduction known as *alternation of generations*. Other medusae never have a polyp stage and directly produce their kind. All medusae are over nine-tenths fluid, and some have been reported to contain about 99 per cent by weight of water.[1]

Reproduction.—Reproduction among the Coelenterata is either sexual or both sexual and asexual. Coelenterates having only the medusoid form reproduce sexually. Those having only the polyp stage reproduce either sexually or both sexually and asexually. Those coelenterates in which there is the alternation of the polyp with the medusoid stage have asexual reproduction confined to the former and sexual reproduction to the latter.

In *sexual reproduction* sperms are discharged into the coelenteron whence they find their way to the exterior through the mouth. They drift about until they enter the coelenteron of another individual, where they unite with ova produced in the endoderm. A ciliated free-swimming larva, the *planula*, develops from this union and ultimately leaves the parent through the mouth. After a short free life the planula attaches itself by the anterior end, and a new opening is made on the end opposite to the end of attachment. Forms having only the medusoid stage release the products into the water, and other medusae develop directly from these.

In *asexual reproduction* a new polyp buds from some part of the body wall of the parent, from the oral part of the polyp (calicinal), from a rootlike extension (stolonal), or from some part of the common connective tissue. Reproduction of the asexual type may also take place by *fission*, in which one polyp divides to form two new ones; or by *rejuvenescence*, whereby a new polyp seems to form through the disintegration of its parent (Fig. 34).

[1] GORTNER, R. A., The water content of medusae, *Science*, vol. **77**, pp. 282–283, 1934.

Budding takes place in the soft parts of the organism, and in some instances there may be as many as three generations on a single organism. Frequently the buds leave the parent polyp and settle down by themselves. If they do not leave the parent immediately, skeletal material may be built around the place of connection of the two. Buds that die before depositing skeletal substance by their own activity, but after the parent has built such around and above the places of their attachment, show their former presence by small openings in the wall of the parental exoskeleton. Such pores, known as *mural pores*, are present in the so-called honeycomb corals and are thought to represent sites where buds originated but failed to develop into mature individuals.

Reproduction by budding leads to the formation of colonies commensurate with the extent to which it proceeds, and the individuals of such colonies usually are connected by a common fleshy tissue known as *coenosarc*. After a space has been fully occupied, further budding results in an immense mortality because of the lack of room for the newly created individuals.

In reproduction by *alternation of generations* some of the asexually produced buds of the colony develop the special function of producing small medusae, which ultimately become free swimming. Upon attaining maturity these medusae release sexual products which mutually unite with their opposites from other medusae. This union of male and female elements produces an embryo which, after a developmental period as a free-moving individual, becomes attached and matures into a sessile polyp which through budding may form a colony.

The colonial habit is very well developed among the Coelenterata, especially among the reef-building corals, which have built during the geologic past, and are still building, extensive rocky reefs composed to a greater or lesser degree of their stony exoskeletons. Many living coelenterates are without the colonial habit, and many extinct corals likewise did not form colonies.

THE EXOSKELETON

Most sessile coelenterates secrete an external supporting and protective structure commonly referred to as a *skeleton* or an *exoskeleton*. It is not to be confused, however, with the true internal skeleton found in the sponges and in the backboned animals.

The skeletons of this phylum are of two kinds: (1) a loose, nonrigid structure composed of minute skeletal elements secreted in the mesogloea; and (2) a rigid framework of calcareous or horny substances secreted by the ectoderm arranged in a great variety of forms which are true exoskeletons. The former are uncommon, whereas the latter are very numerous.

The first type of skeleton, found among many of the Alcyonaria, consists of horny or calcareous spicular bodies of irregular shapes (Fig. 35) secreted in the mesogloea. These skeletal elements often remain loose, but they may also become cemented together by horny or calcareous matter to form a more or less rigid structure. This may be a basal plate, or it may consist of tubes of different lengths (Fig. 36 *D–G*).

Exoskeletons of the second type, being secreted by the ectoderm, reproduce the irregularities of that surface. Hence if the body wall of the organism is crenulated, the skeletal wall will be likewise. Numerous skeletal structures come into existence because of certain relations which are exhibited by the ectodermal surface and the adjacent stony matter. These will be discussed later.

Development of the Exoskeleton.—The embryonic skeleton of a typical coelenterate has the shape and appearance of a little, hollow, conical cup and is known as the *prototheca* (earliest cup). From this simple beginning, by additions at its upper end, arise a great variety of skeletal types depending upon the way in which the polyps bud and grow.

The small conical or tubular cup secreted by a polyp about and under itself is designated a *corallite*. This is more or less horn shaped, if small and young, but with age it tends to become cylindrical. Under conditions of excessive budding, necessitating utilization of all space, the corallites become prismatic. The upper part of the corallite, or that part occupied by the polyp, is known as the *calyx*. The adult skeletal structure, whether composed of a single corallite or of a great number, is a *corallum* (plural, *coralla*). Hence in the case of the solitary corals, which remain conical or tubular throughout life, the skeleton is both a corallite and a corallum. In all other instances two or more corallites combine to form a corallum.

A mature exoskeleton may be a single isolated cone partly filled with internal structures; a hemispherical mass of calcareous matter resembling a button or biscuit; a horny or calcareous framework resembling a bush or tree; or a massive irregularly shaped domal structure composed of many cylindrical or prismatic tubes more or less tightly packed together.

CLASSIFICATION

In the subdivision of such a varied group of organisms as are included in the phylum Coelenterata, consideration should be given to the following:

1. Phylogenetic relations where they can be determined.
2. Character of the soft parts of the animal where they can be studied directly or determined from fossil structures.
3. Structural and architectural features of the exoskeletons.
4. Detailed internal structures.
5. Convenience of grouping.

On the basis of these considerations the authors divide the Coelenterata into the following groups, not all of which are of equal taxonomic rank.

1. **Hydrozoa**—Living and fossil, fresh-water and marine, individual or colonial coelenterates, having both polyp and medusoid stages. The geologic range is from the Lower Cambrian to the Present.
2. **Stromatoporoidea**—A heterogeneous assemblage of extinct marine organisms bearing resemblances to both sponges and hydrozoans. They range from the Ordovician to the end of the Devonian, and several genera have been described from the Permo-Carboniferous of Farther India.
3. **Graptozoa**—Extinct marine organisms remotely resembling certain hydrozoans but not closely related to any known living coelenterates. Some students state that they show important similarities to the Bryozoa. The range is from the Cambrian to the Devonian with a single species described from the Chouteau formation of the Mississippian.
4. **Scyphozoa**—Living and fossil medusoid coelenterates without a polyp stage or with a very limited one. The medusoid stage is well developed. Fossils have been reported from the Lower and Middle Cambrian, Permian, and Jurassic.
5. **Anthozoa**—Solitary and colonial, living and extinct, fleshy and stony corals with large exoskeletons of complicated structure and variable architecture. There is no medusoid stage. The group appears to begin in the early Ordovician and extends throughout geologic time to

the Present.[1] This is probably the most important group of the coelenterates.

6. **Ctenophora**—Peculiar, exclusively medusoid coelenterates without cnidoblasts and having no preservable skeletal structures. The geologic range is undetermined.

Class Hydrozoa[2]

The Organism.—The *Hydrozoa* are typically bell-shaped or vaselike coelenterates with tentacles surrounding the mouth, which is situated in the center of the oral disk. The mouth opens directly into the coelenteron and is without an esophagus. The coelenteron is undivided and without mesenteries; hence the corallites in which the organism lives have no radial partitions. Individuals are small, usually not exceeding 2 or 3 mm. in diameter and slightly more in height. They may be typical polyps, specialized polyps (generally with reproductive functions only), or medusae. Hence they are sometimes described as *dimorphic* or *polymorphic*. The fully formed medusae have a velum.

Some groups of hydrozoans have an alternation of generations in which a polyp stage alternates with a medusoid stage. Medusae bud from specialized polyps of the colony, which differ in shape as well as in function from the normal food-getting polyps and are surrounded by a transparent bulblike, horny structure known as the *gonotheca*. Normal polyps live in vaselike cups termed *hydrothecae*. The specialized polyps are nourished by normal polyps, with which they are connected by coenosarc, and it is often difficult to differentiate between individual and colony. Any of the normal polyps can produce new polyps by budding, but the latter tend to remain attached. Medusoid forms lacking the polyp stage reproduce sexually. Polyp forms lacking the medusoid stage reproduce both sexually and asexually. In all of the cases just cited the reproductive organs are almost always of ectodermal origin.

[1] The genus *Mackenzia* from the Middle Cambrian of British Columbia was assigned by C. D. Walcott, (*Smith. Misc. Coll.*, vol. 57, No. 3, p. 54, 1911) to the Holothurians. A. L. Clark (*Science*, vol. 35, p. 277, 1912) suggested that the organism is an Actinarian, and, if this is correct, the range of the Anthozoa extends to the Middle Cambrian.

[2] Hydrozoa—Gr. *hydor*, water + *zoon*, animal; an animal dwelling in water.

Hydrozoa that reproduce asexually without detachment of the buds develop colonies which may expand into large masses of various shapes. In such colonies each polyp is in some manner connected with those adjacent by common fleshy coenosarc, and ordinarily they do not tend to come into extremely close contact. The ectoderm of the polyps and the underside of the connective coenosarc secrete an exoskeletal framework of horny or calcareous material. That secreted by the coenosarc connects and surrounds the cavities occupied by the polyps and consists of more or less structureless skeletal matter known as *coenenchyma.* Forms having a horny exoskeleton of definite shape are illustrated by living *Obelia* (Fig. 22 *A*) and *Tubularia.* The extinct graptolites also resemble the Hydrozoa in this respect. Colonial associations of calcareous exoskeletons without definite shape are illustrated by the living *Millepora* (Fig. 23). The extinct stromatoporoids have a somewhat analogous skeletal structure.

Habitat and Geologic History.—The Hydrozoa live mainly in marine waters at the present time, and all species secreting skeletons of horny or calcareous substance are confined to that habitat. The few forms living in fresh water have no hard parts and hence have little chance of leaving any fossil evidence of their existence. Both polyps and medusae occur in each of the aquatic habitats.

Fossil remains of the Hydrozoa are found in rocks ranging in age from the Lower Cambrian[1] to the most recently formed deposits. Inclusion in the Hydrozoa of the stromatoporoids and graptolites, the usual reference in textbooks of paleontology and zoology, greatly enlarges the group.

Classification.—The Hydrozoa have been subdivided in several different ways, with the Hydrocorallinae and the Siphonophora recognized by nearly all authors. The classification which follows is that in common use.

Order 1. **Leptolinae**—Hydrozoa with a fixed polyp stage alternating with a medusoid stage. Cnidoblasts are limited to the ectoderm. Skeleton flower-like or dendritic and composed of horny or calcareous matter which is sometimes preserved. The group includes such well-known forms as *Hydra, Hydractinia, Sertularia, Tubularia, Obelia* (Fig. 22 *A*),

[1] Ruedemann, R., Camptostroma, a Lower Cambrian floating hydrozoan, *Proc. U. S. Nat. Mus.*, vol. 82, art. 13, pp. 1–8, pls. 1–4, 1933.

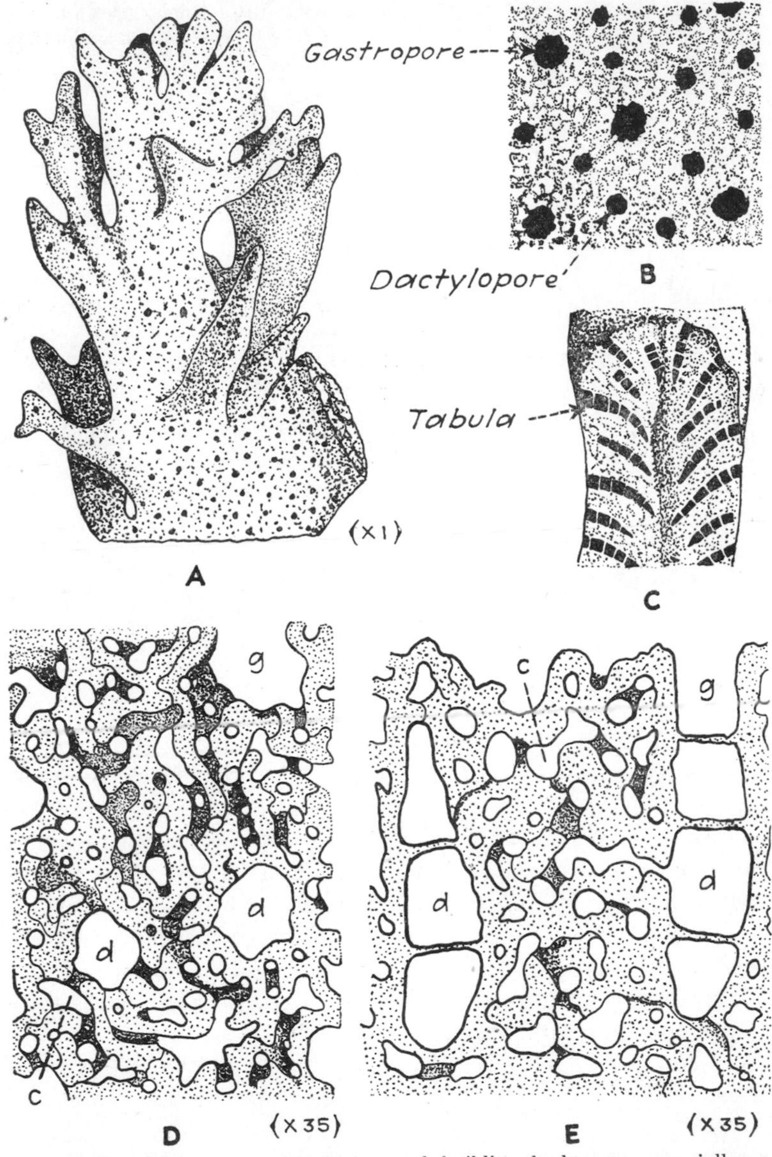

FIG. 23.—*Millepora*, an important rock-building hydrozoan, especially on present coral reefs. *A*. Complete colony. *B*. Portion of surface, magnified, showing gastropores and dactylopores separated by coenenchymal matter. *C*. Vertical section, magnified, showing tabulated zooidal tubes (gastropores and dactylopores). *D*. Tangential section, much magnified, showing gastropores (*g*), dactylopores (*d*), and coenosarcal canals (*c*). *E*. Longitudinal section same as *D*. (*After Nicholson and Lydekker, with slight modifications*)

and *Campanularia*. Fossil forms are known from the Lower Cambrian[1] to Recent. Certain *Hydractinia* are said to be common in the Jurassic of the Mediterranean region.

Order 2. **Trachylinae**—Hydrozoa without a known fixed polyp stage. All individuals are mobile medusae, some of which are known to develop directly from an ovum. Cnidoblasts are present in part of the endoderm. The character of the medusae makes it unlikely that they would leave fossil evidence of their existence, and the geologic history is unknown.

Order 3. **Hydrocorallinae**—naked dimorphic polyps connected with coenosarc. The coenosarcal base of the colony secretes a dense massive calcareous exoskeleton. This skeletal structure is composed of calcareous fibers, in which there are two varieties of tubular openings corresponding to the two types of polyps. The larger tubes (*gastropores*) house the feeding polyps, whereas the smaller (*dactylopores*) house those acting in a protective capacity. Tabulae divide the older part of the tubes into compartments.

Some species, like the living *Millepora* (Fig. 23), are very important reef builders, and skeletons of this order are known as early as the Triassic.

Order 4. **Siphonophora**—colonial pelagic hydrozoans in which the individual polyps show extreme polymorphism. The colony is frequently fastened to a float (*pneumatophore*) of its own making. No fossil record is known except a few specimens questionably interpreted as floats.[2]

Group Stromatoporoidea

The Stromatoporoidea comprise a heterogeneous group of extinct organisms which have left as fossils large calcareous masses of variable shapes and structures. Since these exoskeletons do not reveal much concerning the character of the organisms which built them, the group has been shuffled by investigators from one phylum of organisms to another, and even now its affinities are still a matter of debate. Because of this uncertain state of classification, the authors favor placing the entire group provisionally in the Coelenterata as an independent subdivision, recognizing that such a disposition is more a matter of convenience than of scientific accuracy. It is pos-

[1] Ruedemann, R., Some new Middle Cambrian fossils from British Columbia, *Proc. U. S. Nat. Mus.*, vol. 79, art. 27, pp. 1–18, 1931; *op.cit.*, 1933.

[2] Ruedemann, R., Paleontologic contributions from the New York State Museum, *N. Y. State Mus. Bull.* 189, p. 22, 1916.

sible that certain so-called stromatoporoids may be sponges or algae.[1]

Character of the Exoskeleton.—The fossil skeletal structures of this group are spheroidal, domal, dendroid, columnar, or encrusting masses composed of calcium carbonate and characterized by more or less complicated internal structure. Shape and size appear to have little significance, for both vary greatly within a single species.

The internal structure may be divided into two distinct varieties—*hydrozooid* and *beatricoid.* In order to study the internal framework of a colony, polished surfaces and thin sections must be prepared. For this reason stromatoporoids

[1] Stromatoporoids (some or all) have been classified as algae, foraminifers, sponges, hydrozoans, tabulate corals, bryozoans, and cephalopods. Probably the earliest serious study of the group was made by Baron von Rosen in 1869 (Über die Natur der Stromatoporen, und über die Erhaltung der Hornfasser der Spongien in fossilien Zustande). He concluded that they are horny sponges which have been calcified. Nicholson, in his "A Monograph of British Stromatoporoids," made a very thorough investigation of the group and arrived at the conclusion that they are coelenterates, with affinities closest to certain types of Hydrozoa. He classified the Stromatoporoidea into two large subdivisions: (1) a "milleporoid" group including forms characterized by his so-called "Zooidal tubes" and (2) a "hydractinoid" group which lacked such structures. Parks, in his various studies of the stromatoporoids (*Univ. Toronto Studies* 4, 1907; 5, 1908; 6, 1909; and 7, 1910), followed Nicholson in classification but doubtfully questioned the existence of the zooidal tubes—the basis of the subdivision described above. In 1914 Heinrich (*N. Jahrb. f. Min.*, etc., No. 23, pp. 732–736, 1914, translated by C. M. LeVene, *Jour. Geol.*, vol. 24, pp. 57–60, 1916) denied the existence of the zooidal tubes and separated Nicholson's two groups. His hydractinoid group was designated "true stromatoporoids," and his milleporoid group was excluded from the stromatoporoids altogether. Heinrich subdivided the true stromatoporoids into two families: (1) the *Actinostromidae*, characterized by massive fibers; and (2) the *Stromatoporidae*, having "fibers not massive (porous or perforated)." Twitchell in 1928–1929 (*Amer. Midland Naturalist*, vol. 11, pp. 270–302) concluded that the "true stromatoporoids" of Heinrich "were the ancestors of the modern *Demospongiae* [*Desmospongiae*], *and themselves were sponges.*" Finally, Parks, in a paper read at the 1933 meeting of the Paleontological Society of America, concluded that some of the so-called stromatoporoids are strikingly similar to certain Foraminifera.

With such a division of opinion as now exists among the students of the group, it seems best to separate it entirely from all of the other subdivisions of the Coelenterata but still to include it in the phylum until there is some consensus of opinion as to its disposition.

have never been very popular objects of investigation among paleontologists.

The *hydrozooid* type of structure consists essentially of numerous closely spaced concentric laminae separated by radially directed solid or hollow pillars. The latter cause the interlaminar spaces to be divided into many small cuboidal chambers or cells. If the concentric and radial elements are easily recognizable, a section cut across the laminae will show the radial pillars dividing the interlaminar spaces into small cells, and the section will exhibit a characteristic latticed pattern. This type of framework is well shown in *Clathrodictyon* (Fig. 24 *A*, *B*). In some genera, however, the concentric and radial elements are not recognizable as such, and the exoskeleton becomes a continuously reticulated structure. The genus *Stromatopora* illustrates such an internal framework. In addition to the two extremes just described, there are many forms which occupy an intermediate or gradational position in respect to skeletal make-up.

Exoskeletons of the *beatricoid* type have a columnar shape and are characterized by a hollow, tabulated, axial tube surrounded by a zone of vesicular structure. The latter zone is composed of many convex or concave imbricating laminae, which in some species are crossed by radial pillars. This type of structure is named from the genus *Beatricia*, in which it is well shown (Fig. 24 *L–N*).

In life it is thought that the entire upper and lateral surfaces of a colony were covered with polyps connected by coenosarc. In certain instances the polyps seem also to have been connected by a system of minute, delicate fleshy tubes which ramified the upper part of the exoskeleton. Each individual built around itself small tubular or solid pillars upon which the succeeding lamina was constructed. The laminae appear to represent stages of growth and may correspond in some degree to the tabulae in the Anthozoa. In some stromatoporoids the surface of the laminae is characterized by conspicuous nodes and shallow pits on or in which may be stellate or rosette systems of minute grooves or channels. These are known as *astrorhizae* (Fig. 24 *D*) and have been variously interpreted.

Geologic History.—The stromatoporoids were among the most important rock makers in the Ordovician, Silurian, and Devonian

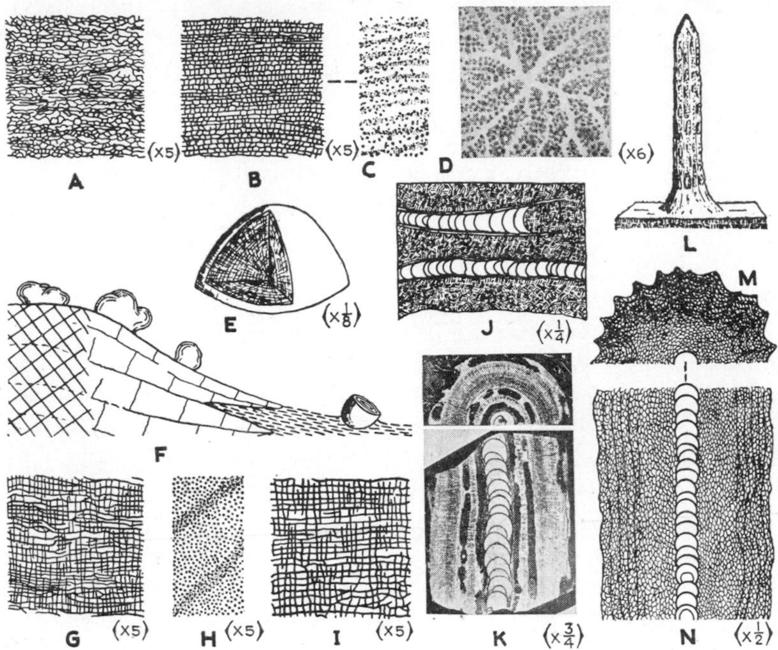

FIG. 24.—Stromatoporoidea. *A–C. Clathrodictyon* from the Niagaran of Quebec: *A*, vertical section of *C. vesiculosum; B*, vertical section of *C. vesiculosum minutum; C*, tangential section of *B. D. Stromatopora antiqua* from the Niagaran of Ontario; tangential section showing astrorhizae. *E.* A colony of *C. vesiculosum*, sectioned to show internal structure. *F.* Colonies of *C. vesiculosum* in position of growth as observed on a Silurian bioherm of northern Indiana. The small colony to the extreme right was torn loose from the biohermal mound and rolled down the slope to be buried finally in the mud of the interreef lagoon. *G–I. Actinostroma tenuifilatum* from the Niagaran of Ontario: *G, I*, vertical sections showing prominence of radial pillars; *H*, tangential section showing numerous pillars. *J–K. Cryptophragmus antiquatus* from the Ordovician. *J*, two small, partly preserved colonies sectioned to show the internal structure. This is the usual method of preservation. Specimen from Ordovician at Kentland, Ind. *K*, transverse and longitudinal sections of a specimen from the Ordovician of Ontario, showing the width of the complete colony. *L.* Diagram to illustrate probable position of growth of *Beatricia. M–N. Beatricia undulata* from the Ordovician (Ellis Bay) of Anticosti Island: *M*, transverse section showing central tube and general cystose structure; *N*, longitudinal section showing tabulated central tube and general cystose structure. *M* and *N* are somewhat diagrammatic. It is not definitely known that the curved diaphragms of the central tube were convex distally. (*A, B, C, G, H, and I after Parks; D after Nicholson; K after Raymond.*)

seas and were also important contributors to the reefs or *bioherms* of those times.[1] *Beatricia* and *Cryptophragmus* are important Ordovician stromatoporoids; and *Clathrodictyon*, *Actinostroma*, and *Stromatopora* are typical of the Silurian and Devonian of North America. *Clathrodictyon* is also present in the late Ordovician (Fig. 24).

Group Graptozoa[2]

The Graptozoa are extinct, exclusively colonial and marine organisms which secreted a supporting and protective exoskeleton of chitinous material, with the separate individuals housed in small cups or pits along a chitinous stalk. During fossilization all of the constituents of the chitin except the carbon disappeared, so that graptolites are nearly always preserved in the form of carbonaceous films resembling scroll-saw blades or hieroglyphics written on the rock (whence the name *graptolite*—Gr. *graptos*, written, + *lithos*, rock). These remains are most abundant in black shales, but they are also found in shales of other colors, as well as in limestones and sandstones. Specimens found in limestone afford the best opportunity for study, as they may be released from the matrix with hydrochloric acid and suspended in some such transparent substance as glycerin. These specimens frequently have been little compressed, and hence show the original dimensions and structures accurately.

The Exoskeleton.—So far as is known from the fossil record, the graptolites were exclusively colonial, with the entire colony surrounded by a chitinous covering known as the *periderm*. The colony arose by serial budding from the primary or embryonic cup, the *sicula* (Fig. 25 *A*), which was built by the initial polyp. The sicula is a conical or dagger-shaped structure and was attached either to the bottom, or to some type of float, by a hollow, threadlike tube known as the *nema* or *nemacaulus*. One,

[1] Cumings, E. R., and Shrock, R. R., Niagaran coral reefs of Indiana and adjacent states and their stratigraphic relations, *Bull. Geol. Soc. Amer.*, vol. 39, pp. 579–620, 1928. Cumings, E. R., Reefs or bioherms, *ibid.*, vol. 43, pp. 331–352, 1932. Fenton, M. A., A Devonian stromatoporoid Reef, *Amer. Midland Naturalist*, vol. 12, pp. 195–202, 1931. Fenton, C. L., Niagaran stromatoporoid reefs of the Chicago region, *ibid.*, pp. 203–212.

[2] Graptozoa—Gr. *graptos*, written + *zoon*, animal; referring to the fact that the carbonized remains of the originally chitinous exoskeletons resemble writing.

two, or four buds were given off by the initial polyp, and these secreted about themselves conical or cylindrical *hydrothecae* (variously designated as thecae, cells, cellules, calices, cups, and denticles), which were so arranged as to open at their bases into a common canal. The *apertures* of the hydrothecae were at first simple or slightly contracted, but in more highly specialized forms they took on various shapes and were often furnished with tiny spines (Fig. 27 *I*).

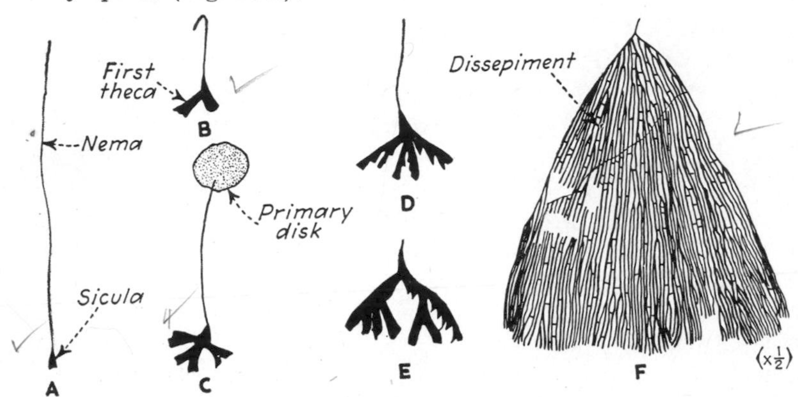

FIG. 25.—Growth stages of a dendroid graptolite (*Dictyonema flabelliforme*) from the Upper Cambrian of New York. *A*. Sicula with long nema. *B*. Sicula and first theca matured. *C*. Young rhabdosome with nema and primary disk. *D–E*. Somewhat more advanced rhabdosomes showing bifurcation of branches; and in *E*, the first dissepiment. (*A–E*, ×2½.) *F*. A normal and approximately mature rhabdosome. (*After Ruedemann.*)

After the formation of the first hydrotheca (or hydrothecae if the buds came off in pairs or in quartets), all subsequent buds arose from the bases of preceding polyps, with which they remained in contact throughout life. The resulting colony (known as a *rhabdosome*, *polypary*, or *stock*) was a bladelike structure with the hydrothecae arranged in a continuous series along one row (uniserial), two rows (biserial), or four rows (quadriserial). These blades in some species had an axial supporting rod known as the *virgula* (Fig. 27 *K*). A group of rhabdosomes similar to those just described, and often attached to some type of float, has been named a *synrhabdosome*. A dendritic or bushlike framework results when the bladelike rhabdosomes are held together by supporting transverse bars known as *dissepiments*. In such an exoskeleton the hydrothecae are usually in the form of small pits on the surface of the branches.

In every case mentioned above, the sicula is on the proximal end of the rhabdosome, and the latter is attached at its proximal end to the nemacaulus (Fig. 25).

Habitat.—Some colonies were fixed to the sea bottom and hence were a part of the benthos; some were attached to seaweeds or other floating objects; and still others were attached to floats of their own making (Figs. 25 *C*, 27), in which respect they are comparable to the present-day *Siphonophora*. The planktonic forms attained world-wide distribution and are very important for intercontinental correlation and for reconstruction of ancient lands and seaways.

The fact that graptolites are found most abundantly in black shales does not indicate that they lived in great abundance in the waters beneath which such sediments were accumulating but rather that the waters over such bottoms may not have been normally marine, hence not unlikely destructive to most salt-water organisms.[1] When the graptolites drifted into these waters from their home in the open sea they were killed, and their remains sank to the bottom where they were preserved because of the absence of scavengers. On bottoms with sufficient circulation to eliminate the organic matter and to produce conditions favorable for benthonic organisms, graptolite remains are usually absent. Their absence in such cases is thought to be due to the destruction of the chitinous skeletons by scavengers.

Geologic History.—Graptolites began as simple dendroid forms in the Upper Cambrian; attained their main acme of development in the Ordovician; arose during the Silurian to a second minor acme, with the dominant divisions different from those in

[1] The presence of marcasite and pyrite (FeS_2) in graptolite-bearing shales indicates that the muds and immediately overlying waters probably contained hydrogen sulphide and that the waters as a consequence were really poisonous. The blackness of the shales proves that reducing conditions were also present on the bottom. In this connection see Ruedemann, R., Stratigraphic significance of the wide distribution of graptolites, *Bull. Geol. Soc. Amer.*, vol. 22, p. 234, 1911. Grabau, A. W., Origin, distribution, and mode of preservation of the graptolites, *Mem. Inst. Geol., Nat. Res. Council China*, pp. 1–52, 1929. Grabau, A. W., and O'Connell, M., Were the graptolite shales as a rule deep or shallow water deposits?, *Bull. Geol. Soc. Amer.*, vol. 28, pp. 959–964, 1917. Marr, J. E., The Stockdale shales of the Lake District, *Quart. Jour. Geol. Soc.*, vol. 81, pt. 2, pp. 113–133, 1925. Ruedemann, R., *Mem.* 2, *Geol. Soc. Amer.*, pp. 43–52, 1934.

the Ordovician; and then almost completely disappeared at the close of the Silurian, with only a few stragglers persisting through the Devonian and possibly into the early Mississippian. The disappearance at the close of the Silurian and the beginning of the Devonian may perhaps be correlated with the advent of the fishes, which appeared in great numbers at that time. The dendroid or fan-shaped forms were the earliest to develop and also the last to survive. The more specialized types are mainly confined to the Ordovician and Silurian.

Biologic Affinities.—After having been referred to various subdivisions of the Organic World (algae, sponges, sertularian and plumularian hydrozoans, and bryozoans), the graptolites have come to be placed by most authors in the Coelenterata, either as a separate subdivision or as an extinct group of Hydrozoa. Since they have been extinct so long and do not seem to be very closely allied to any known existing animals, their exact biologic affinities are still in question. Grave doubt has recently been thrown on the classification as Coelenterata by Ruedemann and Ulrich.[1] These investigators present rather strong evidence for the statement that the graptolites are "an early and long extinct branch of the bryozoans." The present authors, however, prefer to retain the group in the Coelenterata, but as a distinct subdivision, pending further investigations into their biologic relations.

Classification.—Classification of the group is based largely on the arrangement of the hydrothecae, the presence or absence of a virgula, and the shape and character of the skeletal framework. The Graptozoa have been divided into the two orders of *Dendroidea* and *Graptoloidea;* and the latter into two suborders, the *Axonolipa* (without a virgula) and the *Axonophora* (with a virgula).

ORDER DENDROIDEA[2]

The *Dendroidea* include graptolites with fan-shaped rhabdosomes composed of branches or stems joined together into a trellis-like framework by means of transverse bars (dissepiments).

[1] RUEDEMANN, R., and ULRICH, E. O., Are the graptolites bryozoans? *Bull. Geol. Soc. Amer.*, vol. 42, pp. 589–604, 1931.

[2] Dendroidea—Gr. *dendron,* tree + *oid,* like; referring to the treelike appearance of the rhabdosomes.

The hydrothecae are either small pits in, or cups upon, the branches. They are not present on the dissepiments. In the funnel-shaped forms the hydrothecae lie on the inside surface of

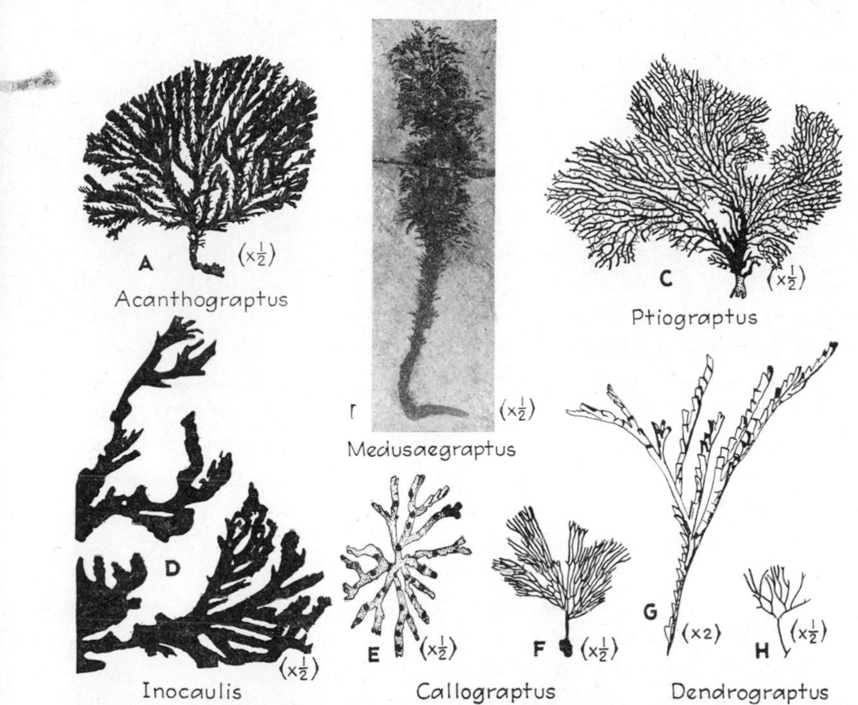

FIG. 26.—Dendroid graptolites. *A. Acanthograptus granti*, a nearly perfect rhabdosome, from the Silurian (Niagaran) of Ontario. *B. Medusaegraptus mirabilis* from the Silurian (Lockport) of New York. *C. Ptiograptus percorrugatus*, an almost complete rhabdosome showing many dissepiments, from the Middle Devonian of Kentucky. *D. Inocaulis granti*, part of a large rhabdosome, from the Silurian (Niagaran) of Ontario. *E. Callograptus staufferi*, a compressed rhabdosome showing pits on the branches, from the Upper Cambrian (Trempealeau) of Minnesota. *F. Callograptus compactus*, an incomplete rhabdosome with adhesion disk, from the Ordovician (Utica) of New York. *G. Dendrograptus hallianus*, an incomplete rhabdosome showing the thecae, from the Upper Cambrian (Trempealeau) of Wisconsin. *H. Dendrograptus ontarioensis* from the Silurian (Niagaran) of Ontario. (*D and H after Bassler; all others after Ruedemann.*)

the branches. Most of the dendroid graptolites, especially the more massive shrublike forms such as *Medusaegraptus* (Fig. 26 *B*), seem to have been attached to the bottom and to have grown in an upright position. This habit of growth very likely accounts for the local distribution. Such forms as *Dictyonema*, which attained world-wide distribution, must have been attached to some type of float, at least in the younger growth stages (Fig. 25).

The earliest of the Dendroidea are found in the Upper Cambrian; the last probably in the Devonian, although a doubtful form has been reported from the early Mississippian. The last survivors are thought to have been the more primitive and less progressive types, and this may account for their survival after the more specialized forms had become extinct.

Typical examples of the order are *Dictyonema* (Cambrian-Devonian), *Callograptus* (Cambrian-Silurian), *Ptiograptus* (Devonian), *Acanthograptus* (Silurian), *Inocaulis* (Ordovician-Devonian?), and *Dendrograptus* (Cambrian-Silurian) (Fig. 26).

ORDER GRAPTOLOIDEA[1]

The Graptoloidea are characterized by rhabdosomes or synrhabdosomes in which the hydrothecae have uniserial (monoprion), biserial (diprion), or quadriserial arrangement. Both the rhabdosomes (not the synrhabdosomes) and hydrothecae exhibit bilateral symmetry. The latter are usually conical or bell-shaped, although they often show considerable variation in shape, and are ornamented in some cases by small spines. In life the inhabitants of the hydrothecae are thought to have been more or less connected by coenosarc. The hydrothecae were in communication by means of a common canal enclosed in the periderm. The order is subdivided, on the basis of the presence or absence of a virgula, into the *Axonolipa* and *Axonophora*.

Axonolipa.—This suborder consists of those forms which lack a virgula and in which the hydrothecae develop by progressive budding, first from the sicula and afterward from the bases of preceding hydrothecae. The arrangement of the latter may be uniserial, biserial or quadriserial. Most Axonolipa seem to have been floating forms attached to seaweeds or similar objects, but a few may have been attached to the bottom. Typical genera are *Didymograptus*, *Tetragraptus*, and *Bryograptus* (uniserial), *Dicranograptus* (biserial), and *Phyllograptus* (quadriserial). This suborder is particularly characteristic of the Ordovician.

Axonophora.—Graptolites belonging to this suborder have a virgula in the rhabdosome. Only uniserial and biserial arrange-

[1] Graptoloidea—Gr. *graptos*, written + *oid*, like; resembling writing.

ments of the hydrothecae are known. The virgula is a simple rod in the forms with a uniserial arrangement (monoprions) lying

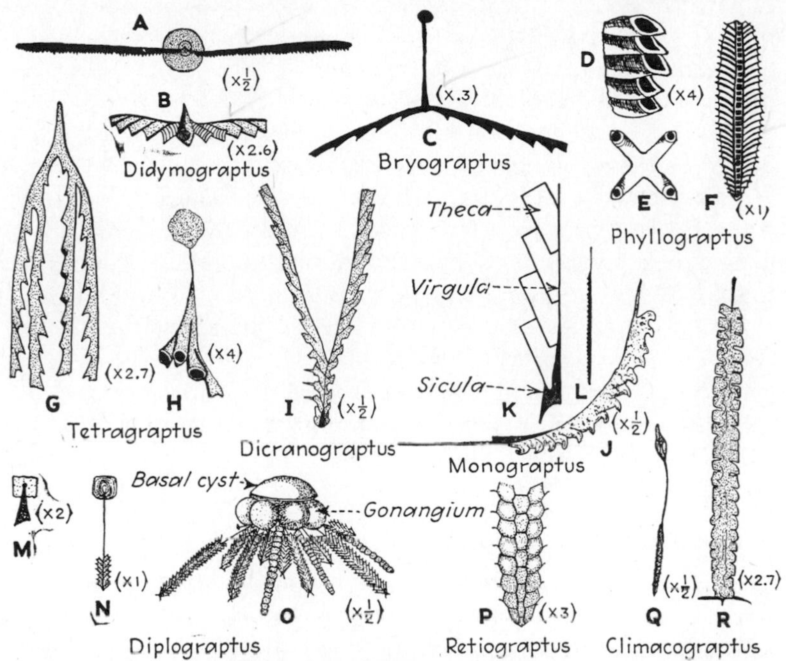

FIG. 27.—Graptoloidea. *A. Didymograptus patulus*, a nearly mature rhabdosome with central disk. *B.* A young rhabdosome of the same species showing sicula and first few thecae. *C. Bryograptus lapworthi*, a young rhabdosome with fragment of primary disk. *D. Phyllograptus ilicifolius*, a few thecae much enlarged to show character of aperture. *E.* Diagram showing the quadriserial arrangement of the thecae in this genus. *F. Phyllograptus angustifolius*, a nearly complete rhabdosome. *G. Tetragraptus pendens*, proximal portion showing sicula and thecae. *H. I. fruticosus*, a young rhabdosome showing primary disk, nema, sicula, and first few thecae. *Dicranograptus nicholsoni*, part of a rhabdosome showing sicula (in black) and thecae. *J. Monograptus flexilis*, a rhabdosome showing nema, sicula, virgula, and thecae. *K.* Diagram of a rhabdosome of *Monograptus*, with structures indicated. *L.* Diagram to illustrate the usual appearance of fossils of this genus. *M. Diplograptus pristis*, the sicula. *N.* A young rhabdosome of *D. pristis* attached to the basal cyst. *O.* A complete synrhabdosome of *D. pristis* with basal cyst, gonangia or reproductive organs, and numerous complete or incomplete rhabdosomes. *P. Retiograptus geinitzianus*, a portion of the reticulated rhabdosome. *Q. Climacograptus parvus*, rhabdosome with inflation of nemacaulus. *R. C. modestus*, an almost complete rhabdosome. (*E, K, and L are diagrammatic; J from the Wenlock shales of England, after Elles and Wood; all other figures are of specimens from the Lower or Middle Ordovician of New York and are after Ruedemann.*)

in a depression on the dorsal side of the rhabdosome. In the diprions (rhabdosomes with the hydrothecae in biserial arrangement) it is double and is enclosed by the coalescence of the periderm of each half of the rhabdosome, except in the *Retiolitidae*, in which it is placed on opposite sides of the coenosarc with one part straight and the other having a zigzag arrangement. In most graptolites the periderm is generally continuous and complete, but in the Retiolitidae it is much attenuated and is supported by a network of chitinous fibers. Each rhabdosome begins as a sicula attached to a float by a nema (nemacaulus), and the new polyps develop adjacent to the sicula at the distal end. Successive generations grow toward the float. The life history of a typical representative of this suborder is shown in Fig. 27 *M–O*.

Genera typical of the suborder are *Monograptus* (uniserial), *Climacograptus* (biserial), and *Retiograptus* (with a reticulated periderm). The group appeared in the Ordovician, attained its major development in the Silurian, and disappeared before the beginning of the Devonian.

Class Scyphozoa[1]

The Scyphozoa are free-swimming, discoidal, and umbrella-shaped medusae with a downwardly directed mouth, gastrovascular pouches, and numerous radial canals. The polyp stage is uncommon but does occur in some forms. The umbrella is without a velum, and the margin is usually lobed and equipped with tentacles. The mouth occupies a central position on the underside of the body. Individuals are often large, and forms 2 m. in diameter and with tentacles 40 m. long have been described. Living forms have many cnidoblasts and often are a source of annoyance on seaside swimming beaches. Recent investigations show that at certain stages of growth specimens may be as much as 99 per cent water.

Obviously, an organism of the composition just described stands little chance of leaving any trace of its existence, yet fossil remains have been reported. This evidence is in the form of molds of the upper and lower surfaces and mud fillings of the gastric pouches. Fossil specimens referred to the Scyphozoa have been described from the Lower Cambrian of New York, Sweden, Russia, and Bohemia; from the Middle Cambrian of

[1] Scyphozoa—Gr. *skyphos*, cup + *zoon*, animal; referring to the resemblance of the scyphozoan to an inverted cup.

British Columbia (*Peytoia*) and Alabama (*Brooksella* and *Laotira*) (Fig. 28); from the Permian of Saxony; and from the Jurassic of Solnhofen, Bavaria. The identity of some of these specimens has been questioned, and there appears to be considerable doubt as to their exact nature. As known at present, the fossils are of

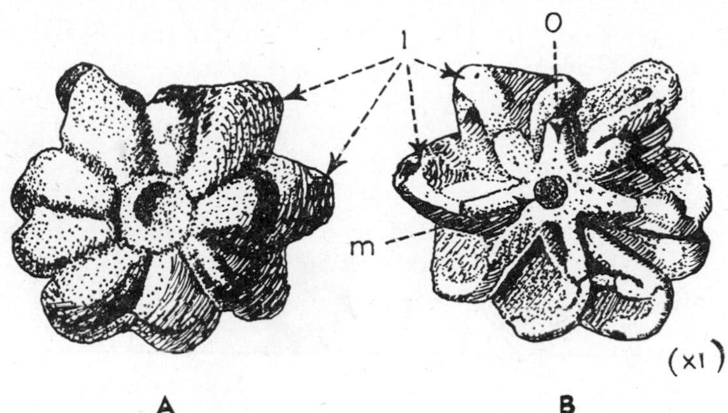

FIG. 28.—*Brooksella alternata*, supposedly a siliceous filling of the internal cavity of a Middle Cambrian medusoid organism. This interpretation has been questioned. The specimen is shown as viewed from above and below. *A*. View of upper surface showing nine lobes (*l*) and a trace of the furrow in the ring about the central disk. *B*. View of underside showing narrow lobes (*l*) and what appear to be oral arms (*o*) leading to a central depression (*m*), which may possibly indicate the position of a primitive "mouth." (*After Walcott.*)

little importance to the paleontologist, for they are very rare and difficult of identification when found.

CLASS ANTHOZOA (ACTINOZOA)[1]

The Organism.—Only polyps are found in the Anthozoa, and they differ from those of the Hydrozoa in the following respects: (1) They possess mesenteries and hence secrete septate exoskeletons; (2) the mouth, which is elongated in the plane of bilateral symmetry, opens into the coelenteron through a gullet with an ectodermal lining; (3) the tentacles are hollow and are connected with the coelenteron; (4) the polyps are generally larger in the Anthozoa; and (5) the sexual products are produced in the endoderm. Not all polyps secrete a skeleton, but those

[1] Anthozoa—Gr. *anthos*, flower + *zoon*, animal; referring to the flower-like appearance of the polyp when it has its tentacles extended.

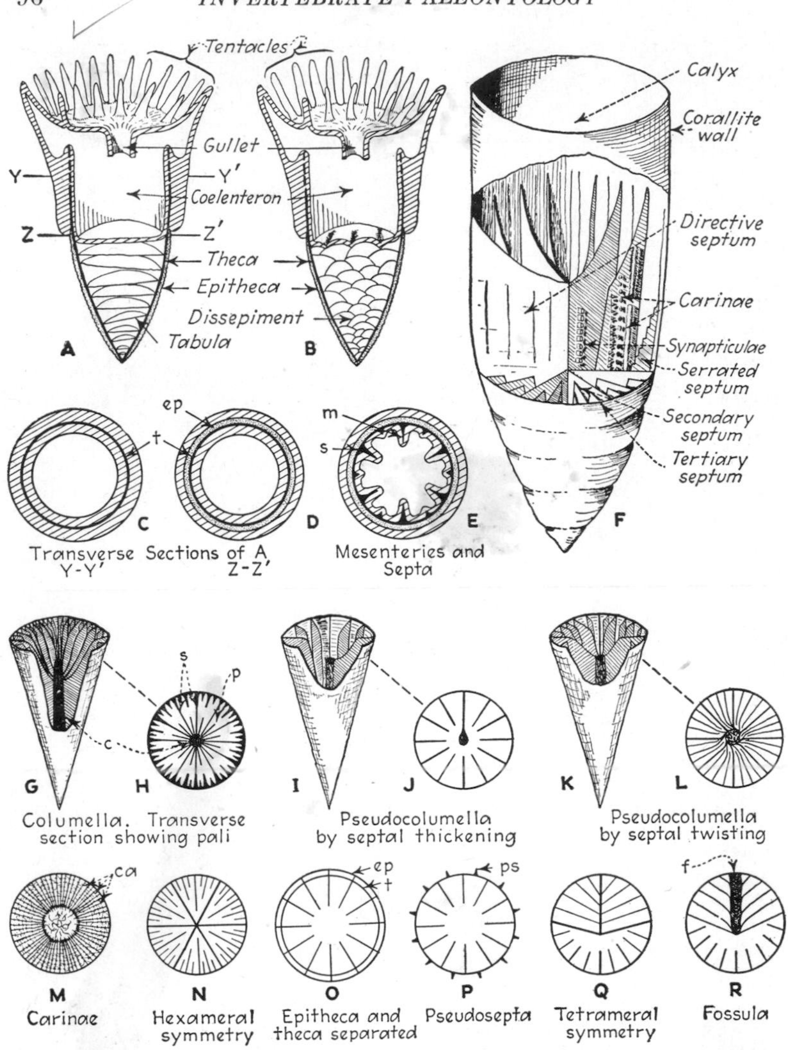

FIG. 29.—Anthozoan exoskeletal structures. *A*. Polyp and tabulated corallite. *B*. Polyp and dissepimental corallite. *C*. Transverse section in upper part of corallite showing only the theca (*t*). *D*. Transverse section at base of calyx showing epitheca (*ep*) and theca (*t*). *E*. Transverse section of septate corallite occupied by a polyp (*m*, mesentery; *s*, septum). *F*. Diagrammatic corallite showing numerous internal structures. *G*. Corallum with columella. *H*. Transverse section of *G*, showing columella (*c*), pali (*p*), and septa (*s*). *I*. Corallum with pseudocolumella produced by thickening of the free edge of a septum. *J*. Transverse section of *I*. *K*. Corallum with pseudocolumella produced by the twisting of the septa. *L*. Transverse section of *K*. *M*. Transverse section of a corallite showing septa and carinae (*ca*). *N*. Same as *M*, showing hexameral arrangement of the septa. *O*. Transverse section of a corallite show-

that do build that structure of horny or calcareous material. The "stony corals" are a group in which the skeleton is composed of the latter substance.

Relation of the Animal and Skeleton.—The coelenteron is divided into compartments by radially directed inward folds of the body wall or the mesenteries. There may be four or six or some multiple of these figures. Corresponding in some degree with the development and position of these mesenteries are wrinkles on the exterior or ectodermal surface of the polyp. Since the stony supporting and dividing structures of the exoskeleton are secreted by the ectoderm, it follows that the inward folds of the entire body wall will have counterparts in the exoskeletons in the form of radially directed, platelike partitions. Such vertical plates, arranged, as are the mesenteries, in cycles of four, six, or some multiple of these numbers, are referred to as *septa* (singular, *septum*) (Fig. 29 *E–F*). These divide the internal cavity of the exoskeleton into more or less equal compartments and are usually best developed in the lower and older part of the corallite. The upper and larger part of the corallite which houses the polyp is known as the *calyx* (cup) (see Fig. 29 *F*).

The septa may be of equal length and thickness throughout, or they may vary in these respects. In some cases they become considerably thickened on the edges. They are always arranged in several cycles. The first cycle is designated the *primary*, and the septa in that cycle are known as the *primary* or *directive* septa. These may be longer or shorter than those added subsequently and may also differ among themselves in length. They range from 4 to 12 in number. Between the septa of the primary cycle other cycles are intercalated progressively until the number may be over a hundred. The edges of the septa may be smooth, serrated, or granulated. The sides are usually more or less granulated. Many septa have rows of small nodes which in some instances are united to form ridges. If these ridges are disposed vertically, they are referred to as *carinae* (singular, *carina*) (Fig. 29 *F*, *M*). Conical or cylindrical transverse bars arranged at right angles to the surface of a septum are known as *synapticulae*. In some species these unite to bind the septa

ing the theca (*t*) and epitheca (*ep*) separated. *P*. Same, showing pseudosepta (*ps*). *Q*. Same, showing tetrameral arrangement of the septa. *R*. Same, showing fossula (*f*) in a tetracoral.

together and thereby form a more rigid structure. If one of the directive septa fails to develop fully, its place will be marked by a depression known as a *fossula* (ditch) (Fig. 29 *R*, 32 *B*, *I*). The number and character of the septa are of great systematic importance.

Septa are usually bound together at or near the outer edges by secretions from the ectoderm. This binding material, which takes the form of a conical or prismatic wall, is designated the *theca*. Subsequent stony additions may be made on the exterior of the theca by overhanging ectoderm (Fig. 29 *A–B*). These additions constitute the *epitheca* (upon the theca). The theca is usually smooth, but commonly it is annulated by more or less faint growth rings. The epitheca very frequently possesses annular rugosities that are disposed parallel to the upper edge of the corallite as it existed at the time when any particular part of the epitheca was formed. In some corals the septa project beyond the theca and thus appear on the exterior. If an epitheca develops in these forms, it may not be in actual contact with the theca (Fig. 29 *O*). In certain other forms septa-like ridges show on the epitheca. If these do not coincide in position with the real septa, they are known as *pseudosepta* (Fig. 29 *P*).

In small corallites the polyp extends to the bottom, but as the organism grows and adds to the top of the structure, the basal part is abandoned and is partitioned off by horizontal or oblique plates which bridge the interseptal spaces. Such floorlike partitions are known as *tabulae* (singular, *tabula*) if they extend entirely across the central area of the corallite or *dissepiments* if they extend from one septum to another or if they join above or below with similar incomplete plates (Fig. 29 *A–B*). Tabulae may be concave upward, convex upward, or flat, and they may or may not be deflected upward or downward at the margins where they join the inner wall of the corallite. They are subject to much variation in distance from each other, and this same irregularity is true of the dissepiments. The latter structures may give to the corallites a *vesicular* character. In some forms only tabulae are present; in others only dissepiments; and in still others one part of the corallite may have the former and another part the latter. In a few species the interior becomes filled with vesicle-like structures, the septa tend to disappear, and the terms tabulate and dissepimental no longer apply.

Rarely a species is found in which the corallite possesses no internal structure.

Among certain types of corals the septa do not extend to the center of the corallite, and there arises from the base a more or less conical structure known as the *columella* (Fig. 29 *G–H*). This is the counterpart of an indentation in the base of the polyp and may be either columnar or leaflike in shape. It is usually solid but may be formed of more or less twisted rods or thin lamellae. In other species of corals the septa extend to the center of the corallite, where the free edges become twisted together and project as a conical mass above the bottom of the calyx, thus forming what is known as a *pseudocolumella* (Fig. 29 *K–L*). The same structure may come into existence by the thickening of one of the directive septa along its free edge (Fig. 29 *I–J*). A few species of corals have narrow vertical plates in one or more cycles inserted between the columella and the septa. These are known as *pali* (Fig. 29 *H*).

Reproduction and Ontogeny.—Reproduction takes place both asexually and sexually. New individuals formed by budding ordinarily remain attached to the parent and thereby aid in building the colony. In sexual reproduction a free-swimming larva is formed. This ultimately attaches itself to some foreign object on the bottom and develops into a new individual. Upon settling down, the larva assumes the shape of a thin biscuit, modifying that general shape to conform to any irregularities on the object to which it has become attached. It first secretes a *basal plate*, and soon afterward the basal portion of the animal develops four or six folds, between which are soon formed a corresponding number of bladelike radial upgrowths of the basal plate. These are the primary septa of the skeleton, and ultimately in almost all cases they become united at the outer edges by the theca. This complete structure, roughly conical or cup-shaped, constitutes the embryonic exoskeleton or the *prototheca*. Rarely growth may end soon after this stage, and a buttonlike, septate skeleton may result as illustrated by *Hadrophyllum* (Fig. 32 *B*) and *Fungia* (Fig. 33 *E*). Usually, however, the animal continues to grow and develops many cycles of mesenteries and an equal number of cycles of septa in the skeleton, until there may be more than a hundred of these. The number is always some multiple of the number of primary septa. In order to place itself in a favorable position with respect to other organisms on the bottom the polyp more or less continuously extends its exoskeleton upward, and this necessitates progressive abandonment of the earlier parts of the structure. As the polyp thus moves upward in its exoskeleton it builds supporting structures beneath itself.

Habitat.—The Anthozoa at the present time are exclusively marine, and it is thought that such has always been the case. They tend to be confined to shallow waters [under 180 m. (600 ft.)], though some range to great depths. The reef-building corals inhabit depths not exceeding 76 m. (250 ft.) and require temperatures not lower than 68°F. The temperature condition limits the distribution in existing seas to a belt about 60 deg. wide extending around the earth about evenly divided on each side of the equator (Fig. 30). In this belt are found many extensive land areas of which some of the rocks are composed to a considerable degree of the broken and macerated remains of coral colonies, along with the stony skeletons of associated organisms. Ancient reefs (bioherms) of similar character have been described from many parts of the world. Whether the ancient reef corals required conditions of temperature and depth like those of the modern coral seas cannot be stated with certainty. Not all living corals, however, are confined to warm waters. Some are found in rather cold waters, and it is likely that similar forms lived in the geologic past.

Classification.—The Anthozoa are subdivided on the basis of the following considerations into four subclasses—Tetracoralla, Hexacoralla, Alcyonaria (Octocoralla), and Tabulata:

1. Arrangement and character of the septa.
2. Size, shape, and relations of the corallites.
3. Presence or absence of internal structural features such as tabulae, dissepiments, columellae, etc.
4. Character of the coralla.

Subclass Tetracoralla (Rugosa)

The Tetracoralla comprise a group of extinct, exclusively Paleozoic corals with *simple* (solitary) or *compound* (colonial) coralla. The former are referred to as cup corals because of shape. The latter may be branching forms or compact masses of generally domal shape. The name *Rugosa* has been applied

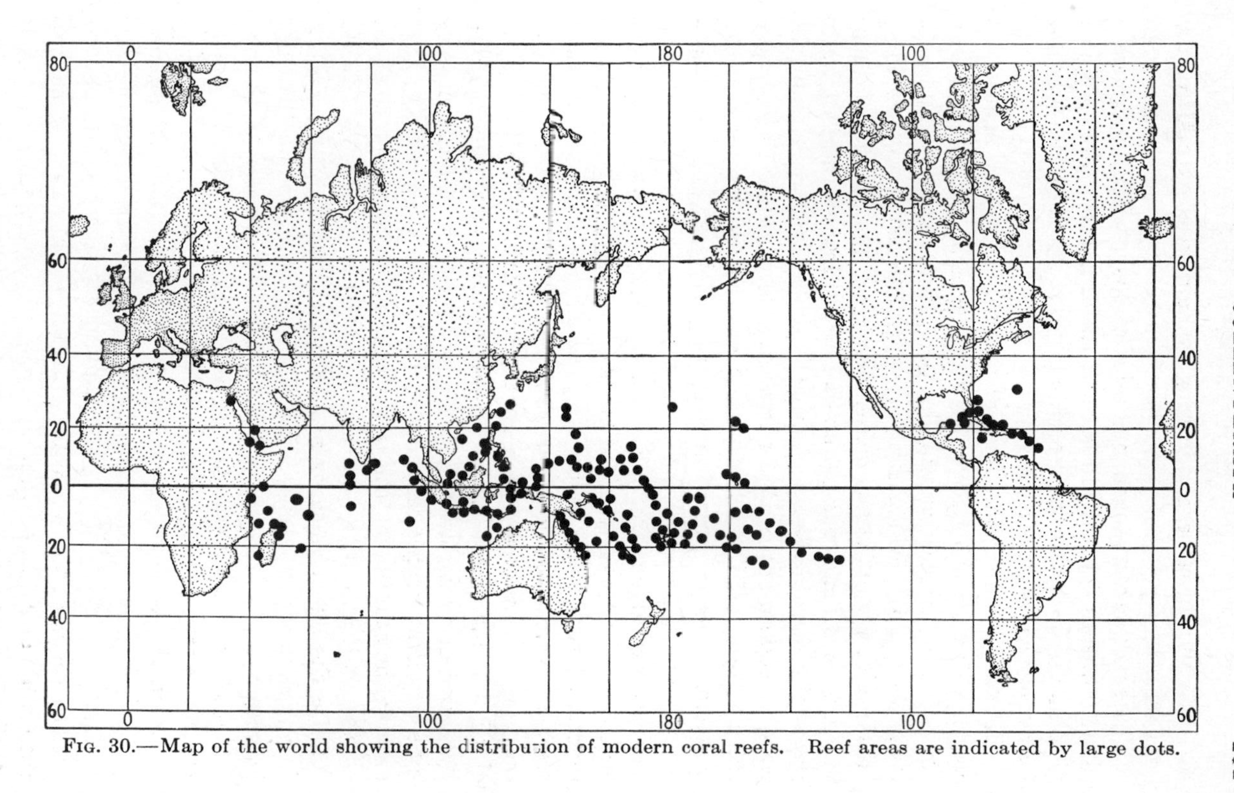

FIG. 30.—Map of the world showing the distribution of modern coral reefs. Reef areas are indicated by large dots.

to this group because of the roughly annulated exterior of the corallites.

The septa are arranged in cycles of four, with fundamental bilateral symmetry, modified in the mature part of the corallites of some species by secondary radial symmetry (Fig. 29 *Q*). The four directive septa of the primary cycle are so disposed as to divide the corallite into four unequal quadrants. Succeeding septa are added in cycles of four or multiples of that number, whence the name Tetracoralla (Gr. *tetra,* four). The main directive septum, which is usually longer than the other three but may be almost wanting and indicated by a fossula, is designated the *cardinal septum* (Fig. 32 *D–F*). The one diametrically opposite is the *counter septum.* This may be longer than the cardinal septum, as in *Lophophyllum,* or so short as to be inconspicuous and indicated by a fossula. In the early growth stages these two together form a single septum located in the plane of symmetry and really represent the initial septum of the corallite. The two remaining directive septa, referred to as *alar septa,* arise on opposite sides of the cardinal septum, and, through enlargement of the space between themselves and that septum, their summits reach positions approximately 90 deg. from the cardinal septum. The four directive septa, therefore, divide the cavity of the corallite into four quadrants of somewhat unequal size. If any primary septum fails to develop, its position is marked by a *fossula.* Such a feature often indicates the position of the cardinal or counter septum but only rarely occurs in place of the alar septa (Fig. 31).

Once the directive septa are formed, new septa arise successively on opposite sides of the cardinal septum, one on each side at a time, and also one on the counter side of each of the alar septa. The manner and order of development are shown in Fig. 31. The interior of the corallite may contain such structures as tabulae, dissepiments, vesicular tissue, synapticulae, and carinae. The theca is ordinarily well developed and imperforate. Epithecal additions often cause annular rugosities on the exterior surface of the corallite. Such are especially characteristic of the simple or single coralla.

A simple corallum, if small, may have the shape of a cone, top, or button; large coralla usually become cylindrical in the mature part. Compound or colonial coralla are composed of many individual corallities loosely or tightly grown together. Coenosarcal tissue does not seem to have connected the solitary polyps, as is the case in the Hydrozoa, but connective tissue of a similar sort may have existed in some of the colonial groups.

The form of the polyp is not known except as it may be inferred from the architecture and structure of the exoskeleton. It is assumed that reproduction was exclusively sexual in some forms

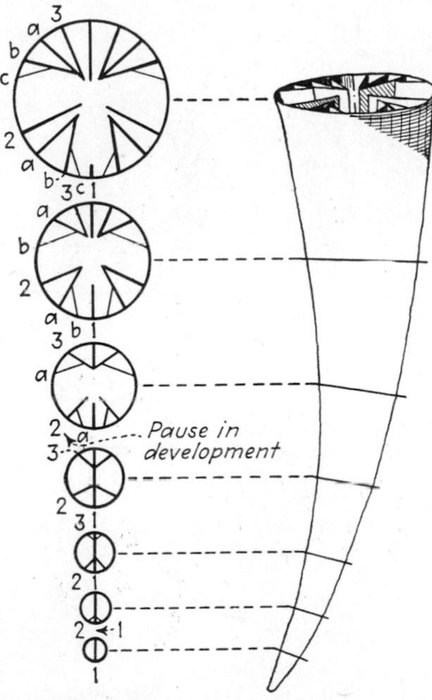

FIG. 31.—Diagram showing the order of development of septa in a tetracoral. The sections are taken from the apex to the base of the calyx at approximately the intervals shown. (*Based on data by Carruthers.*)

and that most solitary polyps were produced sexually. It is further assumed that the original or first individual of a colony usually developed through sexual reproduction and that additions were of asexual origin or budded from older individuals of the colony. The character of the budding can be inferred from the position of the buds with respect to the parents. The buds occupy both lateral and calicinal positions.

The Tetracoralla are considered ancestral to the Hexacoralla, but the exact groups which were responsible for the ancestry as well as the time at which transition from the former to the latter

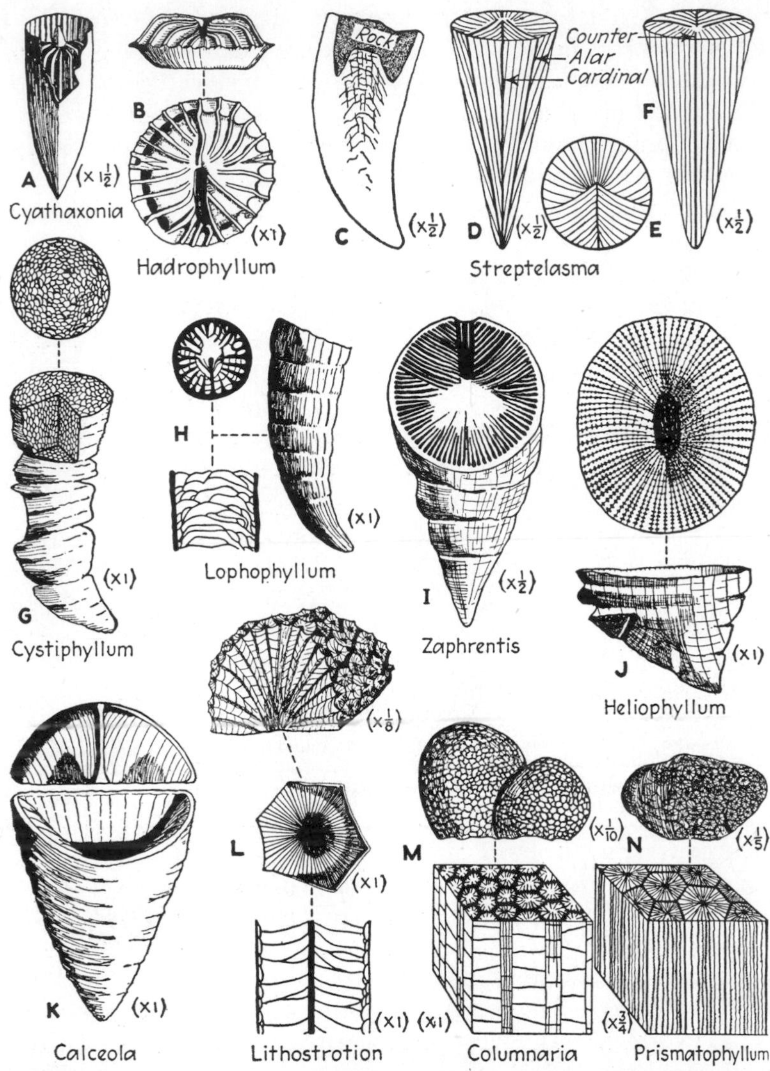

Fig. 32.—*Tetracoralla*. *A*. *Cyathaxonia cornu* from Carboniferous of Belgium. *B*. *Hadrophyllum aplanatum* from Pennsylvanian of Texas, showing prominent septa and fossula. *C*. *Streptelasma corniculum* from the Ordovician of Kentucky, with the corallum sectioned longitudinally. Tabulate and dissepimental structure apparent only in axial part of corallum. The calyx is filled with sediment. *D*. *Streptelasma corniculum* from Ordovician of Kentucky, with theca ground away so that the ends of the septa may be seen. *E*. Same as *D* but transversely cut to show the symmetry of the septa. *F*. Same as *D*. *G*. *Cystiphyllum vesiculosum* from the Devonian of Michigan showing the very vesiculose internal structure produced by dissepiments. *H*. *Lophophyllum eruca* from the Carbonif-

began is still a speculative matter.[1] They made their first appearance in the Chazy of the Ordovician; attained their maximum, both in abundance and in number of species, in the Silurian; and then gradually declined to the end of the Paleozoic. Fossil forms are most abundant in calcareous strata and in many instances are excellent index fossils.

The subclass Tetracoralla is usually divided into the following five families: Cyathaxonidae, Palaeocyclidae, Zaphrentidae, Cyathophyllidae, and Cystiphyllidae.

Cyathaxonidae.—The members of this family have small, simple, turbinate or horn-shaped coralla which lack both tabulae and dissepiments. The septa appear to have radial arrangement, and the only differentiation is in length. The directive septa vary in length, whereas subsequent septa are of equal length. If there is an epitheca, it is thin. A columella may be present but is generally absent. The coralla rarely exceed an inch in length. Members of the family are usually not abundant, and care must be taken lest the young of other families be referred to this. The geologic range is from the Silurian to the Permian. *Cyathaxonia* from the Carboniferous limestone of Europe is a typical genus (Fig. 32 *A*).

Palaeocyclidae.—Individuals of the Palaeocyclidae have small, simple coralla which have the shapes of disks, buttons, or cushions. The horn shape so characteristic of the Tetracoralla is never present. Tabulae and dissepiments are lacking, but septa are strongly developed and are arranged in two or more series with semiradial symmetry. The epitheca is well developed. There are few species in this family, and individuals are rarely abundant. The family is known only from the Silurian to the Carboniferous. *Hadrophyllum* from the Devonian and Pennsylvanian is representative (Fig. 32 *B*).

[1] Robinson, W. J., The relationship of the Tetracoralla to the Hexacoralla, *Conn. Acad. Arts, Trans.* 21, pp. 145–200, 1917; The ancestry of the Hexacoralla, *Amer. Jour. Science* (5), vol. 6, pp. 424–426, 1923.

---

erous of Scotland. *I. Zaphrentis* sp. from the Devonian at Louisville, Ky. *J. Heliophyllum* sp. from the Devonian of Michigan showing extensive development of carinae. *K. Calceola sandalina* from the Devonian of the Eifel, Germany, showing a corallum with the operculum. *L. Lithostrotion canadense* from the Mississippian of Indiana. *M. Columnaria alveolata* from the Ordovician (Saluda) of Kentucky. *N. Prismatophyllum davidsoni* from the Devonian of Michigan. (*A after Zittel with modifications; H after Nicholson and Lydekker, with slight modifications; K after Stebbing.*)

Zaphrentidae.—The Zaphrentidae have simple, horn-shaped or cylindrical coralla which may grow to rather large dimensions. Specimens over 60 cm. (2 ft.) in length occur in the Devonian at Louisville, Ky., and forms 45 cm. (18 in.) long are present in the Silurian of the Ringerike district of Norway. The numerous well-developed septa are arranged in more than one series and show distinct bilateral symmetry. Complete development of tabulae is common, and dissepiments are also generally developed. In a few species the tabulae are irregular, and in some instances this condition is responsible for a somewhat vesicular internal structure. They may be horizontal or oblique, and often they turn upward or downward where they join the interior surface of the theca. The theca is formed by fusion of the septal bases and is often covered with epitheca. The cardinal septum is marked by a fossula in numerous species. A pseudocolumella is present in some species and may be formed by the twisting together of the free ends of the septa and then upgrowth into a cone or by the enlargement and elevation of the free edge of the counter septum. Because of the rather complex internal structure in members of this family, accurate identification requires the preparation of transverse and longitudinal sections of the corallum.

The family ranges from the Ordovician to the Permian. Individual coralla are commonly abundant, and many species are excellent index fossils. Genera that illustrate the different structures typical of the family are *Streptelasma* from the Ordovician, with more or less vesicular tissue and imperfect tabulae; *Zaphrentis* (Silurian to Carboniferous), with numerous irregular tabulae and few dissepiments; and *Lophophyllum* (Carboniferous), with well-developed tabulae, no dissepiments, and a prominent pseudocolumella formed by the enlargement of the free edge of the counter septum (Fig. 32 *C–F*, *H–I*).

Cyathophyllidae.—The Cyathophyllidae include both simple and compound corals, the latter being the more common. The simple forms are conical or cylindrical. Colonial coralla are composed of cylindrical or prismatic corallites, depending upon the manner of growth, and often exhibit considerable variation in structure. The numerous thin, radially arranged septa may or may not reach the center of the corallite. The members of the second series or cycle of septa are about as long as the directive septa, which in most cases are not easily determined. Carinae are strongly developed in some species. The marginal part of the corallite is filled with dissepiments but lacks tabulae. The latter, however, are strongly developed in the central portion where dissepiments are missing. Fossulae are rarely present. The theca is prominent, but the epitheca has variable development. A columella or pseudocolumella may or may not be present. Identification usually requires the preparation of transverse and longitudinal sections.

This family ranges from the Ordovician to the Carboniferous, with maximum development in the Silurian and Devonian. Individual and colonial coralla are often extremely abundant, and certain members of the family played an important role in the construction of Silurian and Devonian bioherms or reefs. Many species are excellent index fossils.

Characteristic genera of the Cyathophyllidae are the simple or colonial *Cyathophyllum* (Ordovician to Carboniferous); *Heliophyllum* (Devonian), with simple or colonial coralla characterized by a strong development of carinae; *Lithostrotion* (Mississippian), with colonial growth and a conspicuous styliform columella; the colonial *Columnaria* (Ordovician to Devonian), with dissepiments present or absent and, except for absence of mural pores, resembling a favosite coral; and the colonial *Prismatophyllum* (Silurian to Devonian), with prismatic corallites and well-developed, radially arranged septa (Fig. 32 *J*, *L–N*).

Cystiphyllidae.—The coralla of the Cystiphyllidae are usually simple, with the septa thin or wanting. There are no tabulae or dissepiments, but the interior contains much vesicular structure or compact *stereoplasm*. Certain species possess a calcareous *operculum* or lid. In some forms the septa are well developed; in others they are numerous but short; and in still others they are developed only as ridges on the interior surface of the theca. The family may or may not be a natural one, for the only common character is the presence of vesicular structure in the central part of the corallite, and it seems likely that this particular feature may have developed independently in several groups of the Tetracoralla.

Members of the family range from the Silurian to the Carboniferous. Individuals are common but rarely abundant, and all species are good index fossils. Representative genera are the horn-shaped *Cystiphyllum* (Silurian to Devonian) with its vesiculose interior and the operculated subturbinate *Calceola* (Devonian to Carboniferous) (Fig. 32 *G*, *K*).

Subclass Hexacoralla

The Hexacoralla have single or compound exoskeletons with the septa arranged in a hexameral (Fig. 29 *N*) (rarely pentameral, heptameral or octameral) system. The polyps of this subclass have cycles of mesenteries which exhibit the same type of arrangement as the septa. Some polyps, as the anemones, are without exoskeletons throughout life; others secrete a horny or calcareous exoskeleton which may have any of the internal or external structures characteristic of the Coelenterata.

The first six septa formed, the directive septa, usually can not be differentiated from those added later except on the basis of length. New septa arise between the six directive septa by intercalation; hence the first cycle (directive septa) numbers six; the second, six; the third, twelve; the fourth, twenty-four; etc. Septa of each cycle are as a rule shorter than those of the preceding. Radial symmetry is conspicuous in the septal arrangement of adult corallites, but bilateral symmetry is shown in the soft parts of the animal and occasionally in the exoskeleton.

The Hexacoralla are now generally recognized as being confined to Mesozoic and Cenozoic rocks.[1] *Calostylus* from the Silurian of Gotland, formerly referred to the Hexacoralla, has been shown to belong to the Tetracoralla; *Palaeacis* from the Mississippian of North America and Scotland has been referred to the Tabulata; and all other supposed Paleozoic Hexacoralla have been assigned to some other subdivision of the Coelenterata.[2]

Two theories have been proposed for the derivation of the Hexacoralla. The first postulates that the Tabulata, Tetracoralla, and Hexacoralla had a common ancestry in some very early Paleozoic coral. Unlike the two other groups, however, the Hexacoralla did not develop the skeleton-forming habit during the Paleozoic, hence left no record of existence during that time. It was not until the early Mesozoic that this habit was

[1] Robinson, W. J., The ancestry of the Hexacoralla. *Amer. Jour. Science*, (5), vol. 6, pp. 424–426, 1923.

[2] Robinson, W. J., The relationship of the Tetracoralla to the Hexacoralla, *Conn. Acad. Arts, Trans.*, 21, pp. 145–200, 1917.

suddenly acquired, and since that time a rather abundant fossil record has been made. This theory does not seem to have gained much acceptance, and it does not seem to be in accord with the facts.[1] The second theory holds that the Hexacoralla descended directly from the exclusively Paleozoic Tetracoralla. The actual transition is thought to have taken place either very late in the Paleozoic or very early in the Mesozoic, since the true hexacorals do not appear until Middle Triassic. The facts as known at the present time favor the second theory.

The hexacorals are the dominant coralline forms in existing seas. Not only are they making very important contributions to existing reefs but they played a similar role during the Mesozoic and Cenozoic.

The Hexacoralla are divided into three orders: Actinaria, Madreporaria, and Antipitharia. The *Actinaria* comprise the fleshy "sea anemones," which do not secrete hard parts, and hence are unknown in the fossil state. The *Madreporaria* are the so-called "stony corals" and are among the most abundant and variable of all living coelenterates. They secrete a variety of calcareous exoskeletons and have left a good fossil record. The *Antipitharia* secrete a horny exoskeleton which does not lend itself to fossilization very easily, hence the order has little fossil representation.

Order Madreporaria

Madreporaria are corals with bilateral symmetry, a thick body wall, and typically hexameral (rarely pentameral, heptameral or octameral) arrangement of mesenteries and septa. The calcareous exoskeleton exhibits apparent radial symmetry and may be a simple or compound corallum of large size. Compound coralla possess the same complex internal structure as is found in other coelenterates. Madreporarian exoskeletons may be distinguished from those of the Tetracoralla by the hexameral arrangement of the septa and the absence of distinct bilateral symmetry; from those of the Tabulata by the development of many conspicuous septa; and from the Alcyonaria by the arrangement of the septa in the exoskeleton. It is also possible to differentiate easily between the living organisms of the Hexacoralla

[1] Robinson, W. J., *op. cit.*, pp. 151, 159–160, 1917.

and the Alcyonaria, for the former have numerous cycles of mesenteries, whereas the latter have only eight and these are arranged about the mouth in a single cycle. The shape of the madreporarian corallum depends largely on the way budding takes place. If conditions are favorable it may grow to be several meters across.

The Madreporaria have been subdivided into 10 families which can be grouped conveniently into the two suborders of *Aporosa* and *Perforata*. The basis for this dual division is the nature of the exoskeletal structure. In the first suborder the septa and theca are compact; in the second they are perforated by pores. The Aporosa may be considered direct descendants of the Paleozoic Tetracoralla, and the Perforata probably descended in turn from the Aporosa, although they too may have developed directly from the tetracorals. It has also been suggested that the Perforata were derived from the Archaeocyathinae of the Cambrian, but such a derivation does not seem very likely.

Suborder Aporosa.—In the *Aporosa* the simple or compound exoskeleton is not perforated. Dissepiments and synapticulae may be absent or present. Septa are usually well developed though there is not always a theca. The corallum shows considerable variation in size and shape and conical, discoidal, and mushroom-shaped coralla are typical. Genera representative of this large suborder are *Turbinolia* (*Turbinolidae*) (Tertiary to Recent), with a simple conical corallum possessing septa which project beyond the theca to form prominent longitudinal ribs; *Flabellum* (*Turbinolidae*) (Tertiary to Recent), with a flattened conical corallum; *Thecosmilia* (*Astraeidae*) (Triassic to Tertiary); and *Fungia* (*Fungidae*) (Post-Pliocene to Recent), with a simple discoidal corallum of which the upper surface is composed of many prominent septa united by synapticulae and projecting on the underside as serrated ribs (Fig. 33).

Suborder Perforata.—The *Perforata* construct a calcareous exoskeleton which is built up of small calcareous elements (*sclerites*) between which lie empty interstices of variable size. The corallites are septate, and the interseptal spaces are either with or without dissepiments and synapticulae. If a theca is present, it is formed by the fusion of the outer edges of the septa. The coralla are simple or compound. The geological range of

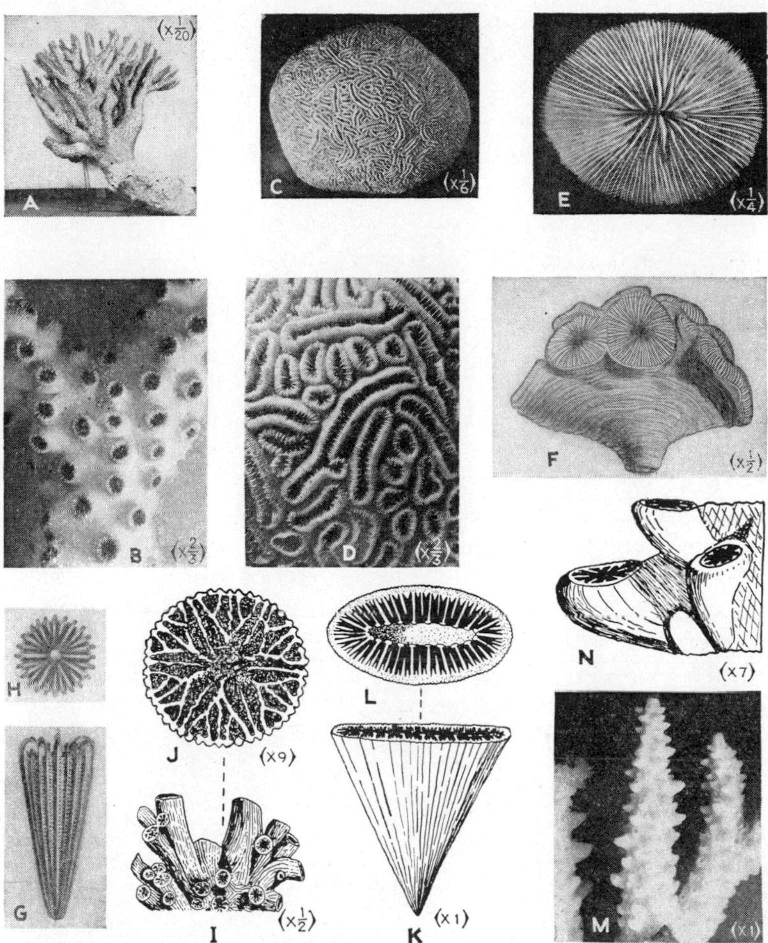

Fig. 33.—Living and fossil Madreporaria. *A*. Complete corallum of a modern madreporarian shown attached to part of the substratum. *B*. Portion of a branch of *A* showing nature of corallites. *C–D*. *Dichocoenia:* *C*, the complete hemispherical corallum; *D*, portion of surface showing the nature of the corallites. *E*. *Fungia* from the Fiji Islands, a solitary corallum. *F*. *Thecosmilia annularis* from the Coral Rag of England. *G–H*. *Turbinolia sulcata* from the Eocene: *G*, the complete corallum showing the exterior of the costate theca; *H*, transverse section showing columella and primary and secondary septa. *I–J*. *Dendrophyllia dendrophylloides* from the London Clay, England: *I*, portion of a corallum; *J*, transverse section enlarged to show nature of septal arrangement. *K–L*. *Flabellum* from the Lower Cretaceous of England: *K*, complete corallum showing characteristic flattened shape; *L*, transverse section of calyx showing nature and arrangement of septa. *M–N*. *Madrepora* from the Indian Ocean: *M*, distal part of several small branches; *n*, small portion of a branch enlarged to show nature of corallites. (*F–H after Nicholson and Lydekker; I–J after Edwards and Haime.*)

the group is Mesozoic to Recent. Representative genera are *Dendrophyllia* (*Eupsammidae*) (Cenozoic to Recent), with a branching corallum composed of cylindrical corallites in which there are numerous septa and a spongy columella; and *Madrepora* (*Acroporidae*) (Tertiary to Recent), characterized by large coralla and one of the important reef builders of the present time (Fig. 33).

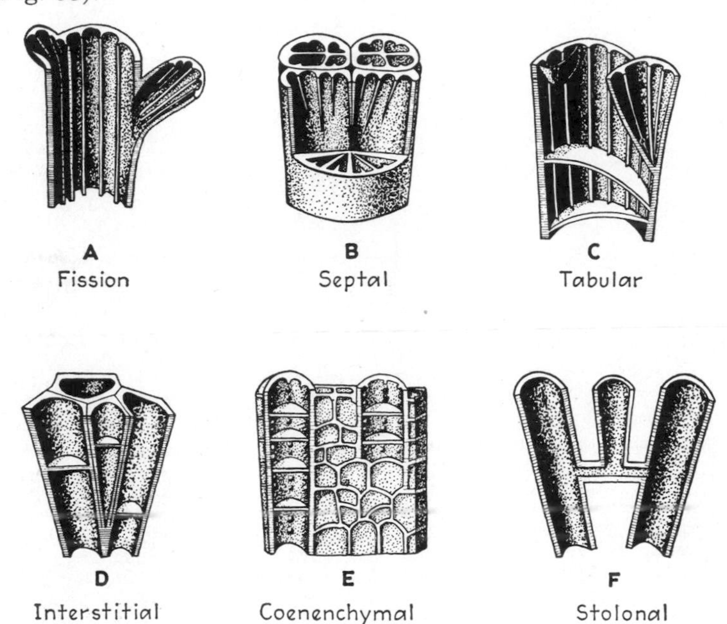

FIG. 34.—Methods of budding among the Coelenterata. (*From Grove, after von Koch, with modifications.*)

ORDER ANTIPITHARIA

The Antipitharia secrete a horny skeleton which is not known to occur in the fossil state, although it seems that such is altogether possible. They are generally known as the "black corals."

Subclass Alcyonaria (Octocoralla)

The Alcyonaria are characterized by the possession of eight mesenteries and eight broad, pinnately fringed or plumose tentacles that form a single cycle about the mouth. The polyps rarely occur singly. They usually combine to construct large coralla which increase in size by some form of asexual reproduction (Fig. 34). The group includes the sea pens and fans, dead-man's-fingers, and organ-pipe corals of present seas, none of which is known to have been fossilized.

The skeletal matter is horny or calcareous, but it is not always developed. The calcareous bodies (*sclerodermites*) (Fig. 35) which comprise the exoskeleton may occur detached in the mesogloea or ectoderm, or they may become closely packed together to form a solid or hollow, horny or calcareous axis (*sclerobasis*) (Fig. 36 *H–I*) or base, about, on, or within which the polyps live. Sometimes these elements are so combined as to produce regularly tabulated tubes. With growth and multiplication of the polyps, the coralla increase in dimension. The compound corallum may be in the form of a rod (sea pen), a fan-shaped meshwork (sea fan) (Fig. 36 *H–I*), a massive structure composed of large and small tabulated tubes closely packed together, bushy growths as in the precious corals, and globular or encrusting masses. In certain of the massive, tube-bearing coralla there are large, septate, and tabulate tubes, known as *autopores*, and smaller, more numerous closely tabulate tubes designated *siphonopores* (Fig. 36). The large autopores are occupied by complete individuals; the small siphonopores, by minute, incomplete individuals which do not have tentacles and which are connected to each other and to the polyps of the autopores by coenosarc. Such a corallum is illustrated in Fig. 36 *D–G*, and it is thought that the extinct Heliolitidae had such structure.

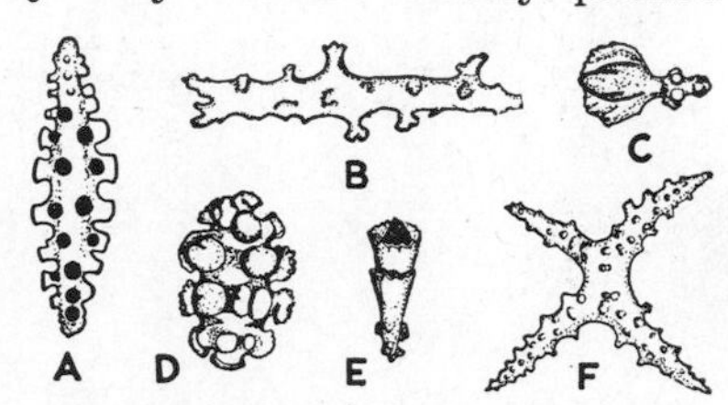

FIG. 35.—Calcareous skeletal elements (sclerodermites) of Alcyonaria, highly magnified (*A–C*, *E–F*, ×150; *D*, ×140). (*After Kölliker.*)

The subclass has been divided into six families—Alcyonidae, Pennatulidae, Gorgonidae, Tubiporidae, Helioporidae, and Heliolitidae.[1] They range from the Ordovician to Recent and

[1] The Heliolitidae have been assigned to the Alcyonaria on the basis of general resemblance to the Helioporidae and possession of dimorphic corallites. There are, however, always 12 pseudosepta. The family is extinct and is confined to the Paleozoic. If this family were omitted from the Alcyonaria, that subclass would range from Triassic to Recent.

are known to have been abundant during several geologic periods.

Alcyonidae.—The Alcyonidae do not construct a firm skeleton. The sclerodermites remain detached in the mesogloea and ecto-

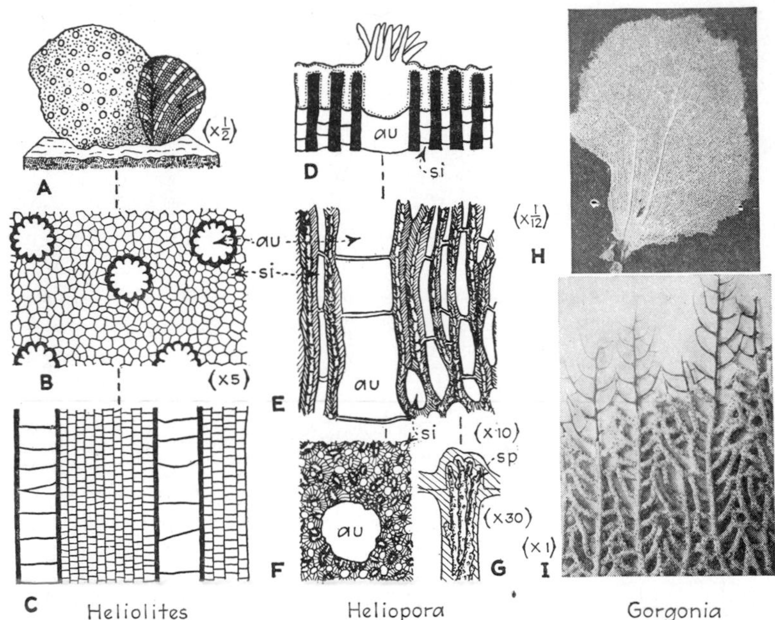

FIG. 36.—Alcyonaria. *A–C. Heliolites interstinctus* from the Silurian: *A*, a small corallum in position of growth, sectioned to show the general internal structure; *B*, tangential section, enlarged to show septate autopores (*au*) and prismatic siphonopores (*si*); *C*, longitudinal section, enlarged to show difference between the tabulae in the two types of tubes. *D–F. Heliopora caerulea*, a living alcyonarian: *D*, diagram to show the relation of the animal to its exoskeleton. The autopore (*au*) is occupied by an autozooid; the siphonopores (*si*) by siphonozooids. Exoskeletal material is shown in black. *E*, longitudinal section of a small part of an exoskeleton showing the microscopic structure of the walls of the autopore (*au*) and the siphonopores (*si*); *F*, transverse section of an autopore and numerous siphonopores showing radial structure of the exoskeletal elements. *G. Sarcophyton*, longitudinal section of the wall between two siphonopores showing the calcareous spicules (*sp.*) as they are disposed in life. *H–I. Gorgonia acerosa: H*, a complete colony; *I*, portion of distal part of colony, enlarged to show chitinous axes of branches and leathery cover perforated by small pores in which the hydrozooids reside. (*D adapted from Moseley; E and F after Nicholson and Lydekker; G adapted from Moseley.*)

derm. It is difficult for such bodies to be fossilized, but they have been reported from the Cretaceous of Bohemia (Cretaceous to Recent).

Pennatulidae.—The Pennatulidae are characterized by dimorphic polyps which construct a horny skeleton resembling a slightly tapering pencil or pen, the small end of which is embedded in sand or mud. These have seldom been fossilized but are known from the Triassic to Recent.

Gorgonidae.—The Gorgonidae build dendritic or fan-shaped coralla (Fig. 36 *H–I*) which are composed of horny substance, either entirely or in combination with calcareous matter. The sea fans and red precious coral used in jewelry are secreted by polyps of this family. Horny skeletons are known from the Tertiary, and calcareous ones from the Cretaceous and Tertiary (Cretaceous to Recent). *Gorgonia*, the common sea fan, is typical of the family (Fig. 36 *H–I*).

Tubiporidae.—The exoskeleton of the Tubiporidae consists of many red-colored, calcareous tubes united by horizontal plates. Though it is unknown in the fossil state, there is no reason why the skeleton might not be preserved under favorable conditions.

Helioporidae.—The Helioporidae build a massive, calcareous corallum which consists of two varieties of tubular corallites, the larger designated autopores and the smaller siphonopores. The autopores are provided with septa-like vertical plates which in the living forms do not correspond in position to the eight tentacles or mesenteries. These are appropriately designated *pseudosepta* but should not be confused with similarly designated structures in the Tetracoralla. The autopores are cylindrical, whereas the siphonopores are prismatic. Both are more or less closely tabulate. The former develop from the coalescence or fusion of several of the latter, which in turn increase by budding. Fossils of this family range from the Cretaceous to Recent. *Heliopora* (Cretaceous to Recent) is a representative genus of the family. It has a massive or ramose corallum composed of autopores with 12 to 25 slightly developed pseudosepta and small closely tabulate nonseptate siphonopores (Fig. 36 *D–G*).

Heliolitidae.—The Heliolitidae comprise an extinct group of octocorals restricted to the Ordovician, Silurian, and Devonian. The organism is unknown, but certain inferences may be drawn concerning its character from a comparison of the coralla of this family and the Helioporidae. The coralla of the Heliolitidae are globular, pyriform, ovoidal, or encrusting bodies, consisting of cylindrical, septate, and tabulate autopores embedded in a coenenchyma of closely packed, and closely tabulate, cylindrical or prismatic siphonopores. Each autopore ordinarily has 12 pseudosepta. These may be well developed and conspicuous, or they may be mere ridges or rows of spines and seem to be absent in some species. The autopores originate through coalescence or fusion of the siphonopores.

Although it is not certain that the Heliolitidae should be assigned to the Alcyonaria, because of the great gap between their last appearance in the Devonian and the first appearance of the Helioporidae in the Cretaceous, the close resemblance of the exoskeletons to those of the Helioporidae suggests genetic relationships. For that reason they are included in the Alcyonaria.

The genus *Heliolites* (Silurian to Devonian) illustrates the distinctive skeletal structures of the family and should be compared with *Heliopora* (Fig. 36 *A–C*).

Subclass Tabulata

The Tabulata constitute an extinct order of Paleozoic and Mesozoic corals. They were invariably colonial and constructed calcareous exoskeletons composed of long tubular or prismatic corallites, always with a great development of tabulae (whence the name Tabulata). The coralla are of many shapes and rarely exhibit a distinct form. The shape seems to have been determined to a large extent by conditions on the bottom where the organisms lived. Septa are usually poorly developed and when present consist of rows of nodes or spines or mere ridges on the interior surface of the corallite wall. If present, they are arranged in multiples of 6 and usually do not number over 12. (It is this character that has caused some investigators to suggest that the subclass be included in the Hexacoralla.) In many species septa are not apparent. There are no dissepiments, synapticulae, or columellae. The corallite walls are ordinarily thick and independent, so that it is often possible to separate individual corallites from a corallum (Fig. 37 *D*). In one group of tabulate corals the walls of the corallites are perforated by variously arranged pores, known as *mural pores*, which are generally thought to represent points where abortive budding took place (Fig. 37 *C–E*).

The tabulate corals range from the Ordovician to the Pennsylvanian, with a few forms persisting to the end of the Mesozoic.[1] Many index fossils are included in the group, but their value is somewhat decreased because of long stratigraphic range. They were important contributors to Paleozoic reefs (bioherms), especially in the Silurian of the Michigan Basin, on Anticosti Island, in Gotland and in Esthonia, and in the Devonian of many parts of the world. Five families have been erected: Favositidae, Halysitidae, Syringoporidae, Auloporidae, and Chaetetidae.

Favositidae.—The Favositidae include most of the so-called "honeycomb corals," in which the prismatic corallites are tightly packed together, but the walls of individuals are independent so that individual corallites may be separated. The coralla vary greatly in shape and attain diameters of several feet. They are commonly globular but may be pyriform, explanate, conical, dendroid, or encrusting. The polygonal corallites range in diameter from 1 to 10 mm. The walls are perforated by small mural pores. These are situated either in the angles or on the sides of the corallite, the former in reality being at the extreme edge of a side. Pores lie immediately above the tabulae, and the number in each intertabular space is some multiple of the number of sides in the corallite. If there is one pore per side, it may be in the center of the intertabular wall or alternately on opposite sides. If there are two pores, they are arranged symmetrically on each side of the middle. The genus *Calapoecia* has the pores so numerous that the corallite wall is reduced to a meshwork (Fig. 37 *H*). The earliest favosite (*Paleofavosites*) has pores at or very near the angles (Fig. 37 *E*), but later forms have them nearer the middle of the sides. The latter apparently developed from the former. Mural pores constitute the distinctive feature of the Favositidae.

Septa are either absent entirely or poorly developed. If present, they are usually faint ridges or rows of spines and nodes. The tabulae are generally very numerous, are situated at regular or irregular intervals, are ordinarily disposed horizontally, though they may be placed obliquely to produce a vesicular appearance, and are frequently depressed around mural pores. The calices are in most cases simple, but in some forms the walls

[1] Zittel, K. von, "Text-book of Paleontology," vol. 1, p. 117, 1913 (1927).

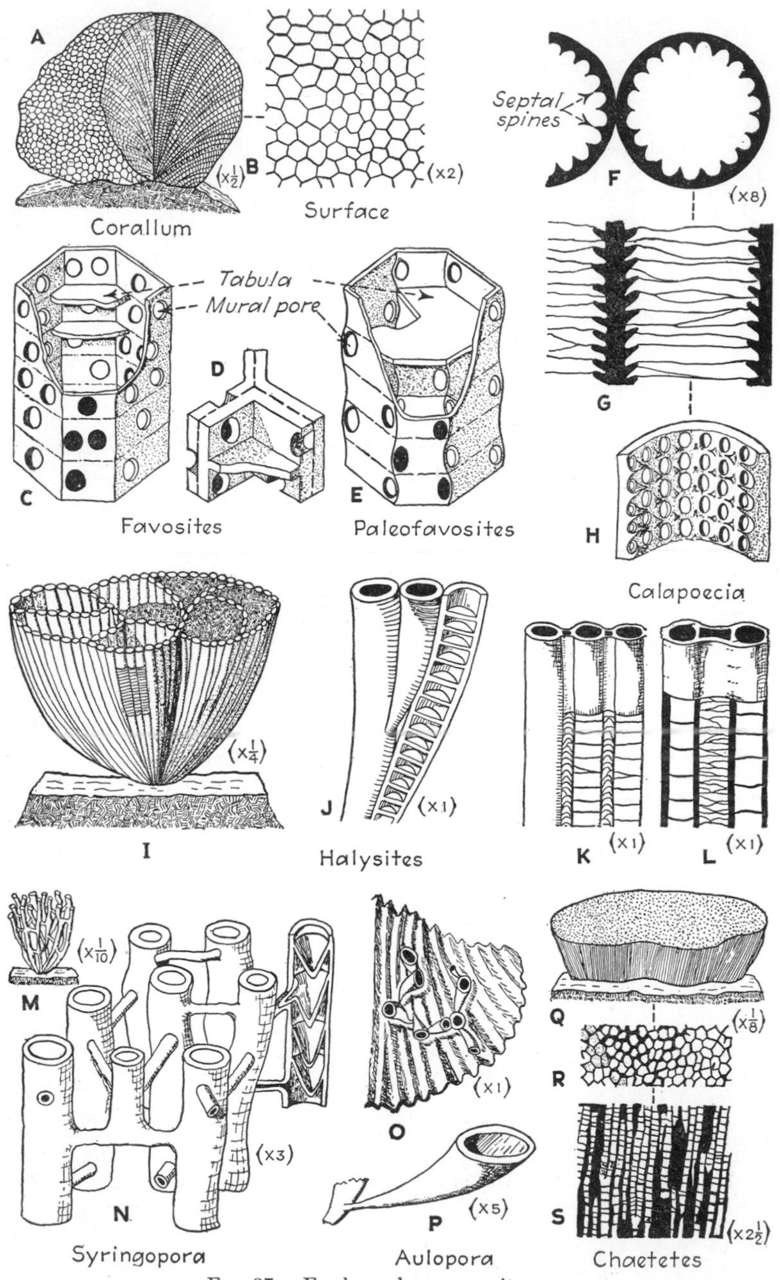

FIG. 37.—For legend see opposite page.

of the corallites are thickened toward the upper ends by layers of stereoplasm to produce a circular opening in a prismatic corallite. The underside of the corallum is frequently covered by an epitheca.

Favositidae range from the Ordovician to the Carboniferous and occur throughout the world. Coralla are commonly abundant, and certain species were important in the construction of many Paleozoic coral bioherms and coral beds (biostromes). Most forms are good index fossils for determining large stratigraphic units. *Favosites* (Ordovician to Carboniferous) illustrates the important structural features of the family (Fig. 37 *A–D*).

Halysitidae.—The Halysitidae constitute the so-called "chain corals." The corallum is composed of long cylindrical corallites joined to each other along the more constricted edges to form palisade-like walls which are joined into a labyrinthine arrangement. A transverse section across one of these walls has the appearance of a chain composed of many small links, whence the name of the family (Gr. *halysis,* chain). The corallites are elliptical in transverse section and are from one and one-half

---

FIG. 37.—Tabulata. *A–D. Favosites hemisphericus* from the Devonian at Louisville, Ky.: *A*, a small corallum in position of growth and sectioned to show internal intensely tabulate character; *B*, portion of the surface magnified to show polygonal outline of the corallites; *C*, a single corallite much magnified to show the relation between mural pores and tabulae; *D*, diagram to show the relation of mural pores to the double wall made by adjacent corallites. *E. Paleofavosites prolificus*, from the Upper Ordovician of Anticosti Island; diagram of a single corallite showing the relation of the mural pores to the tabulae and corners or angles of the corallite. *F–H. Calapoecia canadensis* from the Ordovician of Manitoba: *F*, transverse section of two corallites showing prominent septal spines; *G*, longitudinal section showing septal spines and tabulae; *H*, diagram of a portion of the corallite wall (minus the tabulae) showing the reticulated character caused by the large number of mural pores. *I–L. Halysites: I*, a complete corallum in position of growth with part of the exoskeleton weathered out of the matrix and part still embedded in it; *J*, diagram of three corallites showing the method of budding and presence of tabulae; *K*, *H. catenularia*, a species consisting of alternating large and small tabulated corallites, from the Silurian of Quebec; *L*, *H. catenularia amplitubulata*, showing differently sized and tabulated corallites, from the Lower Helderberg of Quebec. *M–N. Syringopora: M*, a complete corallum in position of growth; *N*, diagram to show relations of adjacent corallites and internal structure (infundibuliform tabulae). *O–P. Aulopora serpens* from the Devonian of Wisconsin: *O*, the corallum in position of growth attached to the surface of a brachiopod shell; *P*, a single corallite somewhat enlarged showing the method of budding. *Q–S. Chaetetes* from the Pennsylvanian (Des Moines) of Indiana: *Q*, a complete corallum in position of growth; *R*, a small portion of the surface magnified to show nature of corallites and presence of toothlike structures; *S*, longitudinal section showing method of formation of new corallites. (*F–H, K–L after Lambe.*)

to two times as wide in one diameter as in the other at right angles. They are usually joined in the line of the longer diameter. They may all be of the same size, or larger ones may alternate with smaller ones, not more than half so large. The maximum width attained by the larger corallites is about 3 mm. The walls of the corallite are thick and are covered on their free sides by a much wrinkled epitheca. Tabulae are numerous and range from horizontal to concave upward. Septa are absent or very poorly developed. If present, they appear as faint ridges or rows of spines and number 6 or 12. There are no mural pores. Budding took place on the edges of the long axes of the corallites, and usually only a single bud formed at a time on an edge (Fig. 34). If two buds developed on the same edge simultaneously, the single palisade split into two walls, and in this way the labyrinthine structure arose.

The Halysitidae first appear in the Upper Ordovician, attain maximum development and distribution in the Silurian, and disappear almost immediately after the beginning of the Devonian. *Halysites* (Fig. 37 *I–L*) is the only genus in the family, and its species are excellent index fossils.

Syringoporidae.—The Syringoporidae have been called "organ-pipe" corals, but there are also members of the Alcyonaria (Tubiporidae) that merit equally such an appellation. The coralla are of irregular shape ranging from dendritic or globular to encrusting. Some are more than 50 cm. (2 ft.) in diameter. The corallites are cylindrical and range in diameter from 2 to 8 mm. The walls are comparatively thick and considerably wrinkled. The corallites are united at intervals along the sides by hollow connecting processes or by horizontal expansions. They are rarely in contact and are usually separated by distances ranging from two to five times the diameter of the corallite. Septa, if present, are inconspicuous. The tabulae are quite numerous in some forms and very concave upward, appearing in many species as invaginated funnels. There are no mural pores. Budding appears to have been marginal, with as many as six buds developing at once in a whorl, or it may have taken place in such a way as to attach the bud to one of the crossbars (Fig. 34 *F*).

The family ranges from the Ordovician to the Carboniferous, with maximum development in the Devonian. *Syringopora*

(Ordovician to Carboniferous) is a representative genus (Fig. 37 *M–N*).

Auloporidae.—The Auloporidae have a creeping, branching, or reticulated corallum, composed of cylindrical or trumpet-shaped corallites 2 to 10 mm. in greatest diameter. The walls of the corallites are relatively thick, somewhat wrinkled, and imperforate. The septa, if present at all, are mere striations. Tabulae are few or are absent entirely. Budding appears to have been limited, with the new bud forming on the side of the polyp shortly after the corallite had attained mature dimensions. A typical corallum resembles a series of small trumpets or vases with the base of each attached to the side of some other. Members of the family are not particularly common and do not have much stratigraphic value. Some investigators consider them the young or immature individuals of the Syringoporidae.

The Auloporidae range from the Ordovician to the Carboniferous. The genus *Aulopora* (Fig. 37 *O–P*), with the same range as the family, is typically a creeping form and is representative of the group.

Chaetetidae.—The Chaetetidae are characterized by massive coralla composed of tightly packed, very small, tubular or prismatic corallites, seldom over 1 mm. in diameter. The corallite walls are imperforate. Septa are absent, but some corallites may have a toothlike projection extending outward from the wall. This is thought to represent an incomplete corallite wall at a point where budding took place. The tabulae are mainly horizontal and may be remote or quite abundant and regularly spaced.

The family ranges from the Ordovician to the Carboniferous, and a few members occur in the Mesozoic. *Chaetetes* (Carboniferous to Jurassic) is a representative genus (Fig. 37 *Q–S*).

Class Ctenophora[1]

The Ctenophora, sometimes termed "comb jellies" because of certain comblike swimming structures, are pelagic coelenterates without a polyp stage or colonial habit. If tentacles are present, they number only two. Cnidoblasts are lacking, but their place is taken, in a sense, by small *adhesive cells*. The animal moves

[1] Ctenophora—Gr. *kteis*, comb + *phoros*, bearing; referring to the comblike swimming structures possessed by the animal.

by means of cilia which are fused to form comblike swimming structures arranged in eight meridional rows. The group, because of the perishable nature of the organism, has left no known fossil record.

APPENDIX TO THE COELENTERATA

ARCHAEOCYATHINAE[1]

The Archaeocyathinae comprise a group of peculiar coral-like organisms which appeared in the Lower Cambrian and vanished by the close of the same period.[2] Ancient bioherms made by these organisms have been found in Labrador, Sardinia, and South Australia, and isolated specimens, occasionally in large numbers, have been reported from New York and Nevada, Normandy, Spain, Scotland, Siberia, North China, Punjab, and Antarctica.

The exoskeleton is a double-walled, solitary, turbinate, conical or subcylindrical structure with apparent radial symmetry. The space between the two walls is filled with porous, radially arranged septa, which end at the inner wall; and porous tabulae, which likewise are confined to the *intervallum* part of the skeleton. The internal and external walls (theca?), like the septa, are also perforate. Synapticulae are developed on the septa of some species (Fig. 21 *A*).

The way in which the skeletal matter of these ancient fossils was built is unknown. Nothing is known of the fleshy part of the body or the method of sexual reproduction. Asexual reproduction by budding is known to have existed.

Because of certain structural features similar to those observed in sponges, the Archaeocyathinae have often been included in the Porifera, and Taylor states that "they are more closely allied to the Phylum *Porifera*, than to any other group of the animal (or vegetable, *pace* Von Toll) kingdom." The authors prefer to follow the ultimate conclusions reached by Taylor and include the Archaeocyathinae in the Coelenterata but as a group of uncertain taxonomic position within the phylum. These conclusions are

[1] Archaeocyathinae—Gr. *archi*, ancient + *cyathus*, cup; referring to the cuplike shape of these ancient coral-like fossils.

[2] Taylor, T. G., Archaeocyathinae from the Cambrian of South Australia with an account of the morphology and affinities of the whole class, *Mems. Roy. Soc. South Australia*, vol. 2, pt. 2, 188 pp., 1910.

that the Archaeocyathinae probably represent an ancestral group common to both the calcareous sponges and the calcareous coelenterates (Fig. 38).

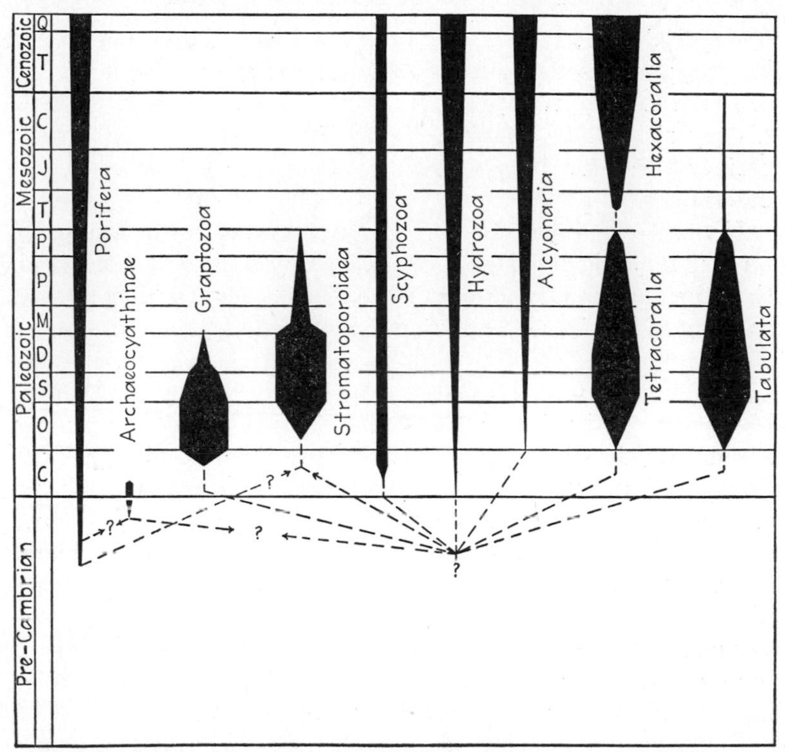

FIG. 38.—Diagram showing the geologic history of the Coelenterata, based on the fossil record. The Hexacoralla are believed to have evolved from the Tetracoralla, though the transition during the early Triassic is not represented by fossils. The position of the Archaeocyathinae is uncertain. They may have been derived from the Porifera or from the Coelenterata, or they may have been ancestral to certain divisions of either or both phyla. Although the Stromatoporoidea have for a long time been included in the Coelenterata, some recent opinion favors the view that certain members of the group may be sponges. The Graptozoa, like the Stromatoporoidea, have usually been placed in the Coelenterata, but recent investigations suggest that the group may be related to the Bryozoa. The dashed lines in the diagram connect each of the large subdivisions with the parent stock but are not intended to indicate the times at which those subdivisions separated from the stock.

The limited vertical range (Lower Cambrian) and the extensive geographic distribution, coupled with the ease of identification, render the Archaeocyathinae of great value for stratigraphic purposes regardless of exact biologic affinities. For this reason, if for no other, it has seemed advisable to include a short discussion of them.

EVOLUTION OF THE COELENTERATA

Fossil Coelenterata range from the Lower Cambrian to the Recent, and various groups of the phylum have been more or less common in some marine waters during every period of geologic history since the beginning of the Paleozoic. During certain periods there has been a great profusion of both species and individuals.

If the Archaeocyathinae are truly ancestral to the Anthozoa, a possibility which has been recognized by some paleontologists, then the phylum Coelenterata certainly had its inception at least as early as the Lower Cambrian if not earlier. That the beginning of the coelenterates does lie in the early millennia of the Cambrian or before is further evidenced by the finding of fossil Hydrozoa in the Lower Cambrian,[1] possible medusae in the Middle Cambrian, and graptolites in the Upper Cambrian (Fig. 38). By early Ordovician the Hydrozoa, Stromatoporoidea, and Graptozoa were well established, the Scyphozoa were present in numbers (if the so-called "medusoid" fossils are correctly identified), and the Tetracoralla and Tabulata of the Anthozoa were beginning to develop.

From their beginning in the Lower Cambrian the Hydrozoa have persisted throughout geologic time and are still present in large numbers in marine and fresh waters.

The Stromatoporoidea, making their first known appearance in the early Ordovician and using calcareous substance for exoskeletons, have left an abundant fossil record to the end of the Devonian when they appear to have become extinct in Europe and America but persisted in Farther India to the end of the Paleozoic. It does not seem likely that they were ancestral to any later group of organisms.

The Graptozoa appeared in the Upper Cambrian but very likely originated at an earlier date. They flourished in great abundance, in both species and individuals, during the Ordovician and Silurian, leaving a large assemblage of fossil representatives in rocks of those ages. They very rapidly waned during the

[1] Ruedemann, R., Camptostroma, a Lower Cambrian floating hydrozoan, *Proc. U. S. Nat. Mus.*, vol. 82, (art. 13,) pp. 1–8, 1933.

Devonian, and by the end of that period or very early in the next—the Mississippian—they had become extinct. They, like the Stromatoporoidea, seem not to have left any descendants. Because of their dominantly planktonic habit they attained world-wide distribution, and today their remains are among the most valuable of all fossils for intercontinental correlation.

The Anthozoa do not seem to have left any fossils before the beginning of the Ordovician, unless the genus *Mackenzia* from the Middle Cambrian of British Columbia is an anthozoan, in which case the range is extended to the Middle Cambrian. Early in the Ordovician, however, all of the large subdivisions, except the Hexacoralla, appeared, and by the end of the period they were well established as to both number of species and abundance of individuals. The Tetracoralla rapidly reached their zenith in the Middle Paleozoic and then became less and less important toward the close of the era. The first Hexacoralla with exoskeletons appeared in the Upper Triassic. The ancestral stock may have been the Tetracoralla, the Tabulata, or Hexacoralla without exoskeletons. Since the first appearance, there has been a progressive increase in numbers until now the Hexacoralla are the most important coral group. The Tabulata appeared first in the Middle Ordovician and reached maximum development by the Silurian and Devonian. They apparently continued through the Mesozoic but were no longer one of the dominant groups, and they do not seem to have left any descendants. The Alcyonaria or Octocoralla, from their possible beginning in the Ordovician (Heliolitidae) to their condition at the present time, have never been an important coral group. One subdivision, the Heliolitidae, became extinct by the end of the Devonian.

The Archaeocyathinae, whatever their biologic affinities, belong to the Lower Cambrian exclusively so far as is known at the present time. Whether or not they gave rise to the calcareous sponges and the calcareous coelenterates is a question that must await its final answer in future investigations.

COELENTERATA AS ROCK BUILDERS

The first true animal bioherms and biostromes appear to have been made in the Lower Cambrian by the Archaeocyathinae. Such structures have been found in Labrador, Sardinia, and

Australia. Probably the oldest known true coral bioherm is in the Lower Ordovician (Chazy) of Vermont,[1] where a favositoid coral (*Lamottia*) and a hydrocoralline (*Stromatocerium*), together with pelmatozoans and bryozoans, comprise a biostrome or bioherm nearly half a mile long. Stromatoporoids made important contributions to calcareous sediments during the Middle Ordovician, in some cases forming thin biostromes; and the *Columnaria*, *Paleofavosites*, and *Halysites* beds of the Upper Ordovician are well known. It was not until the Silurian, however, that extensive reef building went on. One of the most extensive reefs of the Silurian is the so-called "Great Barrier Reef" which almost encircles the Michigan Basin. This feature is a broad belt of isolated bioherms stretching, with interruptions, from northern Wisconsin, through northeastern Illinois by way of Chicago, across northern Indiana and Ohio, into the northern peninsula of Michigan, and into western Ontario. In some places in northern Indiana the belt is 50 miles wide. The bioherms were built by stromatoporoids, tabulates, tetracorals, and algae, with the assistance of such usual reef denizens as echinoderms, worms, brachiopods, mollusks, and trilobites. Extensive coralline deposits are present in the Silurian of Anticosti Island. In Europe the famous "ball stones" of England, the reefs of the island of Gotland, and those of Esthonia all belong to the Silurian.

Reef building continued into the Devonian, so that bioherms and biostromes of stromatoporoids and corals are abundant, though usually not on such a grand scale as during the preceding period. The famous "Reef" at Louisville, Ky., which is really a coral biostrome, has long been known as a rich collecting ground. Stromatoporoid bioherms are well developed in Iowa and Michigan. In Europe the great Devonian coral bioherms of the Eifel district and the Devonian and Carboniferous biohermal masses of Belgium have long been famous.[2] The closing epochs of the Paleozoic do not seem to have been very favorable for reef-

[1] Raymond, P. E., The oldest coral reef, *14th Rept., Vt. State Geologist*, pp. 72–76, 1924.

[2] Grabau, A. W., Paleozoic coral reefs, *Bull. Geol. Soc. Amer.*, vol. 14, pp. 337–352, 1903. Dupont, E., Sur l'origine des calcaires devoniens de la Belgique, *Bull. Acad. Roy. Belgique*, ser. 3, T. 2, pp. 264–280, 1881; Sur les origines due calcaire carbonifère de la Belgique, *ibid.*, ser. 3, T. 5, pp. 211–229, 1883.

building corals or for the stromatoporoids, although the Chaetetidae are responsible for extensive accumulations in the Oswego limestone of southern Kansas.

Throughout the Mesozoic and Cenozoic the coelenterates continued to build biohermal masses and biostromal layers. Such have been reported from the Upper Triassic of California and British Columbia, from the Oligocene of Texas, etc. At the present time there is extensive reef building in all seas between 28 deg. N. and S. lat., and among these the Great Barrier Reef along the northeast coast of Australia is by far the best known[1] (Fig. 30).

References

Stromatoporoidea

Fenton, C. L.: Niagaran stromatoporoid reefs of the Chicago region. *Amer. Midland Naturalist*, vol. 12, pp. 203–212, 1931.

Fenton, M. A.: A Devonian stromatoporoid reef (Petoskey, Michigan), *Amer. Midland Naturalist*, vol. 12, pp. 195–202, 1931.

Heinrich, M.: On the structure and classification of the Stromatoporoidea. *N. Jahrb. f. Min.* etc., 1914, No. 23, pp. 732–736, 1916. (Trans. by C. M. LeVene, *Jour. Geol.*, vol. 24, pp. 57–60, 1916.)

Nicholson, H. A.: A monograph of British stromatoporoids. Palaeontographical Society, vols. 39, 42, 44, and 46, 1886–1892.

Parks, W. A.: The stromatoporoids of the Guelph formation in Ontario. *Univ. Toronto Studies*, geol. ser. 4, 1907.

———: Niagara stromatoporoids. *Ibid.*, No. 5, 1908.

———: Silurian stromatoporoids of America. *Ibid.*, No. 6, 1909.

———: Ordovician stromatoporoids. *Ibid.*, No. 7, 1910.

———: Systematic position of Stromatoporoidea. *Geol. Soc. Amer., Proc.* for 1933, pp. 344–45, 1934; *Jour. Paleontology*, vol. 9, pp. 18–29, 1935.

Twitchell, G. B.: The structure and relationships of the true stromatoporoids. *Amer. Midland Naturalist*, vol. 11, pp. 270–302, 1928–1929.

Graptozoa

Bassler, R. S.: Dendroid graptolites of the Niagaran dolomite at Hamilton, Ontario. *U. S. Nat. Mus., Bull.* 65, 76 pp., 1909.

Ruedemann, R.: Graptolites of New York. Pt. 1. Graptolites of the lower beds. *N. Y. State Mus., Mem.* 7, pp. 455–803, 1904; pt. 2, Graptolites of the higher beds. *Ibid.* 11, 583 pp., 1908.

[1] Saville-Kent, W., "The Great Barrier Reef of Australia, its products and potentialities," W. H. Allen & Co., London, 1893. Yonge, C. M., "A year on the Great Barrier Reef," G. P. Putnam's Sons, New York, 1930.

———: The Cambrian of the Upper Mississippi Valley. Pt. 3, Graptolitoidea. *Bull. Pub. Mus. City of Milwaukee*, vol. 12, pp. 307–348, 1933; *Science*, n. s., vol. 80, p. 15, 1934.

———: Paleozoic plankton of North America. *Geol. Soc. Amer., Mem.* 2, 1934.

ULRICH, E. O., and RUEDEMANN, R.: Are the graptolites bryozoans? *Bull. Geol. Soc. Amer.*, vol. 42, pp. 589–604, 1931.

SCYPHOZOA

WALCOTT, C. D.: Fossil medusae. *U. S. Geol. Surv., Mon.* 30, 1898.

ANTHOZOA

CUMINGS, E. R.: Reefs or bioherms? *Bull. Geol. Soc. Amer.*, vol. 43, pp. 331–352, 1932.

DANA, J. D.: "Corals and Coral Islands." 3d ed., Dodd, Mead, & Company, Inc., New York, 1890.

DARWIN, CHARLES: "The structure and distribution of coral reefs." 344 pp., New York (1896), 1889.

DAVIS, W. M.: The coral reef problem. American Geographical Society, New York, 596 pp., 1928.

GARDINER, S.: "Coral reefs and atolls." 181 pp., Macmillan & Company, Ltd., London, 1931.

GRABAU, A. W.: Paleozoic coral reefs. *Bull. Geol. Soc. Amer.*, vol. 14, pp. 337–352, 1903.

———: "Principles of Stratigraphy." 1,185 pp., A. G. Seiler and Company, 1913.

HICKSON, S. J.: An introduction to the study of recent corals. *Pub. Univ. Manchester*, biol. ser., 4, 257 pp., 1924.

SAVILLE-KENT, W.: "The Great Barrier Reef of Australia." W. H. Allen & Co., London, 1893.

VAUGHAN, T. W.: Corals and the formation of coral reefs. *Smith. Inst., Ann. Rept.*, 1917, pp. 189–276, 1919.

WOOD-JONES, F.: "Corals and Atolls." 392 pp., Lovell Reeve Company, London.

YONGE, C. M.: "A year on the Great Barrier Reef." 246 pp., G. P. Putnam's Sons, New York, 1930.

ARCHAEOCYATHINAE

TAYLOR, T. G.: Archaeocyathinae, from the Cambrian of South Australia, with an account of the morphology and affinities of the whole class. *Mems. Roy. Soc. South Australia*, vol. 2, pt. 2, 1910.

CHAPTER V

WORMS

INTRODUCTION

For many years paleontologists have used the term "worms" for a great variety of fossil remains of questionable origin such as trails, burrows, castings, etc., which were doubtless made by organisms of widely diverse character and uncertain relationships. Almost any vague, fossil organic structure with a long, round body or any marking made by an organism of similar shape was very likely to be referred to this heterogeneous assemblage. The name was also used to some extent by zoologists, particularly those of generations preceding the present. As different groups of these so-called worms were studied carefully, some were shown to represent developmental stages in the life histories of higher animals. Others were found to possess structures which ally them with other phyla. These removals effected, there still remain, however, four major divisions of wormlike organisms, each of which is given by zoologists the rank of a phylum. Paleontologists, however, still prefer to use the indefinite category "Worms," since no classification can be constructed on the basis of the fossil record.

The four phyla included in the worms are the *Platyhelminthes* or flatworms; the *Nemathelminthes* or threadworms; the *Trochelminthes* or wheelworms or wheel animalcules; and the *Annelida* (*Annulata*) or segmented worms. The last phylum is the only one which has left a fossil record of any importance, although fossil representatives of the first two phyla have been reported. The Trochelminthes are unknown in the fossil state.

The Organism.—Worms are bilaterally symmetrical, more or less elongated, flattened or cylindrical animals with a mouth at one end and an anal opening at the other. There is a ventral (under) and dorsal (back) surface. The organism in some cases is segmented; may possess or lack lateral appendages and *parapodia*—small, ciliated muscular processes used as limbs—

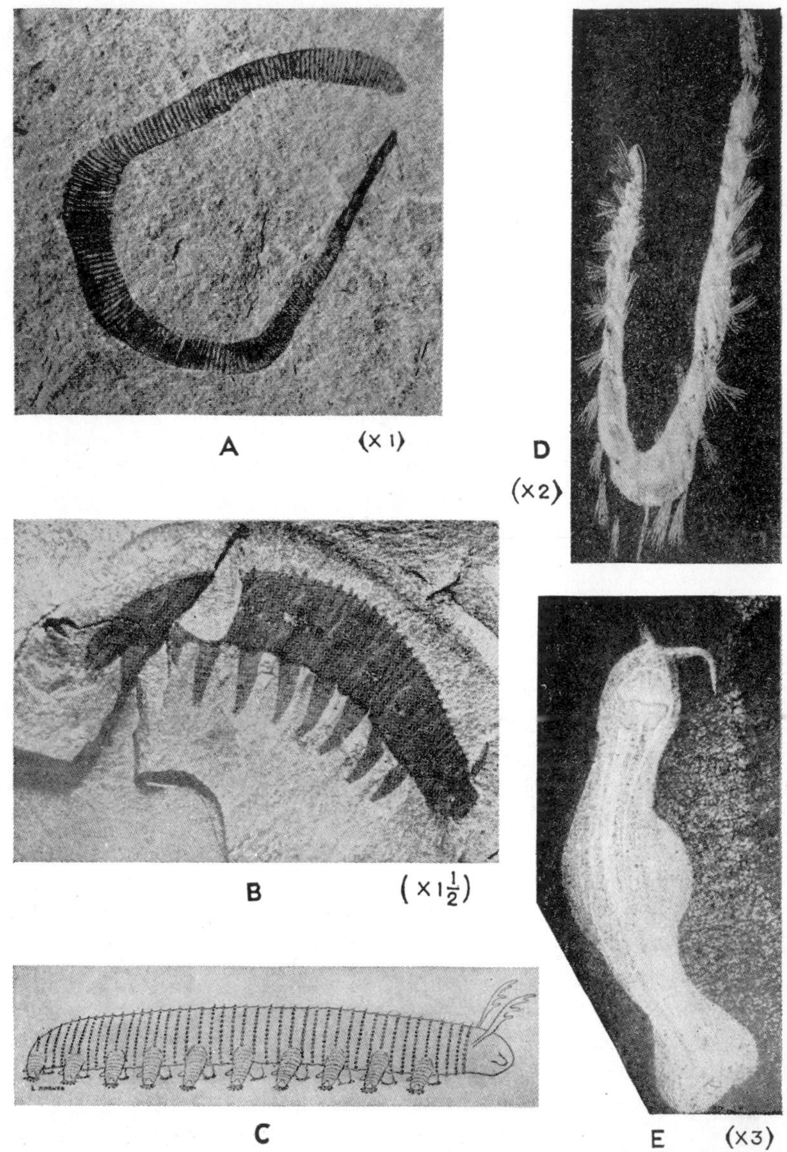

FIG. 39.—Fossil worms. *A. Protoscolex batheri* from the Silurian (Lockport) of New York. *B–C. Aysheaia pedunculata* from the Middle Cambrian (Burgess) shale of British Columbia: *B*, an almost complete specimen; *C*, conjectural restoration of an individual. *D. Canadia setigera*, a slender, flattened specimen showing setae, from the Middle Cambrian of British Columbia. *E. Amiskwia sagittiformis*, a flattened specimen from the Middle Cambrian of British Columbia. (*A after Ruedemann; B after Hutchinson; C from Hutchinson after Krause; D-E after Walcott.*)

and in some instances secretes or constructs a resistant protective covering. The body wall is composed of three well-developed layers—*ectoderm, endoderm,* and *mesoderm.* There is usually a dermal muscular system, a fairly well-developed excretory system, a distinct nervous system with ganglia and a simple brain (all of ectodermal origin), and numerous other structures which mark the animals as rather complex organisms. Respiration is effected by any part of the surface or by special structures, as *gills (branchiae)* and parapodia. The sexes may or may not be distinct.

Worms have had a very long geologic history. They are thought to have been in existence in the Pre-Cambrian and to have been the general ancestral stock of several groups of higher organisms.

Because of limited development of hard parts, fossil worms are extremely rare in the geologic column, and few described species are based on complete skeletal structures or individuals. Identification of fossil worms has been based largely on three types of remains: (1) horny jaws; (2) calcareous, chitinous, or agglutinated tubes; and (3) impressions, films, burrows, trails, tracks, castings, etc.

Worms are extremely abundant at the present time, both in species and in individuals, and an approximately equal abundance may be postulated to have obtained throughout much of their past history. Many divisions now living have no known fossil representatives, and there must have been many groups, long since extinct, of which there is no record among either fossil or living forms.

Character of the Fossil Record.—The fossil record of worms, in general, is scanty and unsatisfactory. Under certain very unusual environmental conditions of entombment the entire organism may be exquisitely preserved, in some cases even without the loss of any of the most delicate structures. Such a condition prevailed during the deposition of the Middle Cambrian Burgess shale of British Columbia, and as a consequence this terrane has yielded a large number of wormlike creatures, many of which leave little to be desired so far as preservation is concerned[1] (Fig. 39 *B, D–E*). Two other unusual cases of

[1] Walcott, C. D., Middle Cambrian annelids, *Smith. Misc. Coll.*, vol. 57, No. 5, 1911.

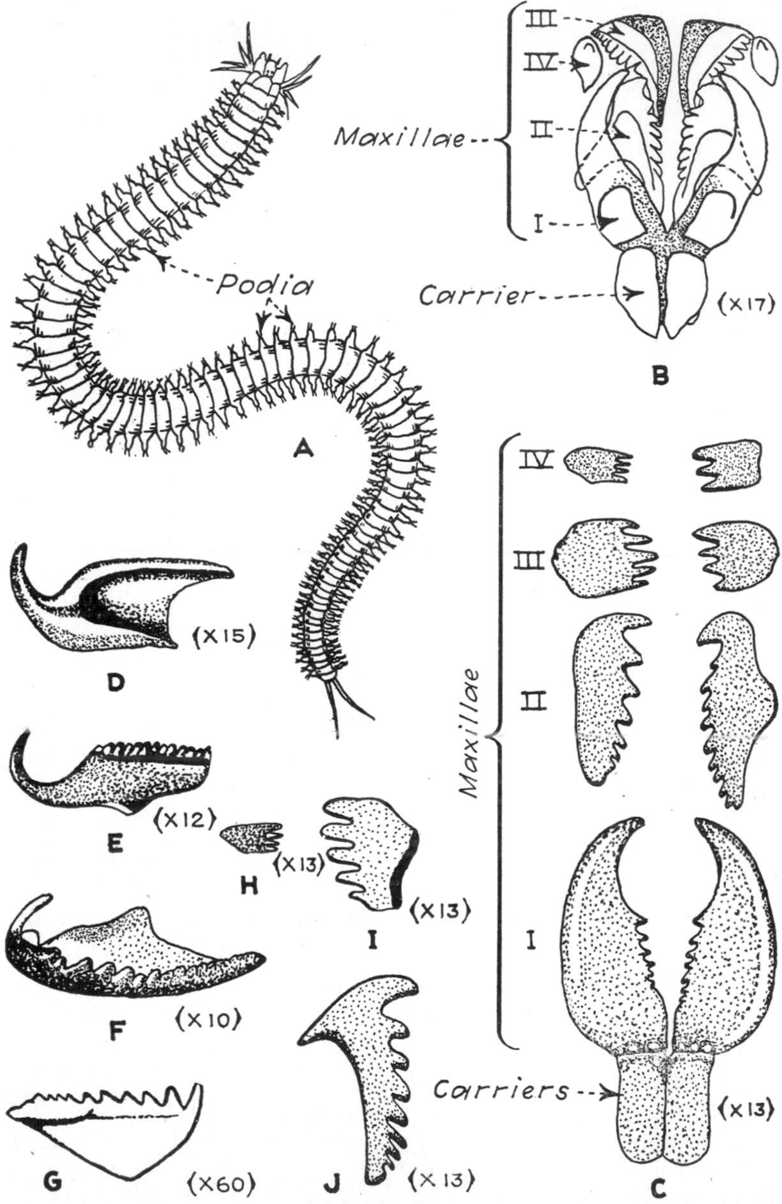

FIG. 40.—Living and fossil Polychaeta. *A. Nereis cultrifera*, a free-living polychaete worm. *B. Diopatra ornata*, a living polychaete worm; the complete jaw apparatus with the jaws in living position. *C. Arbellites* sp., a schematic representation of the jaw apparatus of a Devonian genus closely similar to the

preservation are those of Silurian worms. One genus closely resembling *Serpulites* has been found as thin carbonaceous films in strata of this age in the vicinity of Chicago,[1] and well-preserved specimens of *Protoscolex* (Fig. 39 *A*) and *Bertiella* have been reported from the Silurian of New York.[2]

Worm jaws, appropriately designated *scolecodonts*[3] (Gr. *skolex*, worm, + *odous*, tooth), have been reported from strata of almost every system since the beginning of the Paleozoic. Many of these were first identified as *conodonts*—toothlike structures which have generally been attributed to primitive fish.[4] Very recently, however, it has been pointed out that conodont assemblages found in the Quadrant shale (Pennsylvanian) of Montana represent some kind of jaw apparatus. There is little in these assemblages suggesting fish teeth but much suggesting close relations with the jaw apparatus of certain annelid worms.[5] The exact nature of conodonts, therefore, is still apparently an open question.

In some horizons scolecodonts are very abundant, and in some instances thousands are known to be present in a cubic foot of rock. They are commonly of microscopic size, vary greatly in form (Fig. 40), and are composed of about 50 per cent volatile matter and about 45 per cent silicon dioxide.[6] Until very

[1] WELLER, S., A new type of Silurian worm, *Jour. Geol.*, vol. 33, pp. 540–544, 1925.

[2] RUEDEMANN, R., Some Silurian (Ontarian) faunas of New York, *N. Y. State Mus. Bull.* 265, pl. 14, 1925.

[3] CRONEIS, C., and SCOTT, H. W., *Bull. Geol. Soc. Amer.*, vol. 44, p. 207, 1933.

[4] ULRICH, E. O., and BASSLER, R. S., A classification of the toothlike fossils, conodonts, with descriptions of American Devonian and Mississippian species, *U. S. Nat. Mus., Proc.*, vol. 68, art. 12, 63 pp., 5 figs., 11 pls., 1926.

[5] SCOTT, H. W., The zoological relationships of the conodonts, *Jour. Paleontology*, vol. 8, pp. 448–455, 1934.

[6] CRONEIS, C., personal communication, Jan. 8, 1935.

living *Arabella*. *D–J*. Scolecodonts from Paleozoic worms: *D*, *Glycerites sulcatus excavatus*, a maxilla I from the Upper Ordovician of Ontario; *E*, *Arabellites cornutus*, same as *D*; *F*, *Lumbriconereites basalis*, probably a maxilla IV from the Middle Silurian of Ontario; *G*, *Oenonites tacitus*, from the Ordovician (Decorah) of Minnesota; *H*, *Eunicites mutabilis*, maxilla IV from the Upper Devonian of New York; *I*, maxilla III, same as *H*; *J*, *Eunicites anchoralis*, a maxilla II from the Upper Devonian of New York. (*A after Thomson; B after Moore; C after Eller; D–F after Hinde; G after Stauffer; H–J after Eller.*)

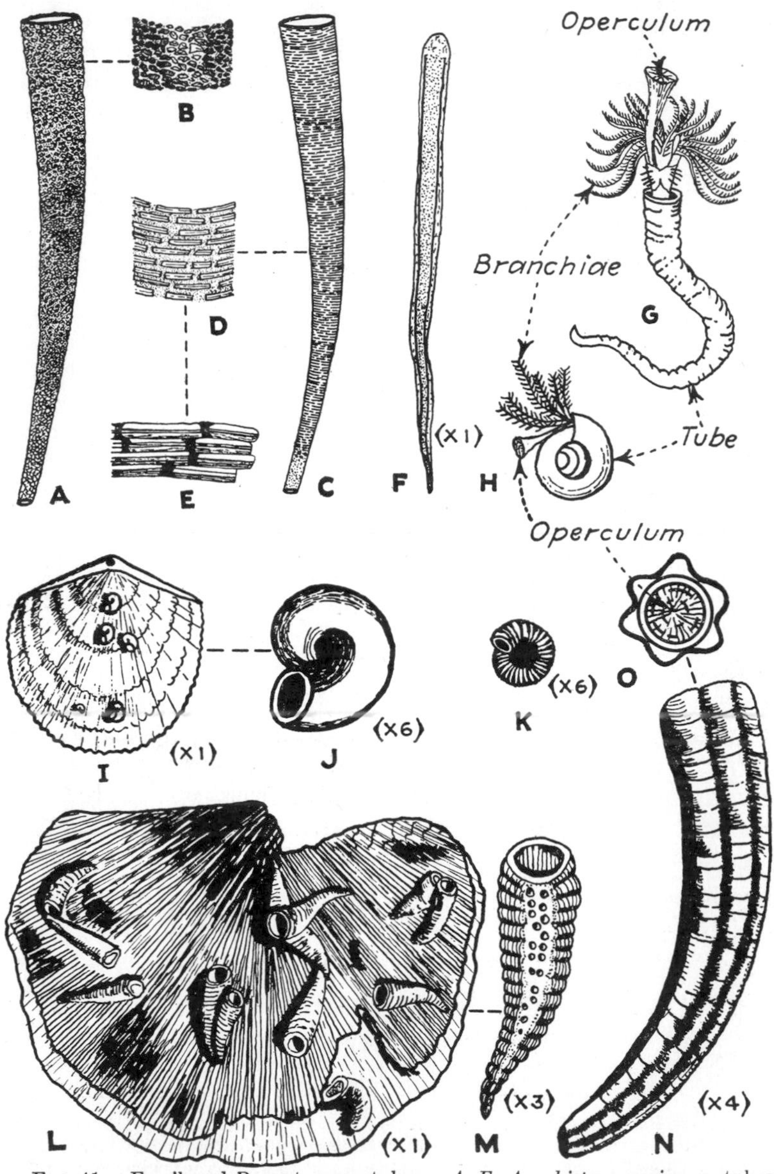

FIG. 41.—Fossil and Recent worm tubes. *A–E. Amphictene auricoma*, tubes of a living annelid: *A*, tube composed of quartz grains cemented together by an organic cement; *B*, portion of *A* enlarged to show nature of quartz grains; *C*, tube composed of sponge spicules arranged in a very symmetrical manner; *D*, *E*, portions of *C* enlarged to show the arrangement of the spicules. *F. Serpulites*

recently little attention has been given to these fossils, but at the present time the strata are being eagerly searched for them.

Fossil worm tubes composed either of calcareous matter or of foreign particles cemented by calcareous or dermal matter are of common occurrence in the geologic column (Fig. 41). The former have been found in strata ranging in age from Ordovician to Recent, and in some formations they comprise large parts of certain beds, as in the *Serpulitenkalk* (Lower Cretaceous) of Brunswick and the *Serpuliten Sandstein* (Lower Cretaceous) near Dresden, Germany. The tubes of *Serpula* have also been found in Cretaceous and Tertiary strata of other countries and are present in great abundance in certain parts of modern tropical seas. Here they live on the bottom, and their calcareous tubes (Fig. 41 *G*) are frequently cemented together to form tangled biohermal masses. Such structures, known as *Serpula atolls*, occur on the coast of Bermuda. The small coiled tubes made by *Spirorbis* are found occasionally in the geologic column from the Ordovician to the Recent and are common in existing water bodies (Fig. 41 *H–K*). *Cornulites* and related forms are found in strata ranging in age from Ordovician to Devonian. They are not usually abundant and may be easily overlooked (Fig. 41 *L–M*). Some annelids construct tubes composed of foreign materials cemented with calcareous or chitinous secretions (Fig. 41 *A–E*). An example is the living genus *Sabellaria*, of which the tubes may so firmly bind sand accumulations as to build reeflike bodies as on the coast of Brittany. Material of these tubes includes quartz grains, sponge spicules, echinoderm spines and fragments, foraminiferal tests, oyster shells, other worm tubes, etc.[1]

[1] McIntosh, W. C., *Ann. and Mag. Nat. Hist.*, vol. 12, pp. 1–18, Figs. 4–8, 1894; Etheridge, R., Jr., *Geol. Mag.*, vol. 7, pp. 109–115, 171–174, 215–222, 258–266, 304–307, 362–369, 1880.

intermedius from the Frankfort shale (Ordovician) of New York. *G. Serpula contortuplicata*, a living tubicolar worm with an operculated calcareous tube. *H. Spirorbis communis*, same as *G* but coiled. *I. Spirorbis* sp., coiled calcareous worm tubes cemented to the brachial valve of *Atrypa*, from the Devonian of Michigan. *J.* One tube of *I* enlarged. *K. Spirorbis arkonensis* from the Devonian of America. *L–M. Cornulites* [*Ortonia*] *conica*, calcareous tubes of a tubicolar annelid cemented to the valve of *Rafinesquina*, and one tube considerably enlarged. The specimens are from the Ordovician of Ohio. *N–O. Hamulus onyx*, an operculated calcareous annelid tube from the Upper Cretaceous of Tennessee. (*A–E after Anderson; F after Ruedemann; G–H, K, after Nicholson and Lydekker; L–M after Nicholson; N–O after Wade.*)

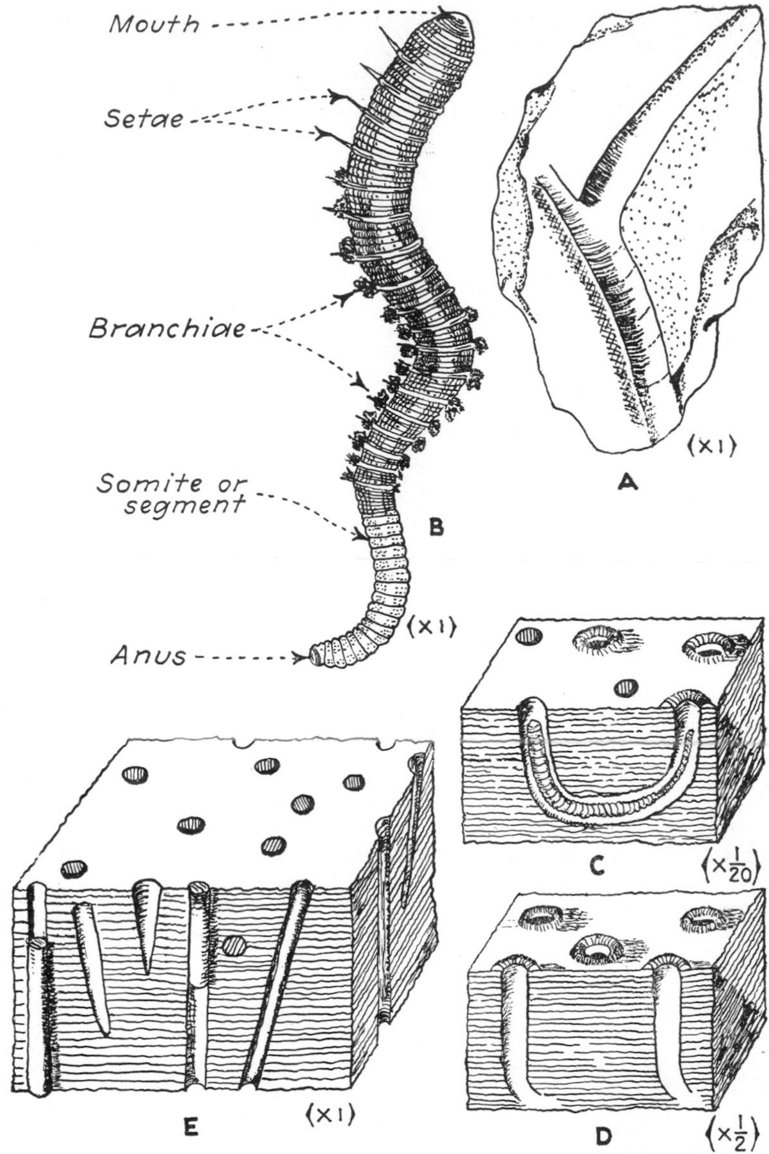

FIG. 42.—*A. Planolites corrugatus*, supposed filling of a burrow made by a Pre-Cambrian worm, from the Algonkian (Greyson shale) of Montana. *B–C. Arenicola marina*, the common "lobworm"; *B*, entire animal as viewed from the left side; *C*, diagram to illustrate the U-shaped burrow made by the worm. The animal feeds at one extremity and casts off excreta at the other. These burrows may extend downward into sand for several feet. *D. Arenicolites chemungensis*,

Burrows and borings made by modern worms are very common and often show interesting characteristics (Fig. 42). There are many similar structures in all sedimentary rocks from Pre-Cambrian to Recent times, but whether they represent the work of worms in all cases is uncertain. Many may be inorganic. Burrows known as *Scolithus* (Fig. 42 *E*) are especially abundant in Cambrian strata and have long been considered to have been made by worms, but recently these have been interpreted as possible phoronid burrows.[1] The puzzling *Arthrophycus* and *Daedalus* from the Lower Silurian (Medinan), originally considered of plant origin, have been interpreted by Sarle[2] as probable worm burrows.

Modern sea bottoms contain many *excremental* or *fecal pellets.* Some of these are known to have been made by worms. Certain small fossilized spherical bodies, referred to as *coprolites* or *castings,* may have been formed by worms in the same manner. In some instances their origin seems fairly clear (Fig. 43 *A*), but often there are no known means of determining how they were formed.

The literature of paleontology contains many figures of trails, tracks, tubes, burrows, and other indefinite structures of probable organic origin, some of which have been attributed to worms or wormlike creatures. In the majority of cases, however, their origin is questionable, and they are usually of little or no value for stratigraphical purposes.

Classification.—The following classification is based on the nature of the soft parts of the animal. It is impossible in the present state of knowledge to classify worms on the basis of the fossil record.

[1] Fenton, C. L., and Fenton, M. A., *Pan-Amer. Geol.*, vol. 61, p. 348, 1934. Also see James, J. F., *Bull. Geol. Soc. Amer.*, vol. 3, pp. 32–44, 1892.

[2] Sarle, C. J., The burrow origin of Arthrophycus and Daedalus (Vedillum) (abstract), *Science*, n s., vol. 22, 1905, p. 335; *Rochester Acad. Sci., Proc.* 4, pp. 203–210, 1906.

---

a burrow from the Devonian (Chemung) of New York, which may have been made by a worm similar to the living *Arenicola*. *E. Scolithus*, the common early Paleozoic burrow usually attributed to some type of worm. The hollow or filled tubular burrows are usually vertical or slightly inclined. (*A after Walcott; B after Thomson; D after Whitfield.*)

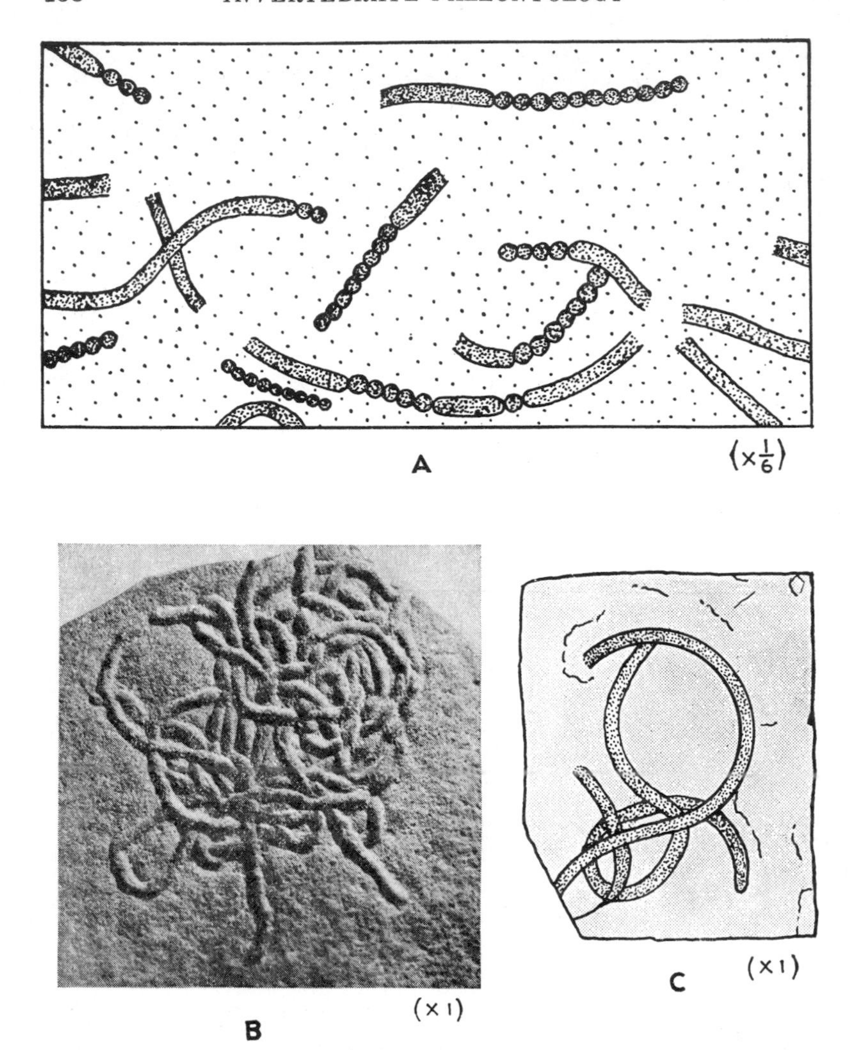

Fig. 43.—Fossil worm castings and trails. *A.* Probable castings of large worms, in the Salem limestone (Mississippian) of Indiana. *B. Lumbricaria,* from the Jurassic of Solnhofen, Bavaria, usually considered as castings of a worm. *C. Helminthoidichnites meeki,* a trail from the Algonkian of Montana. This trail may also have been made by a mollusk or crustacean. (*C after Walcott.*)

PHYLUM PLATYHELMINTHES[1]

The *Platyhelminthes* comprise a group of dorsoventrally flattened worms, commonly designated the "flatworms." They are generally unsegmented, almost always without an anal opening, and mainly parasitic in habit.

The phylum is divided into four classes: Turbellaria (Planaria), Trematoda, Cestoda, and Nemertinea. The *Turbellaria* are free-living, fresh-water flatworms with a ciliated outer surface. They are unknown as fossils. The *Trematoda* are parasitic, possess an anterior sucking disk, and have a well-developed digestive system. The liver fluke, which is parasitic in sheep, is a living example of the class. There are no known fossil representatives.[2] The *Cestoda*, including the notorious tapeworm, are endoparasites without a digestive cavity. They do not seem to have been fossilized. The *Nemertinea* are free-living, marine worms which are appropriately designated "ribbon worms." They range in length from 6 to 175 mm. Living forms are burrowers, and it is very likely that ancestral members of the class made trails and burrows on ancient sea bottoms. Some of the trails in the geologic column may have been left by the Nemertinea, but no differentiation can be made from similar structures made by other free-living worms.

PHYLUM NEMATHELMINTHES[3]

The *Nemathelminthes* are the so-called "roundworms" or "threadworms." They have an elongated, cylindrical body which is usually without an anal opening. Some forms are free living, but others are parasitic. The former are threadlike, and one of the best known is the black "horsehair worm," which was once believed by uninformed people to originate from a horsehair placed in water. The parasitic forms are extremely

[1] Platyhelminthes—Gr. *platys*, flat + *helmins*, *helminthos*, worm; referring to the flattened nature of the worm.

[2] The only reported fossil representatives of the Platyhelminthes are parasitic forms, found in insects from the Carboniferous and Tertiary. These are usually referred to one of the two classes which now show a parasitic habit.

[3] Nemathelminthes—Gr. *nema*, thread + *helmins*, *helminthos*, worm; referring to the threadlike appearance of the worm's body.

dangerous to the containing hosts. They are reported to have been found as fossils in insects of both Carboniferous and Tertiary age, and a Middle Cambrian genus (*Amiskwia*) (Fig. 39 *E*) has been reported from British Columbia.[1]

The phylum has been divided into three classes: Nematoda, Acanthocephala, and Chaetognatha. The *Nematoda* are small round worms with the body pointed at both ends. Free-living forms dwell in fresh or salt water. Some forms are parasitic. *Trichina*, the so-called pork worm, is an endoparasite in swine and is often so abundant that one ounce of pork may contain as many as 80,000 individual parasites. The *Acanthocephala*, or hook-headed worms, are extremely formidable intestinal parasites in vertebrates. The *Chaetognatha* are the arrow-worms which often occur in such abundance in the surface waters of the ocean that the water resembles a jelly. The fossilized wormlike creature (*Amiskwia*), found in the Middle Cambrian Burgess shale of British Columbia and mentioned above, has been referred to this class.[2]

PHYLUM TROCHELMINTHES[3]

The *Trochelminthes* are the well-known "wheel animalcules" or "rotifers," so named because of the appearance of rotation produced by vibration of cilia. These cilia are disposed in tufts and bands on the anterior apex or on the central circumference of the animal and are responsible for locomotion. The worms of this phylum are of microscopic size and are very abundant in stagnant pools, gutters, and like places.

Most worms have a growth stage resembling the form shown by a mature individual belonging to this phylum. This is known as the *trochophore* or *trochospheric stage* (Fig. 44) and is also found in the early growth stages of corals, echinoderms, bryozoans, brachiopods, and mollusks, suggesting a phylogenetic relation

[1] Walcott, C. D., Middle Cambrian annelids, *Smith. Misc. Coll.*, vol. 57, No. 5, p. 112, pl. 22, Figs. 3–4, 1911.

[2] Walcott, *loc. cit.*

[3] Trochelminthes—Gr. *trochos*, wheel + *helmins*, *helminthos*, worm; referring to the fact that when moving through the water the organism resembles a rotating wheel. This resemblance is due to the vibration of cilia.

between these five groups and the worms. No Trochelminthes are known to occur as fossils.

PHYLUM ANNELIDA (ANNULATA)

The *Annelida* (*Annulata*) comprise those animals that most nearly fit the popular conception of a worm, although some members of the phylum depart considerably from that conception. The body is fundamentally an elongated, cylindrical, or flattened tube with a mouth at one end and an anal opening at the other. Except for one division of the phylum, the body is divided both internally and externally into a number of rings or segments of which the internal segments may not coincide with the external. These segments are known as *somites* or *metameres*, and in a typical annulated worm each has small muscular processes (parapodia) developed on both sides of the plane of bilateral symmetry in the animal (Fig. 40 *A*). The parapodia function for locomotion and respiration. Respiration is also accomplished in some forms by the surface of the skin or by structures known as gills (branchiae) (Fig. 41 *G–H*). Many annelids have coarse, hairlike, chitinous bristles (*setae*) on both segments and parapodia (Fig. 42 *B*). In typical members of this phylum the organs are also segmented, so that in many respects a somite is a complete structural unit. Many individuals have the ability to regenerate lost or injured parts, and in some instances it is possible to graft one individual upon another. Depending upon the species, an individual may be of one sex, or it may be hermaphroditic.

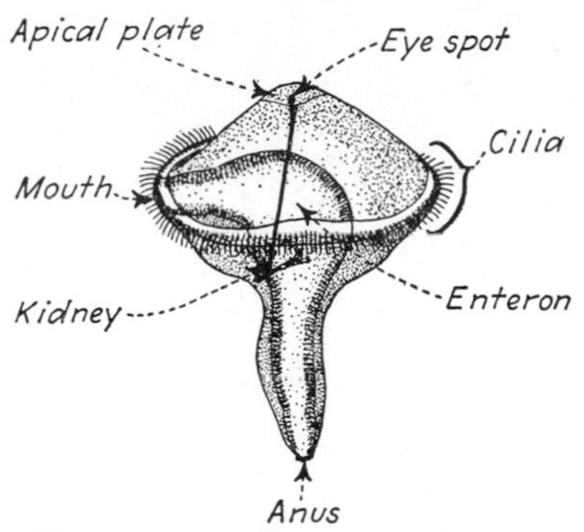

Fig. 44.—Trochophore of *Polygordius neapolitanus*, a very primitive worm belonging to the Archiannelida. (*Adapted from Fraipont.*)

The Annelida have had a long geologic history and have been of much greater biologic and geologic importance than ordinarily is realized. The phylum has been divided into the following four classes: Chaetopoda, Sipunculoidea (Gephyrea), Archiannelida, and Hirudinea.

Class Chaetopoda

The *Chaetopoda*, which include the common earthworms, fresh-water worms, and marine annelids, comprise a group of worms characterized by a segmented body. The segments are usually similar, and each contains a compartment of the body cavity, a part of the alimentary canal, and numerous other more or less well-developed organs. Each side of a somite is equipped with a pair of parapodia which serve for both locomotory and respiratory functions. Chitinous setae, which are developed in the epidermis, are found on both somites and parapodia, or are limited to one or the other.

The chaetopods are equipped with tiny chitinous jaws and numerous other minute chitinous plates (*denticles*). These are possible of fossilization. The jaws, recently given the name scolecodonts, have been reported from various geologic formations, and at the present time are receiving considerable study. It is altogether possible that worms of this class have also left fossil records in the form of burrows, trails, etc., but such structures are often difficult, if not impossible, to identify definitely.

The Chaetopoda have been subdivided into the following four subclasses: Polychaeta, Oligochaeta (earthworms), Myzostomida (parasitic on Echinoderma), and Echiurida (marine worms). Of these only the first group has left a known fossil record of any importance. Members of the Myzostomida are reported to have infested the columnals of Jurassic crinoids, and some fossil trails and burrows may have been made by the Echiurida.

Subclass Polychaeta

The Polychaeta are carnivorous, marine worms possessing numerous setae which are not restricted to the parapodia. The latter are *biramous* and have the setae best developed in the free forms. Members of this subclass have tiny chitinous jaws which are frequently found fossil (Fig. 40). Since living forms burrow extensively, it is possible that many of the burrows found in the geologic column were made by polychaetes. It has also been suggested that certain of the Pre-Cambrian polychaetes were the ancestors of the Paleozoic trilobites.

Four orders have been erected: *Archichaetopoda*, *Phanerocephala* (*Errantia*), *Cryptocephala* (*Sedentaria* or *Tubicola*), and

Miskoa. The first order is an aberrant group without known fossil representation. The last order is now extinct and was limited to the early Paleozoic.

ORDER PHANEROCEPHALA (ERRANTIA)

Members of this order are free-swimming, predaceous worms with a well-developed head and a protrusible proboscis armed with powerful chitinous jaws. The individual segments are generally similar throughout the length of the body. The parapodia are also well developed and are provided with ringlets or tufts of minute hairlike processes known as *cirri.*

The Phanerocephala live in shallow water where they burrow in the sand and mud or construct tubes. The scolecodonts (Fig. 40) of the geologic column are thought to have come very largely if not wholly from members of this order. Many trails or castings, such as *Lumbricaria* (Fig. 43 *B*), found in the Jurassic limestone of Solnhofen, Bavaria, and the peculiar excremental structures (Fig. 43 *A*) found in several other formations, are probably attributable to individuals of this group of worms, although *Lumbricaria* has recently been interpreted as the casting of a holothuroid.[1] *Conodonts* were once thought to be the jaws of worms of this order but are now generally considered as structures of fish (see footnote, page 133).

A living representative of the Errantia is *Nereis*, a worm common along the New England coast, where it is known as the "sandworm" because of its habit of burrowing in the sand and mud between tide levels (Fig. 40 *A*). The worm secretes a mucilaginous substance which cements the sand grains together, and this enables the burrow to remain open. The animal has a set of powerful jaws which grind up materials taken into the mouth. Excremental material is ejected into the burrow posterior to the animal, and, as this commonly is of considerably finer grain than the surrounding mud or sand, the filled tubes are readily apparent, particularly since the fecal materials differ in color from the surroundings.

ORDER CRYPTOCEPHALA (SEDENTARIA OR TUBICOLA)

Worms of this order are herbivorous, and permanently inhabit chitinous or calcareous tubes of their own construction. These

[1] FENTON, C. L., and FENTON, M. A., *Pan-Amer. Geol.*, vol. 51, pp. 291–292, May, 1934.

are attached to some foreign object either as single individuals or in clusters. The individual organism has neither a protrusible proboscis nor jaws; but a head is present though it is frequently small. Members of the order live mainly in shallow water and under certain favorable conditions build large masses composed of tangled and intertwined calcareous tubes. The "serpula atolls" of Bermuda are made by worms of this division. These are circular structures ranging from 9 to 12 m. in diameter, of which the central lagoons constitute four-fifths or more of the width.

The fossil record of the Cryptocephala consists mainly of different types of horn-shaped tubes (Fig. 41). Some of these are attached to foreign objects, such as brachiopod shells, and often occur as clusters. Their first appearance is in the Ordovician with the well-known coiled tube *Spirorbis*. *Serpula*, *Hamulus*, and the puzzling *Cornulites* (also called *Ortonia* and *Conchicolites*) are common Paleozoic fossils. *Serpula* secretes long calcareous tubes in which the animal resides, and there may be a lid or *operculum* which can be drawn downward into the tube to protect the organism (Fig. 41 *O*). These tubes, generally attached to some foreign object, consist of concentric layers of calcareous matter and leathery substance, detrital particles cemented by calcareous material, or calcareous matter entirely.

ORDER MISKOA

This extinct order was erected to include a group of remarkably well-preserved wormlike creatures found in the Middle Cambrian Burgess shale of British Columbia.[1] The fossils show similar segments and parapodia throughout the length of the body. There seems to have been a protractile proboscis and a straight body cavity, and the internal structures do not appear to have been specialized in the segments. The order is known only from the Cambrian, unless several genera (*Protoscolex*, *Bertiella*, and *Eotrophonia*), which have been described from the Upper Ordovician of Ohio and the Silurian of Illinois and New York, belong here.[2]

[1] WALCOTT, *loc. cit.*

[2] ULRICH, E. O., Observations on fossil annelids and descriptions of some new forms, *Cin. Soc. Nat. Hist., Jour.* 1, pp. 87–91, 1878. RUEDEMANN, R., *ibid.*, 1925.

The genus *Aysheaia* (Fig. 39 *B–C*), originally described and assigned to this order by Walcott,[1] has been restudied recently by Hutchinson[2] and assigned to a position close to the Onychophora of which the genus *Peripatus* is the only living representative. Hutchinson includes the Onychophora as a class under the Annelida, referring the Middle Cambrian *Aysheaia* to the extinct order *Protonychophora* and the living terrestrial *Peripatus* to a second order, the *Euonychophora*. Other investigators include the Onychophora in the Arthropoda as an appendix to the Crustacea, and in the present work the class will be considered again under the Crustacea.

Subclass Oligochaeta

In this subclass there are no definite parapodia or cirri, and only a few setae are found on a segment. The head is not distinct. Members of the group live either in fresh water or in soil, but the subclass is thought to have descended from marine ancestors belonging to the Polychaeta. More than four-fifths of the species of this subclass are earthworms which live in the soil or under stones along shores. There are no known fossil representatives, and it seems unlikely that any of the burrows, trails, and castings were made by members of the subclass.

Subclass Myzostomida

Individuals of the Myzostomida are small, discoid or oblong, aberrant annelids without external ornamentation. They live as internal or external parasites on crinoids, asteroids, and ophiuroids. The larva is trochospheric, suggesting that the group may be a modified branch of the Polychaeta. There are no known fossils, though it has been reported that they infested the columnal segments of Jurassic crinoids.

Subclass Echiurida

The Echiurida comprise a small group of marine worms including such forms as *Echiurus*, *Epithesostoma*, and *Saccosomus*. There is no known fossil record.

[1] Walcott, *ibid.*, pp. 109 *ff.*

[2] Hutchinson, G. E., *Proc. U. S. Nat. Mus.*, vol. 78, pp. 14–24, pl. 1, figs. 1–2, 1930.

Class Sipunculoidea (Gephyrea)

The Sipunculoidea are a group of wormlike organisms of uncertain zoological affinities. They are devoid of segmentation in the adult condition, possess no parapodia, and lack setae. The larva is trochospheric.

It has been suggested that the tubes known as *Scolithus*, common in certain Lower Paleozoic formations, were made by species of Sipunculoidea. Four Middle Cambrian genera, *Ottoia*, *Banffia*, *Pikaia*, and *Oesia*, have also been assigned to this class.[1]

Class Archiannelida

These are the simplest of all Annelida and comprise a group of small, segmented marine worms without parapodia or setae. The class comprises the single family *Polygordiidae*, of which *Polygordius neapolitanus* is a representative species. The larva of this species is a typical trochophore, and its metamorphosis into the adult worm is similar to that in the Polychaeta (Fig. 44). No representative of the class is known to occur in the fossil state, though occurrence has been predicted.[2]

Class Hirudinea (Leeches)

The leeches always have 34 "segments," a smaller number of somites, and suckers at both ends of the somewhat flattened body. They are fresh water, marine, or terrestrial in habitat, carnivorous in diet, and some are parasitic. Parapodia are not present, and locomotion on a solid substratum is accomplished in the same manner as by a measuring worm. They are also good swimmers. There is as yet no known fossil record.

GEOLOGIC HISTORY OF THE WORMS

Worms appeared sometime in the Pre-Cambrian if the trails and burrows attributed to them are correctly identified (Figs. 42 *A*, 43 *C*). Confirmatory evidence for such an early origin is found in the remarkable assemblage of fossils preserved in the Middle Cambrian Burgess shale. This fauna contains 11 genera of worms belonging to widely separated families and clearly

[1] Walcott, *loc. cit.*
[2] Walcott, *ibid.*, p. 111.

indicates that a long developmental period must have preceded the time of burial, for the fundamental characters of all of the classes had been developed before the middle of the Cambrian. Many tracks, trails, burrows, castings, etc., found in Cambrian rocks have been attributed to worms, but it seems probable that some of these structures may have been made by other organisms.

By Ordovician time worms had developed the ability to secrete calcareous tubes in which to live, and *Spirobis* and *Cornulites* are common Ordovician and later Middle Paleozoic fossils. The former is still in existence.

From the Silurian to the Present, fossils attributed to worms have been reported from almost every important subdivision of the geologic column. As was the case with the Cambrian remains, it seems more than likely that not all of the tracks, trails, castings, burrows, impressions, and jaws or teeth found in later geologic deposits were left by worms. In many cases, however, the remains are of such a character that reference to the worms seems correct.

In spite of local abundance at times, fossil worms have never been significant from the stratigraphical point of view, but they have great importance in shedding light on the possible ancestry of numerous groups of Paleozoic organisms. There is good evidence that the Arthropoda, the most highly developed of all invertebrates, are descended from some type of segmented worm. The Mollusca, Brachiopoda, Bryozoa, Echinoderma, and possibly also the Coelenterata may all have had their inception in some wormlike creature. There are investigators who hold the opinion that the first primitive fish developed from some type of worm. Hence the lowly worm may constitute a link in the long chain which connects man with the Pre-Cambrian protozoans.

GEOLOGIC WORK OF THE WORMS

Throughout geologic time the worms have served a very important function on the sea bottom and in the soil mantle on the land. This function has been to modify the sediments as they passed through the alimentary tracts. Chewing and grinding actions reduce the materials to a finer state of division, and chemical action imposed on the sediments as they pass through the animal body causes certain changes to take place.

At the present time worms assume great importance as modifiers of unconsolidated sediments and as transporting agents carrying such materials from one place to another. Some land areas have as many as 50,000 earthworms to the acre, and it has been estimated that these annually transport 18 tons (1/5 in.) of soil to the surface.[1] In this vast transfer of material the soils and sediments suffer mechanical disintegration in the mouth and then chemical modification during passage through the alimentary tract where the intestinal juices are active. The materials have not only been transferred from one point to another, but they have been changed somewhat during the transfer.

Boring and burrowing worms are of great importance on many muddy and sandy bottoms. The so-called "lobworms" (Fig. 42 *B*), which inhabit "sand flats exposed at low tide on the coast of Northumberland, England and the adjacent coast of Holy Island [and many other similar areas], eat the sands through which they burrow and bring their excreta to the surface in the same way as the earthworms."[2] It has been estimated that the individual castings on the coast of Northumberland average 84,423 per acre at any given time and around 50,000,000 per square mile. Where the worms are in greatest abundance, it is estimated that they bring 3,147 tons of material to the surface of every acre annually. All of this material has passed through the intestinal tract of the animal, where it has undergone more or less modification. These lobworms burrow to a depth of 2 ft. or more, and hence at least 2 ft. of the bottom muds and sands are being subjected to this slow churning process (Fig. 42 *B–C*). It is thought that the entire 2-ft. layer passes through the worms in about two years.[3]

It thus seems quite clear from a study of living worms that they play a most important role in the modification of unconsolidated muds and sands, and there is abundant evidence of their work in ancient geologic formations.

[1] DARWIN, C., "Formation of Vegetable Mold," 1881.

[2] TWENHOFEL, W. H., "Treatise on Sedimentation." 2d ed., p. 148, 1932.

[3] DAVIDSON, C., *Geol. Mag.*, vol. 38, pp. 489–493, 1891.

CHAPTER VI

ECHINODERMA[1]

INTRODUCTION

The Echinoderma (Echinoderms) are a group of exclusively marine animals of Cambrian or earlier origin. The living divisions of the phylum are designated by names which call attention to some characteristic feature. Thus there are the starfish (*Stelleroidea*), subdivided into the true starfish (*Asteroidea*) and brittle stars (*Ophiuroidea*); sea urchins (*Echinoidea*); sea cucumbers (*Holothuroidea*); and feather stars and sea lilies (unstalked and stalked *Crinoidea*, respectively). These forms are typical representatives of the four classes into which living echinoderms are usually placed. During the Paleozoic there were three other classes: *Cystoidea*, *Edrioasteroidea*, and *Blastoidea*, as well as a single subclass of the Stelleroidea (*Auluroidea*), but none of these has survived to the present, and consequently they are not so well known as living forms.

The echinoderm body is encased in a calcareous test of globular, spheroidal, or discoidal shape or in a leathery skin or integument having an ellipsoidal or star shape and containing isolated calcareous plates. The spiny or prickly character of the test or the skin has given the name to the phylum.

The ancient ancestry of the Echinoderma, the rather unique appearance of the tests, the fair abundance of remains in the geologic column, of which some are excellently preserved, and the great abundance of certain forms in existing seas have encouraged extensive study of the phylum. Many ancient species are good index fossils.

[1] Echinoderma—Gr. *echinus*, spiny + *derma*, skin—"spiny or prickly-skinned" animals. The Greeks applied the name *echinos* to the hedgehog as well as to the sea urchin, both of which have a prickly exterior. The term *echinus* has been continued for a certain sea urchin.

THE ANIMAL AND ITS HABITS

General Considerations.—The Echinoderma show a marked advance over the Coelenterata in the possession of a true body cavity (*coelom*) with a distinct stomach, an intestinal tract separating the mouth from the anal opening, and a distinctly localized nervous system. There is also a crude circulatory system without a heart or regular circulation.

The coelom contains the intestinal tract or *gut* and a complicated hydraulic apparatus, known as the *water-vascular system,* which in some groups performs the dual functions of locomotion and respiration. The intestine may be straight, curved, or coiled. The mouth and anus may be on the same side of the body, as in the crinoids; diametrically opposite, as in some echinoids and starfish; or they may occupy intermediate positions as in certain echinoids. Whatever the relation, however, they always lie in the plane of the fundamental bilateral symmetry common to all echinoderms.

Symmetry of the Body.—In many echinoderms the original bilateral symmetry is often obscured by well-developed secondary radial symmetry which is almost always pentamerous. In recent echinoids certain species have developed a second bilateral symmetry which coincides with the original and which necessarily distorts the radial arrangement so characteristic of that class. The arrangement and position of the mouth and anal opening, as well as of other structures in the body and on the test, change with alteration in the symmetry. Sessile or attached forms usually have radial symmetry, whereas forms that move about actively almost always have developed a bilateral arrangement in which the mouth has tended to migrate toward the front of the animal and the anal opening toward the rear.

In the majority of echinoderms the body is divided into five radially disposed parts. These may be in the form of free arms, as in the starfish, or fixed radial areas, as in the sea urchins. They may branch, but the arrangement almost always tends to be pentamerous. The arms and corresponding fixed radial areas are termed *ambulacra.* Spaces between the ambulacra are termed *interambulacra.* The ambulacral areas are frequently described as *rays*, and the interambulacral as *interrays.*

The Water-vascular System.—In certain living echinoderms (echinoids and stelleroids) the radial pentamerous symmetry is very well exhibited by numerous canals, tubes, sacs, and vessels which together constitute the so-called water-vascular system. Water is carried throughout the body in this hydraulic apparatus, and extensions to the exterior serve the dual functions of locomotion and respiration (Fig. 45). Water enters the system through a perforated plate, known as the *sieve plate* or *madreporite*, situated on the upper part of the organism, and passes downward through a tube or canal, designated the *stone canal*, into a circular *ring canal* surrounding the mouth. The ring canal gives off five *radial canals* which have ambulacral position. On each side of a radial canal are small bag-like closed tubes (*ampullae*, *diverticula*). The ends of these reach the exterior through pores in the test and are provided with small suckers which aid them in performing a locomotory function. For this reason they are known as *tube feet* or *podia* (Fig. 45).

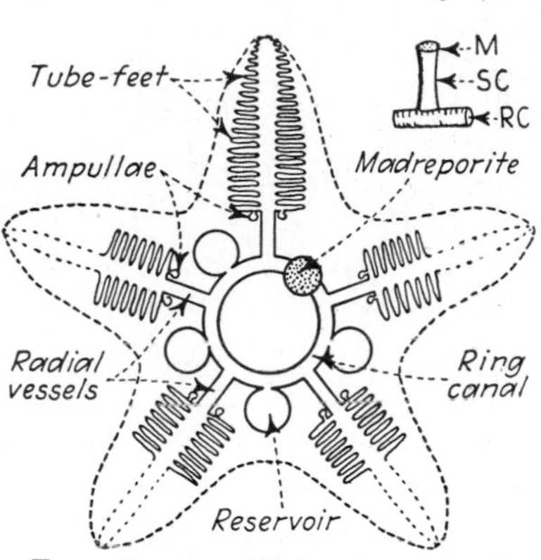

FIG. 45.—Simplified schematic diagram illustrating the structure of the water-vascular system of a starfish. The madreporite (*M*) communicates with the ring canal (*RC*) through the vertical stone canal (*SC*), as shown in the small diagram at the upper right. Ampullae are shown on only the first pair of tube feet.

The water-vascular system was first developed in the primitive Cystoidea (*Aristocystites*) in the form of irregularly arranged canals ramifying the plates of the test (Fig. 47). In the more complex Cystoidea these gave place to various types of pores known as diplopores, pore rhombs, etc. The Blastoidea have the pores confined to the ambulacral areas. These connect interiorly with peculiar sac-like structures known as *hydrospires* produced by the folding of certain parts of the test (Fig. 50 *E–F*). The pores in the crinoids are also arranged along the ambulacra. In the asteroids and echinoids the water-vascular system reaches the highest degree of development.

Ambulacra and Food Grooves.—In most echinoderms five conspicuous ambulacra or ambulacral areas radiate from the

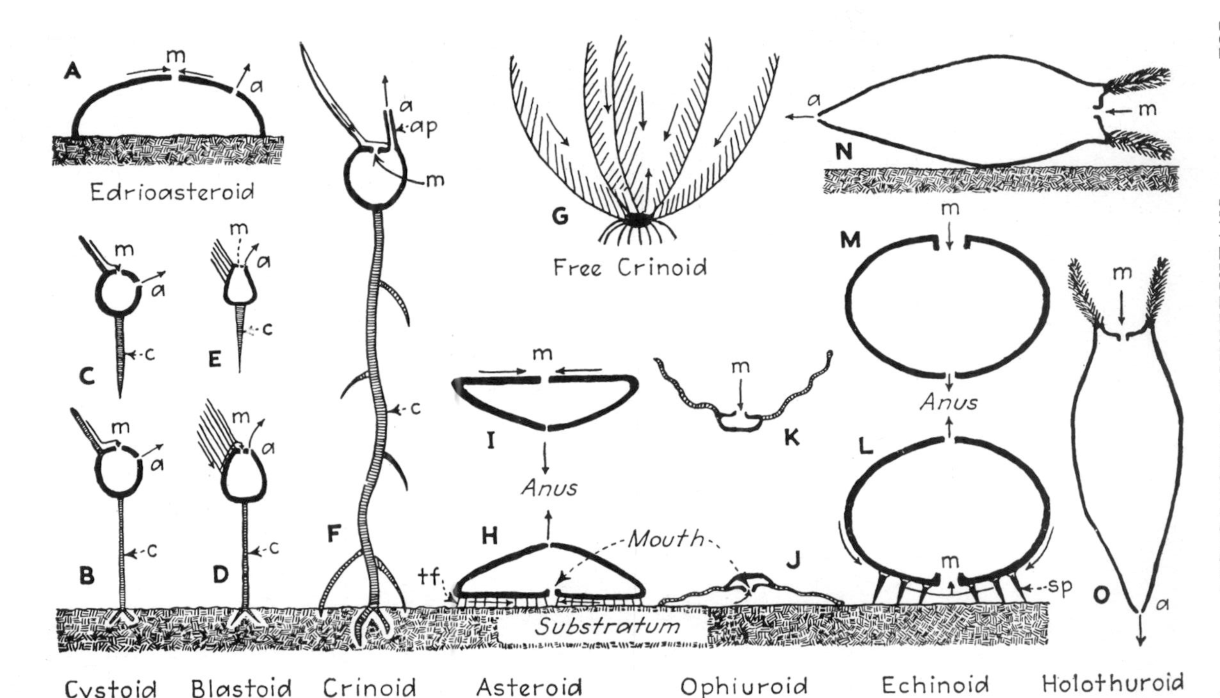

Fig. 46.—Schematic diagram to show the living positions of the various echinoderms and to illustrate the similarity of their structures. All sections are cut in the plane of symmetry, which includes the mouth (*m*) and anus (*a*). The arrows indicate the direction of food- and waste-bearing water currents. The test or leathery integument is shown

mouth. Lying along the radius of each ambulacrum is a food groove provided with small cilia which by a lashing motion drive a current of water and the contained food particles toward the mouth. Elongation and branching of the food grooves greatly increase the food-gathering area of the animal. One large crinoid, *Pentacrinus*, which lived during the Jurassic, had a food-groove system totaling many hundreds of feet.

In some echinoderms the food grooves are open, and the food-bearing current is exposed at all times, but in many crinoids the food grooves are roofed over by minute *covering plates*.

Attachment.—The echinoderms in present seas are almost exclusively vagrant or sessile benthos, and it is thought that most ancient forms were likewise bottom dwellers. The vagrant forms have an irregularly shaped test exhibiting distorted radial symmetry. The attached forms have a *stem*, which elevates them above the bottom. This terminates below in some form of anchoring device. Some living echinoderms have a stem in the early growth stages but lose it by the time maturity is attained (Fig. 46).

Habitat and Habits.—Echinoderma are of very great importance on the bottoms of existing seas where they utilize the excretal matter of living animals as well as the bodies of dead organisms for food. It has been said that "an ocean without echinoderms might become a putrid cesspool." Starfish prey on worms, echinoderms, mollusks, and fish, and upon the oyster banks their depredations are tremendously destructive. Like certain other echinoderms, starfish have the ability to regenerate lost parts; hence when an angry oyster fisherman tears one of the animals apart, thinking that he has destroyed it, he may unwittingly increase the number of individuals. The voracity of these creatures is well illustrated by a large starfish (*Luidia*

---

by a heavy, solid line.

A. An edrioasteroid cemented to the substratum. *B*. Cystoid attached by stem (*c*) and with one arm shown. *C*. Free cystoid with short stem. *D*. Stemmed blastoid with a few brachioles shown. *E*. Free blastoid with a feebly developed stem. *F*. Stemmed crinoid with one arm, covering plates and tegmen shown. The anus is elevated on an anal proboscis (*ap*). *G*. Free-living crinoid with prominent arms and short cirri. *H*. An asteroid in living position, held above the bottom by tube feet (*tf*). *I*. Same inverted. *J*. An ophiuroid in living position. *K*. Same inverted. There is no anus. *L*. An echinoid in living position, held off the bottom by spines (*sp*). *M*. Same inverted. *N*. A holothuroid on the bottom. *O*. Same turned with the mouth upward. Two tentacles are shown.

clathrata), with arms 145 mm. long, which was picked up dead on the beach at Sarasota, Fla. The starfish had swallowed a sand dollar (*Mellita*) 60 mm. in diameter, and its death apparently was due to its inability to disgorge the shell of the prey.

Holothurians and certain of the echinoids perform a very important function in passing large quantities of mud and sand through their bodies for the purpose of extracting the contained organic matter. As a result of this action inorganic materials are affected both chemically and physically, and the organic materials may be eliminated. It seems likely that similar activities were characteristic of ancient echinoderms, and it is thought that the apparently unfossiliferous character of many marine limestones may be attributed, at least in part, to the destruction of the fragile shells by such scavengers.

Modern Echinoderma are characteristically gregarious in habit, preferring to live in colonies, assemblies, or "gardens." Because of this, where living echinoderms are found at all, they are usually present in great abundance. Urchin assemblies, such as that of *Melonechinus* at St. Louis, Mo., and crinoid gardens, such as the famous locality of Crawfordsville, Ind., show that ancient forms were similarly gregarious. Echinoderms are present in existing seas in prodigious numbers, as illustrated by the familiar urchin assemblies along certain coasts and the great numbers of starfish in some waters. The *Challenger* Expedition dredged 10,000 feather stars (unstalked crinoids) in a single haul from fairly deep water, and brittle stars (ophiuroids) are known to be equally abundant. Echinoderms of all kinds are exclusively marine and seem always to have been confined to that environment. Consequently, finding an abundance of echinoderms in a geologic formation indicates that it is marine. Living forms are found in depths ranging from tidemark down to 6,000 m. (3¾ miles) and in practically all latitudes.

Many organisms live in commensalism with echinoderms. Protozoans, sponges, annelid worms, mollusks, and arthropods feed upon the excreta of certain forms. *Igoceras*, a Mississippian gastropod, sat upon or beside the anal opening on certain crinoids and in some cases was actually cemented to the upper surface of the crinoid skeleton. A little fish, known as *Fierasfer*, crawls into the mouth of holothurians or among the arms tail first and is afforded protection thereby. Many nematodes, trematodes, and other worms are parasitic on or in echinoderms.

Ancestry.—The ancestry of the Echinoderma is very ancient. The first members of the phylum appear in the Cambrian, and from that time to the present they have lived in greater or less abundance in every geologic period. Ontogenies of species so far worked out indicate that some Pre-Cambrian annelid worm was very likely the ancestor of the phylum. The evolutionary tree and the importance of the phylum at various times in geologic history are shown in Fig. 74.

THE TEST

The *test* or *exoskeleton* of the typical echinoderm is a hollow, globular, pear-shaped, spheroidal, or star-shaped structure, composed either of a leathery integument studded with calcareous plates or of a series of calcareous plates arranged in symmetrical or asymmetrical manner. The plates are usually situated in the skin of the animal, so that during life the test is covered by dermal tissue. This tissue actually permeates pores in the plates with the result that the test is truly of internal origin. The surface of the tests of many forms is covered by numerous spines composed of the same material as the test proper. Grooves, ridges, nodes, tubercles, and other structures may also ornament the exterior surface of the plates.

The plates are typically composed of calcium carbonate. Some living echinoderms have in addition a small percentage of magnesium carbonate, and with the carbonates usually is mingled more or less chitinous matter. The plates may be united firmly to form a rigid test capable of retaining shape upon burial. In many forms, however, the individual plates are held together by fleshy, cartilaginous or dermal matter, so that when the animal dies the test falls apart or is crushed by the weight of the overlying sediments. In one group, the Holothuroidea, the skeletal structure consists of many small spicular calcareous elements usually in unattached positions in the body of the organism, and only very rarely are these united into any sort of continuous structure.

The side of the globular test on which the mouth is situated is designated the *oral, actinal,* or *ventral* side; the opposite side, where the anus may be located, is known as *aboral, abactinal,* or *dorsal*. In sessile forms the oral side is upward, and the aboral downward. In free forms the oral side is downward except in the case of the holothurians, which have the mouth anterior and the anus posterior (Fig. 46). Some species of echinoderms (echinoids) have a calcareous structure, known as "Aristotle's lantern," encircling the mouth. This has five strong *teeth* which are operated by the action of a set of powerful muscles. The muscles are attached to processes on the test known as the *perignathic girdle* (Fig. 68). By the use of this mastigatory apparatus the organism is able to cut holes in shells and the most resistant rock, and on storm-beaten, rocky coasts they drill holes in which they live protected from the waves.

Taken as a whole the echinoderm test exhibits the same radial pentamerous symmetry (or such symmetry distorted by a second development of bilateral symmetry) as that shown by the animal; hence there is an ambulacral area on the test corresponding to the same area of the body, and there is often an interambulacral area joining together the adjacent ambulacra. The food grooves on the test are underlaid and margined by calcareous plates and in some species may be covered. In the simplest and oldest forms of Echinoderma the food grooves are short and lie directly upon the oral surface of the test. The original number in the animal stock from which the echinoderms descended is not definitely known, but there are some indications that only three grooves were present originally. The five grooves possessed by most echinoderms are thought to have developed from the three by the branching of two of them. The development in the earlier members of extensions of the grooves beyond the oral area gave a wider gathering ground for food, and branching of the grooves, which apparently took place very early, made them still more efficient. This stage of development is typical of the cystoids and the edrioasteroids. The blastoids developed marked ambulacral areas and lined the edges of the food grooves with small jointed appendages, termed *brachioles* (Fig. 50 *E*), which in some cases were equipped with very small segmented, bristle-like appendages known as *pinnules*. The food grooves were continued on the brachioles from the oral surface of the test but were not extended on to the pinnules. Branching *arms* or *brachia* (large jointed structures of more massive character than brachioles), in many cases with pinnules, represent the last step in the development of the food-gathering apparatus. Such an apparatus was present on some cystoids and on most crinoids (Fig. 51 *F–G*).

Echinodermal test fragments are of frequent occurrence in marine strata throughout the geologic column and are very commonly associated with ancient reef deposits, and even today echinoderms are among the common denizens of the coral-reef environment. The plates, because of method of construction and subsequent changes, usually act as a single crystal of calcite and hence exhibit calcite cleavage when broken. This property sets echinoderm plates apart from shell matter found in other organisms. Certain echinoderm fragments may even be identified as to species, though ordinarily satisfactory identification requires a larger part of the test.

STRATIGRAPHIC RANGE

The Echinoderma first appear in the Cambrian, and subsequently fossil remains are present in greater or less abundance in rocks of all later systems. The stemmed and sessile forms flourished greatly during the Paleozoic, but most of them became extinct at the close of the era. Vagrant forms, subordinate in numbers and species during the Paleozoic, rapidly expanded in both respects in the early Mesozoic, and at the present time these form by far the greatest majority of living echinoderms (Fig. 74).

CLASSIFICATION

The Echinoderma are subdivided into classes on the following characteristics:

1. Presence or absence of stem or place for attachment on the dorsal side of the body. The stem commonly serves as a means of attachment, though in certain forms this function is lost.
2. Presence or absence of fixed or movable arms or ambulacra.
3. Character of test and arrangement of skeletal elements.
4. Character of the water-vascular system.

Using these various characters the Echinoderma have been divided into two subphyla and seven classes as follows:

Pelmatozoa
(Stemmed or attached)
- Cystoidea—Cystoids (extinct)
- Edrioasteroidea—(extinct)
- Blastoidea—Blastoids (extinct)
- Crinoidea—Feather stars and sea lilies (living)

Eleutherozoa (Free and vagrant)....	Stelleroidea—Starfish and brittle stars (living) Echinoidea—Sea urchins and sand dollars (living) Holothuroidea—Sea cucumbers (living)

A comparison of the above classes shows that they comprise a closely related group of animals. If all are so oriented that the mouth is up, then it is seen that in each class the five radially arranged arms or ambulacra radiate from the more or less centrally located mouth. In a very general way the arms of the true starfish, brittle star, crinoid, and holothuroid are homologous to the ambulacral areas of the cystoid, edrioasteroid, blastoid, and echinoid. If the starfish is turned over so that the mouth is up, then the lower side corresponds to the base of the cystoid, blastoid, and crinoid, and the upper side on which the five ambulacra radiate from the mouth is similar to the upper surface of the three groups just mentioned. In order to orient the starfish with the echinoid the arms of the former must be bent dorsally until they almost meet; then union along the margins of the arms would produce a skeletal structure similar to that of the echinoid. The holothuroid differs from the starfish in having the central part of the body elongated into an ellipsoidal form and in having the mouth anterior (Fig. 46).

SUBPHYLUM PELMATOZOA[1]

Cystoids, edrioasteroids, blastoids, and crinoids form a group of closely related echinoderms. The body of the animal is encased in a boxlike structure known as the *calyx*. This is hollow and composed of numerous calcareous plates firmly or loosely fastened together and ordinarily, although not always, is anchored to the bottom either by a jointed *stem* or *column* or by direct cementation. The stem is made of small, calcareous, disk-shaped plates with a central perforation. These are known as *columnals* and are placed one above another to form a cylindrical structure which is completely surrounded by a fleshy dermal covering (Fig. 51). Usually its base terminates in an anchor or holdfast system, in which the branches are similar to the main stem in structure but differ from it in being much smaller. On the upper surface of the calyx there are usually

[1] Pelmatozoa—Gr. *pelma, atos,* the sole of the foot + *zoon,* animal; referring to the fact that representatives are attached to the bottom by stems and roots.

five food grooves leading to the central mouth. These commonly have pentamerous arrangement, and each may be continued from the surface of the calyx on to the upper surface of an arm. In some forms there are no arms, but the ambulacra are lined with brachioles, upon which the food grooves are extended, or with pinnules which do not carry such extensions. In some crinoids the oral surface is covered by a leathery integument or a roof of calcareous plates known as the *tegmen* (Fig. 51 *B*). The mouth is generally central, is surrounded by an area designated the *peristome*, and, if beneath the tegmen, is said to be *subtegminal.* The food grooves are often roofed over by small *covering plates,* and the anal opening is usually on the upper surface within the arms. The table below (Table 2) shows the chief characters and the stratigraphic range of the different classes in the subphylum.

TABLE 2.—RANGE AND ESSENTIAL CHARACTERS OF THE PELMATOZOA

Class	Food grooves	Plate arrangement	Pores	Range
Cystoidea	Food grooves on surface	Irregular	Pore plates	Cambrian-Permian
Edrioasteroidea	Curved food grooves	Irregular	Pores in ambulacra	Cambrian-Carboniferous
Blastoidea	Ambulacra and brachioles	Regular	Pores and hydrospires	Ordovician-Permian
Crinoidea	Free arms	Regular	Outgrowth of radial canals	Cambrian-Recent

CLASS CYSTOIDEA[1]

The cystoids are stemmed or stemless echinoderms with a globular, ovoidal, or hemispheroidal test composed of a variable number of calcareous plates (13 to over 200) arranged with or without symmetry. The mouth is near, or in the center of, the oral surface and in some forms is covered by five small plates. The anus is usually situated on the oral side in an eccentric position. It is frequently closed by five or more triangular

[1] Cystoidea—Gr. *cystis,* bladder + *oid,* like; calling attention to the bladder-like appearance of the test.

calcareous plates, which make a valvular pyramid (Fig. 48 *A*), or by a variable number of small plates. Some cystoids have one or two small openings between the mouth and the anus and in the same plane. One of these is surmised to have been for genital functions. The other is supposed to have provided for the entrance of water (Fig. 48 *A–D*).

The Calyx.—The plates of the calyx are quadrangular, pentagonal, hexagonal, or polygonal and are united by close suture. They range in number from 13 in *Cryptocrinus* (exclusive of the small plates connected with the mouth and those comprising the tegmen) to over 100 in *Echinosphaerites*. Only exceptionally do the plates have regular arrangement and shape; hence the pentamerous symmetry characteristic of most echinoderms is absent. Calyx development in the Cystoidea proceeds from many plates with irregular arrangement to few plates and symmetrical arrangement.

In addition to the larger openings into the interior of the calyx, certain or all of the calyx plates are perforated by minute pores. These pores have been used as a basis for classification of the Cystoidea (Fig. 47). In some forms they are arranged singly; in others they are in pairs and are then known as *diplopores*. These pores reach the exterior at right angles to the surface of the plates and represent the terminations of tiny, single or branching canals which ramify the plates, beginning on the inner surfaces. The pores may terminate on tubercular elevations or in depressions. In another group, pores or canals are so arranged on certain of the calyx plates as to form rhomb-shaped areas. These are designated *pore rhombs*, and each always lies upon contiguous plates with the suture between the plates passing through the rhomb along one of the diagonals. Pores on opposite sides of the suture are connected by minute tubes that ramify the middle layer of the plates and extend directly across the suture. The pores also communicate with short canals passing vertically through the plates. A peculiar form of the rhomb, known as *pectinate*, has the two parts situated on contiguous plates and separated externally by a nonporous interval. The two parts may vary in form and size, and in some cases one of the parts may become obsolescent. The functions performed by the various types of pores and pore rhombs are unknown, but it has been suggested that the entire apparatus of pores, canals, etc., functioned as a primitive kind of water-vascular system.

Ambulacral Areas and Arms.—In the Cystoidea the ambulacral areas or food grooves are generally simple and are rarely branched. They are short in most species and may be situated on the tegmen, on the arms, or on the tegmen and the upper

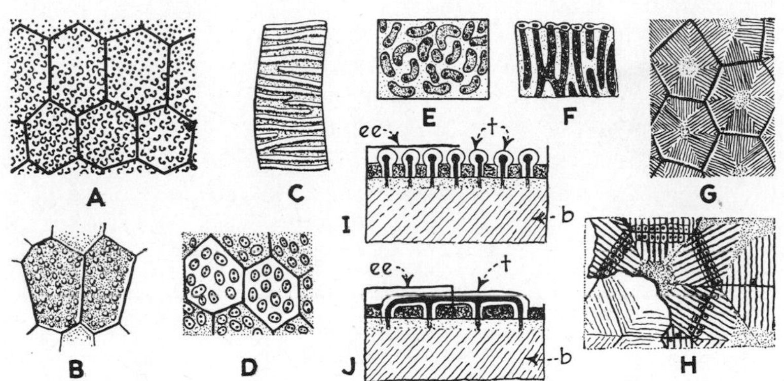

Fig. 47.—Cystoid plates. *A*. Part of the calyx of *Aristocystites*, showing plates perforated by single and horseshoe-shaped pores. *B–C*. *Aristocystites bohemicus* from the Ordovician of Bohemia. *B*, inner surface of two calyx plates showing simple pores; *C*, vertical section of part of a plate showing transverse tubes which terminate at both ends in pores. *D*. *Craterina bohemica*, from the Ordovician of Bohemia, plates with external epidermis removed to show diplopores. *E–F*. *Aristocystites bohemicus: E*, part of a plate bearing diplopores; *F*, vertical section of part of a plate showing relation of pores and tubes. *G–J*. *Echinosphaerites infaustus* from the Ordovician of Bohemia: *G*, a few plates showing pore rhombs, with tiny surface canals; *H*, plates with external epidermis partly removed to show tubes of pore rhombs; *I*, section transverse to tubes and parallel with the edge of the plate showing parallel tubes (*t*) communicating internally with the body. The external epidermis (*ee*) is shown in the left half of the diagram; *J*, section along the longest tube of the pore rhomb showing tube crossing suture between adjacent plates and communicating with interior. The left half of the diagram has the external epidermis in place. (*After Barrande.*)

surface of the calyx (Fig. 48 *K*). Often they are roofed over by alternately arranged covering plates. A few cystoids seem to have been without grooves of any kind. Most known cystoids have five food grooves, but there is some evidence for the statement that the ancestors of the first echinoderms had only three grooves and that the pentamerous arrangement developed by branching of two of the original grooves. In the earliest species of cystoids the symmetry of the ambulacral grooves is imperfect, but in later forms pentamerous radial symmetry is present.

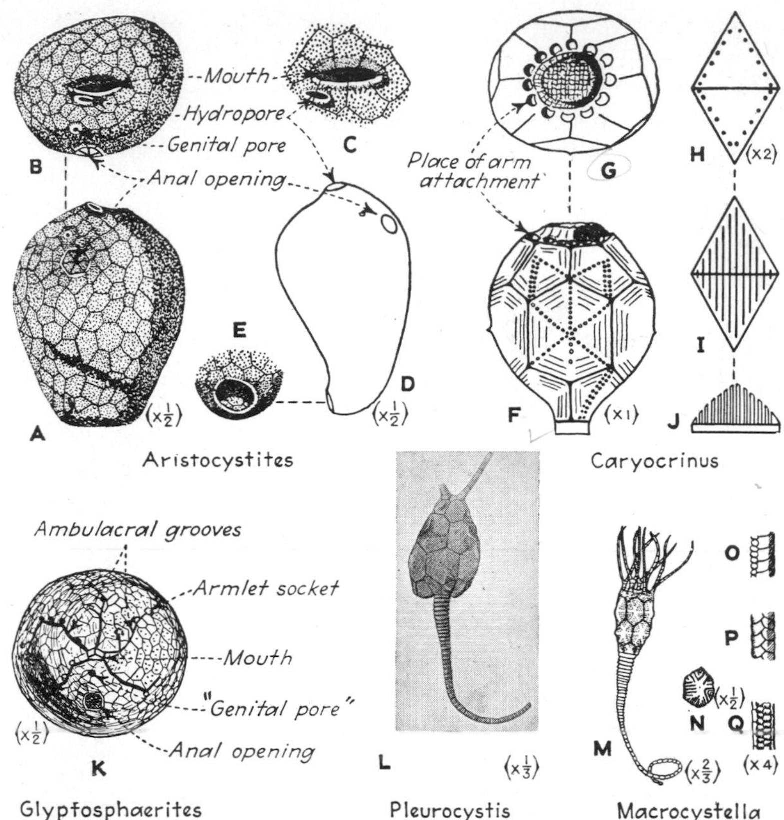

Fig. 48.—Cystoidea. *A–E. Aristocystites bohemicus* from the Ordovician of Bohemia. *A*, an almost complete specimen with only the basal termination missing. The anal opening is closed by a valvular pyramid composed of numerous triangular plates; *B*, top view of *A*, showing the four openings into the test. The test is somewhat deformed; *C*, enlarged view of the mouth region showing the nature and arrangement of the perforated plates; *D*, outline of a complete specimen with three openings visible; *E*, enlarged view of the basal portion of the test showing the prominent concavity. *F–J. Caryocrinus ornatus*, a common Silurian cystoid: *F*, a complete test showing the nature and arrangement of the plates, pore rhombs, and places where the arms were attached. The pore rhombs are not well preserved on the specimen. *G*, top view of *F*; *H*, surface view of a pore rhomb showing the pores; *I*, section parallel to the surface of the test showing the course of the internal tubes; *J*, transverse section. *K. Glyptosphaerites leuchtenbergi* from the Ordovician of Russia. Upper surface of test showing the five ambulacral grooves, the mouth covered by oral plates, the anal opening without the covering plates, the supposed genital pore, and the places of attachment of the armlets. *L. Pleurocystis filitextus*, an Ordovician cystoid. *M–Q. Macrocystella mariae* from the Cambrian of England: *M*, side view of complete specimen; *N*, single plate of a large specimen; *O–Q*, side, dorsal, and ventral views of a portion of a brachiole. (*A–E after Barrande; H–J after Wachsmuth and Springer; K after Nicholson and Lydekker; L after Kirk; N–Q after Bather in Lankester's "A Treatise of Zoology."*)

Arms are nearly always poorly developed and, if present, range in number from 2 as in *Pleurocystis* to 13 as in *Caryocrinus*. They are composed of small calcareous plates which are arranged either in a single row (uniserial) or in a double row (biserial) as shown in Fig. 48. On the inner or upper side of each arm is a small groove protected by minute covering plates. These grooves are extensions of the larger ambulacral grooves that lie on the calyx. The arms range from delicate brachiole-like structures to very robust forms. Rarely they are provided with tiny pinnules.

Attachment.—Primitive cystoids such as *Aristocystites* were attached to the bottom by the dorsal apex of the test and hence did not have a stem (Fig. 48 *D*). Many cystoids possessing segmented stems were free and unattached. Others were attached by means of a stem. The stems of free forms progressively decrease in diameter with distance from the calyx, with the result that the distal termination is pointed (Fig. 46). Columnals usually are disk shaped and are united along smooth or striated surfaces, in rare cases overlapping one another. In a few species the columnals in a part or in the whole of the stem are not round but are serially arranged to make a round stem. The stem is pierced by a wide central canal.

Classification.—The Cystoidea are the oldest and the least specialized of the Pelmatozoa and perhaps even of the echinoderms. They appear to be ancestral to both Blastoidea and Crinoidea. They first appear in the Cambrian, the maximum development was attained in the Silurian, and the class became extinct by the close of the Paleozoic.

Cystoids vary greatly in form, structure, and symmetry. Pores of some kind are present in the calyx plates of most species, and these afford one of the chief means of differentiating the cystoids from other Pelmatozoa. Four orders have been erected to include the members of the class. Their similarities and differences are indicated in Table 3.

ORDER AMPHORIDEA

Cystoids of this order have no radial symmetry in either the food grooves or the calyx plates. The calyx varies in shape from globular to ellipsoidal and may possess or lack a stem. Food grooves have only a limited development in some families

TABLE 3.—SHOWING THE ESSENTIAL CHARACTERS AND GEOLOGIC RANGE OF CYSTOIDEA

Order	Pores	Symmetry	Range
Amphoridea	Numerous, single pores	None	Cambrian-Ordovician
Rhombifera	Pore rhombs	Food grooves and some calyx plates	Ordovician-Silurian
Diploporita	Diplopores	Food grooves and some calyx plates	Ordovician-Silurian
Aporita	No pores	Food grooves and calyx plates	Cambrian-Permian

but in others are extended and branched. The calyx plates contain pores and canals, but there are no pore rhombs. This order includes the most primitive of the cystoids with one genus, *Aristocystites*, resembling the embryo of an echinoderm covered with plates. The range of the order is from the Cambrian to the Ordovician inclusive.

Representative genera are the stemless *Aristocystites* (Fig. 48 *A–D*), *Anomalocystites*, and *Malocystites*, all from the Ordovician. The first genus has an ellipsoidal or pyriform calyx with numerous irregularly arranged plates, without food grooves, and without brachial processes. The calyx was attached directly by the aboral side. The oral surface has four openings—the mouth, anus or *vent*, *genital pore*, and *water pore*. *Malocystites* has a globular calyx, long branched food grooves provided with brachioles, and a feebly developed stem.

ORDER RHOMBIFERA

Representatives of the Rhombifera exhibit radial arrangement of the food grooves, which are borne largely on brachioles and in some species on the calyx plates. Pore rhombs are invariably present. Individuals of some species may be abundant locally. The order ranges from Ordovician to Silurian.

A typical genus of this order is the well-known Ordovician and Silurian *Caryocrinus* (Fig. 48 *F–J*). This genus has a somewhat globular calyx in which the plates are arranged in cycles with hexamerous symmetry. The base is dicyclic (two cycles). There are 6 to 13 feebly developed arms. Plates of the calyx possess pore rhombs except for those of the summit which are imperforate. The food grooves and mouth are subtegminal, and the anus, on the outer margin of the ventral surface, is protected by a valvular pyramid. There is a long stem composed of cylindrical segments. *Pleurocystis* from the Ordovician is a second representative genus (Fig. 48 *L*).

ORDER DIPLOPORITA

The members of this order possess diplopores (whence the name) but lack pore rhombs. The food grooves, and to some extent the calyx plates, have radial symmetry. The former are prolonged upon the brachioles which line their edges. The order is confined to the Ordovician and Silurian. A representative genus is *Glyptosphaerites* from the Ordovician (Fig. 48 *K*). This has a globular calyx composed of irregularly arranged plates and short ambulacral grooves.

ORDER APORITA

The Aporita include a considerable number of cystoids which cannot be placed in any of the three orders just described, and it is altogether likely that some genera now placed in this order may ultimately be classified differently. Food grooves and calyx plates exhibit a radially symmetrical arrangement, and the former are borne on arms around the mouth. The calyx plates lack both pore rhombs and pores, hence the name Aporita (without pores). This is one of the oldest orders of Cystoidea and is the one with the longest range [Cambrian to Permian (?)].

The Cambrian genus *Macrocystella* (Fig. 48 *M–Q*), a rather highly developed cystoid, has been referred to this order. It is characterized by a pyriform calyx in which the plates are arranged in three cycles of five each. There are five branched brachioles and a rapidly tapering stem by which the animal may have attached itself to the bottom. The radiating folds of the calyx plates are strongly marked, but there are neither pores nor pore rhombs.

Class Edrioasteroidea[1]

It is by no means certain that this division should be given rank coordinate with the other classes of Pelmatozoa.[2] Some paleontologists prefer to include it as an order under Cystoidea. In the Edrioasteroidea the calyx is generally flexible and is composed of numerous irregularly arranged calcareous plates which in some forms are imbricating. The complete test has a discoidal shape, certainly due in part to flattening at the time of burial. From the central mouth on the upper surface of the

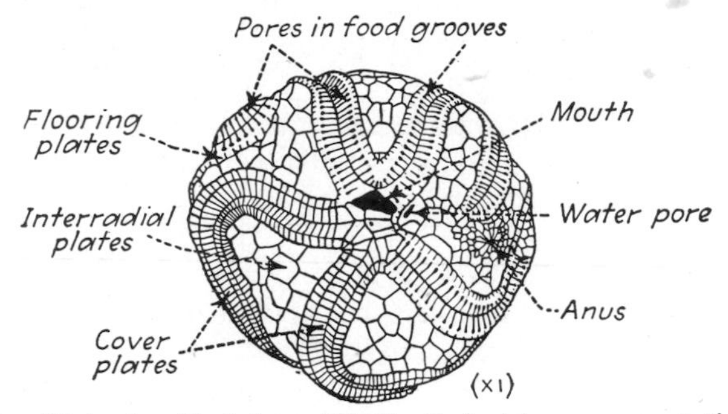

Fig. 49.—*Edrioaster bigsbyi*, a Middle Ordovician representative of the Edrioasteroidea. The aboral side shows the mouth, anus, water pore, and ambulacra. Cover plates are shown on only two of the ambulacra. (*After Bather.*)

test radiate five falciform, unbranched ambulacral grooves which extend to the outer edge of the test and are recumbent on the surface. In life these grooves were roofed over by small covering plates which could be lifted up. Minute pores lie between or pierce the plates of the ambulacral grooves. The anus and a water pore lie in the posterior interambulacral area, and the two adjacent ambulacra, comparable to the *bivium* of the echinoids, curve around them (Fig. 49). The anus may be covered by a valvular pyramid. Tube feet were probably present during life and were connected with the interior through the pores in the ambulacra.

[1] Edrioasteroidea—Gr. *edrion*, dim. of *edra*, seat + *aster*, star, + *oid*, like. The test has the appearance of a little cushion with a star on top. The star is formed by the five recumbent ambulacral grooves.

[2] Bassler, R. S., The classification of the Edrioasteroidea, *Smith. Misc. Coll.*, vol. 93, No. 8, pp. 1–11, 1 pl., 1935.

The edrioasteroids are either primitive or degenerate pelmatozoans. The fact that they appear in the Lower Cambrian suggests that they are the former. They possess features similar to those in the cystoids in the form of irregularly arranged plates, and they resemble the asteroids in apparently having had the ambulacral grooves provided with tube feet. The group seems to represent a stock close to the cystoids but one which early became attached by the dorsal surface (Fig. 46 *A*) and subsequently adapted the various bodily and skeletal structures to that mode of life. The range is from Cambrian to Carboniferous.

A representative genus of this unique "class" is *Edrioaster* (Ordovician) (Fig. 49) with a flexible, discoidal test composed of thin, usually imbricating plates perforated by fine pores and attached by the dorsal surface. The five ambulacral grooves are protected by small covering plates.

Class Blastoidea[1]

The Blastoidea are extinct, short-stemmed or stemless pelmatozoans with a relatively small, rigid, pear-shaped or globular calyx. The calyx exhibits excellent radial symmetry (usually pentamerous) and is composed of 13 *primary* calcareous plates—three *basals*, five *radials* or *forked plates*, and five *interradials* or *deltoids* (Fig. 50 *D, G*). Radiating from the centrally located mouth are five unbranched, more or less petaloid ambulacral areas. The mouth is located beneath a vault of small calcareous plates, and the ambulacral grooves were protected in life by a double row of tiny covering plates. Since the vault over the mouth joins directly with the covering plates of the ambulacra, there was thus in life a continuous roof over the entire food-groove system. The plates of this roof are nearly always missing in fossil forms.

Small brachioles, in some cases provided with pinnules, were, and in a few fossils still are, attached along the lateral margins of the ambulacral areas in a single or double row. True arms are not developed. A hydraulic apparatus, known as a *hydrospire*, lies along and beneath the lateral margin of each ambulacrum and is connected with the surface of the ambulacral area through small pores along the margin. Orally, the hydrospires

[1] Blastoidea—Gr. *blastos*, sprout or bud + *oid*, like; calling attention to the resemblance of a blastoid to a flower bud.

open through five pairs of large elliptical pores (*spiracles*) situated at the points of the deltoid plates.

The Calyx.—The calyx of a blastoid is pyriform, globular, ovoid, clavate, or bell shaped and exhibits perfect radial symmetry. The 13 primary plates are arranged in three cycles—the basal cycle with 3 plates, the radial with 5 plates, and the interradial with 5 plates. Two of the basal plates are large and of equal size; the third is considerably smaller. The five deeply incised or forked radials lie immediately above the basal cycle. In most blastoids the radials are the largest plates, and as a consequence they form the major part of the calyx. Because the radials fork orally, inclosing part of the ambulacrum between the two parts of the plate, they are often designated *forked plates*. The five interradials—triangular plates resembling the Greek letter delta, whence they are known as *deltoid plates*—comprise the third cycle of the calyx and lie near the summit in notches made by the junctions of the radials. The deltoid cycle is interrupted by the ambulacral areas. The deltoid plates are nearly always small and in some cases are partly hidden (Fig. 50 *B–C*).

The Ambulacra.—The ambulacra of a blastoid are the most conspicuous features of the calyx, and they give to its summit the appearance of a flower bud, a resemblance reflected in the name of the class (Fig. 50). The ambulacra are always five in number and extend with radial symmetry from the centrally located pentamerous mouth. They may be broad or narrow, long or short, and pointed at one or both ends. They usually are slightly depressed below the surface of the calyx, but in some forms they are level with the surface or even elevated to some degree above it. In a typical blastoid each ambulacral area is divided into two symmetrical parts by a prominent median longitudinal groove, known as the food groove or ambulacral groove. This in life was roofed over by a double row of covering plates. The ambulacral groove lies along the median line of a long pointed plate, referred to as the *lancet plate*, which constitutes the larger part of the ambulacral area. In some genera, such as *Pentremites*, a second plate known as the *under lancet plate* lies beneath the median part of the lancet plate (Fig. 50 *E*). Since the lancet plate is somewhat narrower than the complete ambulacrum, there is an interval separating it from the sides of

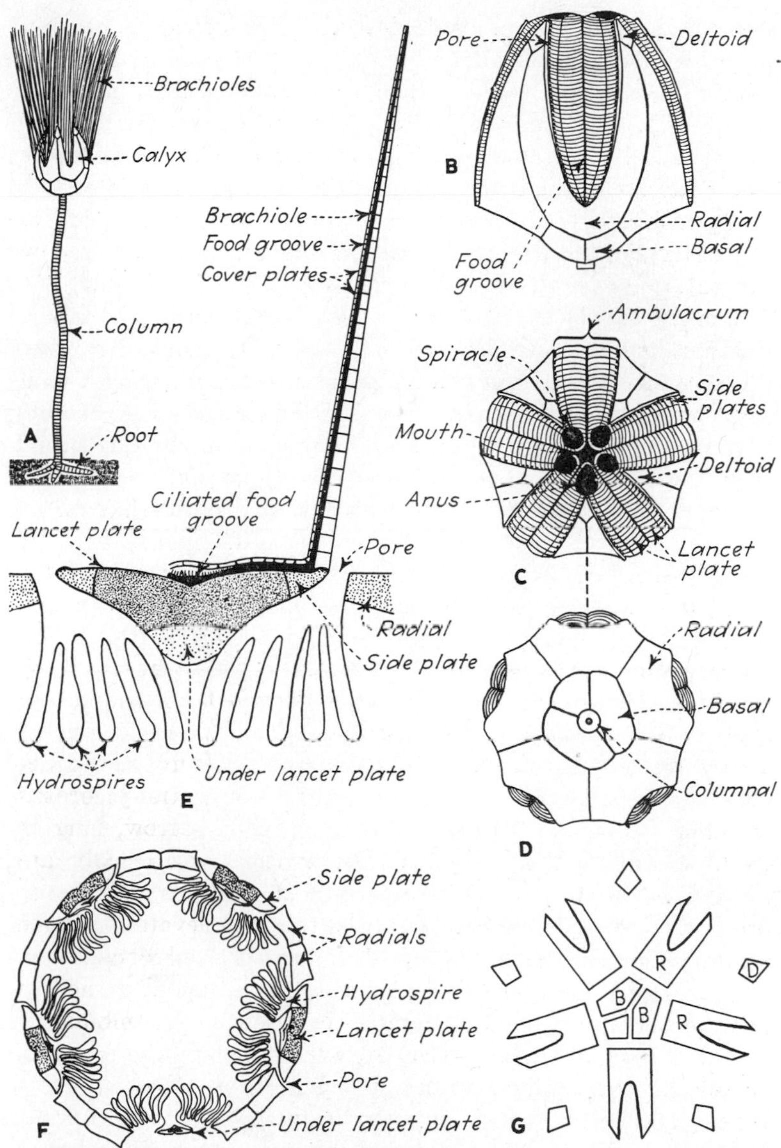

Fig. 50.—Blastoidea. *A*. Schematic diagram to show an attached blastoid in living position. *B–G*. *Pentremites*, the common Mississippian blastoid: *B–D*, lateral, oral, and basal views, respectively, of the calyx; *E*, schematic transverse section of the mid-portion of an ambulacrum as it appeared in life, with a brachiole shown along only one margin; *F*, transverse section of the calyx of *P. pyriformis* at about the mid-point of the ambulacrum, with one ambulacrum removed; *G*, diagram to show analysis of the main calyx plates (*B*, basal; *R*, radial; *D*, interradial or deltoid). (*F after Wachsmuth and Springer.*)

the radial plate that partly incloses it. This space is occupied on each side by small plates, known as *side plates*, which may overlap the lancet plate sufficiently to conceal it partly or completely. In some species the side plates are separated from the radials by a second series of small plates designated *outer side plates*. A single row of small marginal pores is present along each side of the ambulacrum, being on the side plates if the outer side plates are absent but on the latter if they are present.

The two equal sides of the lancet plate are traversed by minute grooves disposed at right angles to the ambulacral groove and opening into it. These smaller grooves may be thought of as branches of the main food groove. They extend across the side plates nearly to the margin of the ambulacrum, ending near a tiny dome which was the place of attachment of a brachiole. From this point the food grooves continued outward from the surface of the calyx along the brachioles. The path, therefore, of a food particle acquired at the extremity of a brachiole was down the brachiole to the transverse groove, along that groove to the median ambulacral groove, and thence to the mouth on the summit of the calyx.

At the apices of the deltoid plates between adjacent ambulacra are 5 or 10 circular, elliptical, or slitlike openings—the spiracles—which connect with the hydrospires. These have been considered as genital openings by some and as outlets of the water-vascular system by others. The latter view is now generally held. If the number of spiracles is five, each is divided by a median partition so that 10 openings to the hydrospires are present. The spiracle on the posterior side of the calyx is generally larger than the other four, and when specimens are well preserved it is seen to be divided into three parts by two partitions. The middle opening is apparently the anus, for it connects with the interior cavity only, whereas the two side openings connect only with the hydrospires.

The hydrospires, which apparently functioned as respiratory tubes, and possibly also in connection with the discharge of reproductive elements, are one of the most remarkable structures in the blastoid calyx. They lie underneath the lateral part of each ambulacrum, one on either side; hence there are 10 in all (rarely more than 10 may be present). Structurally the hydrospire is a simple, flattened, calcareous tube, of which the thin walls have been more or less crenulated and folded in such a way that the cavity appears to be composed of a series of parallel tubes with incomplete walls. Internally the hydrospire is closed except where it is connected with the marginal pores along the side of the ambulacrum and orally where it terminates in the spiracles. It is thought that in life water entered the hydrospires through the marginal pores and then moved orally until it escaped through the spiracles. It is possible, however, that the current may have moved in the opposite direction.

Brachioles and Stem.—The living blastoid very likely resembled a brush turned upside down, for the ambulacral areas had the margins lined with small segmented appendages known as brachioles, and these in turn were often pinnulated. A tiny ciliated food groove is thought to have lain along the inner surface of each brachiole, and along this trough the food particles moved on the way to the mouth. This groove in some forms is known to have been roofed over by tiny calcareous covering plates. In general, the covering plates of the mouth, ambulacra, and brachioles, as well as the brachioles and pinnules themselves, are rarely found on fossil blastoids, as they very readily fell apart when the animal tissue holding them together decomposed.

The *stem* of sessile blastoids is rarely preserved in its entirety, though it is known to have served the function of attachment in many forms. The *columnals* are usually round and are pierced by a small central canal. The stem in life was probably completely inclosed in some sort of dermal covering. Death brought decomposition of the flesh and separation of the plates; hence they are rarely found attached to the calyx. The stem in all cases is short, rarely attaining a length as great as 15 cm.

Geologic History.—Nothing is known of the ontogeny of the Blastoidea. They appear to have developed from some cystoidean ancestor late in the Cambrian or early in the Ordovician. *Asteroblastus* from the Ordovician seems to be an intermediate form suggesting such ancestry.

The blastoids range from the Ordovician to the Permian, reaching a climax during the Mississippian, when they were extremely abundant in North America. Certain limestones have been called *Pentremital* because of the great numbers of the genus *Pentremites*.

Classification.—The Blastoidea have been subdivided into two orders—*Protoblastoidea*, characterized by a variable number of calyx plates; and *Eublastoidea*, with a definite and limited number of plates. An earlier classification subdivided the class into the *Regularia*, with five similar ambulacra; and the *Irregularia*, with four similar and one unlike ambulacrum. All forms of the latter group can be placed in the Eublastoidea

The Protoblastoidea, an exclusively Ordovician order, have a large and variable number of plates in the calyx. The structural features show that members of this order are closely linked with the Cystoidea, from which they seem to have descended. *Asteroblastus*, a stemmed form with five ambulacra, brachioles, and plates perforated by diplopores, but without hydrospires or poriferous ambulacral plates, is representative of the order.

The Eublastoidea have the calyx composed of 13 plates. There are prominent ambulacral areas lined with brachioles and pinnules, and there are always hydrospires. *Pentremites* (Fig. 50), probably the best known genus among the blastoids, is a typical representative of the order. The small calyx has the appearance of a flower bud because of its shape and the conspicuous pentamerous ambulacral areas. The circlet of five spiracles, one larger than the rest and containing the anus, surrounds the pentamerous centrally located mouth. The order ranges from the Ordovician to the Permian.

Class Crinoidea[1]

General Considerations.—The Crinoidea include the sea lilies and feather stars of existing seas and the stone lilies of the geologic column. The class was thought to be extinct until about 60 years ago when a dredge brought up living examples from the sea bottom, and subsequently the *Challenger* Expedition dredged as many as 10,000 unstalked individuals in a single haul. Investigations which have been carried on since the first discovery have shown that crinoids are still an important element in marine faunas in both shallow and deep waters. They are known to live between 52° S. lat. and 81° N. lat.

Crinoids are gregarious organisms tending to live in assemblies or "gardens" of immense populations, as shown by the *Challenger*

[1] Crinoidea—Gr. *crinon*, lily + *oid*, like; referring to the lily-like appearance of the skeleton.

haul mentioned above. They also seem to prefer relatively clear waters and favor especially the vicinities of coral reefs. The sporadic occurrence of fossil crinoids in the geologic column indicates that the ancient forms were also gregarious, and the association of the remains with limestones and reef deposits shows that they preferred clear water in the past.

Most ancient crinoids were attached to the bottom and elevated above it by a stem or column. The stem ranges in length from 25 mm. (1 in.) to more than 21 m. (70 ft.), as Quenstedt is said to have traced a stem in the rocks for 21 m. without finding either the end attached to the calyx or the one rooted to the bottom. The normal length is from 30 cm. (1 ft.) to 90 cm. (3 ft.). The stem is fastened to the bottom by some anchoring apparatus, such as small rootlike appendages (*cirri*), or directly by cementation. Many interesting devices were developed by ancient crinoids, depending upon the environment in which they lived (Fig. 51). One form, *Scyphocrinus*, is supposed to have had a bulbous root or a float (*Camarocrinus*). *Holopus* was attached directly without a stem.

Free crinoids have no root system or anchoring apparatus, and the stem nearly always is very feebly developed or entirely absent. Many such forms, however, do have a stem in the early growth stages, but in maturity this structure is lost, although in some cases there is a well-developed holdfast arrangement by which the organism attaches itself temporarily to floating objects. Free forms are known to have lived since the Carboniferous and are represented in existing seas by 580 species and 85 genera. Since the total number of living crinoids is only 650 species and 100 genera, it is apparent that most modern forms are free. These are known as *Comatulidae*. However, in the three species of the comatulids of which the life history has been worked out there is an initial stalked stage.

The Animal.—The living crinoid is incased in a calcareous or horny-calcareous cuplike structure known as the calyx. The upper part of the calyx is covered by a tegmen and is designated the oral side. The mouth is in the center of the oral surface, and it may open through the tegmen or lie beneath it. In the latter case it is said to be subtegminal.

Radiating from the mouth, with pentamerous or rarely hexamerous symmetry, are five ambulacral grooves, which

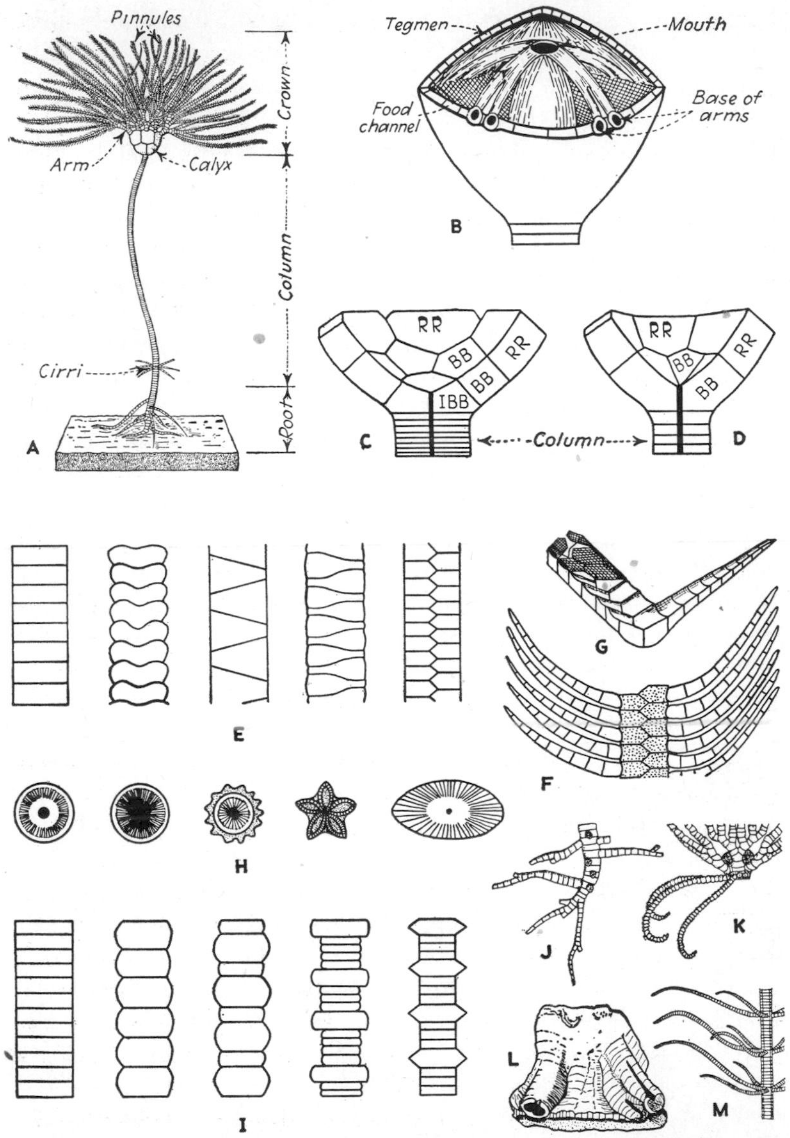

FIG. 51.—Crinoid structures. *A*. A complete crinoid in living position. *B*. Diagrammatic calyx with tegmen and subtegminal mouth. The food grooves radiate from the mouth to points where the arms are attached. The anus is not shown. *C*. A dicyclic calyx (*IBB*, infrabasals; *BB*, basals; *RR*, radials). *D*. A monocyclic calyx. *E*. Uniserial and biserial arms. *F*. A biserial arm with pinnules. *G*. Diagram of arm and pinnule with a few covering plates shown. *H*. Columnals viewed from above. *I*. Columnals viewed from the side. *J–M*.

may lie upon or beneath the tegmen and which are prolonged upon the arms to their distal extremities. The grooves in some species are provided with small calcareous covering plates which can be drawn down to cover and protect the passages (Fig. 51 *G*). Food particles, acquired along the arm and urged along the food grooves by the motion of the cilia, enter the mouth, pass through the esophagus into the stomach, whence the waste products move through the intestines to be expelled finally from the anus or vent, situated in the posterior interradius on the oral surface within the circle of arms. The anus in many species is elevated upon a tube (*anal tube* or *proboscis*) (Fig. 53 *A*), in which case the actual opening is at the summit or on the anterior side. The opening may be covered by calcareous plates.

The *arms* or *brachia* contain prolongations of the body cavity which consist of generative organs, nervous tissue, vessels of the water-vascular system, and podia. These fleshy parts lie on or within the calcareous supporting structures which are composed of many calcareous segments of various patterns.

Crinoids have distinct bilateral symmetry, upon which has been imposed a secondary radial symmetry of either a pentamerous or a hexamerous nature. The plane of bilateral symmetry passes through the mouth and anus or through the anterior ray and the posterior interray.

Every living crinoid and probably every extinct species possesses or possessed a water-vascular system. Below the food grooves in each arm is an ambulacral vessel (*ampulla*) filled with water, from which distensible bodies known as podia are given off on alternate sides. The five ampullae unite around the mouth to form the circumoral *ring canal.* From this ring five short, open tubes extend downward into the body cavity from which water is obtained to supply the ambulacral vessels. Many interambulacral plates are perforated to admit water into the body cavity, and certain crinoids (*Fistulata*) have a madreporite.

Crinoids have a considerable concentration of nervous tissue. There are tubes in various plates of the calyx and in the arms and

---

Roots and cirri: *J*, root system of *Platycrinus; K*, cirri of *Neometra; L*, stumplike root of *Barycrinus?; M*, part of column with cirri of *Comastrocrinus.* (*A–B, E–J, and L after Wachsmuth and Springer, with more or less modification; C–D, parts of E and I after Springer; K and M after Clark.*)

the stem for the passage of the nerve fibers and blood vessels. There is also much muscular tissue.

The Skeleton.—The skeleton of a typical crinoid consists of three structural elements (Fig. 51 *A*)—(1) the *root system*, present as an anchoring device in those species which attach themselves to the bottom or to objects on the bottom; (2) the *stem*, *stalk*, or *column*, which is a flexible, thick-walled, segmented tube connecting with the root system at the lower extremity and with the main part of the skeleton—the so-called *crown*—at the upper extremity; and (3) the crown, composed of the *calyx*, which houses the main part of the animal body, and the *food-gathering system* consisting of five or rarely six arms that radiate from the mouth on the upper surface of the calyx.

THE ROOT SYSTEM.—The majority of extinct crinoids appear to have been attached, but most living forms are free, though, as already mentioned, they often have a holdfast system developed on the under- or dorsal side of the calyx. In stemmed forms the apparatus for attachment consists of numerous spikelike, segmented appendages known as *cirri* and *rootlets*. These adhere to the bottom directly or wrap themselves about objects on the bottom (Fig. 51 *J–M*). *Neometra*, a living stemless genus, has on its dorsal or aboral side in the adult stage a number of small, delicate cirri by which it can moor itself to foreign objects temporarily. It is fastened by a stem only in the early growth stages. Cirri are composed of numerous tiny calcareous plates sufficiently well connected so that they do not disintegrate immediately upon the death of the organism. They are flexible, however, during life.

THE STEM OR COLUMN.—The stem of most crinoids is a more or less flexible structure composed of variously shaped and sized calcareous plates generally arranged in a single series. Each plate has a small central perforation, and these perforations in the column form an axial canal. In life fleshy dermal substance incloses the stem, and a rod or tube of fleshy matter occupies the axial canal, serving to hold the plates together, to give flexibility to the stem, and to perform such functions as are essential to the nutrition of the stem. The stem is always short in living stemmed crinoids, but in extinct forms it ranges from a few centimeters to more than 21 m. (70 ft.). In cross section the stem may be circular, elliptical, quadrangular, pentagonal, or polygonal. The stem plates or columnals are always thin in respect to diameter and may all be of the same size in a stem, or small and large plates may alternate (Fig. 51 *H–I*). The upper and lower flat surfaces along which adjacent columnals join are commonly smooth, but they may be sculptured to aid in interlocking. There is great diversity in ornamentation. The columnals are of common occurrence in marine sediments, particularly from the Ordovician to the Jurassic, but are less common thereafter.

Stems often have small cirri along them at regular intervals, and also similar processes near the base which serve to brace the stem. Such cirri are seldom preserved, but the places of attachment are clearly indicated on the columnals (Fig. 51 *J*).

THE CALYX.—The crinoid body is housed in a dorsal cup or calyx surmounting the stem and constituting the lower part of the crown. The calyx is covered by a vault known as the tegmen (Fig. 51 *B*) and is composed of a variable number of calcareous plates which are arranged symmetrically in cycles about a *centrodorsal* plate (*CD*) (Fig. 52) or, if such is absent, about a central point on the dorsal or aboral surface of the calyx. In successive cycles outward and upward from the centrodorsal plate, or a point corresponding to its position, are the *infrabasals* (*IBB*) (not always present), *basals* (*BB*), *radials* (*RR*), and *brachials* (*Br*). Between the radial plates are interradials (*iR*), and between the brachials are interbrachials (*iBr*). The infrabasals, radials, and brachials occupy a radial or ambulacral position in the calyx; the basals, interradials, and interbrachials have interambulacral position. The infrabasal cycle is frequently absent, and interradials and interbrachials may not be present. The size of the calyx is directly dependent upon the number and size of the plates that compose it. Calices without infrabasals are known as *monocyclic*, whereas those with infrabasals are *dicyclic* (Fig. 51 *C–D*). The simplest calyx would be monocyclic and consist of basals and radials only. Large calices are produced when brachials and interbrachials participate in the formation. In such calices the tegmen is enlarged through the incorporation of *ambulacral* and *interambulacral* plates (Fig. 53 *C*). The largest calyx so far discovered is that of the genus *Uintacrinus*, which is known to have measured more than 20 cm. in diameter, and when the arms were outspread the crown was 240 cm.

(8 ft.) across. Most calices do not exceed 25 mm. (1 in.) in diameter.

Primarily there are five infrabasals, five basals, and five radials, but in a dicyclic calyx the infrabasals often become fused to

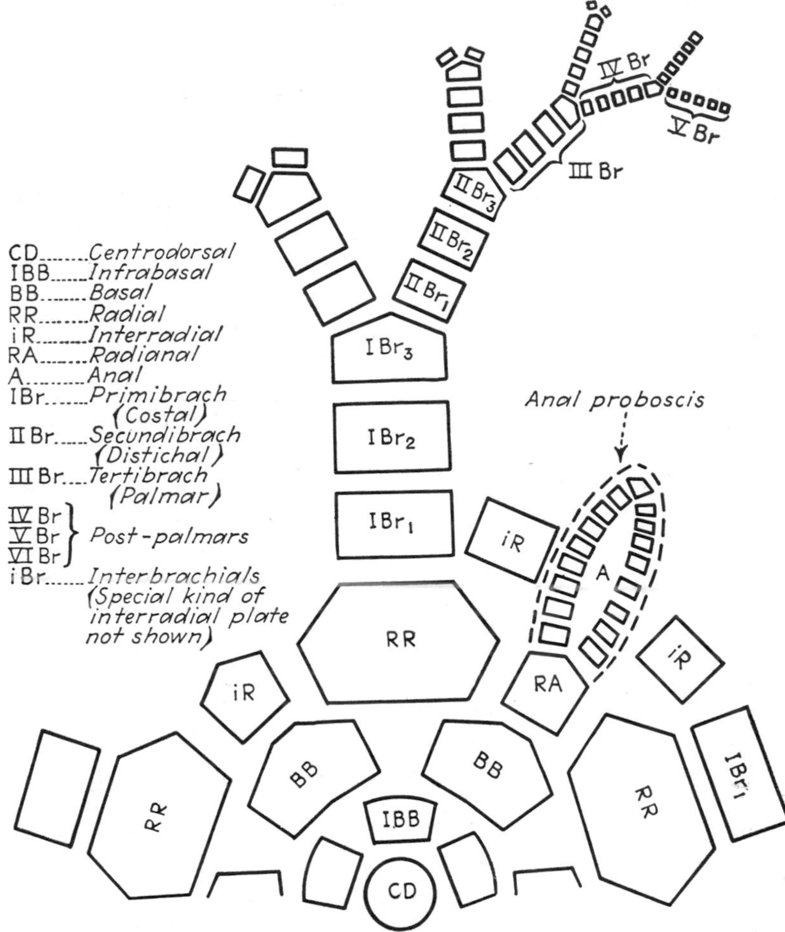

FIG. 52.—Diagram illustrating the usual method of analyzing a complete dorsal cup (calyx minus the tegmen) and the arms

make four, three, or two plates or even only a single one. Similar reduction may also take place in the basals of some monocyclic forms. Radial plates in some cases divide to form several *compound radials,* those below designated as inferradials and those above superradials. There are usually five radials in the cycle, but in certain species a sixth plate, known as the *radianal* (*RA*), is intercalated between adjacent radials in the posterior interambulacral position. Other *anal* plates may also develop above the radianal, particularly if there is a proboscis.

All plates above the radials are assigned to the arms or brachia and are designated as *brachials* of various kinds, but all brachials which enter into the calyx are also considered as part of that structure. Brachials participating in the calyx are termed *fixed*, whereas all others are *free*. All brachials from the radials to and including the first *axillary* (the plate which gives off two arms) are known as *primibrachs* (I*Br*) or *costals*. The second series from the first axillary to and including the second are *secundibrachs* (II*Br*) or *distichals*. The third series are known as *tertibrachs* (III*Br*) or *palmars*. All other brachials beyond are designated as *postpalmars* (IV*Br*, V*Br*, VI*Br*, etc.). Pinnules are found on the arms of many crinoids and are variously arranged with respect to the arm plates (Fig. 51 *F–G*).

The Arms or Brachia.—Arms are present in all crinoids, and the number is usually five. Each arm, with all of its branches, carries food grooves to its distal extremities, except that these are not extended on to pinnules. The grooves, which in some forms total several meters in length, are protected by small covering plates known as *ambulacrals* and *adambulacrals* (side plates) (Fig. 51 *G*). Branching is very common in the arms and follows the three general types *isotomous* (equally bifurcating), *heterotomous* (unequally bifurcating), and *pinnulate* (branching only once and bearing pinnules). Early crinoids have five simple, unbranched arms without pinnules. This probably represents a primitive condition. As noted later, this condition represents a stage in the ontogeny of the three living crinoids of which the life history is known. In all living and fossil crinoids the arm plates are perforated by a single or double canal, which contains nerve cords in living forms and is thought to have contained such cords in fossil forms. This canal extends either through the radials or lies in a furrow upon the inner surface and ends in the basals.

The arm plates are arranged either uniserially or biserially. Simple uniserial arms have each plate of the same thickness on each edge and arranged one above another. In more complex forms of uniserial arms the arm plates are thicker on one edge than on the opposite, and the thick side of one plate alternates with the thin side of another. In the biserial arms the plates are wedge shaped, and either the whole or a part of each arm is composed of the interlocking plates (Fig. 51 *E*).

THE TEGMEN.—The oral part of the calyx is covered by a rooflike vaulted structure known as the tegmen (Fig. 51 *B*). This may be a horny or leathery integument in which large or small plates are embedded, or it may be a dome of calcareous plates. It often has a central opening for the mouth. There is always an eccentric opening for the anus, and this may be placed on the summit or anterior side of a conical elevation composed of calcareous plates or dermal matter studded with such plates. This elevation is the anal tube or proboscis (Fig. 53 *A*).

Five triangular plates, designated *orals*, surround the mouth or cover it, one being situated in each of the five angles between the ambulacra. The acute apices of the plates are directed toward the mouth, and they are separated by the ambulacral grooves. The latter are floored by ambulacral plates, and interambulacral plates are in the spaces of the tegmen bounded by the grooves, the oral plates, and the edge of the tegmen.

Evolution and Ontogeny.—The life history of crinoids is known in only three living species. The eggs are produced by generative organs residing in the arms and reach the exterior through the ambulacral grooves. They are fertilized externally while attached to the pinnules or the arms. At the proper time the egg membrane bursts, and an elongate-oval, bilaterally symmetrical, gastrula-like embryo is released. This embryo has an anterior tuft of cilia and is encircled by five ciliated bands. The appearance is much like the trochospheric larvae of certain annelid worms at this stage of development. Internally, there are visible the rudiments of five oral plates, five basal plates, and three or five infrabasal plates, all arranged in horseshoe-shaped bands. There are also 11 similarly shaped columnals. The embryo has a mouth and anus with a nearly straight intestinal tube between them. There is a third opening known as the *hydropore* (Fig. 73).

After swimming about for a few hours by means of the cilia, the embryo attaches itself by its anteroventral surface; the cilia disappear; the mouth, anus, and hydropore shift to the free end of the body; and other changes cause the original character of the embryo to be pretty largely lost. The shifting of the mouth and anus forms a loop to the intestine. The five oral plates take the form of a pyramid over the ventral (now upper) part of the organism, the five basals arrange themselves in corresponding position on the dorsal part of the animal, and the infrabasals take position below the basals; below the infrabasals are the columnals. At the base of the stem a lobate plate is developed for attachment. The organism has now attained the cystoid stage.

There next develop between the orals and the basals five radials and an anal plate, the latter gradually moving upward with the orals into the ventral disk. The three circlets of radials, basals, and infrabasals together comprise the *patina*. Above each radial plate then develops a series of plates to form the arms, which grow very rapidly through the addition of new plates on the distal ends. The column increases in length through the addition of new columnals at the junction of the column and the calyx, until there are about 25. The highest plate of the column becomes concave upward and convex downward and increases in dimensions, covering first the infrabasals, later the basals, and it may even cover the radials. Ultimately it fuses with the plates that are covered and becomes a single plate known as the centrodorsal. At this stage of growth the crinoid is said to be at the pentacrinus stage.

The oral and anal plates now begin to be resorbed; the arms, at first free from the base, branch on the third primibrach to make 10 unbranching arms which are free above the first secundibrach; and the button-shaped centrodorsal plate develops cirri and becomes detached from the rest of the column. From this point onward the animal leads a free life.

From the ontogeny it appears that the early crinoids had calices composed of infrabasals, basals, radials, and orals, with simple arms branching from the third primibrach. It may be assumed that an unbranched arm preceded the branched condition. The arms of the mature crinoids of which the ontogenies are known are pinnulate, but pinnules are lacking on the arms in the early growth stages. Also, in the early stages the arms are free from the base up, suggesting that this character existed in the parent stock. The ontogenies further suggest that the crinoids were derived from some cystoidean stock and ultimately from a wormlike ancestor.

The evolution from cystoid to crinoid took place either in the Pre-Cambrian or during the early Cambrian. The *Larviformia* division of the simple *Inadunata* is perhaps to be considered nearest the ancestral stock. The members have the calyx composed of not more than three cycles of plates, and the arms are free above the radials. All are small, and *Allagecrinus* is almost microscopic. *Haplocrinus* and *Pisocrinus* are other forms that are not far from the stem stock, but neither of them has been found so early as the Ordovician. *Hybocrinus*, from the Ordovician and belonging to the *Fistulata*, has its plates like those of the larval stage of known crinoids, and the orals bear traces of hydrospires, suggesting a stock from which the blastoids might have been evolved. *Hybocystis*, another Ordovician fistulate genus, has food grooves extending upon the radials and even upon the basals, suggesting relations with the cystoids. Evidence strongly suggests that the crinoids and blastoids developed from a common stock with the early stages more or less parallel.

Stratigraphic Range.—Crinoids are reported from the Cambrian as isolated plates supposed to belong to this class. They became common in the Ordovician, and in some localities during the Silurian they flourished abundantly. Certain calcareous formations, such as those at Port Byron, Ill., and Racine, Wis., contain a great abundance of crinoidal remains. The class was also well represented during the Devonian but did not reach the climax of development until the Mississippian, when the shallow seas in several different parts of the world teemed with them. The world-famous localities at Crawfordsville, Ind., and at Keokuk and Burlington, Iowa, are in strata of this age. The crinoids continued into the Pennsylvanian with some decrease in vigor, though still important. Thereafter, however, there seems to have been a decrease in the number of species, at least in shallow waters. How much of this apparent decline is real and how much a matter of preservation and discovery remain to be determined. At the present time there are about 650 species assigned to 100 genera. Stalked forms appear to have dominated during the Paleozoic, with unstalked forms coming in toward the end. Since the Paleozoic the latter have gradually increased in number, so that at the present time they constitute nearly 90 per cent of known living species.

Without known exception the crinoids are marine; consequently finding an abundance of crinoidal remains in a formation indicates that the inclosing rock is of marine origin or was formed closely adjacent to marine conditions. Because of the gregarious habit of crinoids their remains may be found in great profusion at one locality and only sporadically or not at all in surrounding areas. This local abundance is first found in the Ordovician, the strata of which furnish fairly good specimens at various points in North America. The Niagaran strata of Dudley, England, of Gotland, and of Anticosti, as well as correlative formations in the states from New York to the Mississippi River, have crinoidal remains in local abundance, but unfortunately the material is mainly fragmentary, and complete crowns are not common. Good Devonian localities for crinoids are in the Eifel and adjacent areas in Germany and in New York, in Michigan, and about the Falls of the Ohio at Louisville, Ky. There are good localities in Mississippian strata in Belgium, near Moscow in Russia, and in Great Britain. The most famous of Mississippian localities, however, are at Crawfordsville, Ind., and Burlington and Keokuk, Iowa. In the former locality crinoids have built large mounds or lenses of coarsely crystalline limestone, known as *crinoidal bioherms*. In the majority of these bioherms columnal plates dominate, and complete calices are very rare. In later life among many living crinoids the crown separates from the stem and continues as plankton, whereas the stem is deserted and left behind to form a deposit on the bottom. It may be that such a condition accounts for some bioherms' having many calices, whereas others have only stem plates.[1] From the Indiana and Iowa localities have come many of the specimens found in the great museums of the world and figured in textbooks in all languages. The region about Kansas City has yielded many excellent crinoids from Pennsylvanian strata, and Permian strata of the island of Timor contain a remarkable crinoidal fauna. There are few famous Mesozoic localities; one of the best known is in the Niobrara chalk of Kansas from which slabs carrying great numbers of *Uintacrinus* have been collected.

[1] Stockdale, P. B., Bioherms in the Borden group of Indiana, *Bull. Geol. Soc. Amer.*, vol. 42, pp. 707–718, 1931. Kirk, E., The structure and relationships of certain Eleutherozoic Pelmatozoa, *Proc. U. S. Nat. Mus.*, vol. 41, pp. 1–137, 1911.

Crinoids are excellent index fossils for some horizons, and they would be even more useful if they were found more abundantly and over wider areas. Species usually have very limited vertical ranges, thus adding to the stratigraphic value. Because of limited geographic distribution and marked gregarious habit, however, the actual usefulness is greatly lessened.

Classification.—The following classification is that proposed by Wachsmuth and Springer and A. H. Clarke and is based on the following features:

1. Character of arms; whether free above the radials or partly incorporated in the calyx as brachials.
2. Character of the calyx; whether union of plates gives rigidity or flexibility.
3. Growth of stem; whether new columnals are added beneath the basal rings of the calyx or beneath the top stem joint.
4. Presence or absence of tegmen.

The Crinoidea are divided into four orders—*Camerata, Flexibilia, Inadunata,* and *Articulata.* The Inadunata are ordinarily subdivided into the *Larviformia* and *Fistulata.* The essential characters of the different divisions are shown in the chart below (Table 4).

Table 4.—Chart Showing the Essential Characters and Geological Range of the Four Orders of Crinoidea

Order	Mouth and food grooves	Calyx	Calyx plates	Arms	Range
Camerata	Not exposed	Rigid	Some brachials	Pinnules	Ordovician-Permian
Flexibilia	Exposed	Flexible	Some brachials	No pinnules	Ordovician-Mississippian
Inadunata:	Mouth not exposed	Rigid	No brachials	With or without pinnules	Ordovician-Triassic
Larviformia	Mouth not exposed	Rigid	No anal plates	No pinnules	Silurian-Mississippian
Fistulata	Mouth not exposed	Rigid	Anal plates	With or without pinnules	Ordovician-Triassic
Articulata	Exposed	Flexible	With or without brachials	Pinnules	Triassic-Recent

ORDER CAMERATA

The Camerata are frequently referred to as the "box crinoids" because of the rigid calyx and solid tegmen that covers the oral surface in most species. The monocyclic or dicyclic calyx contains the lower brachials and has all its plates rigidly united. The mouth and food grooves are completely covered, with the covering plates in many instances a part of the tegmen, and hence they are subtegminal in position. The anus is subcentral on the oral surface and is frequently elevated on the end of an anal tube. The arms are uniserial or biserial and are pinnulate. The order makes its appearance in the Ordovician and becomes extinct in the Mississippian.

Platycrinus (Fig. 53) is a typical representative of the order. It has a rotund, monocyclic calyx composed of large radials in contact all around and three basals of which two are large and of equal size and the third smaller. The brachials and interbrachials are only slightly represented in the calyx. The arms are uniserial in the lower part and biserial in the upper. The elliptical stem is typically twisted. The genus ranges from the Devonian through the Mississippian.

ORDER FLEXIBILIA

The Flexibilia have the lower brachials incorporated in a flexible calyx by lateral union, by interbrachials, or by a plated skin. The tegmen is flexible, and the well-defined ambulacra are roofed with movable covering plates. The mouth is supra-tegminal, open, and surrounded by symmetrically arranged oral plates. The grooved arms are nonpinnulate. The dicyclic calyx is composed of three unequal infrabasals, five basals, five radials, and five brachials, all more or less united by muscular articulation. The stem is round. The order makes its appearance in the Ordovician and becomes extinct in the Carboniferous. *Taxocrinus* (Fig. 54 *A–B*) is a typical genus.

ORDER INADUNATA

The Inadunata have the arms free above the radials so that the calyx consists only of radials and lower plates. The monocyclic or dicyclic calyx is rigid, as the plates are firmly united with each other. It is nearly always small. The mouth is

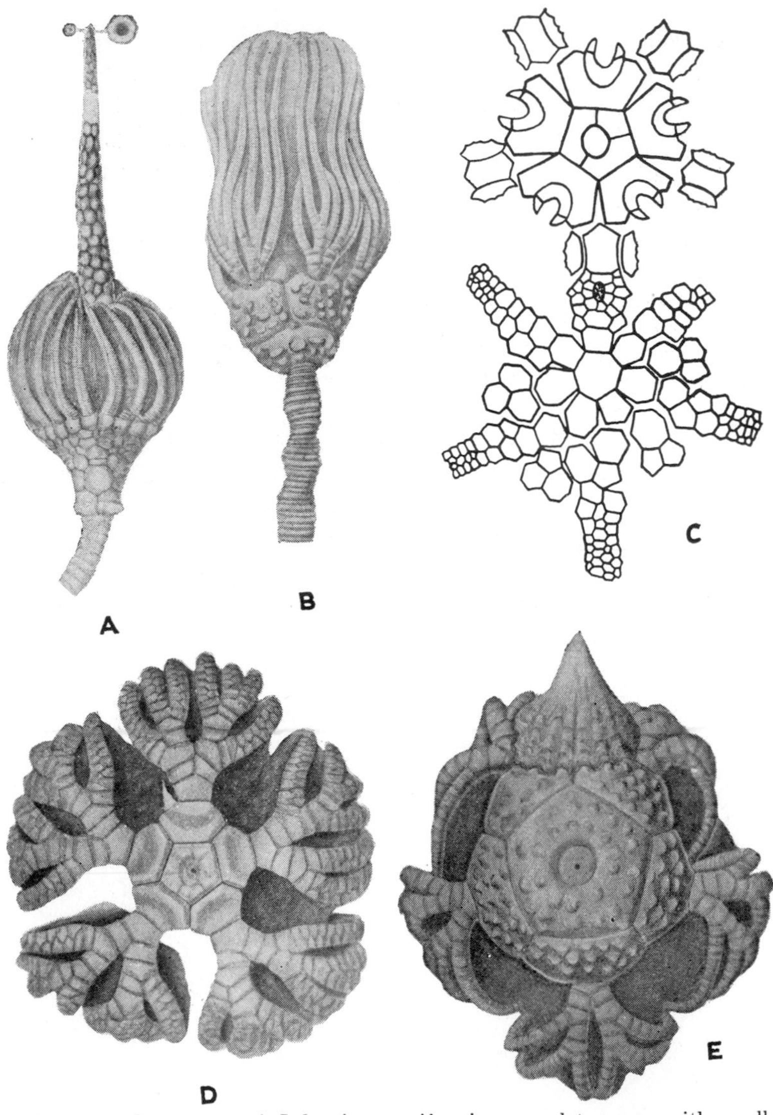

FIG. 53.—Camerata. *A. Lobocrinus pyriformis*, a complete crown, with a well-developed anal proboscis and the upper part of the column, from the Mississippian (Burlington) of the Mississippi Valley. *B–E. Platycrinus*, a very common Mississippian camerate crinoid: *B*, *P. hemisphericus*, a complete crown from the Mississippian (Keokuk) of Indiana and Iowa; *C*, analysis of the calyx of *Platycrinus*, including the tegmen and the basal portions of the arms; *D*, *P. subspinosus*, from the Burlington of Iowa, showing a basal view; *E*, *P. hemisphericus*, a complete crown with the shell of *Igoceras*, a gastropod, over the anal opening. (*A after Meek and Worthen; B, C, and E after Wachsmuth and Springer; D after Meek and Worthen.*)

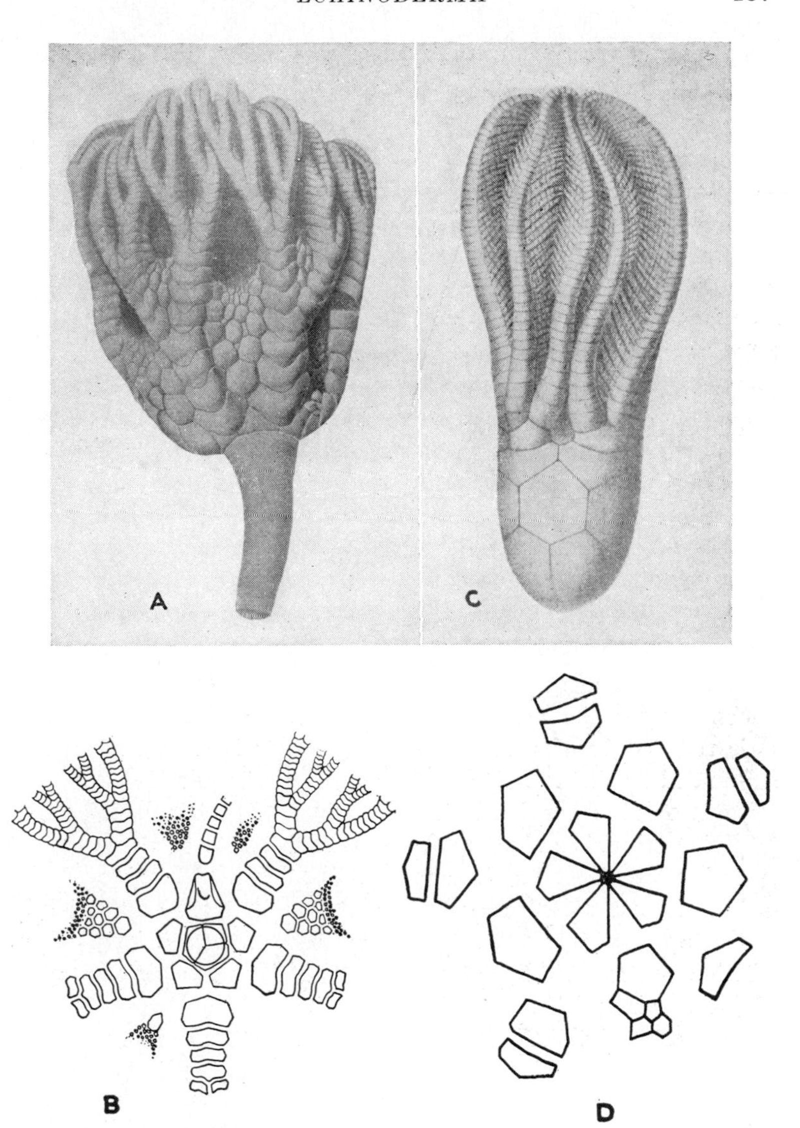

Fig. 54.—Flexibilia and Inadunata. *A. Taxocrinus praestans*, a complete mature crown and a small portion of the column, from the Mississippian of Indiana. *B.* Analysis of the crown of *Taxocrinus*. *C. Agassizocrinus dactyliformis*, a common crinoid in the Upper Mississippian of America. *D.* Analysis of the calyx of *Agassizocrinus*. (*A–B after Springer; C from Meek and Worthen, after a figure by Roemer in Brown's "Leth. Geog."; D after Hall.*)

subtegminal, and the ambulacra are on the surface of the tegmen. The anal opening may penetrate the interradials, or it may be situated between two radials or their appendages. The arms are with or without pinnules.

This group includes the simplest crinoids known. It was well represented during the Paleozoic, and a single family continued into the Triassic. The suborder *Larviformia* includes the very simple forms; the *Fistulata* are farther advanced. *Agassizocrinus* (Mississippian) is a representative genus (Fig. 54 *C–D*).

ORDER ARTICULATA

The Articulata are characterized by a small, dicyclic calyx in which the infrabasals and in some cases also the basals are atrophied, resorbed, or otherwise modified. The leathery tegmen is studded with calcareous plates. Both mouth and ambulacral grooves are exposed, but the latter are often bordered by plates capable of being brought down to cover them. Oral plates are present in the young but are often absent in adults. The calyx plates are united by articulation; hence the calyx is flexible. The free, movable arms are uniserial and pinnulate. There is no concavity for the reception of the stem, and in some forms it is reduced to a single plate. The order is thought to have descended from the *Fistulata* suborder of the Inadunata, since these two orders overlap in the Triassic. The Articulata include all living crinoids and range from the Triassic to the Present.

Apiocrinus (Fig. 55) is a typical fossil representative of the order. It has a long stem rooted to the bottom and swelling at the top to merge gradually with the base of the pyriform calyx, which is surmounted by branching arms. The calyx is composed of five basals and three cycles of radials.

Neometra (Fig. 51 *K*) is a typical example of a living, stemless crinoid, and *Pentacrinus* (Fig. 55 *C*) represents the living stalked forms.

SUBPHYLUM ELEUTHEROZOA[1]

The Eleutherozoa are stemless echinoderms which may be subdivided into three groups on the basis of bodily structure,

[1] Eleutherozoa—Gr. *eleutheros*, free + *zoon*, animal—"free-animals"; referring to the fact that representatives of this group are free living rather than attached.

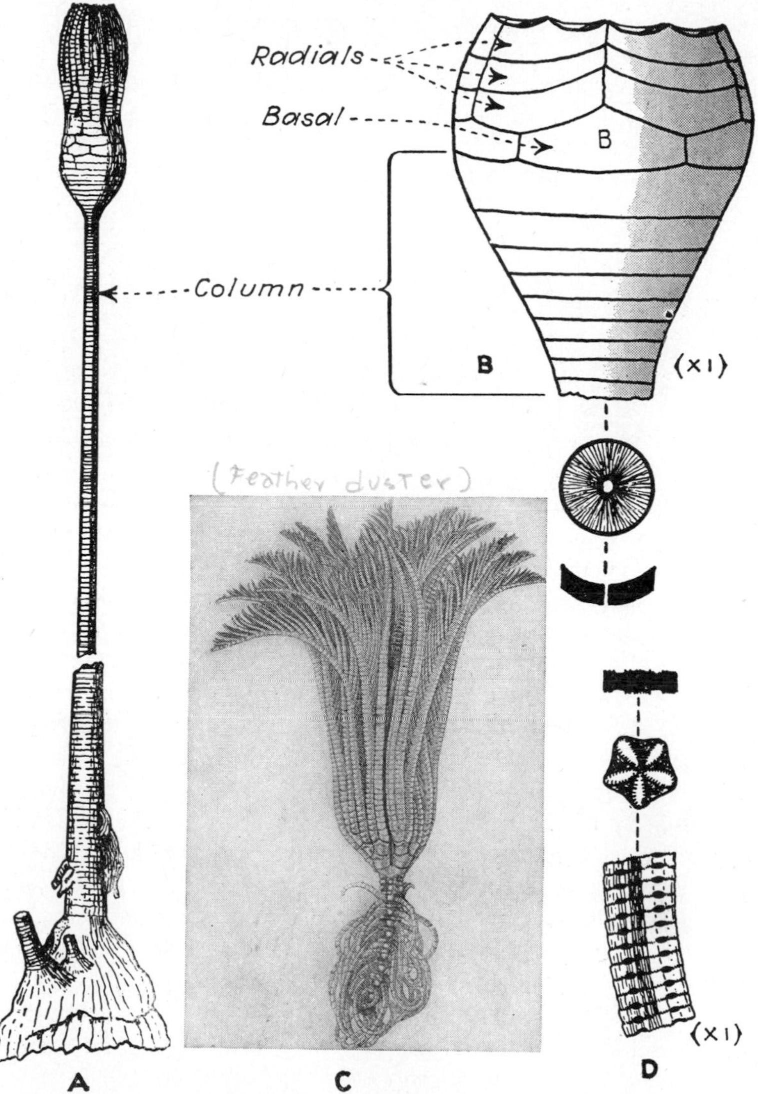

FIG. 55.—Crinoidea (Articulata). *A. Apiocrinus roissyanus* from the Jurassic. *B. Apiocrinus parkinsoni* from the Jurassic of England, showing the calyx, part of the column, and one columnal as seen from above and as sectioned transversely. *C. Pentacrinus maclearanus*, a living stalked crinoid. *D. Pentacrinus asteriscus*, a small fragment of the column from the Jurassic (Lias) of England. One columnal is shown as viewed from above and from the side. (*A, C after Nicholson and Lydekker.*)

character of the food-gathering system, and nature of the test or skeletal matter. The body of the animal may be incased in a leathery integument, as in the *Stelleroidea* and *Holothuroidea;* or in a globular, hollow test, composed of calcareous plates, as in the *Echinoidea.*

Class Stelleroidea[1]

The Stelleroidea, or starfishes, are stemless echinoderms with a star-shaped body consisting of a central disk from which five or more arms radiate (Fig. 57). In contrast to the pelmatozoans, the starfish has the oral side down, the aboral up. If a crinoid were detached from its stem and turned upside down with the arms extended, it would have the position of a starfish (Fig. 46). The mouth is situated in the center of the oral side of the central disk. The food grooves or ambulacra lie on the under- or oral side of the arms and radiate from the central mouth, usually with pentamerous radial symmetry. The hollow arms are provided with extensions of numerous body organs, and all starfish carry a vessel of the water-vascular system beneath each ambulacral furrow (Fig. 45), generally interior to the plates flooring the furrow. Small lateral extensions from the radial vessel pass between the flooring plates to the outside where they become podia or tube feet.

The body of the starfish is not inclosed in a rigid or flexible calcareous box, as is the case with pelmatozoans and echinoids, but instead has a leathery integument which is given strength by small, irregular calcareous plates that may or may not be united or by calcareous spines and other ornamental structures (Fig. 58 *C*).

The Stelleroidea appear first in the Cambrian and occur as rare specimens in marine formations from that time to the present. The geologic range of any given species is short, and if they were more abundant they would make good index fossils. Because of rare occurrence, however, the stratigraphic value is small. In present seas members of the class are extremely

[1] Stelleroidea—N. L., fr. F. *stellérides,* fr. L. *stella,* star + Gr. *oid;* referring to the starlike appearance of the stelleroid.

common. They are vagrant benthos and play an important role as predators on many bottoms.

Classification

Stelleroidea may be divided into three subclasses—*Asteroidea*, *Auluroidea*, and *Ophiuroidea*. The Auluroidea are extinct forms confined to the Paleozoic, but the other two subclasses have living representatives. The Auluroidea and Ophiuroidea have a rather sharply defined central disk, whereas in the Asteroidea the central part merges gradually into the arms. Prolongations of the viscera extend into the hollow arms only in the last named group. The madreporite in the asteroids is large and is situated on the aboral side of the body; in the auluroids it is small and on the oral side; and in the ophiuroids one of the oral plates performs its function. Asteroidea and Auluroidea have ambulacral grooves on the arms. Ophiuroidea lack these. Two of the arms or rays of the Asteroidea and Ophiuroidea have the madreporite between them, and these two rays form the *bivium*. The other three rays are termed the *trivium*. The plane of symmetry passes through the madreporite and bisects the bivium. The skeletal structure of the arms in the different subclasses is shown in Fig. 56. The Auluroidea seem to be intermediate between the other two subclasses.

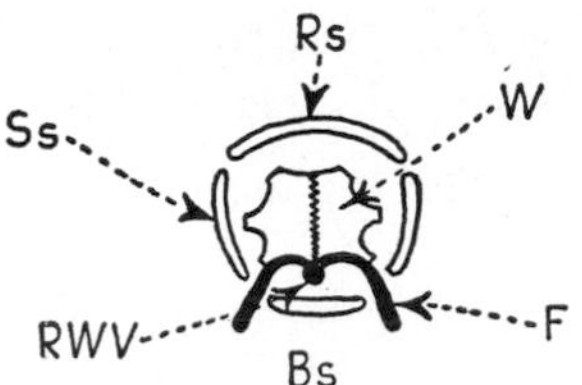

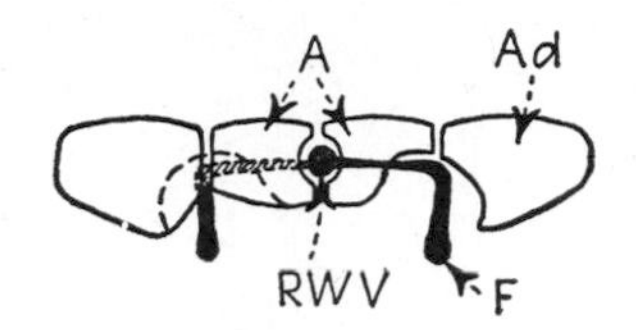

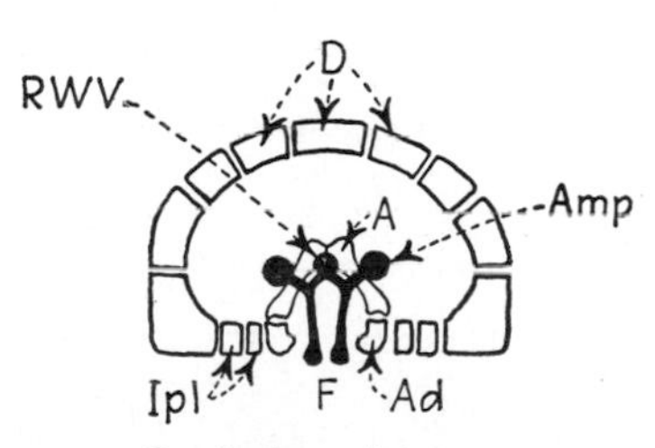

FIG. 56.—Arm structure in the Stelleroidea. *A*. Transverse section of an ophiuroid arm showing the ventral (*Bs*), lateral (*Ss*), and dorsal (*Rs*) shields, the vertebral ossicles (*W*), the radial water vessel (*RWV*), and the podia (*F*). *B*. Transverse section of an auluroid arm showing the alternating ambulacralia (*A*), the adambulacralia (*Ad*), radial water vessel (*RWV*), and podia (*F*). *C*. Transverse section of an asteroid arm showing dorsal (*D*) and marginal skeletal elements, accessory ossicles (*Ipl*), adambulacralia (*Ad*), ambulacralia (*A*), radial water vessel (*RWV*), and podia (*F*). (*Much simplified after Schuchert.*)

Subclass Asteroidea

The Asteroidea have star-shaped or pentagonal bodies consisting of 5 to 40 or more simple, more or less flattened, unbranched arms which radiate from a central disk that is not set off sharply from the arms (Fig. 57). Prolongations of the viscera extend into the hollow arms, and a single arm torn from the body may develop into a new individual. The ambulacral grooves extend from the centrally located mouth to the ends of the arms where they terminate in a simple calcareous plate known as the *ocular*.

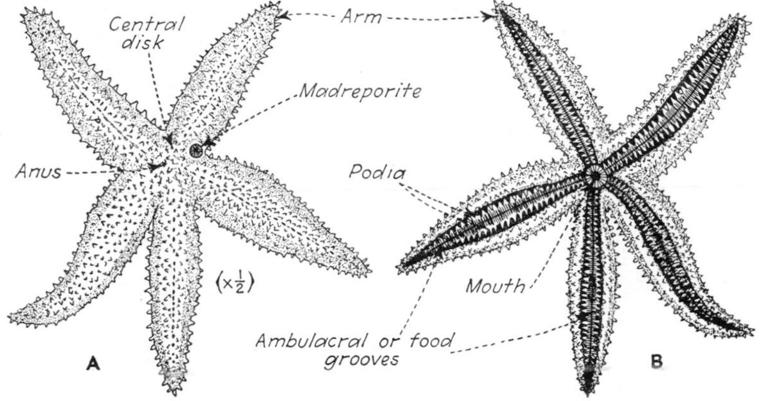

FIG. 57.—*Asterias forbesi*, a common starfish along the Maine coast. *A*. Aboral view. *B*. Oral view.

This plate carries an organ sensitive to light. The ambulacra are plentifully provided with tube feet fitted with suction disks (Fig. 45). The mouth, situated in the center of the oral surface, has a pentagonal margin due to the projection of five pairs of calcareous plates known as orals. The anus is on the upper or aboral side of the body near the center and is very small. Adjacent to it and in interambulacral position is the madreporite or sieve plate. On the edge of the poorly defined central disk and between the bases of the arms are pores from which the genital products are extruded.

The *skeleton* of the asteroid consists of detached or united calcareous plates which touch along the edges, overlap, or unite in reticulate fashion, and the whole is covered by a leathery integument and muscular tissue. In some species the plates and the surface bear movable spines known as *pedicellariae*. There is considerable variation in the form of the skeletal elements (Fig. 58). In recent species the ends of the ambulacral plates are apposed along the median line of the ambulacrum like the rafters of a roof, but in Paleozoic species these are arranged in alternate rows and are inclined toward each other at a small angle. Pores through which the tube feet protrude are present along the junctions of adjacent plates. The ends of the flooring plates (or roofing plates) fit against a second series of ambulacral plates

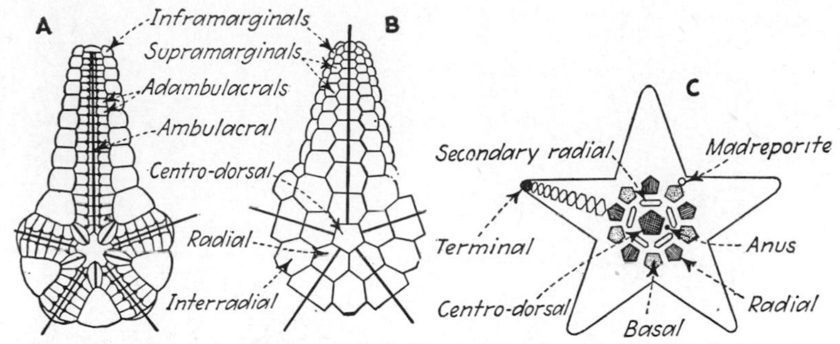

FIG. 58.—The asteroid test. *A–B.* Ventral (oral) and dorsal (aboral) views of the theoretical phylembryo of the Stelleroidea, based on *Hudsonaster*. *C.* Diagram showing the relations of the chief plates of the apical system in the young starfish. (*A–B after Schuchert; C after Parker and Haswell.*)

(*adambulacrals*), and the latter in turn may be bounded by several kinds of marginal plates (Fig. 59).

At present there is much difference of opinion on the classification of the Asteroidea. The size of the marginal plates in the arms has been used as a basis for erecting two orders—*Phanerozonia*, with large and conspicuous plates; and *Cryptozonia*, wherein the plates are small. The former includes most of the Paleozoic and later fossil asteroids. Each order is represented by numerous living species.

The earliest and simplest representatives of Asteroidea appear in the Cambrian. *Hudsonaster*, an Ordovician and Silurian genus, is typical of the early asteroids, and in the plates of the aboral surface it closely resembles the young individuals of living forms (Fig. 59). *Asterias* (Fig. 57) is a typical modern starfish.

Subclass Auluroidea

The Auluroidea constitute an extinct group of starfish with simple unbranched arms originating from a fairly well-defined central disk. The skeleton of the arms consists of four rows of calcareous plates, with the plates of adjacent rows arranged in alternating positions. The two middle rows are composed of ambulacral plates, the other two of adambulacral or marginal plates. In the auluroids the arm plates are never united to form vertebral ossicles as in the ophiuroids. There seem to have been no extensions of the body cavity into the arms, and the ambulacral

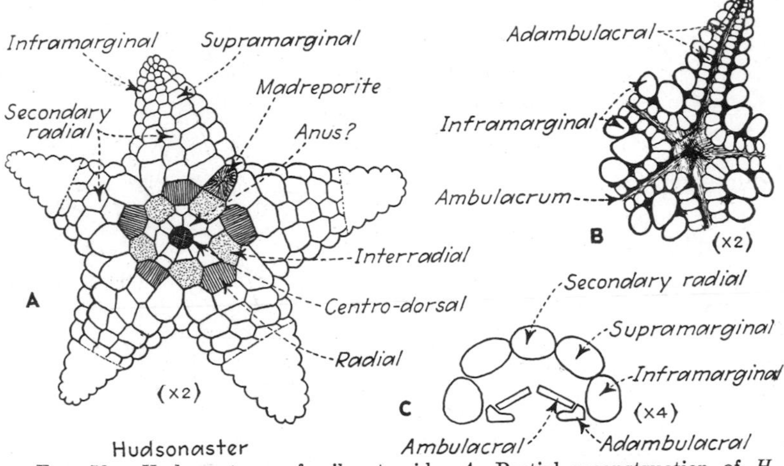

FIG. 59.—*Hudsonaster*, a fossil asteroid. *A*. Partial reconstruction of *H. incomptus*, from the Upper Ordovician (Richmond) of Ohio, showing the aboral surface. *B*. Oral view of *A*. *C*. Diagrammatic transverse section of the arm showing the different plates. (*Slightly modified after Schuchert.*)

grooves were very likely open. The radial vessels of the water-vascular system lay in grooves excavated in part from apposed ambulacral plates (Fig. 56 *B*). The Auluroidea are supposed to have branched from the parent stock of the Asteroidea in the Cambrian or early Ordovician. They range from the Ordovician to the Carboniferous and attained maximum development in the Silurian and Devonian.

Subclass Ophiuroidea

The Ophiuroidea (brittle stars) have a sharply defined central disk containing the digestive, genital, and other organs of the body and segmented, snakelike, flexible arms that radiate from the disk with radial symmetry (Fig. 60). There is no extension of the viscera into the arms. The genital organs lie in interambulacral positions near the stomach, whence the genital products are discharged at the bases of the arms through slitlike furrows or through pores in some fossil forms (Fig. 60 *C*). The mouth is situated in the center of the oral surface on the underside. There is no real anal opening.

The skeletal elements of the animal are incased in a leathery integument and muscular tissue. This integument is frequently

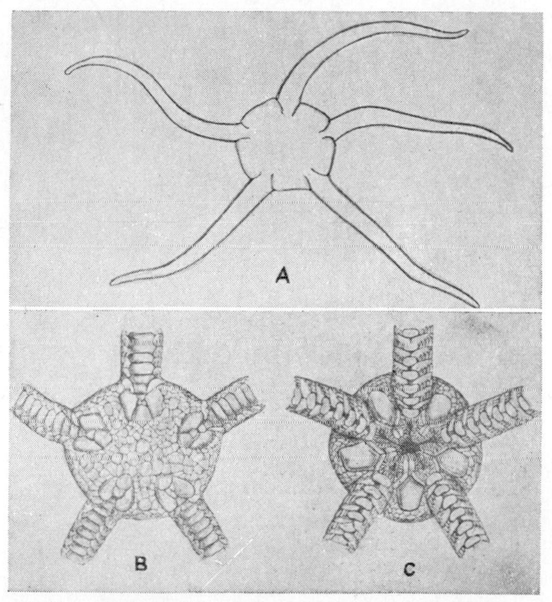

FIG. 60.—*Ophiuroidea. Ophioglypha lacertosa. A.* Outline of the entire individual (×¾). *B.* Aboral surface of the central disc (×1⅓). *C.* Oral surface showing the mouth and genital fissures (×1⅓). (*After Nicholson and Lydekker.*)

covered with small calcareous plates and may be spiny. A large central plate is present in some forms on the aboral surface, and there may be five pairs of plates (*radial shields*) at the places where the arms originate. About the mouth are five *mouth shields,* one of which functions as a madreporite. *Side mouth shields,* to which are attached tooth-bearing jaws, lie between the mouth and the mouth shields.

The arms are long, very flexible, and frequently branched, and the name of "serpent star" has arisen from the twisting, snakelike motions of the arms made by the animal as it wriggles and rows itself along the bottom. The skeletal structure of the arm consists of a single, median series of calcareous elements termed *vertebral ossicles.* Each ossicle originates from the fusion of four adjacent plates. The ossicles articulate with each other by means of domelike elevations on each side. Each series of vertebral ossicles is margined by four rows of thin plates, of which two rows are on the oral surface marginal to and on either side of the row of vertebral ossicles and two rows are on the aboral side (Fig. 56 *A*). There usually are no ambulacral furrows

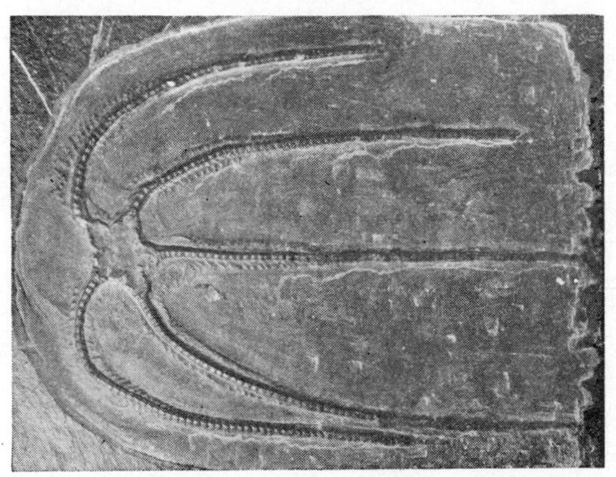

Fig. 61.—*Ophiura decheni,* a fossil ophiuroid ($\times \frac{1}{3}$) from the Lower Devonian of Germany showing the dorsal aspect of the central disk.

on the arms, but the lower sides of the ossicles are indented or grooved to receive the radial water vessel. Beneath the water vessel lie blood tubes and nerve cords. Small extensions of the radial water vessel pass through tubes in the lateral margins of the vertebral ossicles to the exterior to form tube feet. These are without terminal suction disks and have no locomotory function, although they do aid in respiration.

The Ophiuroidea appeared in the Devonian and supposedly descended from the Auluroidea. They do not seem to have become abundant before the Triassic. They are quite common in existing marine waters, in which they are known as sand stars, brittle stars, branching stars, and basket starfish. The *Challenger* Expedition dredged brittle stars by the hundredweight from the Atlantic. Fossil forms, however, are always rare and have little stratigraphic value. *Ophiura,* from the Devonian, is representative of fossil genera (Fig. 61), and *Ophioglypha* (Fig. 60) is a modern form.

mid term

CLASS ECHINOIDEA[1]

General Considerations.—The Echinoidea, variously known as sea urchins, heart urchins, sand dollars, sea chestnuts, and sea porcupines, are echinoderms possessing alimentary, reproductive, nerve, and water-vascular systems within an enclosing superficial, semiglobular, heart-shaped, or planoconvex-shaped test. This test, which in life is inclosed in a dermal integument, is composed of radial columns of calcareous plates which bear movable spines of various kinds. The pentamerous symmetry exhibited by both test and inclosed animal is superimposed on an original bilateral symmetry. The plane of the latter passes through the mouth and anus in such a way as to place the madreporite in the right anterior interambulacrum.

Echinoids differ from starfish in having no free arms. If the arms of the latter were bent upward and backward until the ends met at the dorsal pole and were then bound together by interambulacral areas, the general architecture of an echinoid would be produced (Fig. 46). Echinoids differ from most pelmatozoans in having no stem and no free arms, a reversed position with respect to the substratum. and interradial instead of radial reproductive organs.

The Animal.—The individual echinoid has the usual organs of an echinoderm, with a mouth on the under- or oral side, an anal opening on the top or aboral side or on the side opposite the mouth if the latter is not centrally located, and a digestive tract (esophagus, stomach, and ciliated intestine) connecting the two openings. The mouth is surrounded by a leathery skin known as the *peristome,* and the anus by a similar structure designated the *periproct.* On one side of the periproct, in the right anterior interambulacrum, is the madreporite through which water enters the stone canal on its way to a circular tube, the ring canal, surrounding the esophagus. The latter tube sends off five radial vessels—one along each of the ambulacral areas. Small saclike tubes, given off from these radial vessels on the inside of the test, extend through pores in the test wall to the surface to form tube

[1] Echinoidea—Gr. *echinus,* a hedgehog or sea urchin + *oid,* like; hence resembling either of the two animals just named.

feet (Fig. 62). Some of these are provided with suction disks and function as organs of locomotion, as in the Asteroidea, whereas others serve for respiratory purposes. There is a nerve ring around the esophagus with a nerve cord extending along each ambulacrum in a position beneath the circulatory tube. The genital organs hold an interradial position on the dorsal side, and the products are exuded through genital plates in the upper part of the test (Figs. 65, 67).

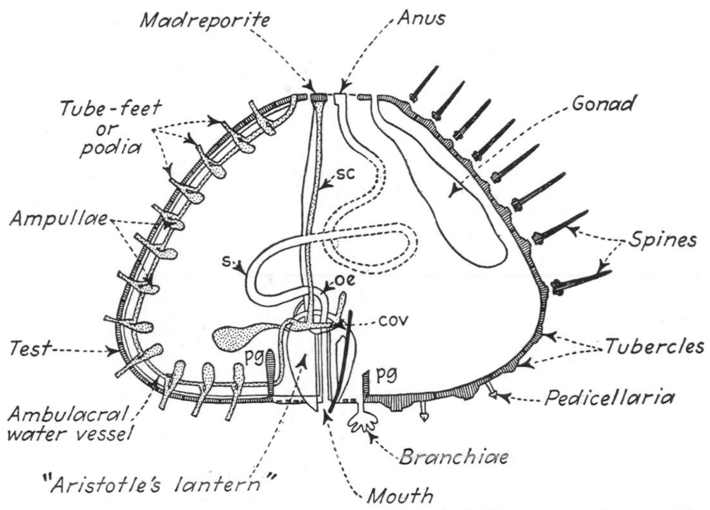

FIG. 62.—Diagrammatic transverse section of *Echinus*, a modern echinoid. *cov*, circumesophageal vessel of the water-vascular system; *oe*, esophagus; *pg*, perignathic girdle; *s*, stomach; *sc*, stone canal. (*Modified after Bather in Lankester's "A Treatise on Zoology."*)

The Test.—The test of an echinoid is a semiglobular or discoidal body made up of numerous calcareous plates firmly united by their edges to form a rigid boxlike structure. In certain forms some or all test plates may overlap in an imbricating fashion, with the result that the test is flexible instead of rigid. The complete test may be divided into four systems of plates—the corona, the peristome, the so-called oculogenital system, and the periproct. The *corona* constitutes the main part of the test and consists of five ambulacral or radial and five interambulacral or interradial areas. The *peristome*, which consists of a leathery integument studded with small calcareous plates, surrounds the mouth. The *oculogenital system* is composed of 10 plates, arranged in a single or double row around the periphery of the large aboral opening in the test. The plates of this system really form the top of the corona. Within the oculogenital ring is the *periproct,* a leathery integument, which like the peristome is studded with small calcareous plates, and which in addition is perforated by the anal opening. In some echinoids the periproct is situated outside the oculogenital ring.

THE CORONA.—The main part of the echinoid test, the corona, is a hollow, semiglobular or discoidal structure composed of numerous calcareous plates arranged in 10 meridional bands. Five of these, known as the ambulacral areas, alternate with five interambulacral areas. There are from 2 to 20 columns of plates in each of the former and from 1 to 14 in each of the latter. The plates of the ambulacral areas are perforated and have the same position as the internal radial vessels of the water-vascular system. Interambulacral plates are imperforate.

In all modern and nearly all Mesozoic echinoids (*Tetracidaris* excepted) there are two rows of plates in each of the coronal series, although some of the plates may be compound. In Paleozoic forms, however, the number of plates in the interambulacral series ranges from 1 in *Bothriocidaris* (Fig. 69) from the Ordovician to 14 in some species of *Hyattechinus* (Fig. 71 *B*) from the Mississippian and in the ambulacral series from 2 to 16 in *Lepidesthes* (Mississippian-Pennsylvanian) (Fig. 71 *A*).

The corona has two primary openings—the aboral, with the anus and its surrounding periproct and oculogenital systems of plates; and the oral, with the mouth and its peristome. The covering for both openings is leathery and is more or less studded with calcareous plates, with those on the peristome so arranged as to conform with the columns of the corona. If the mouth is at the oral pole and the anus diametrically opposite at the aboral pole, the corona is described as *endocyclic.* In those forms of echinoids in which the mouth and peristome have migrated forward to an anterior position and the anus and periproct backward to a posterior position, the corona is said to be *exocyclic* (Fig. 63).

The endocyclic types of tests characterize those echinoids that move in any direction with equal facility. In echinoids that develop a tendency to move in a single definite direction, the mouth migrates forward, the anus backward, the test develops a second bilateral symmetry coinciding with the original symmetry, and the corona becomes exocyclic.

The plates of the corona are provided with various types of spines and similar processes. The structures are movable and

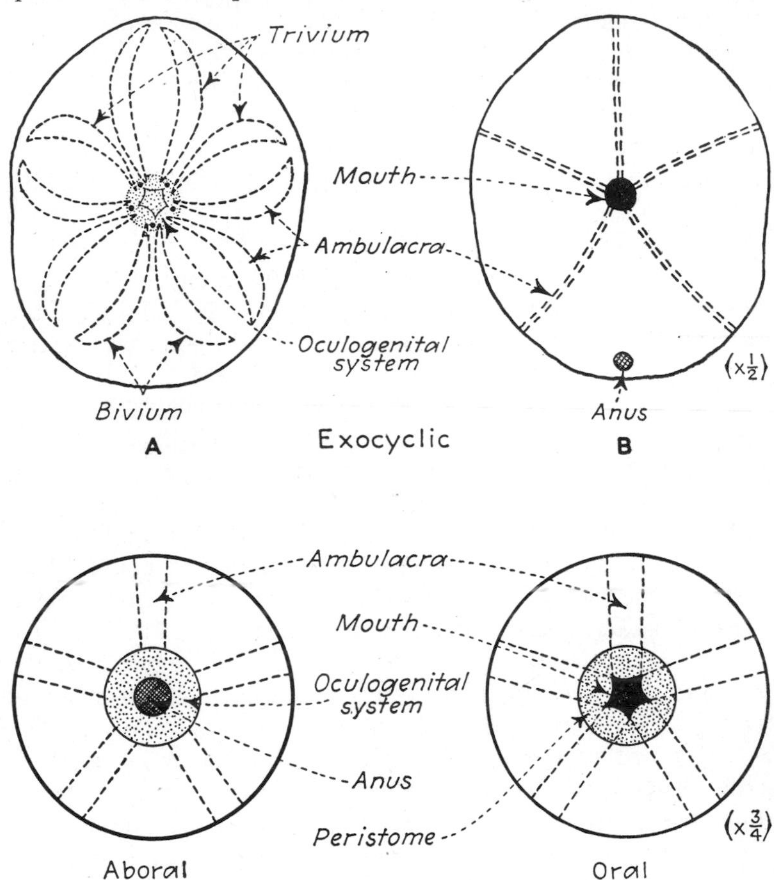

FIG. 63.—Simplified diagrams showing the aboral and oral aspects of an exocyclic (*A–B*) and endocyclic (*C–D*) echinoid. The former are based on *Clypeaster;* the latter, on *Cidaris.*

vary greatly in size, shape, and character (Fig. 64). Spines consist of a *shaft, base,* and *condyle* (*acetabulum*) (a socket fitting upon the tubercle of the test). Some of the spines are used for locomotion, and others serve for defense. *Fascioles* are narrow bands of close granular ornamentation which support short spines and *pedicellariae*. The latter consist of a stem on which is a head equipped with two or more pincer-like valves. They are scattered over the surface of the test. Some spines of the corona are quite long. A large urchin, 15 cm. (6 in.) in diameter, living in Florida waters, possesses spines 30 cm. (1 ft.) long.

The test of the echinoid increases in size through the addition of plates at the aboral termination of the ambulacral and interambulacral columns, the new plates being inserted below the oculars and genitals. Enlargement of the plates already present may also cause some increase in size of the test.

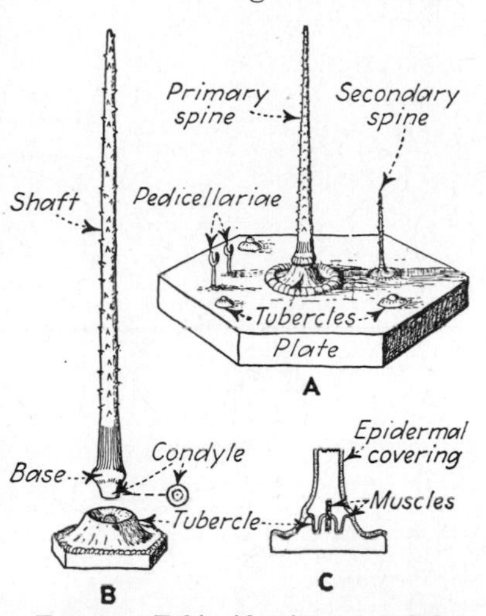

FIG. 64.—Echinoid spines. *A*. Schematic diagram to show a plate with primary and secondary spines and the pedicellariae. *B*. A primary spine elevated above the tubercle to show nature of articulation. *C*. Longitudinal section of basal portion of spine and of tubercle to show relation of soft parts to the articulating spine. (*Based in part on figures by Jackson.*)

AMBULACRA.—Ambulacra are usually continuous from the peristome to the periproct and resemble a band stretching from one pole to the other. In the irregular exocyclic echinoids, however, they may be confined altogether to the dorsal side of the test, and often they resemble the petals of a flower with the middle of each ambulacrum, known as the *ambitus*, much wider than either end. In the latter case the right and left posterior ambulacra may be shorter than the other three and are known as the bivium, whereas the other three constitute the trivium. The middle ambulacrum of the trivium is commonly longer than the other two (Fig. 63 *A*). The plane of symmetry bisects the bivium and intersects both mouth and anus.

Each ambulacrum and each interambulacral area have been given a particular number in a plan devised by Loven in which Roman numerals are used for the former and Arabic for the latter. In order to apply the system the test is placed in natural position with the ventral side down and is viewed from the position of the posterior interambulacrum. The first ambulacrum to the right is given the number I; and the succeeding interambulacrum, 1. Numbering then proceeds counterclockwise to the posterior interambulacrum, which is numbered 5 (Fig. 65). In using such a system the madreporite is in interambulacrum 2, and the anterior ambulacrum is numbered III.

Ambulacral pores are typically in pairs and are rarely unpaired. They tend to lie along the side of the plate nearest the adjacent interambulacrum, with the result that the two columns of

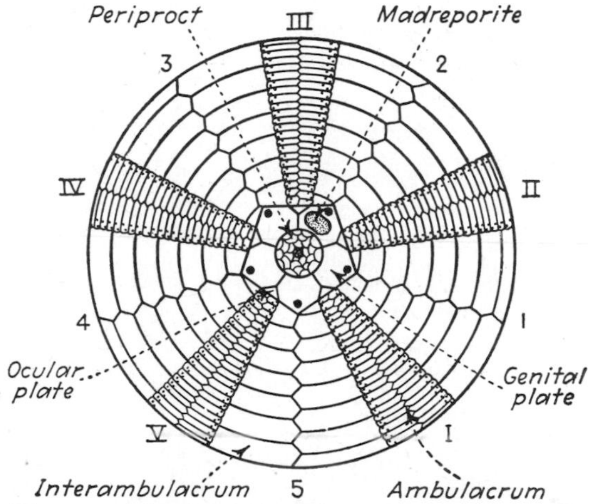

Fig. 65.—Diagram of the aboral view of an echinoid test showing the method of designating the ambulacra and interambulacra. The posterior interambulacrum is No. 5. The madreporite lies in interambulacrum 2.

ambulacral plates have a large nonporiferous area down the middle of the series. If the pairs of pores are situated one above the other in a single continuous series stretching from the peristome to the periproct, the arrangement is said to be *uniserial.* If there are two lines of pores on each side of the ambulacrum, the arrangement is *biserial;* and if more than two, *polyserial* (Fig. 66). A pore pair is sometimes surrounded by an elevated rim, known as a *peripodium,* and the pores of a pair may be united by a transverse furrow. Such pores are said to be *conjugate.*

The Apical System (Fig. 67).—Each ambulacrum terminates at the aboral extremity in a porous plate known as the *ocular,* because of the fact that it contains a light-sensitive organ. This plate has a single pore except in some Paleozoic forms in which there seem to be either two or none. Likewise, each interambulacrum terminates aborally in a *genital plate*, which is also provided with a pore. The plate in the right anterior interambulacrum is greatly perforated and serves as a madreporite. The openings in the genital plates communicate with the genital glands and permit the escape of the reproductive products. The

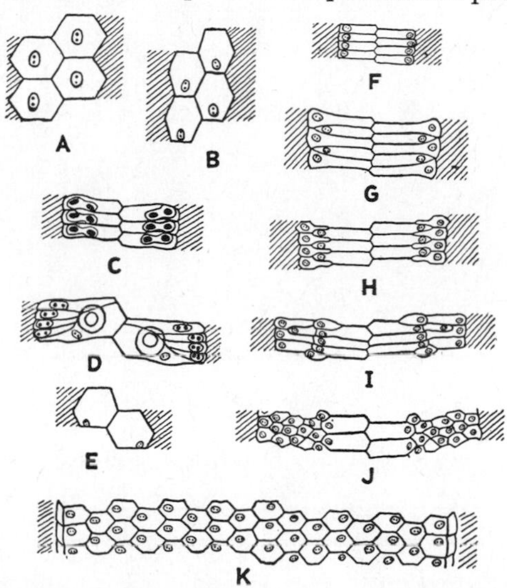

FIG. 66.—Character of the ambulacrum in representative echinoids. The lateral portions of the interambulacra are indicated by inclined lining. No plates of the interambulacra are shown.

A. Bothriocidaris archaica, Ordovician. *B. Goniocidaris caniculata*, Recent. *C. Eucidaris tribuloides*, Recent. *D. Strongylocentrotus dröbachiensis*, Recent. *E. Micraster cor-anguineum*, Cretaceous. *F. Palaeechinus elegans*, Lower Carboniferous. *G. Maccoya burlingtonensis*, Lower Carboniferous. *H. Lovenechinus missouriensis*, Lower Carboniferous. *I. Oligoporus danae*, Lower Carboniferous. *J. Melonechinus multiporus*, Lower Carboniferous. *K. Lepidesthes colletti*, Lower Carboniferous. (*Adapted from Jackson.*)

five oculars and five genitals together comprise the oculogenital system, which forms a ring about the periproct. If the 10 plates of the former constitute a single continuous ring—an arrangement characteristic of Paleozoic echinoids—the oculars are said to be *insert* (Fig. 67). If, however, the oculars are excluded from the genital ring, and the genital plates are in contact and also in contact with the periproct, the oculars are described as *exsert*. This is an arrangement characteristic of many Mesozoic forms. In rings composed of genital plates alone two or more of them may unite, and in one group of echinoids all of the five plates fuse to form a single pentagonal plate. The ocular and genital plates retain apical positions independent of the migration of the periproct and anus.

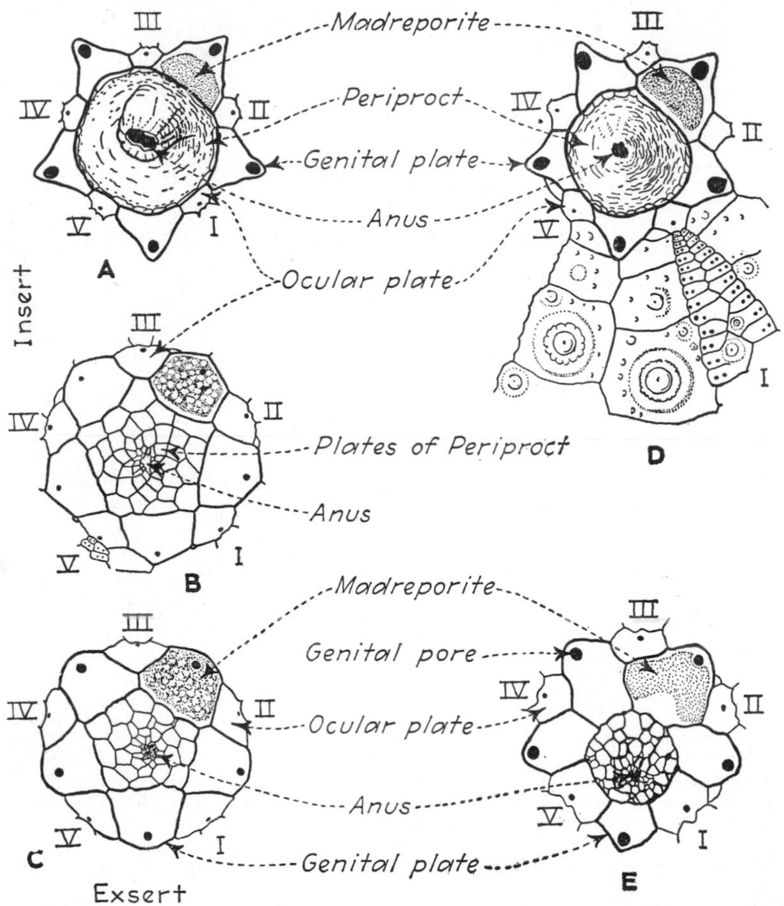

Fig. 67.—Apical systems of Echinoidea. *A. Centrechinus setosus* from Florida waters, with oculars insert. *B. Cidaris affinis*, a modern species, with all oculars insert and with periproctal plates. *C. Eucidaris tribuloides* from Jamaican waters, with all oculars exsert. *D. Centrechinus setosus* from West Indian waters, with oculars I, V, and IV insert. *E. Strongylocentrotus dröbachiensis*, from Massachusetts waters, with oculars I and V insert, the typical character of the species. (*All figures after Jackson.*)

The Periproct.—This structure, which always bears the anal opening, is within the oculogenital ring in the endocyclic echinoids and outside in the exocyclic forms. In the latter it is situated some distance posteriorly from the aboral pole in the median line of the posterior interambulacrum. It may be a simple leathery structure, or it may contain numerous calcareous plates. It is rarely preserved, but its position in the test is generally apparent and serves in systematic classification.

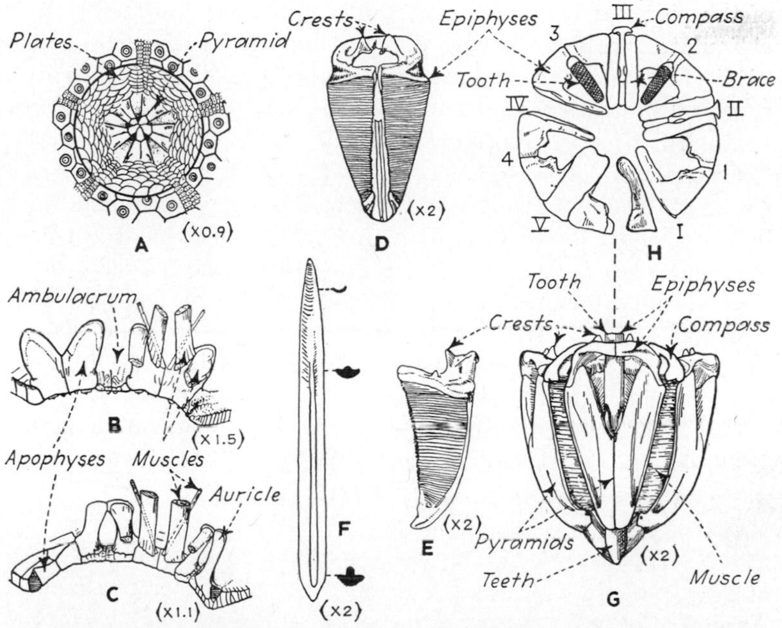

Fig. 68.—The Peristome. *A. Archaeocidaris wortheni* from the Mississippian (St. Louis) at St. Louis, Mo. The complete peristome and basal part of corona restored. *B. Eucidaris tribuloides* from Bahaman waters. Several elements of the perignathic girdle attached to basal part of corona. The muscles are shown attached to one set of elements. *C–H. Strongylocentrotus dröbachiensis* from Maine waters: *C*, same as *B* but somewhat more complex; *D*, pyramid of interradius 4 without the tooth; *E*, lateral view of *D*; *F*, tooth, flattened out, with sections at three points to show nature of cross section; *G*, complete lantern showing teeth in position in the pyramids; *H*, top of lantern to show structure. Teeth are in position in areas 2 and 3 only. Certain other structures are removed. (*All figures after Jackson.*)

The Peristome (Fig. 68 *A*).—The peristome is nearly always oral and central in position (endocyclic). It may be round, pentagonal, or decagonal in outline. In exocyclic echinoids, however, it migrates anteriorly with the mouth but remains on the oral side of the test. The peristome may be naked, or it may be covered by a variable number of plates. The character of the plates has systematic importance.

Many Echinoidea possess a unique mastigatory apparatus known as "Aristotle's lantern," because of its resemblance to an ancient Greek lantern (Fig. 68 *G*). This structure is composed of 40 calcareous pieces of which 5 are powerful teeth. The shapes of the pieces vary with different species, but in all cases certain of the pieces articulate with each other, and the entire structure articulates with a skeletal process, known as the *perignathic girdle*, that surrounds the mouth. By the action of many distinct muscles the teeth are moved back and forth and are capable of cutting many kinds of material (Fig. 68).

Ontogeny.—The early larval stages of the Echinoidea are similar to those of the known Stelleroidea but very unlike those of the Crinoidea. *Bothriocidaris* from the Ordovician has long been considered either the actual ancestor of the echinoids or at least near the ancestral stock. Recently, however, this venerable fossil has been referred to the Cystoidea by some workers. Other investigators take an intermediate stand, stating that it is an echinoid but that it left no descendants. The weight of fossil evidence seems to support Jackson's original classification with the Echinoidea and also the statement that *Bothriocidaris* represents an ancestral stock from which all echinoids evolved.[1]

Ecology.—Living echinoids are exclusively marine, and the group seems always to have been confined to that habitat. All depths from the shallowest waters to the abyss serve as homes. Typically gregarious, they often form immense assemblies on the bottom and function both as predators and as scavengers. Many species eat the bottom materials to obtain the contained organic matter. Some burrow in the mud; others prefer sandy or rocky bottoms; and on wave-beaten, rocky coasts many cut holes in extremely strong rocks in which they live protected from the waves. In quiet waters the same species do not cut holes; hence the tendency seems to be an adaptive one.

Stratigraphic Range.—There are about 2,500 described species of fossil echinoids as compared with about 500 known living forms. The earliest known echinoids are three species of *Bothriocidaris* from the Ordovician of Esthonia. Remains are rare in the Silurian and Devonian, but colonies of many individuals have been found in the Mississippian. A colony of the

[1] CLARK, H. L., The ancestry of the Echini, *Science*, vol. 76, pp. 591–593, 1932.

genus *Melonechinus*, found in the Mississippian at St. Louis, Mo., has furnished specimens to museums all over the world. Echinoid spines and isolated plates are abundant in the Pennsylvanian strata of the Mid-Continent region of the United States, but entire corona are rare. The class flourished in great numbers during the Mesozoic, but the distribution is more or less restricted to colonies in certain formations. In some strata of the Texas Comanchean the genus *Enalaster* can be collected by the hundreds.

TABLE 5.—CHART SHOWING CHIEF CHARACTERISTICS OF THE DIFFERENT ORDERS OF ECHINOIDEA
(Data from Jackson)

Order	Test	Rows of plates		Kinds of plates	Range
		Ambulacrum	Interambulacrum		
Bothriocidaroida	Regular and endocylic	2	1	Simple	Ordovician
Cidaroida	Regular and endocyclic	2	2–4	Simple	Mississippian-Recent
Centrechinoida	Regular and endocyclic	2	2	Compound	Triassic-Recent
Exocycloida	Irregular and exocyclic	2	2	Simple or compound	Jurassic-Recent
Plesiocidaroida	Regular and endocyclic	2	3	Simple	Triassic
Echinocystoida	Irregular and exocyclic	2–4	8–9	Simple	Silurian
Perischoechinoida	Regular and endocyclic	2–20	3–14	Simple	Silurian-Permian

Most fossil echinoids have a very limited vertical distribution and for that reason would be excellent index fossils were they more abundant and more widely distributed. From a practical point of view the fossil echinoids are of less stratigraphic importance in most formations than many other forms.

The earliest species of fossil echinoids had more or less than 20 meridional rows of plates, but the number 20 appears to have become established in the early Mesozoic and has been maintained to the present time. The irregular and exocyclic echinoids appeared during the middle Mesozoic and today are quite common.

Classification.—The following classification of the Echinoidea is that of Jackson and is based on the development and structure of the adult test. Use has been made of such structures as the corona with its ambulacra and interambulacra, the periproct, oculogenital system, peristome, Aristotle's lantern, perignathic girdle, and ornamental processes such as spines.

Table 5 on page 207 presents in synoptic form the chief differences readily observable in the fossils of the various orders.

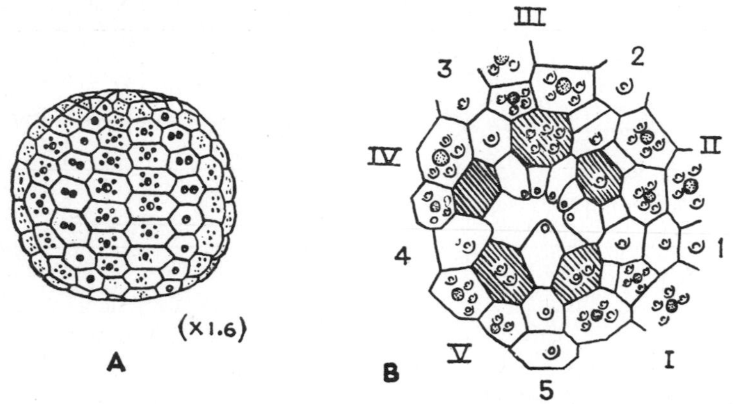

Fig. 69.—*Bothriocidaris globulus*, an ancient echinoid from the Ordovician of Russia. *A*. A complete specimen, with perforate tubercles on both ambulacral and interambulacral plates. *B*. Apical region enlarged to show nature and arrangement of plates. (*From Jackson after Schmidt.*)

ORDER BOTHRIOCIDAROIDA

Members of this order are regular echinoids with a globular test possessing two meridional rows of plates in each ambulacral area and one row in each interambulacrum. The oculogenital ring incloses the periproct. The order has the single genus *Bothriocidaris* (Fig. 69) to which reference has already been made. It is limited to the Ordovician of Esthonia.

ORDER CIDAROIDA

The Cidaroida have a regular, endocyclic test in which the periproct is inclosed by the oculogenital ring. The test has two columns of low, narrow ambulacral plates and two [*Tetracidaris* has four in the wider part of the interambulacrum] columns of pentagonal interambulacral plates. Each of the latter has a large, primary central tubercle and spine. There are also marginal tubercles and spines of secondary character. This order reached its maximum development in the Jurassic and Cretaceous, though it ranges from Mississippian to Recent. There are over 200 species of which the living *Cidaris* (Fig. 70 *E–F*) is a typical example.

ORDER CENTRECHINOIDA

Echinoids of this order have a regular, endocyclic test with two columns of compound plates (2 to 10 elements in each) in each ambulacrum and a like number of simple plates in each interambulacrum. Each part of a compound plate is provided with pore pairs. The peristome is complex, with lantern teeth and other associated structures. The test is covered with primary spines. The order ranges from the Triassic to Recent. There are 11 families and many species. *Strongylocentrotus* (Fig. 70 *C–D*) (Tertiary to Recent) is a representative genus of the order.

ORDER EXOCYCLOIDA

In this order the test is irregular and exocyclic, and the periproct lies outside the oculogenital ring in interambulacrum 5. There are two columns of plates in each of the coronal series, making a total of 20 meridional rows. The ambulacra are usually petaloid, with a bivium and trivium. Most species are bilaterally symmetrical, with the plane passing through the test along the axis, ambulacrum III to interambulacrum 5. There are 12 families in the order, which ranges from the Jurassic to the Recent. This order includes the so-called heart urchins. *Eupatagus*, from the Tertiary, is a representative genus (Fig. 70 *A–B*).

ORDER PLESIOCIDAROIDA

Members of this order have a regular endocyclic test with two columns of plates in each ambulacrum and three columns in each interambulacrum. The genital plates largely cover the aboral surface, and the oculars are exsert. Periproct and peristome are centrally situated, but their structures are unknown. The order is based on a single tiny specimen (*Tiarechinus*) from the Triassic of the Tirol.

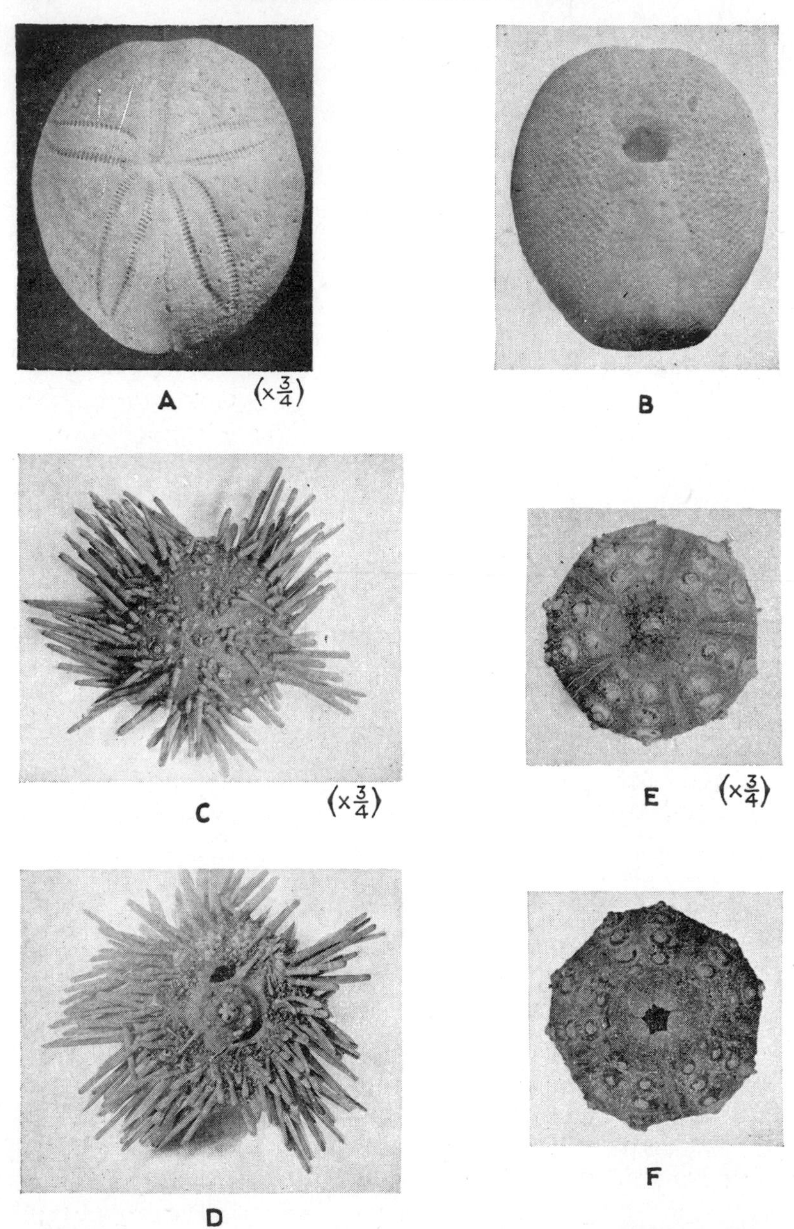

FIG. 70.—*Echinoidea.* *A–B.* Aboral and oral views of *Eupatagus floridanus* from the Tertiary of Florida. *C–D. Strongylocentrotus* sp., a modern echinoid common in Atlantic waters. *E–F. Cidaris tribuloides*, a modern endocyclic echinoid from Florida waters.

ORDER ECHINOCYSTOIDA

The Echinocystoida have small, irregular, apparently exocyclic spheroidal or flattened tests, with the periproct situated in an interambulacral area. There are two to four columns of low plates in each narrow ambulacral area and eight to nine columns of rather irregular, polygonal plates in each broad interambulacral area. There is a well-developed typical echinoid lantern, but nothing is known of either the periproct or the peristome. The order includes the two imperfectly known genera *Palaeodiscus* and *Echinocystites* from the Silurian of England.

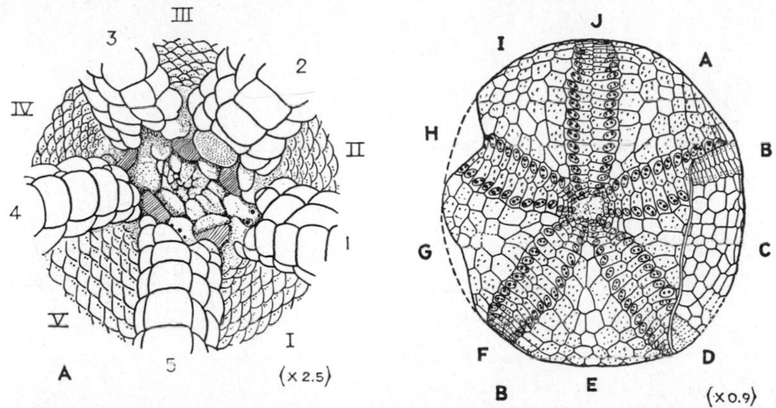

FIG. 71.—Fossil Echinoidea. *A*. *Lepidesthes colletti* from the Mississippian (Keokuk) of Indiana. Aboral view showing simple ambulacra and broad, low, and rounded genitals and oculars. Genital 2 is perforated with madreporic pores. *B*. *Hyattechinus rarispinus* from the Mississippian (Waverly) of Pennsylvania. External mold of ventral surface, and in areas *B*, *C*, and *D* an internal mold of dorsal side. Lettered instead of numbered because the orientation is uncertain. (*After Jackson.*)

ORDER PERISCHOECHINOIDA

This order includes regular Paleozoic echinoids in which the periproct lies inside the oculogenital ring. The ambulacral areas are narrow or wide, with from 2 to 20 columns of simple plates all bearing the single pore pair. There are from 3 to 14 columns of plates in each interambulacrum. Plates may imbricate, and the madreporite is usually not recognizable. The individuals of certain species are frequently large. The order is exclusively Paleozoic, ranging from the Silurian to the Permian. Genera typical of the order are *Archaeocidaris* (Fig. 68 *A*), *Hyattechinus* (Fig. 71 *B*), and *Melonechinus*.

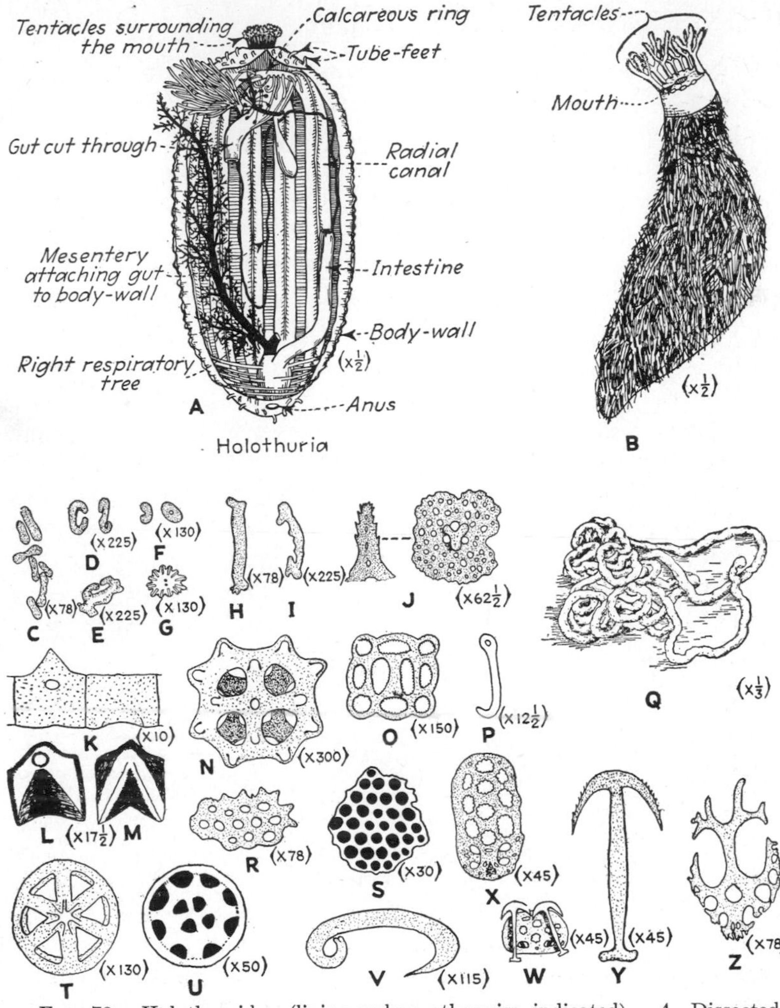

FIG. 72.—Holothuroidea (living unless otherwise indicated). *A*. Dissected holothurian (*Holothuria tubulosa*), viewed from the ventral surface. *B*. *Thyone briarcus* showing external appearance. *C–F*. Miliary granules of several genera. *G*. Rosette. *H–I*. Supporting rods from the tentacles. *J*. Table viewed from above and spine viewed from the side. *K–M*. Radial and interradial pieces of the calcareous ring. The former are perforated. *N*. Normal closed cup. *O*. Accessory perforated plate. *P*. Fossil hook from the Pennsylvanian of Texas. *Q*. Casting made by a living holothurian (*Leptosynapta*). *R*. Perforated plate from the skin. *S*. Perforated plate from the Pennsylvanian of Texas. *T*. Wheel. *U*. Fossil wheel from the Mississippian of Illinois. *V*. Sigmoid body. *W–Z*. Anchors and anchor plates. (*A after Thomson; C–O, L–P, R, T, and V–Z after H. L. Clark et al.; P, U, and S after Croneis and McCormack; Q after C. L. Fenton*)

Class Holothuroidea[1]

The Holothuroidea (sea cucumbers) are elongated, wormlike creatures closely resembling a cucumber, whence the popular name. They range in length from less than 25 mm. (1 in.) to nearly 1 m. Superficially they bear little resemblance to typical echinoderms, but they do possess the fundamental structures characteristic of the phylum.

The wormlike body of the holothurian has a mouth at one end, an anal opening at the opposite extremity, and a looped digestive tract connecting the two openings. The mouth is surrounded by a circlet of 8 to 30 tentacles (Fig. 72 *A–B*).

Modern holothurians, represented by some 750 species, constitute a sharply defined group of marine organisms. They belong to the vagrant benthos and occur abundantly in tropical waters and also in temperate and polar waters, though not in such great abundance. The depth range is from tide level to over 4,500 m. (15,000 ft.). Locomotion is by means of podia or by wormlike extensions and contractions of the body. The food consists of mud and sand that is swallowed in large quantities for the contained organic matter. Excretion is effected by powerful muscles which enable the animal to change its form radically and even to cause the body to be turned inside out. The excrement of the living holothurians emerges in the form of solid threads, 2 to 5 mm. in diameter; and if the animal is irritated, excretion may take place with such violence that the excretal material may be thrown from the animal as much as 7 cm. The first discharge is in the form of an irregular pile, but in the closing stages loosely looped coils are formed (Fig. 72 *Q*). Some of these bear resemblance to the fossil *Lumbricaria*, interpreted as a worm casting. The authors consider it very probable that many fossil wormlike markings may have been formed by holothurians.[2]

[1] Holothuroidea—L. *holothuria*, pl., a sort of water polyp, from Gr. *holothourion*, + *oid*, like; referring to the polyp-like appearance of many species of this group of animals.

[2] The worm-casting interpretation of *Lumbricaria* has been questioned recently by C. L. and M. A. Fenton (Lumbricaria; a holothuroid casting? *Pan-Amer. Geol.*, vol. 61, pp. 291–292, 1934), who observed a burrowing holothurian (*Leptosynapta inhaerens*) make castings of a similar character. In a typical specimen of *Lumbricaria* the animal which formed it must have moved in and out through the ropy excretal matter, whereas the castings

The body of the holothurian is incased in a tough leathery integument that may be prickly like the surface of some cucumbers. There is no true exoskeleton as in all other echinoderms, but there are scattered through the body a number of small calcareous spicular elements which rarely unite to form a very delicate skeletal structure. These elements range to several millimeters in diameter, exhibit a great diversity in character, and are given various names (Fig. 72 *C–P*, *R–Z*).

The simplest of the elements are tiny, irregular grains designated *miliary granules.* Small curved or straight spicular bodies, found in the tentacles and other parts of the body, are known as *supporting rods.* Certain irregularly branched particles occurring in the body wall are described as *rosettes,* and, if they are in the form of a perforated disk, the term *plate* is employed. A plate having a definite projection rising from its mid-point is described as a *table.* A table consists of a *basal disk* and a projecting *spire.* Other particles assume the shapes of hooks, wheels, anchors, cups, etc., and are named after the object which they resemble. All of the elements so far described lie in the body wall, tentacles, or tube feet of the animal.

In certain holothurians additional plates occur around the anal opening and the esophagus. The five calcareous plates surrounding the anus are known as the *anal teeth.* In most holothurians the esophagus is surrounded by a ring of 10 plates referred to as the *calcareous* or *dental ring.* Five of these are known as *radials,* since to them are attached the radial muscles, and the other five, alternating with the radials, as *interradials.*

The Fossil Record.—Holothurians may leave three different types of fossil record—(1) mud fillings or impressions of a part or all of the body; (2) calcareous skeletal elements of great diversity in shape and structure; and (3) castings similar to some worm castings. Fossils of the first type will by their very nature be extremely rare. Some such objects have been referred to the Holothuroidea, but at present there is no consensus of opinion as to the accuracy of identification. Chief among these are the Cambrian *Eldonia* and the Jurassic *Pseudocaudina.* The

---

illustrated by the Fentons appear to have been formed during a single stage of rapid discharge (Fig. 72 *Q*). For this reason the present authors do not subscribe to the suggestion made by the Fentons.

scattered skeletal elements of the second type may be expected in marine deposits and are being recognized and used by micropaleontologists. Holothurian excrementa will always be questionable because of the great similarity to worm castings. On the whole, holothurian remains are of little importance to the average paleontologist, but micropaleontologists may find them useful.

It seems altogether probable that the Holothuroidea were evolved early in the Cambrian from some echinoid ancestor, and hence spicules may be expected from all subsequent strata. Because of resemblance to skeletal structures in many other organisms, however, identification as holothuroidian remains may be difficult.

PHYLOGENY OF THE ECHINODERMA

The fertilized egg of an echinoderm hatches into a ciliated, free-swimming, bilaterally symmetrical embryo, which has a mouth at one end and on the underside and an anal opening at the opposite end. A straight intestinal tube connects the two openings. This embryo bears considerable resemblance to certain annelid embryos, and by most zoologists the echinoderms are postulated to have descended from some wormlike ancestor, which may in turn have been evolved from a simple bilaterally symmetrical animal. The hypothetical ancestor is supposed to have given rise to the various types of echinoderms late in the Pre-Cambrian or early in the Cambrian, for the first true echinoderms appear in the latter period.

This hypothetical ancestral form, which has been named *Dipleurula* (Fig. 73), has never been found, but certain very early and primitive cystoids bear close resemblance to it. A very primitive group of extinct animals, included in the *Machaeridia* and usually considered as Cirrepedia, are thought by Bather[1] to be possibly very early, perhaps aberrant, echinoderms; and another group, the *Carpoidea*, are sometimes placed as a class under Echinoderma, though most authors still include it as a subdivision of the Cystoidea.

Two distinct echinoderm lines are thought to have developed from the hypothetical *Dipleurula* (Fig. 74). One line, composed of free-living forms, constitutes the stelleroids, echinoids, and

[1] BATHER, F. A., "Encyclopedia Britannica," 14th ed., p. 904, 1929.

holothuroids. The other is made up of those forms which fastened themselves to the bottom and became cystoids, blastoids, and crinoids. The primitive Ordovician cystoid *Aristocystites* seems very close to the hypothetical *Dipleurula*, differing only in having a globular, platy test. The crinoids are thought to have

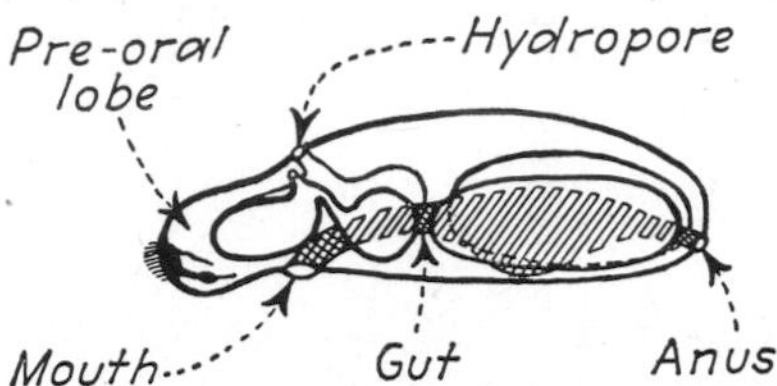

FIG. 73 *A*.—Diagrammatic reconstruction of the hypothetical ancestral *Dipleurula*, with the anterior end (to the left) provided with sensory cilia, a straight alimentary tract, and a well-developed water system. (*After Bather in Lankester's "A Treatise on Zoology"; reproduced by permission of A. & C. Black, Ltd.*)

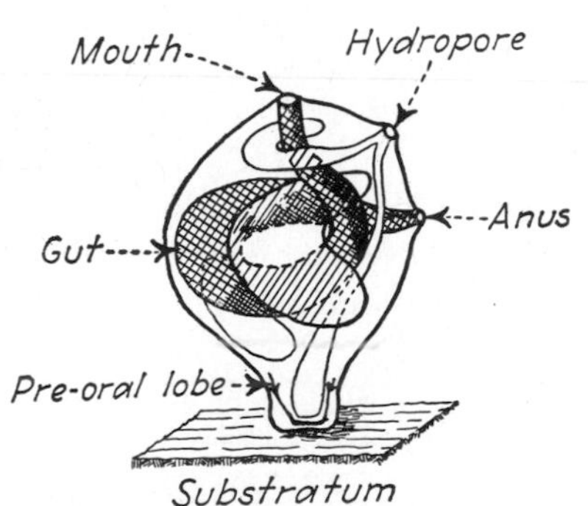

FIG. 73 *B*.—Diagrammatic reconstruction of the supposed primitive ancestor of the Pelmatozoa. With attachment the alimentary tract has become looped with the mouth on the upper surface and the anal opening on the posterior side. The hydropore occupies a position intermediate between the mouth and anus. The preoral lobe has been modified for attachment. *Aristocystites* (Fig. 48) is thought to have represented about this stage of development. (*After Bather in Lankester's "A Treatise on Zoology"; reproduced by permission of A. & C. Black, Ltd.*)

developed from cystoidean ancestors. The cystoids did not survive the Paleozoic, but during their evolution they developed from primitive, irregular, bilaterally symmetrical animals to regular, radially symmetrical forms. This trend is thought to have been due to the fact that they were attached to the bottom. The blastoids, with limited area for food collecting, had a relatively short geologic history but quickly developed perfect radial symmetry. The crinoids, with large food-gathering apparatus in the arms, were the most successful of the sessile echinoderms and have continued, though in diminishing numbers, to the present time.

The free-living forms, with the exception of the exocyclic echinoids, have almost perfect radial symmetry superimposed on

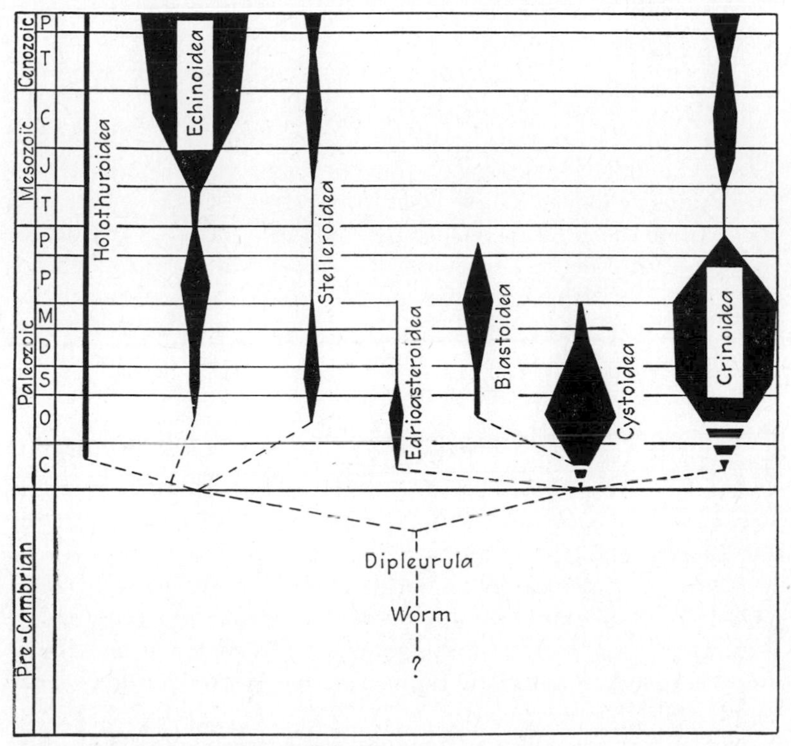

FIG. 74.—The apparent geologic history of the Echinoderma, based on the number of fossil genera. The width of the band indicates approximate abundance. (*Adapted from data by Swinnerton.*)

the original bilateral symmetry. The sea cucumbers appear to be a mature group and are supposed to have been evolved from some echinoid ancestor early in the Cambrian.

ECHINODERMA AS GEOLOGIC AGENTS

Among the echinoderms only the crinoids and echinoids appear to have been important as rock builders during past geologic ages. In cases where these organisms have been instrumental in building up deposits on the ocean bottom, such bodies of rock are almost certain to be local because of the gregarious habit of the animals which built them. The Mississippian bioherms of southern Indiana, composed to a large extent of coarsely crystalline, crinoidal limestone, largely in the form of a crinoidal coquina, illustrate this type of deposit.

Crinoidal remains are almost invariably associated with Paleozoic reef deposits, especially in the interreef stratified rock. Such crinoidal limestones have been reported from the Niagaran of New York, Indiana, and Wisconsin, from the Silurian of the island of Anticosti, and from the Niagaran of Gotland. Some investigators have suggested that these extensive crinoidal deposits have been formed from sessile species torn loose from the bottom during severe storms or from free-living species which drifted into quiet, shallow water to die because of the lack of oxygen. It seems possible, also, that during the time that the main organic reef was being constructed many species during early growth stages were attached to the bottom either on the main reef mound or closely adjacent to it in shallow water and that upon attaining maturity some of these may have abandoned the stems, which are the remains most often found in the vicinity of ancient reefs, and floated away as free-moving organisms to meet death and to undergo burial far from the places of origin.

In the lower Pennsylvanian (Upper Rundle) of Alberta a 60-m. (200-ft.) unit of limestone is almost entirely composed of separated crinoid columnals. Similar rock, of much less thickness, is found in southern Indiana in the Harrodsburg (Mississippian) limestone.

Cystoids are not of common enough occurrence to be of great importance as rock builders, and the same is true of the blastoids. The stelleroids have little in the way of structures for building of rocks, and the skeletal elements of the holothurians would not contribute a great deal.

Certain echinoderms are of great geologic importance because of predatory and scavenging activities. Predatory habits determine to a large extent where certain forms exist, and scavenging is an important contribution to the sanitation of the ocean bottom. In addition to the activities just mentioned, some echinoderms pass great quantities of bottom materials through their digestive tracts for the purpose of extracting the contained organic matter. Passage through a digestive tract must have important chemical and physical effects on these materials, and repeated passages may cause particles to be reduced to a fine state of division.

References

BASSLER, R. S.: The classification of the Edrioasteroidea, *Smith. Misc. Coll.*, vol. 93, No. 8, pp. 1–11, 1 pl., 1935.

BATHER, F. A.: "The Echinoderma," pt. III, A treatise on zoology. Ed. by E. Ray Lancaster, A. & C. Black, Ltd., London, 1900.

———: Studies in Edrioasteroidea. *Geol. Mag.*, 1898, 1900, 1908, 1914, 1915.

CLARK, A. H.: A monograph of the existing crinoids. *U. S. Nat. Mus., Bull.* 82, vols. 1–3, 1921.

———: Cambrian holothurians. *Am. Nat.*, vol. 47, pp. 488–507, 1913.

CLARK, W. B.: The Mesozoic Echinodermata of the United States. *U. S. Geol. Surv., Bull.* 97, 207 pp., 1893.

——— and TWITCHELL, M. W.: The Mesozoic and Cenozoic Echinodermata of the United States. *U. S. Geol. Surv., Mon.* 54, 341 pp., 1915.

CRONEIS, C., and MCCORMACK, J.: Fossil Holothuroidea, *Jour. Paleontology*, vol. 6, pp. 111–148, 1932.

JACKSON, R. T.: Phylogeny of the Echini, with a revision of the Paleozoic species, *Boston Soc. Nat. Hist., Mem.* 7, 491 pp., 1907.

SCHUCHERT, C.: Revision of the Paleozoic Stelleroidea with special reference to North American Asteroidea, *U. S. Nat. Mus., Bull.* 88, 301 pp., 1915.

SPRINGER, F.: The Crinoidea Flexibilia, *Smith. Inst.*, 2 vols., 1920.

WACHSMUTH, C., and SPRINGER, F.: The North American Crinoidea Camerata, *Mus. Comp. Zool., Mems.* 20–21, 837 pp., 1897.

WALCOTT, C. D.: Middle Cambrian holothurians and medusae, *Smith. Misc. Coll.*, vol. 62, No. 3, 1911.

WOOD, E.: A critical summary of Troost's manuscript on the crinoids of Tennessee, *U. S. Nat. Mus., Bull.* 64, 150 pp., 1909.

CHAPTER VII

BRYOZOA[1]

INTRODUCTION

Living bryozoans build tuftlike colonies which bear close resemblance to moss, whence the name "moss animals" sometimes used for the phylum. Collections of "seaweeds" made by amateurs almost invariably contain specimens of bryozoans; in fact, some of the latter make better seaweeds, so far as appearance is concerned, than the plants themselves. Because of this resemblance to plants, early students of the bryozoans referred to them as "zoophytes" (animal-like plants), and even after the true animal character was demonstrated and they had been removed from the plant classification, the descriptive designation moss animals still persisted and, for that matter, is still commonly used.

As early as 1830 Thompson in Ireland demonstrated that each individual bryozoan possesses an alimentary tract, with a mouth, stomach, and anus, and hence showed clearly that the organism must be an animal. Ehrenberg in Germany a year later corroborated the findings of Thompson. Having demonstrated the animal nature of the group, the two workers found that it could not be assigned to any known phylum. Thompson proposed the name *Polyzoa*, calling attention to the many individuals in a colony, a character which, however, is equally applicable to divisions of other phyla. Ehrenberg used the name *Bryozoa*, which calls attention to the resemblance of the colonies to moss. Subsequently, a controversy arose over which name should be used. Thompson's name clearly has priority and is used by English paleontologists. Continental Europeans and Americans, however, have preferred Ehrenberg's.

Individual bryozoans are generally microscopic organisms, are always aquatic and colonial, are usually marine, and con-

[1] Bryozoa—Gr. *bryon*, moss + *zoon*, animal—"moss animal"; referring to the resemblance of a bryozoan colony to a tuft of moss.

struct bushy colonies of membranous, chitinous or calcareous matter. They occur in great abundance in present marine waters in all latitudes, and the fossil record indicates extensive development and wide distribution in past geologic ages. Study of the Bryozoa necessitates much microscopic investigation, and, in the case of the forms which have complex calcareous skeletal structures, thin sections must be prepared. In these studies minute structural details are of paramount importance, and the reports setting forth the results of the investigations are couched in such technical language that the average paleontologist either sends his bryozoan material to a specialist or leaves it unidentified. A popular belief has developed that a lifetime of research is the essential qualification for identification of bryozoans. Recently, one of America's leading students has prepared a very helpful manual on the Bryozoa and has gained the grateful thanks of amateur and professional paleontologists who collect the fossil bryozoans so common in many Paleozoic, Mesozoic, and Cenozoic strata.[1]

The skeletal structures of many bryozoans resemble tabulate corals, and in early studies attempts were made to associate them with the coralline Coelenterata. Hence they often have been referred to as "corallines," and one of the Tertiary formations of England, the "Coralline Crag," is named not from the common presence of corals but from the abundance of Bryozoa. For many years one large group of bryozoans, the *Monticuliporoids*, was included in the Tabulata, a division of the Anthozoa. The total absence of septa, the different method of development, and certain other features made necessary the removal of the group from the Coelenterata and inclusion in the Bryozoa.

Bryozoa are abundant today in all seas and in all latitudes, and a few forms also occur in fresh waters. They appear to live mainly in clear, shallow to deep waters which are provided with adequate circulation. On the bottoms of such waters they are found dwelling upon seaweeds or cemented to shells, rocks, and other foreign objects. They seem to grow very rapidly.

Judging from the fossil record, bryozoans appear to have been abundant during geologic time since the first appearance in the Lower Ordovician. Over 1,500 species have been described

[1] Bassler, R. S., The Bryozoa, or moss animals, *Smith. Inst., Ann. Rept. for* 1920, pp. 339–380, 4 pls. and numerous text figures, 1922.

from Paleozoic strata, over 1,000 species from the Mesozoic, and an additional 2,000 living and Cenozoic species are known.

In recent years the application of micropaleontology to economic geology, particularly petroleum geology, has given

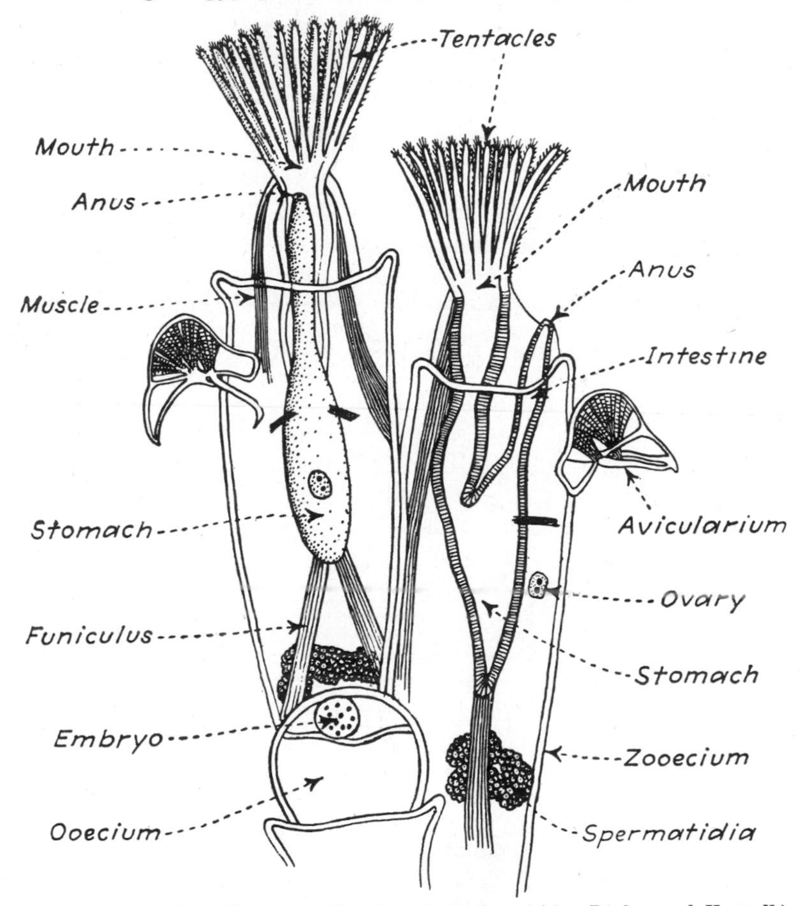

Fig. 75.—A modern bryozoan, *Bugula avicularia.* (*After Parker and Haswell.*)

great impetus to the study of bryozoans. Small fragments of the colonies are frequently recovered from well cuttings and may be identified readily. Since the geologic ranges of bryozoans are generally short and the geographical distribution is commonly extensive, Bryozoa are among the most valuable of microfossils or, for that matter, of any fossils, and it is unfortunate that so few paleontologists are trained to use them.

THE ANIMAL

The individual bryozoan or *zooid* consists of a double-walled membranous, chitinous or calcareous sac or tube, the *zooecium* (animal house), in which the fleshy part of the animal, the *polypide*, is housed. The polypide is composed of the body wall; a U-shaped alimentary tract, consisting of an esophagus, stomach, and intestine, so suspended that the mouth and anus are close together on the upper surface of the animal; and the other struc-

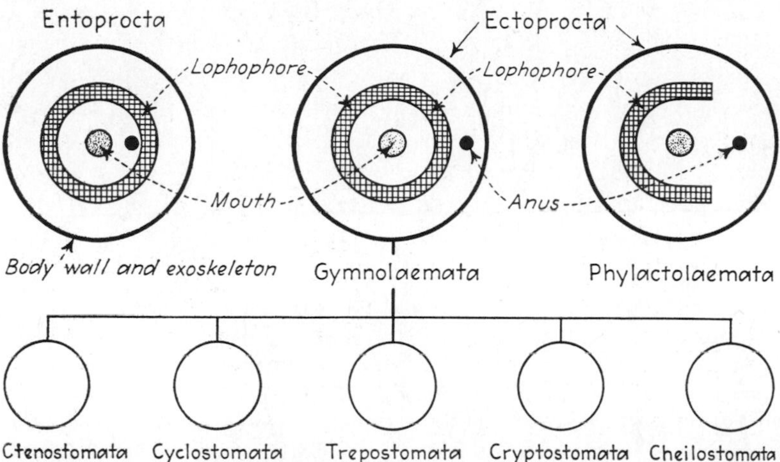

FIG. 76.—Schematic diagram illustrating the essential differences between the major subdivisions of the Bryozoa. The position of the anus and nature of the lophophore are the important differentiating characters.

tures of the fleshy body (Fig. 75). The largest polypides do not exceed 3 mm. in length and 1 mm. in width.

The mouth is surrounded by the *lophophore*, a circular or horseshoe-shaped ridge surmounted by slender, hollow *tentacles* with ciliated surfaces. These tentacles sweep food toward the mouth and also serve for respiratory purposes. The anal opening may lie within the lophophore, as in the *Entoprocta*, but more commonly lies without, as in the *Ectoprocta* (Fig. 76). The zooecium, when membranous, is somewhat flexible, and the upper part may be invaginated so that the lophophore and U-shaped alimentary tract are pulled downward into the sac by the action of certain transverse and longitudinal muscles attached near the mouth and at the base of the lophophore.

The muscles traverse the so-called "visceral cavity," which is a true body cavity filled with fluid (Fig. 75).

Reproduction among the Bryozoa is either sexual or asexual (budding), and the reproductive organs of each sex may occur singly in different individuals or together in the same individual. They are developed in various parts of the body cavity. The ova are fertilized within the animal. Asexual reproduction is usually initiated by a sexually produced individual. In most cases the newly formed buds remain connected and join to build a colony which is limited in size only by the period of time that it is inhabited by polypides. Rarely a bud detaches itself and starts a new colony. In some species a peculiar form of rejuvenation takes place through disintegration of existing structures in a zooid so that they become compacted with the body wall into a round mass known as the *brown body*. A new polypide then develops on the body wall to take the place of the old.

The fertilized ova develop into free-swimming larvae which are structurally similar to a trochophore (Fig. 77). There are a ciliated *apical plate* on the upper side, a mouth and anus on the underside, and a single band of cilia around the periphery of the greatest circumference. A larva, after a short free-swimming period, attaches itself by the oral surface to some foreign object on the bottom and secretes a covering known as the *protoecium* (first house). In some cases it has a primitive bivalved shell during the free-swimming period, but this changes to the protoecium. The internal organs then break down, and a new polypide, the first of the colony, forms. This secretes about itself and around the opening into the protoecium a tubular zooecium, the first of the colony, designated the *ancestrula*. By repeated budding from the ancestrula at first, and from preexisting polypides later, a great variety of colonial structures are formed (Fig. 78). In the early developmental stages bryozoans and brachiopods have a trochophore stage, and in maturity both have lophophores, but there much of the similarity ends, because the skeletal structures are very different.

THE SKELETON

The skeletal structure of the bryozoan is in the form of an external supporting and protecting box or tube, the zooecium. The material is membranous, gelatinous, chitinous, or calcareous.

Of the four materials, chitin may be preserved in an altered form, but only the calcareous substance is readily preserved. Zooecia rarely exceed a millimeter in diameter but may reach many millimeters in length. The skeletal structure produced by the

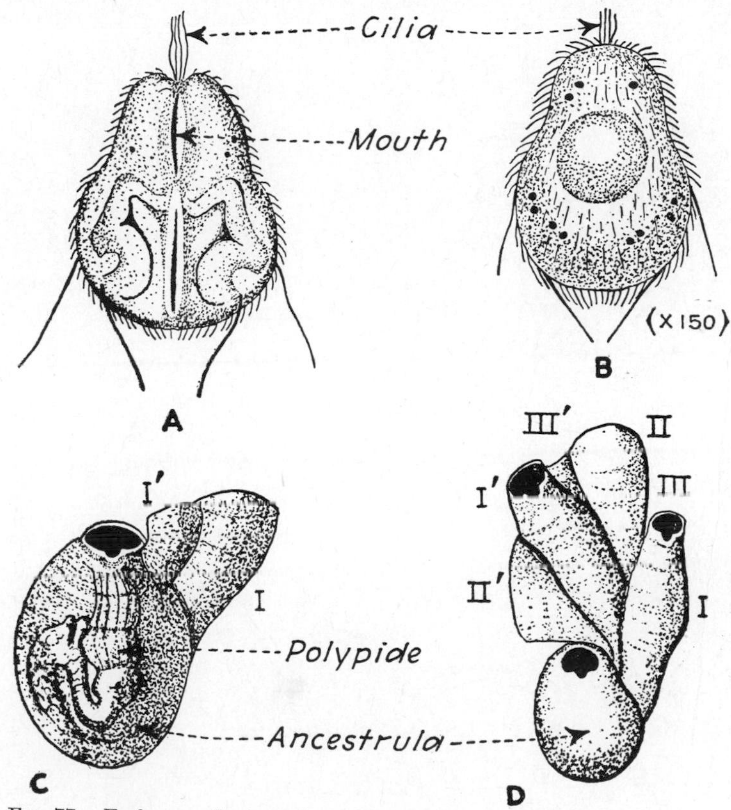

FIG. 77.—Early growth stages in *Mollia granifera*, a modern bryozoan. *A–B*. Oral and aboral faces of a free embryo. *C*. A very early growth stage of the zoarium showing the ancestrula and the two primary buds, one larger than the other. *D*. A somewhat later stage showing three generations of buds. (*From Simpson*.)

union of several zooecia forms a *zoarium*. Zoaria are usually small but may attain dimensions as great as 50 cm. (2 ft.) in greatest diameter.

Zooecia may be conical, urn shaped, cylindrical, or prismatic; and they may be circular, oval, or polygonal in cross section. The opening, generally referred to as the *aperture* or *orifice*, is in some forms as large as the zooecium; in others it is smaller and modified in various ways. It is situated either on the upper

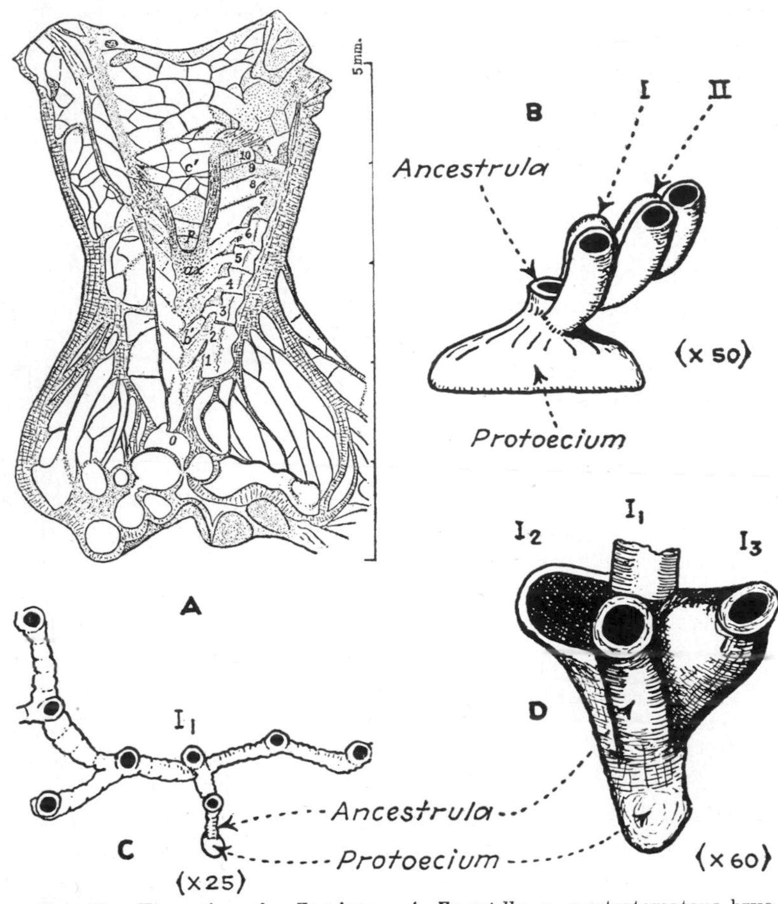

FIG. 78.—Formation of a Zoarium. *A. Fenestella*, a cryptostomatous bryozoan. Section of base of zoarium cutting exactly in the plane of the axis and of the zooecial apertures to the right (1–10). The protoecium is at *o*; the thickening of the axis (*ax*) begins at *b′*; the apex of the cone of expansion of the colony is at *p*; the vesicular tissue (*c′*) above *p* is of secondary origin, forming during the mature and senile life of the colony. *B.* Earliest growth stages of a zoarium of *Fenestella*. *C.* Early growth stage of a cyclostomatous bryozoan, *Stomatopora parvipora*. *D.* Early growth stage of a cheilostomatous bryozoan, *Retepora phoenicea*, from St. Vincent's Gulf, Australia. (*A after Cumings; B based on figures by Cumings; C based on Bassler; D after Cumings.*)

or anterior end of the zooecium or near that end and is either open or closed by a lid known as the *operculum* (Fig. 86). The zooecia may remain unattached except at the points of origin, or they may be compactly cemented together. In the *Ceramoporidae* they are cemented together by vesicular tissue, whereas in many trepostomatous forms, long, prismatic zooecia are attached to each other by the angular edges, leaving small prismatic *mesopores* between. In some species these mesopores are very numerous and may be so concentrated as to give ornamentation to the zoarial surface. In many of the *Fenestellidae* the zooecia-bearing longitudinal bars are connected by transverse bars of vesicular material, termed *dissepiments,* and a lattice-like framework is formed.

In two orders of Bryozoa the zooecia are divided into regularly shaped compartments by complete transverse partitions known as *diaphragms* (*tabulae* in England). Similar structures occur in the mesopores of some species. The diaphragms may extend directly across the zooecium, making a right angle with the walls, or they may be inclined. They closely resemble the tabulae of the tabulate corals and are thought to represent successive growth stages either of a single individual or of a series of polypides. The former seems more probable. In some trepostomatous bryozoans there are incomplete curved transverse partitions which divide the zooecial tube into irregularly shaped compartments. These are known as *cystiphragms.* If the zooecium is cut transversely, these partitions appear as circular or lunate structures within the zooecial wall.

Many Bryozoa have special structures that are devoted to incubation or protection of the eggs. These are generally known as *ovicells* or *ooecia* (Fig. 86). Some authors hold that the compartments produced by the cystiphragms may have served such a purpose. The *marsupium* is a special receptacle for ova attached directly to a zooecium. The surface of the zoarium is sometimes inflated into *gonocysts. Gonoecia* (*gonoecium*) are special zooecia modified for reproductive purposes.

Zooecia of some bryozoans possess peculiar appendicular organs of uncertain function (Fig. 79). One of these organs, the *avicularium,* resembles the head of a bird, and in life the jaws or beak parts are constantly opening and closing with a snapping motion, seizing and rigidly holding small organisms which come too close. *Vibracula* are bristle-like appendages which in life are more or less constantly in motion. It has been suggested that avicularia may perform a protective function because of the snapping motion of the jaws. Both avicularia and vibracula may function in feeding, in alimentation, or in oxygenation, but as yet there seems to be no consensus of opinion as to what functions they actually perform. Neither of the appendages is likely to be fossilized, but the place of attachment on the zooecium is usually marked by a small depression or a blunt spine, either or both of which might be preserved. It has been suggested that the small tubular spines, known as *acanthopores*, common on many trepostomatous bryozoans, may have been places of attachment for structures similar to avicularia

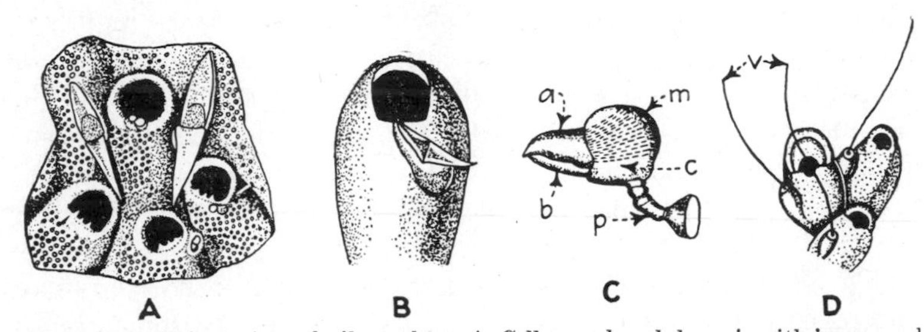

FIG. 79.—Avicularia and vibracula. *A. Cellepora honoluluensis* with immersed avicularia. *B. Eschara sulcata* with a sessile *avicularium*. *C.* Diagram of a pedunculate avicularium (*a*, mandible; *b*, beak; *c*, chamber of avicularium; *m*, muscles; *p*, peduncle). *D.* Three zooecia with vibracula (*v*). (*All figures from Simpson; B after Hincks and Busk.*)

and vibracula. Structures known as *lunaria* (*lunarium*) are present at the aperture on the posterior wall of the zooecia. They are formed from the zooecial wall, which is thickened and curved to a shorter radius and which also usually projects above the plane of the zooecial aperture which it may somewhat overarch. The term relates to the crescentic shape of this structure. It may be seen in the Ceramoporidae and Fistuliporidae (Fig. 81 *M*).

Bryozoan zoaria exhibit great variety in shape, size, and architecture. Incrusting forms are very common and may be responsible for the preservation of the incrusted organic matter. Such zoaria may have the form of a very delicate network or may be thin or thick laminar expansions. Spheroidal and hemispheroidal zoaria are common and seem to have been attached in many cases by a wrinkled basal plate (the *epitheca*). Zoaria resembling trelliswork, lace, or netlike fan-shaped structures are very characteristic of one order. These appear to have been attached to the bottom by a wrinkled or folded basal structure similar to the epitheca. Some zoaria are composed of jointed stems upon which the zooecia are arranged around the axis in a number of longitudinal rows. Lamellar, leaflike, and small dendritic zoaria are especially characteristic of the trepostomatous bryozoans.

The surfaces of the zoaria often show several kinds of ornamentation. A concentration of mesopores gives rise to stellate structures on zoaria of the genus *Constellaria* (Fig. 82 *O*). *Monticules* and *maculae*, so characteristic of the Trepostomata, are composed of zooecia which differ from the average in size or have the apertures elevated (Fig. 82 *B*, *O–P*). The monticule is a rather pronounced dome, whereas the maculae are flat or depressed areas on the surface. *Spines* and *nodes* also ornament the surfaces of some species.

CLASSIFICATION

Several classifications of the Bryozoa have been proposed, but since there is still much to be learned about the phylum, it is probable that no classification now in existence will ultimately prove satisfactory. The classification preferred by the present authors is as follows:

Phylum **Bryozoa**
- Class *Entoprocta*—Bryozoans in which a circular lophophore incloses both the mouth and the anal opening. (None fossil.)
- Class *Ectoprocta*—Bryozoans in which a circular or crescentic lophophore surrounds the mouth only. The anal opening lies outside. (Fossil.)
  - Superorder Phylactolaemata—Fresh-water forms with a crescentic lophophore, mouth protected by an overhanging lip, and no skeleton. (None fossil.)
  - Superorder Gymnolaemata—Almost exclusively marine bryozoans with a circular lophophore surrounding the mouth only. There is a stony skeleton. Almost all fossil and most living forms belong to this superorder. (Fossil.)
    - Order 1. Ctenostomata (extant)
    - Order 2. Cyclostomata (extant)
    - Order 3. Trepostomata (extinct)
    - Order 4. Cryptostomata (extinct)
    - Order 5. Cheilostomata (extant)

The essential characters of the five orders of the Gymnolaemata are tabulated in Table 6.

TABLE 6.—TABLE TO SHOW ESSENTIAL CHARACTERS OF THE FIVE ORDERS OF GYMNOLAEMATA

Order	Composition of zooecium	Shape of zooecium	Character of aperture	Operculum	Diaphragms	Marsupia and appendicular organs	Mesopores	Character of zoarium	Range
Ctenostomata	Horny or membranous, rarely calcified in part	Tubular or conical	Terminal and round	Present	None	None	None	Small, delicate	Ordovician-Recent
Cyclostomata	Calcareous	Cylindrical	Terminal and round	None	Usually none	None	Present or absent	Usually delicate	Ordovician-Recent
Trepostomata	Calcareous	Prismatic or cylindrical	Round or polygonal	Present	Abundantly present	Present probably	Present	Variable, frequently massive	Ordovician-Permian
Cryptostomata	Calcareous	Cylindrical	Round	Present	Present or absent	None	Usually absent	Delicate, but sometimes several inches high	Ordovician-Permian
Cheilostomata	Membranous, chitinous, calcareous	Conical, tubular, prismatic, urn shaped, etc.	More or less anterior, frequently modified	Present	None	Present	None	Delicate or massive, usually not large	Jurassic-Recent

ORDER CTENOSTOMATA[1]

The ctenostomatous bryozoans are simple primitive forms with membranous or chitinous zooecia. The very simple

[1] Ctenostomata—Gr. *ctenon,* comb + *stoma, stomata,* mouth; referring to the comb-shaped operculum which closes the mouth or aperture of the zooecia.

character of the zooecia may suggest proximity to the naked forms from which the Bryozoa were derived. The zooecial tubes, which are commonly isolated, are developed by budding from a distinct tubular *stolon* or *stem*. This is often a threadlike tube which gives off cylindrical stalks, each of which swells at its extremity into the body of a polypide. The aperture of the zooecium is terminal and has a setae-bearing operculum. The latter resembles a comb and is responsible for the name given to the order. Appendicular organs and ovicells are wanting. In some cases the zooecia unite laterally to form thin sheets.

In all known species of Ctenostomata the zooecia are membranous or chitinous and hence not generally capable of preservation. The stolon, however, often becomes calcified in part and may be preserved, though usually no trace of the zooecia will remain. The zoaria either incrust or penetrate the objects on which they occur. They are very small and are preserved mainly in the form of the calcified stolons or small cavities excavated into shells and other objects on which they lived or in which they ramified. The earliest representative of the order (*Heteronema priscum*, Fig. 80 *A–C*) makes its appearance in the Lower Ordovician, Ungulite sandstone of Esthonia, and other genera occur sparingly throughout geologic time to the present. The order is never of much stratigraphic importance.

The genus *Vinella*, with radial stolons, and *Rhopalonaria*, with its pinnately arranged stolons usually represented by minute excavations in shells and corals, are representative Paleozoic genera (Fig. 80). Very few Mesozoic and Cenozoic species have been described, and the order is certainly the least represented in present seas.

ORDER CYCLOSTOMATA[1]

The Cyclostomata possess zooecia which are simple calcareous tubes with thin, minutely porous walls. Zooecial apertures are terminal, round, not contracted, though commonly expanded and bent outward (Fig. 81 *E*), and are without opercula. Internally the zooecia usually lack the numerous transverse partitions so common in trepostomatous and cryptostomatous bryozoans,

[1] Cyclostomata—Gr. *cyclos*, circle + *stoma, stomata*, mouth; referring to the circular aperture of the zooecium.

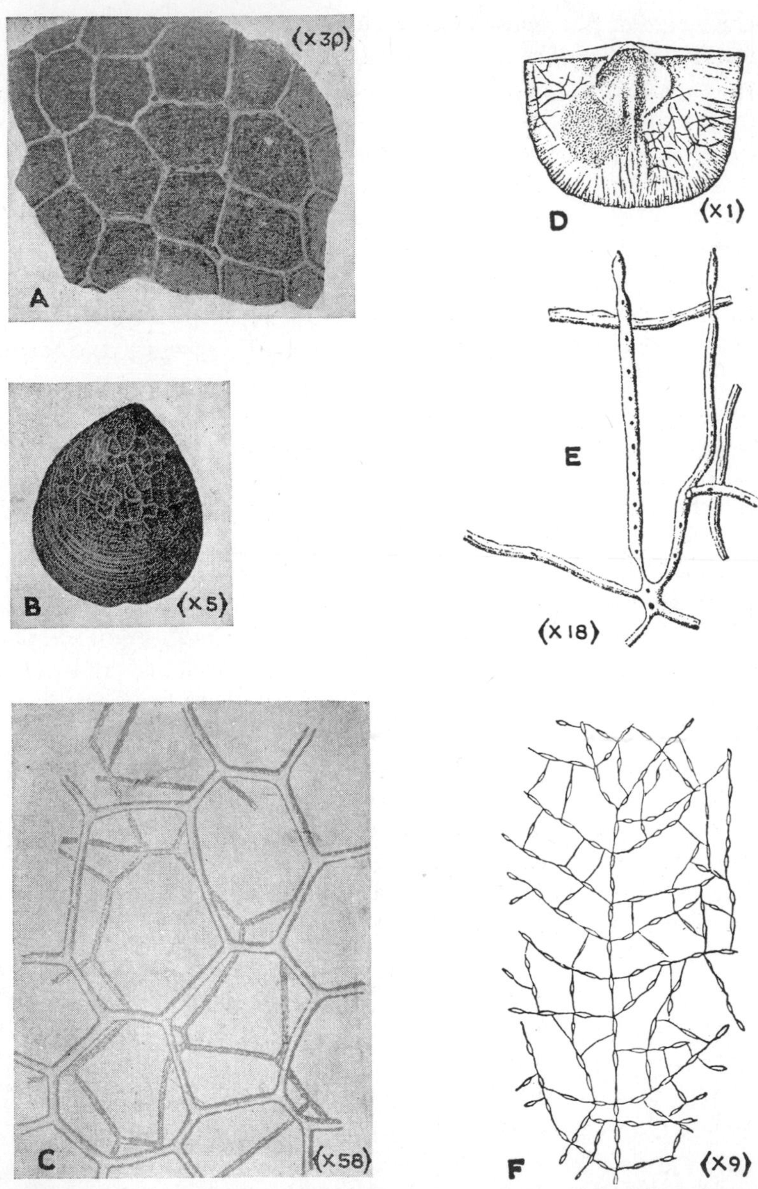

FIG. 80.—Ctenostomata. *A–C. Heteronema priscum* the earliest known bryozoan from the Lower Ordovician of Esthonia: *A*, a small portion of *B* enlarged to show method of branching; *B*, a colony attached to a valve of *Obolus;* *C*, parts of two zoaria with parts of one growing over the other. *D–E. Vinella repens* from the Middle Ordovician of Minnesota: *D*, two zoaria attached to the

and therefore it is usually possible to identify species without preparing thin sections. There are no marsupia or appendicular structures, and the ovicells, when present, are either large zooecia or inflations on the zoarial surface. The ovicells are of great importance in the classification of the order.

The zoaria assume many different patterns. The zooecia may not be supported at the base, but in the Ceramoporidae there are often solid or tubular strengthening deposits, and these may contain mesopores. In many Cyclostomata accessory tubes designated by various terms are developed on the front or back side of the zooecium. These are open or closed and seem to be zooecia which are without polypides. In the simpler forms of zoaria the ancestrula is small and is associated with a bulbous protoecium (Fig. 78 *C*). Subsequent zooids at first branch divergently but later come together, and a closely united colony results. The zooecia are always delicate and small except in the Paleozoic Ceramoporidae which exhibit more massive zoaria.

Stomatopora (Ordovician to Recent), *Corynotrypa* (Ordovician to Devonian), *Spiropora* (Jurassic to Recent), *Diaperoecia* (Cretaceous to Recent), *Crepipora* (Ordovician to Silurian), and *Fistulipora* (Ordovician to Permian) are representative genera of the order (Fig. 81).

Cyclostomata first appear in the Ordovician and immediately become common and diversified, though by no means abundant or important. Incrusting anastomosing branches and somewhat massive zoaria are the rule. A decline began in the Silurian, and thereafter until the Jurassic the order held a subordinate position. In the Jurassic, however, there was a second expansion, and the order again became prolific in species and individuals in the Cretaceous. This was short-lived, however, for by the end of the Cretaceous a second decline set in, and the order was almost immediately reduced to a position subordinate to the Cheilostomata. At the present time there are barely a hundred known species in existing seas.

---

inner surface of a ventral valve of *Strophomena septata; E*, portion of one of the colonies magnified to show a nucleus with five divisions of the tubular stolon radiating from it. *F. Rhopalonaria venosa* from the Upper Ordovician (Richmond) of Ohio. Portion of the reticulate zoarium growing upon a pelecypod. (*A–C after Bassler; D–E after Ulrich; F after Ulrich and Bassler.*)

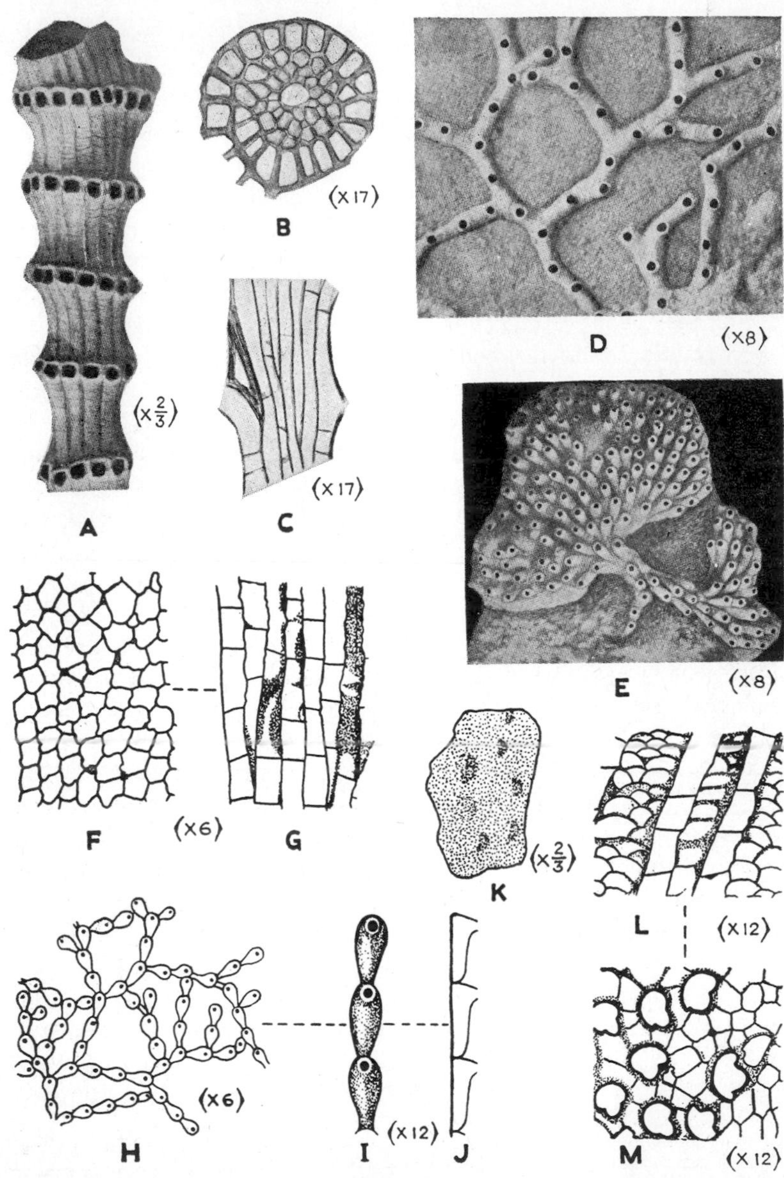

Fig. 81.—Cyclostomata. *A–C. Spiropora majuscula* from the Eocene (Jacksonian) of South Carolina: *A*, a fragmental zoarium; *B*, transverse section; *C*, longitudinal section. *D. Stomatopora contracta* from the Eocene (Midwayan) of Alabama. The type specimen showing the nature of the zoarium. *E. Diaperoecia lobulata* from the Eocene (Jacksonian) of Georgia. An incrusting symmetrical zoarium. *F–G. Crepipora perampla* from the Ordovician ("Tren-

ORDER TREPOSTOMATA[1]

The Trepostomata constitute an exclusively Paleozoic group of bryozoans which flourished during the earlier part of the era, building many stony zoaria (some as large as 2 ft. in diameter) and contributing largely to the formation of many calcareous strata. The colonies are composed of long, coherent, prismatic or cylindrical zooecia with a simple terminal aperture. The aperture is frequently covered with an operculum having a small subcircular opening. The zooecial tubes are divided into regular or irregular compartments by straight, transverse or inclined diaphragms or by cystiphragms. The former may be incomplete, and some are provided with a perforation in the center.

Each zooecial tube is composed of an inner axial region, the *immature region*, and an outer peripheral zone, the *mature region*. The immature part of the zooecium usually constitutes from two-thirds to four-fifths the length of the tube and is prismatic with a polygonal cross section. The walls are thin, and the transverse partitions remote. In the mature region the tube is prismatic or tubular, with polygonal or circular cross section; the walls are much thickened; and the transverse partitions are much closer together (Fig. 82 *C*). This change in the character of the zooecia is reflected in the name of the order and is accompanied by the development of numerous structural features in the mature region. For one thing the zooecia are usually separated by mesopores, and these are scattered among the zooecia as conditions of growth dictated. Marsupia are present, and appendicular organs are thought to have existed in many species, because of the presence of tubular

[1] Trepostomata—Gr. *trepos*, change + *stoma*, *stomata*, mouth; referring to the change in character of the zooecial tubes from the immature or axial region to the mature or peripheral region.

---

ton") of Minnesota: *F*, tangential section showing prominent lunaria and lack of mesopores; *G*, longitudinal section showing distantly spaced diaphragms. *H–J*. *Corynotrypa inflata* from the Ordovician of Ohio: *H*, small portion of a large colony growing upon the concave side of a *Rafinesquina alternata; I*, three zooecia enlarged; *J*, longitudinal section showing internal structure. *K–M*. *Fistulipora foordi* from the Devonian (Hamilton) of Iowa: *K*, a fragmental zoarium showing maculae; *L*, longitudinal section from surface downward; *M*, tangential section showing the conspicuous lunaria and the size and shape of zooecia and mesopores. (*A–E after Canu and Bassler; F–M after Ulrich.*)

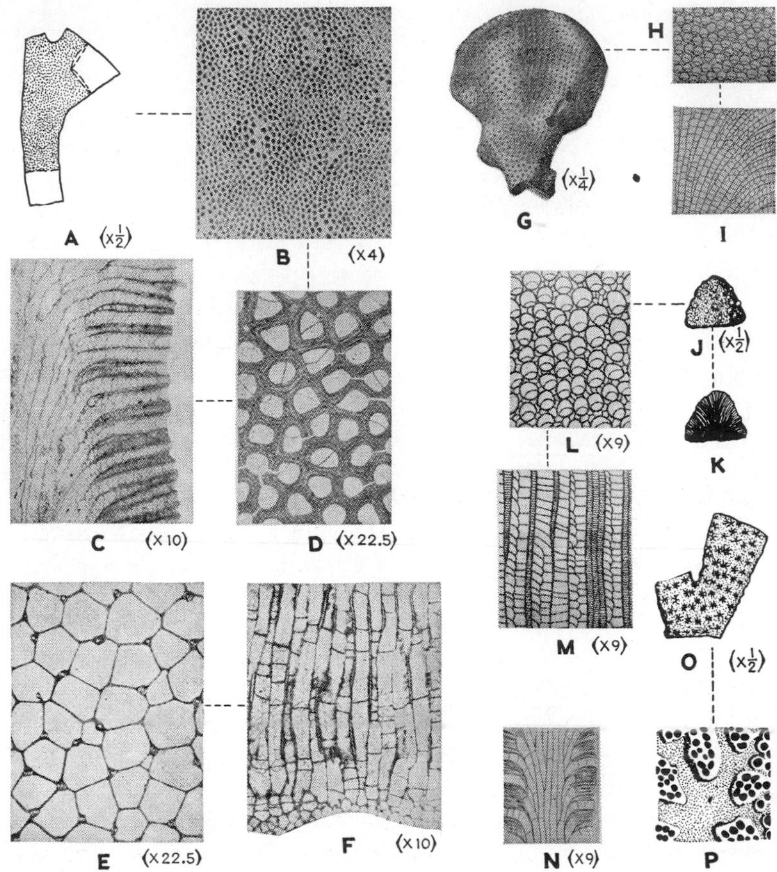

FIG. 82.—Trepostomata (Amalgamata). *A–D. Homotrypa alta* from the Upper Ordovician (Richmond) of Indiana: *A*, a fragmental zoarium; *B*, portion of an unweathered surface showing the stellate maculae; *C*, longitudinal section showing crinkled walls, immature and mature regions, diaphragms, and cystiphragms; *D*, tangential section showing thick walls and communication pores. *E–F. Stigmatella incrustans* from the Upper Ordovician (Richmond) of Indiana: *E*, tangential section showing polygonal zooecia and prominent acanthopores; *F*, longitudinal section showing basal epithecal portion and three mature regions. *G–I. Monticulipora molesta* from the Ordovician of Ohio and Tennessee: *G*, almost complete bifoliate zoarium with characteristic monticuliferous surface; *H*, longitudinal section; *I*, tangential section. *J–M. Prasopora*, a typical Middle and Upper Ordovician bryozoan: *J*, a complete zoarium of *P. conoidea; K*, longitudinal section of *J*, showing the shape of the zoarium; *L*, tangential section of *P. simulatrix* showing zooecia and mesopores (the curved lines within the zooecia are transected cystiphragms); *M*, longitudinal section of *L*, showing closely tabulated mesopores and larger zooecia with diaphragms and cystiphragms. *N. Batostomella spinulosa* from the Mississippian (Chester) of Kentucky. A longitudinal section showing complete mature and immature regions. *O–P. Constellaria constellata* from the Upper Ordovician (Richmond) of Indiana, Ohio,

spines, known as *acanthopores* (Fig. 82 *E–F*), in the zooecial walls of the mature region.

The zoaria have dendroid, tabular, frond, leaflike, globular, hemispherical, lenticular, and irregular shapes, and many were incrusting over everything on the bottom. Such massive types of zoaria were possible because the zooecia in the Trepostomata are directly superimposed on one another to form prismatic and cylindrical tubes. From these tubes additional zooids were budded off and continued to extend the colony. The forms of the zoaria were splendidly efficient in causing the deposition of sediment around them, so that they were more or less directly concerned with the deposition of the rocks in which they were buried. Many zoaria have their surfaces characterized by *maculae* and *monticules*, arranged at regular intervals (Fig. 82 *B, G, J, O, P*). The former are spotlike areas of cells, differing from the average in size, level with the zoarial surface or depressed somewhat below it. They are usually rather inconspicuous, but in some forms they make star-shaped areas. Monticules are elevated areas, and they may be small, sharp tubercles, rounded nodes, or elevated rings completely girdling the zoarium. The size, shape, elevation, and distribution of the maculae and monticules, when used with internal structure, are of use in differentiating species.

Study of this order necessitates patient attention to the minutest details of internal and external structure. For that reason thin sections must be prepared and studied microscopically in order to identify correctly the great number of species. Zoaria of a given species may vary greatly in form and size, but the zooecia and associated structures remain constant. For that reason superficial features cannot be depended on for identification. In the preparation of thin sections it is desirable to prepare two sections of the zoarium. One should be tangential to the zoarium and transverse to the zooecia in the mature region. The second should be an axial section, that is, a section which includes the axis of the branch or stem and shows a longitudinal section of the zooecia. A third section cut transverse to the

---

etc.: *O*, a fragmental zoarium showing the characteristic stellate maculae; *P*, tangential section showing arrangement of zooecia in a macula. (*A–F after Cumings and Galloway; G–P after Ulrich, with slight modifications in some cases.*)

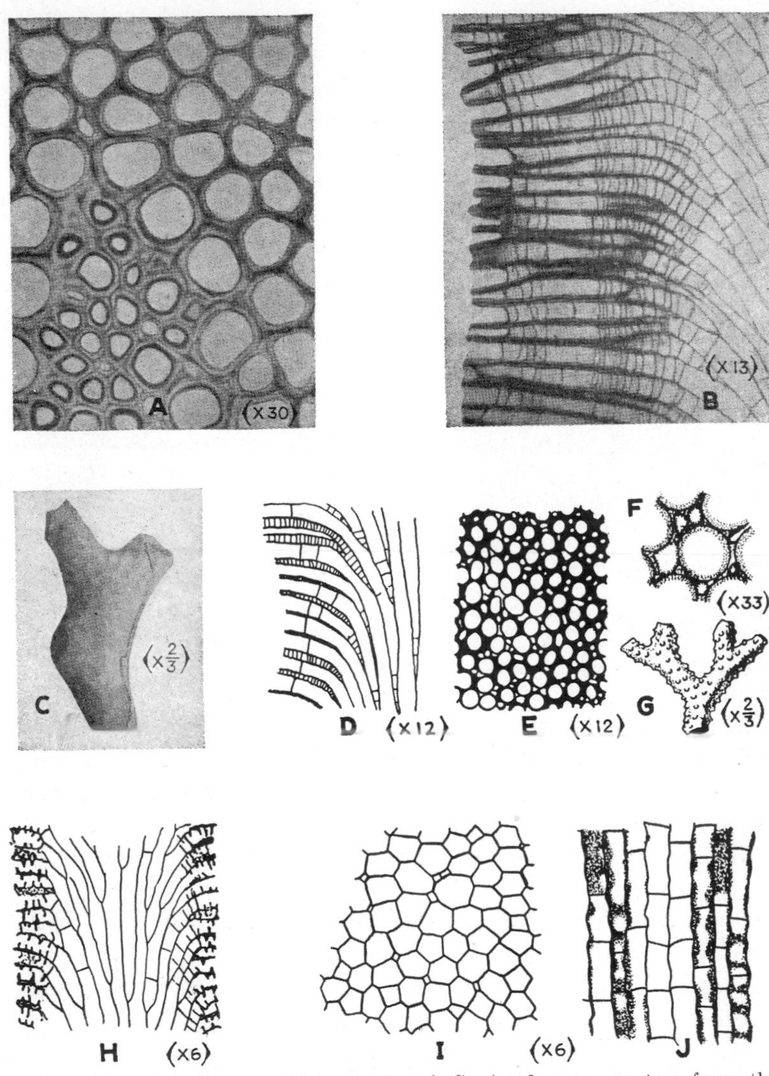

FIG. 83.—Trepostomata (Integrata). *A–C. Amplexopora septosa* from the Upper Ordovician (Richmond) of Indiana: *A*, tangential section showing thick walls and dark division line, faint acanthopores, and a macula of mesopores; *B*, longitudinal section showing nature of mature and immature regions; *C*, a nearly complete zoarium. *D–G. Hallopora pulchella* from the Middle Ordovician of Minnesota: *D*, longitudinal section showing nature of zooecia and mesopores; *E*, tangential section; *F*, magnified view of a single zooecium and surrounding mesopores showing the dark division line characteristic of the Integrata; *G*, incomplete zoarium with characteristic monticuliferous surface. *H. Hemiphragma irrasum* from the Middle Ordovician of Minnesota. Longitudinal section showing complete mature and immature regions and characteristic incomplete diaphragms in

axis of the branch is sometimes desirable, although the first two sections are usually sufficient for accurate identification.

Classification.—Early workers used only external characters of zooecia and zoaria in classifying the Trepostomata, and consequently much confusion resulted. In fact, one large group, the *Monticuliporoids*, was for a long time assigned to the tabulate corals. Only after the internal structure was studied microscopically and the ontogenetic development determined were they removed from that category and placed with the Bryozoa.[1]

Most authors now divide the order into the *Amalgamata* and *Integrata*. The former, including four families, have the calcareous walls of adjacent zooecia so amalgamated or fused together that no line of separation is apparent. In the latter group, composed of three families, the zooecial walls remain distinct, and the wall between adjacent zooecia is double, the division appearing in thin section as a dark line. It has been suggested that this dark line represents the fossilized remains of animal tissue that filled the space when the zooecia were occupied by living polypides. Recently doubt has been cast on the value of the two divisions as natural groups, but as yet no better classification has appeared.

Monticulipora (Ordovician to Silurian), *Homotrypa* (Ordovician to Silurian), *Stigmatella* (Ordovician), *Prasopora* (Ordovician to Silurian), *Batostomella* (Silurian to Permian), and *Constellaria* (Ordovician) are representative genera of the Amalgamata, which ranges from the Ordovician to the Permian (Fig. 82). *Amplexopora* (Ordovician to Silurian), *Hallopora* (Ordovician to Devonian), *Hemiphragma* (Ordovician to Silurian), and *Monotrypa* (Ordovician to Devonian) are representatives of the Integrata, which ranges from the Ordovician to the Devonian (Fig. 83).

ORDER CRYPTOSTOMATA[2]

The Cryptostomata have short zooecia of which the aperture is hidden at the base of a tubular shaft known as the *vestibulum*

[1] CUMINGS, E. R., Development and systematic position of the Monticuliporoids, *Bull. Geol. Soc. Amer.*, vol. 23, pp. 357–370, 1912.

[2] Cryptostomata—Gr. *kryptos*, hidden + *stoma*, *stomata*, mouth—"hid-

the former. *I–J. Monotrypa magna* from the Middle Ordovician of Illinois: *I*, tangential section showing polygonal zooecia; *J*, longitudinal section. (*A–C, after Cumings and Galloway; D–J after Ulrich.*)

(Fig. 84 *B*). The latter is surrounded by a calcareous deposit and opens to the exterior through a variously sized pore. The primitive zooecium in cryptostomatous bryozoans is short and regular in its outline, being pyriform, oblong, quadrate, or hexagonal, with the aperture at the anterior end. These characteristics are also shared by the Cheilostomata, suggesting that

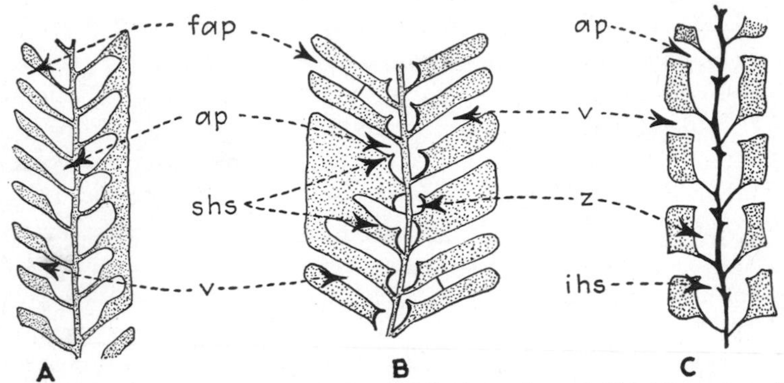

FIG. 84.—Cryptostomata. *A*. Longitudinal section of *Rhinidictya grandis* showing on the left half the false aperture (*fap*), true aperture (*ap*), and vestibulum (*v*). *B*. Longitudinal section of *Rhinidictya fidelis* showing the long vestibuli (*v*) and the prominent superior hemisepta (*shs*). Longitudinal section of *Arthropora simplex* showing zooecia (*z*), vestibuli (*v*), and inferior hemisepta (*ihs*). (*After Ulrich.*)

the Cryptostomata are in reality only Paleozoic Cheilostomata. The former differ from the latter, however, in the following ways:

1. Lack ovicells and avicularia.
2. Have much greater deposits of calcareous matter on the front part of the zooecia.
3. Frequently have a tubular zooecium formed by successive layers of polypides.
4. Zoaria with an uninterrupted width of more than 8 mm. exhibit clusters of cells which differ somewhat in size and in elevation from the average zooecia.

Although the last two features suggest the Trepostomata, the Cryptostomata differ from them in having the immature and mature regions of approximately the same length and in having a *hemiseptum* at the bottom of the vestibulum. The hemiseptum

---

den mouth"; referring to the fact that the true aperture of the primitive zooecium is concealed at the bottom of a tubular vestibule.

is an incomplete plate which extends from the base of the vestibulum downward into the primitive zooecium (Fig. 84 *B–C*). A second such plate sometimes springs from the bottom of the cell and is referred to as the *inferior hemiseptum* to distinguish it from the upper or *superior* one. The function of these is unknown, but it has been suggested that they may have served as supports for movable opercula.

Certain Cryptostomata have ramose zoaria in which there are long, thin-walled prismatic tubes in the axial region. These tubes possess or lack diaphragms. The presence of a hemiseptum, however, serves to distinguish them from all other somewhat similar forms.

The zoaria of this order are branching, dendroid, or lacelike structures which may have the shape of a fan, frond, funnel, or screw (*Archimedes*) (Fig. 85 *E*). They are never massive, are often very delicate, and in some cases range to several inches in length. There are three general arrangements of the zooecia. In the typical cryptostome the zoarium is composed of a double layer of zooecia, arranged back to back, and has the shape of a sword, ribbon, or fan. In other species the zoaria consist of lacelike expansions in which there is but a single layer of zooecia, the back or reverse side being covered by a dense layer of striated or finely granular material. In the third type of architecture the zoaria are ramose, and the zooecia arise from the axis of the more or less cylindrical stem. In this group some zoaria are composed of articulating segments.

It is often possible to identify species of Cryptostomata by the external characters, but in some cases thin sections must be prepared in order to determine the internal structure. Because of the symmetry of the zooecial arrangement and the architecture of many of the zoaria, Cryptostomata are among the most beautiful of bryozoans.

The order appears in the early Ordovician, rises to a climax in the latter half of the Paleozoic, and becomes extinct by the close of the Permian. Fenestellid forms are especially abundant during the Devonian, Mississippian, and Pennsylvanian. Some layers of the famous Salem limestone (Indiana building stone) of Indiana are little more than a matted mass of the zoaria of these lacelike forms, and many Pennsylvanian limestones show them in equal abundance.

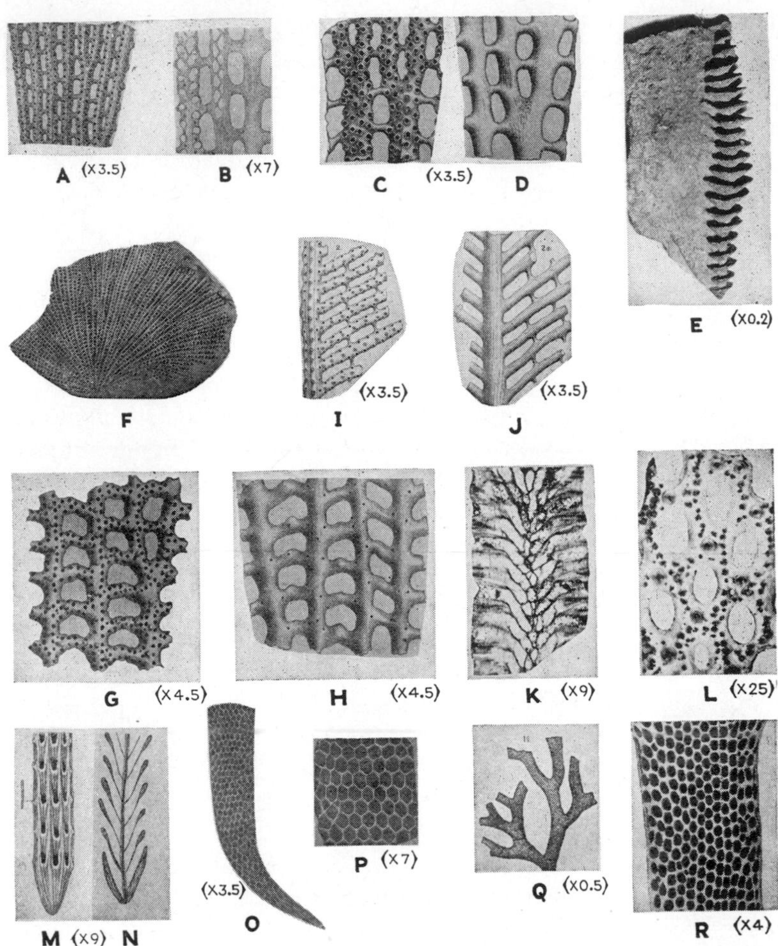

FIG. 85.—Cryptostomata. *A–B. Fenestella triserialis* from the Mississippian (Keokuk) of Kentucky: *A*, celluliferous or obverse face of part of a zoarium showing the double row of zooecia characteristic of the genus; *B*, section of part of zoarium at different levels. At the extreme right is the striated reverse face. *C–D. Polypora varsoviensis* from the Mississippian (Warsaw) of Illinois: *C*, obverse surface showing relative size of branches, number of zooecial apertures, and in some cases covers on the apertures; *D*, reverse striated surface. *E. Archimedes*, a very common Mississippian cryptostome, from the Warsaw of Kentucky. In life a spiral fenestrated band with zooecial apertures encircled the axial screw, but this band is rarely preserved. *F–H. Septopora*, a common Mississippian and Pennsylvanian bryozoan, characterized by zooecia on the dissepiments: *F*, a nearly complete zoarium of *S. biserialis nervata* showing the typical fan shape; *G*, *S. subquadrans*, obverse surface; *H*, reverse surface of a zoarium. *I–J. Ptilopora cylindracea* from the Mississippian (Keokuk) of Kentucky and Iowa: *I*, obverse surface of a specimen from Kentucky; *J*, reverse striated surface of a specimen from Iowa. *K–L. Rhombopora lepidodendroides*

Fenestella and *Polypora* (Silurian to Permian), *Archimedes* (Mississippian), *Septopora* (Mississippian to Pennsylvanian), *Ptilopora* (Devonian to Mississippian), *Rhombopora* (Ordovician to Permian), *Helopora* (Ordovician to Silurian), *Escharopora* (Ordovician), and *Rhinidictya* (Ordovician to Silurian) are representative genera (Fig. 85).

ORDER CHEILOSTOMATA[1]

The zooecia of the Cheilostomata are oval, turbinate, urceolate, quadrate, or hexagonal in outline and are usually closely arranged side by side. Adjacent zooecia are connected by perforations or pores known as *septulae* (Fig. 86). The aperture, which is located near the front end of the zooecium, is closed by a chitinous lip or operculum (whence the name of the order) when the polypide is retracted. It is usually smaller than the diameter of the zooecium and may have projections on its walls known as *cardelles*. Ova often mature in external ovicells which appear as blister-like cavities in front of the apertures. Appendicular organs in the form of avicularia and vibraculae are frequently developed. These organs, because of chitinous composition, are not apt to be preserved as fossils, but their positions may be indicated by structures on the zooecia.

The material of the zooecium varies considerably in character. Some zooecia are composed wholly of calcareous substance; some are partly calcareous and partly membranous or chitinous; and some are entirely membranous or chitinous.

Internally cheilostomatous Bryozoa possess a unique hydrostatic apparatus of which the main organ is the *compensating sac* or *compensatrix*. This process aids in the extrusion and retraction of the polypide. Its relation to the organism is

[1] Cheilostomata—Gr. *cheilos*, lip + *stoma, stomata*, mouth; referring to the chitinous lip which acts as an operculum for the zooecium.

---

from the Pennsylvanian of Indiana: *K*, longitudinal section of a fragmental zoarium; *L*, tangential section very near the surface showing the zooecial apertures and large and small spines. *M–N*. *Helopora spiniformis* from the Middle Ordovician of Tennessee: *M*, basal portion of a zoarium, with small figure one-half natural size; *N*, longitudinal section showing nature of internal structure. *O–P*. *Escharopora angularis* from the Middle Ordovician of Minnesota: *O*, a nearly complete zoarium; *P*, portion of surface of another specimen highly magnified. *Q–R*. *Rhinidictya grandis* from the Middle Ordovician of Illinois: *Q*, a nearly complete zoarium; *R*, portion of surface considerably magnified. (*A–D*, *G–J*, *M–R after Ulrich; F after Nebraska Geological Survey.*)

illustrated in Fig. 86. In forms possessing a compensating sac the polypide can emerge from the zooecium only when an equal volume of water has entered the sac to compensate for the extrusion.

The classification of the Cheilostomata is difficult because of the complexity of the soft parts and the character of the skeleton. For a long time only the skeletal structures were considered,

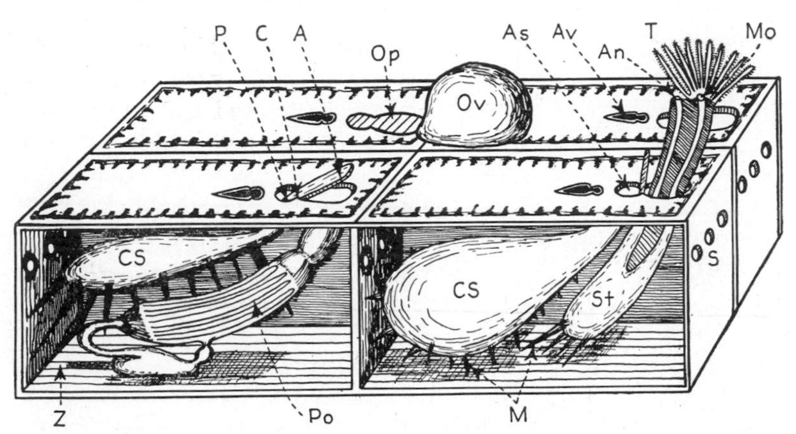

FIG. 86.—Diagrammatic drawing of a modern cheilostomatous bryozoan showing four zooecia (*Z*), with the polypides withdrawn in three and protruding from one. The ornamental calcareous wall is equipped with avicularia (*Av*) and ovicells (*Ov*). The posterior part (*P*) of the operculum (*Op*), which operates on a hinge or the cardelle (*C*), covers the opening (*As*) into the compensating sac (*CS*), and the anterior part (*A*) closes the orifice of the polypide (*Po*). Adjacent zooecia communicate through small pores or septulae (*S*). The compensating sac when filled with water forces the polypide out through the orifice, and the animal is then in a feeding position. The operculum is removed in one zooecium, closed in a second, slightly open in a third, and fully open in the fourth. *An*, anus; *As*, ascopore; *M*, muscles; *Mo*, mouth; *St*, stomach; *T*, tentacles. (*Adapted from Bassler.*)

but it has been shown that a much more natural classification can be built if both the skeletal and soft parts of the animal are considered. Subdivision of the order is based on

1. Functions and processes dealing with reproduction. This necessitates determining the relation between the operculum and the ovicells.
2. The hydrostatic system and the extrusion of the polypide. Fortunately, the form of the aperture illustrates the function of the apparatus, and the presence of cardelles reveals the movements of the opercula. One suborder, the *Anasca,* does not possess a compensating sac. The *Ascophora* possess a sac which communicates with the exterior by a pore known as the *ascopore* (Fig. 86).
3. The nature of the skeletal part of the animal.

All of these features usually can be determined directly, in well-preserved fossils, or by noting the character of associated structures.

The Cheilostomata represent the highest type of development found among the Bryozoa. The order made its appearance in the Jurassic and is thought to have been derived from the Cryptostomata, possibly from Paleozoic Cyclostomata. By the Upper Cretaceous they had become the dominant order of Bryozoa, and they have retained this dominance to the present. The Ascophora range from the Cretaceous to the Recent. *Gastropella* (Tertiary), and *Peristomella*, *Metroperiella*, and *Perigastrella* (Tertiary to Recent) are representative genera of the Ascophora (Fig. 87).

GEOLOGIC IMPORTANCE AND ECOLOGY

Since the first appearance early in the Ordovician, Bryozoa have made substantial contributions to calcareous strata in every period of geologic time. This contribution has been in the form of the calcareous zoaria which they built and upon which they lived until death. Almost any calcareous formation will show some of the zoaria, and certain strata exhibit them in great profusion. At the present time Bryozoa are among the more important denizens of coral reefs, and on ancient reefs and bioherms they seemed to have held a similar position. In the Silurian reefs of the Upper Mississippi valley the fenestrate zoaria of bryozoans are among the more common fossils. In the Ordovician of some parts of the world certain genera (*Batostoma*) are responsible for the construction of low bioherms.

Indirectly, the bushy zoaria must have served an important part in deposition on certain bottoms by checking the currents and causing deposition of materials in suspension or in solution. On the steep peripheral slopes of ancient coral reefs, where they appear to have grown in great profusion, they almost certainly played an important role in intercepting the reef mud and sand, as these moved down the slopes, and very likely aided in the construction of some of the unusually high initial inclinations observed on many reef structures. They seem also to have lived in great profusion on muddy and calcareous bottoms, where they were attached to the bottom directly or incrusted various kinds of objects.

It seems very likely that most large zoaria were not molested greatly by scavengers, for they rarely show fragmentation which

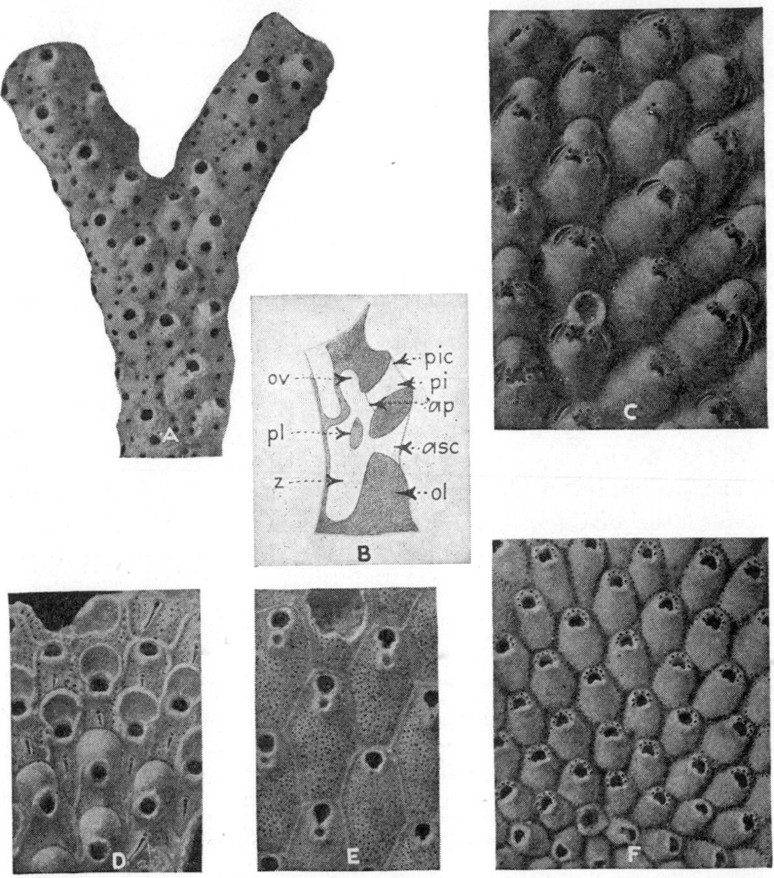

FIG. 87.—Cheilostomata. *A–B. Gastropella ventricosa* from the Eocene (Midwayan) of Arkansas: *A*, a bifurcated zoarium showing large, swollen zooecia and large ascopores; *B*, longitudinal section through a zooecium with ovicell (*ap*, apertura; *asc*, ascopore; *ol*, olocyst; *ov*, ovicell; *pi*, peristome; *pl*, support; *pic*, peristomice; *z*, zooecium). *C. Peristomella falcifera* from the Eocene (Jacksonian) of North Carolina. A well-preserved zoarium of this incrusting species, with both ordinary and ovicelled zooecia and conspicuous long, falciform avicularia. *D–E. Metroperiella* from the Eocene (Jacksonian) of Georgia and North Carolina, respectively: *D*, *M. latipora* showing normal and ovicelled zooecia. *E*, *M. biplanata* showing wide zooecia. *F. Perigastrella oscitans* from the Eocene (Jacksonian) of Mississippi showing ancestrula and neighboring zooecia. (*All figures except B* ×15, *and all after Canu and Bassler.*)

could be attributed to such action. It is considered probable that predators and scavengers were responsible for much of the fragmentation and in some cases almost complete destruction of delicate zoaria which are apparent among fossil accumulations. Both large and small zoaria may frequently have been torn from their moorings by waves and currents and transported to other environments, where the living bryozoans perhaps could not have lived.

EVOLUTION OF THE BRYOZOA

The evolution of the Bryozoa is not clear. The earliest known bryozoan makes its appearance in the early Ordovician, and very soon thereafter four of the five orders appear. The presence of the trochophore larval stage suggests that the Bryozoa descended from some wormlike stock. Whatever the origin, it seems fairly certain that the bryozoans were evolving in the Cambrian and that no record of that evolution is preserved because the earliest forms probably did not have any calcified structures. Some paleontologists are of the opinion that the graptolites are very closely allied to the Bryozoa, if not actually a division of the phylum.

The Ctenostomata, which have little in the way of a skeleton and appear to be close to the ancestral stock, and the Cyclostomata, which are also of fairly simple structure, range from the beginning of known bryozoan history to the present time, though they appear never to have been of very great importance and rarely of considerable abundance. The Trepostomata and Cryptostomata are exclusively Paleozoic, appearing first in the Ordovician and becoming extinct by the end of the era. The Cheilostomata, which constitute the most important modern group, appear first in the Jurassic. A few students have suggested that they may have descended from the Paleozoic Cyclostomata, but most investigators accept the view that they are closest to the Cryptostomata and that they were derived or descended from that order.

GEOLOGIC HISTORY

The earliest known bryozoan is *Heteronema priscum* from the basal Ordovician Ungulite sandstone of Esthonia. It is a very simple ctenostomatous form. Bryozoa are not known to have been common during the first third of the Ordovician, but by the middle of that period four of the orders had become established, and in the upper third, trepostomatous species flourished in great abundance. All four orders persisted through the Paleozoic, but two became extinct at the close of the era (Fig. 88).

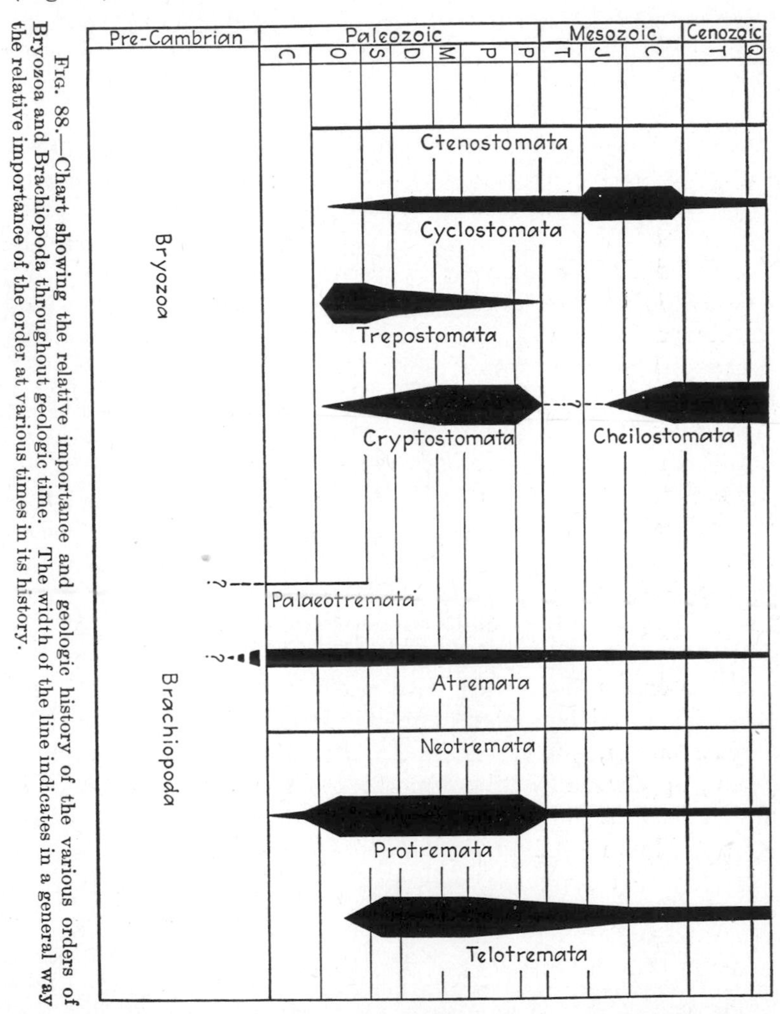

FIG. 88.—Chart showing the relative importance and geologic history of the various orders of Bryozoa and Brachiopoda throughout geologic time. The width of the line indicates in a general way the relative importance of the order at various times in its history.

The Ctenostomata seem never to have been important, as the fossil record is a meager one and the number of living species is few. During the Paleozoic, from the Ordovician to the Permian, the Cyclostomata were common, and perhaps the most abundant were the Ceramoporidae. Thereafter they seem to have declined until the Jurassic, when they reappear in large numbers and continue in equal abundance into the Cretaceous at which time the Cheilostomata became common. The Trepostomata surpassed all other Bryozoa in the early Paleozoic but relinquished the position of dominance to the Cryptostomata in the later part of the era. Both orders became extinct at the close of the Permian. There seems to be good evidence that the Cheilostomata, which made their appearance in the Jurassic, are a continuation of the Cryptostomata stock. In present seas this is the dominant order of the Bryozoa.

References

BASSLER, R. S.: The Bryozoa, or moss animals. *Smith. Inst., Ann. Rept.* for 1920, pp. 339–380, 1922.

CANU, F., and BASSLER, R. S.: A synopsis of American early Tertiary Cheilostome Bryozoa. *U. S. Nat. Mus., Bull.* 96, 87 pp., 1917.

———, and ———: North American Early Tertiary Bryozoa. *Smith. Inst., Bull.* 106, 878 pp., 162 pls., 1920.

CONDRA, G. E.: The coal measure Bryozoa of Nebraska. *Neb. Geol. Surv.*, vol. 2, pp. 11–163, 1903.

CUMINGS, E. R.: Development of some Paleozoic Bryozoa. *Amer. Jour. Sci.*, vol. 17, pp. 49–78, 1904.

———: Development and systematic position of the Monticuliporoids. *Bull. Geol. Soc. Amer.*, vol. 23, pp. 357–370, 1912.

JELLY, E. C.: "Synonymic Catalogue of Recent Marine Bryozoa." 1889.

NICKLES, J. M., and BASSLER, R. S.: A synopsis of American fossil Bryozoa. *U. S. Geol. Surv., Bull.* 173, 663 pp., 1900.

ULRICH, E. O.: American Paleozoic Bryozoa, *Jour. Cincinnati Soc. Nat. Hist.*, vols. 5, 6, 7, 1890.

———: Paleozoic Bryozoa, *Ill. Geol. Surv.*, vol. 8, pp. 283–688, 1890.

———: Lower Silurian Bryozoa, *Geol. Surv. Minnesota*, vol. 3, pt. 1, 1895.

——— and BASSLER, R. S.: A revision of the Paleozoic Bryozoa. Pt. 1, On genera and species of Ctenostomata. *Smith. Misc. Coll.*, vol. 45, pp. 256–294, 1904.

——— and ———: A revision of the Palezoic Bryozoa. Pt. 2, On genera and species of Trepostomata. *Smith. Misc. Coll.*, vol. 47, pp. 15–55, 1904.

CHAPTER VIII

BRACHIOPODA[1]

INTRODUCTION

Until recently most authors have included the Bryozoa and Brachiopoda in the so-called phylum Molluscoidea. The reasons for this association were: (1) The embryos of both groups pass through a trochophore stage; (2) members of both possess a lophophore throughout life; and (3) the digestive and nervous systems in the two groups are similar. The dissimilarities, however, are considered of sufficient importance to warrant raising each division to the rank of phylum and discontinuing the term Molluscoidea. The reasons for this procedure are: (1) The mature animals of the two groups vary greatly, with the ontogeny differing considerably once the larvae have settled down; and (2) there is a fundamental difference in the skeletal structures. The brachiopod is always solitary, always reproduces sexually, and its bivalve shell bears no resemblance to the tubular zooecium of a bryozoan. The bryozoans are usually intensely colonial animals and build a loose, bushy, or compact colony which is composed of many tubes or boxlike zooecia rarely over 1½ mm. in diameter. Entire colonies of Bryozoa are often smaller than single brachiopods.

Brachiopods are bilaterally symmetrical animals which seem always to have lived in a marine habitat. The animal is inclosed in a bivalve shell, with one valve borne in so-called ventral position and the other in so-called dorsal position. One valve usually is more convex than the other, and generally there is an opening for a fleshy stalk in the posterior part of the shell. The plane of symmetry passes through this posterior perforation and divides each valve longitudinally into two symmetrical parts. The general appearance of the shell in many species is that of a

[1] Brachiopoda—Gr. *brachion,* arm + *pous, podos,* foot; referring to the brachia which early investigators thought were homologous with the foot of mollusks.

Roman lamp, in which the fleshy stalk protruding through the posterior opening may be likened to the wick of the lamp. Hence, brachiopods are frequently termed "lamp shells." They are often beautifully and abundantly preserved and are among the most common of fossil animals. There is scarcely a marine formation which does not contain some brachiopod remains. Many species are extremely useful in stratigraphic work because of the ease of identification, common occurrence, and wide distribution.

In mature life brachiopods have always been a part of the sessile benthos. Only during a very short period of the larval stage are they free swimming, and for this reason migration is slow. The individual larvae remain close together and frequently congregate in clusters attached to some foreign object or to the shells of older brachiopods. Each mature brachiopod, however, is a solitary organism. Most species prefer well-oxygenated water of normal salinity, and most fossil forms seem to have favored similar conditions. Certain genera, such as *Lingula*, however, live in mud in which they burrow like the well-known little-neck clam *Mya arenaria*. Some of the mud dwellers have lived from the Ordovician to the present time with essentially little change in shell structure. Such longevity may be due to the stable character of the environment or to the absence of much competition, resulting in little selection of individuals in either case. Living in mud necessitated ability to move, with the result that forms which have adopted this habitat are not permanently fixed in position.

Most living brachiopods inhabit shallow water, and this seems to have been the case with the majority of fossil species. Living forms have been dredged from depths as great as 5,490 m. (18,000 ft.), but so far as is known few species live in very deep water. The known deep sea forms have very thin and fragile shells, and some are so thin as to be translucent or almost transparent. Shallow-water forms tend to have thick shells, and those living in the tidal zone may have them unusually thick. There are about 225 living species divided among about 70 genera. The fossil species are numbered by thousands and are included in several hundred genera.

Brachiopods appear with the earliest animals of the Lower Cambrian and are found fossilized in the marine strata of all subsequent geologic ages to the present. They are often extremely abundant and in some cases constitute the major portion of a rock. The phylum unquestionably originated in the Pre-Cambrian and at the beginning of the Lower Cambrian deployed very rapidly into the various marine environments of the time. Four of the five orders developed before the close of the Cambrian. Throughout the entire Paleozoic the brachiopods were always a very important part of the sessile benthos and attained their maximum development in the middle of the era. The number of genera decreased toward the close of the Paleozoic, and this decline has continued to the present. The most recent classification of the Brachiopoda[1] lists 702 valid genera, of which 456 are Paleozoic, 177 are Mesozoic, and 74 Cenozoic to Recent.

It has been customary to divide the phylum into two classes based on the nature of the union of the two valves. The *Inarticulata* either are without hinge-line structure or with such only poorly developed. This class is the older and the more primitive and represents the ancestral stock of the more specialized *Articulata*. In the Articulata hinge-line structures are well developed and are often quite complex. The Inarticulata include three orders which in increasing complexity are the *Palaeotremata*, *Atremata*, and *Neotremata*. The Articulata are divided into the two orders *Protremata* and *Telotremata*.

THE ANIMAL

Relation of Animal to Shell.—The brachiopod lives inside a calcareous, phosphatic, or chitinous shell composed of two *valves*, which when apposed surround and protect the vital parts of the organism. The shell is generally attached to some object on the bottom by means of a fleshy stalk, known as the *pedicle* or *peduncle*, protruding through an opening in the posterior part of the shell (Fig. 89). This anchoring device may be so short as to extend only a few millimeters beyond the shell or may range to several centimeters in length. In *Lingula* it is contractile and does not function for attachment but has the distal end modified into a tool for burrowing. In some brachiopods the pedicle is lost in maturity, and the animal is attached by cementation or

[1] Schuchert, C., and LeVene, C. M., Fossilium Catalogus, I. Animalia, Pars. 42, Brachiopoda (*Generum et Genotyporum et Bibliographia*) 140 pp., 1929.

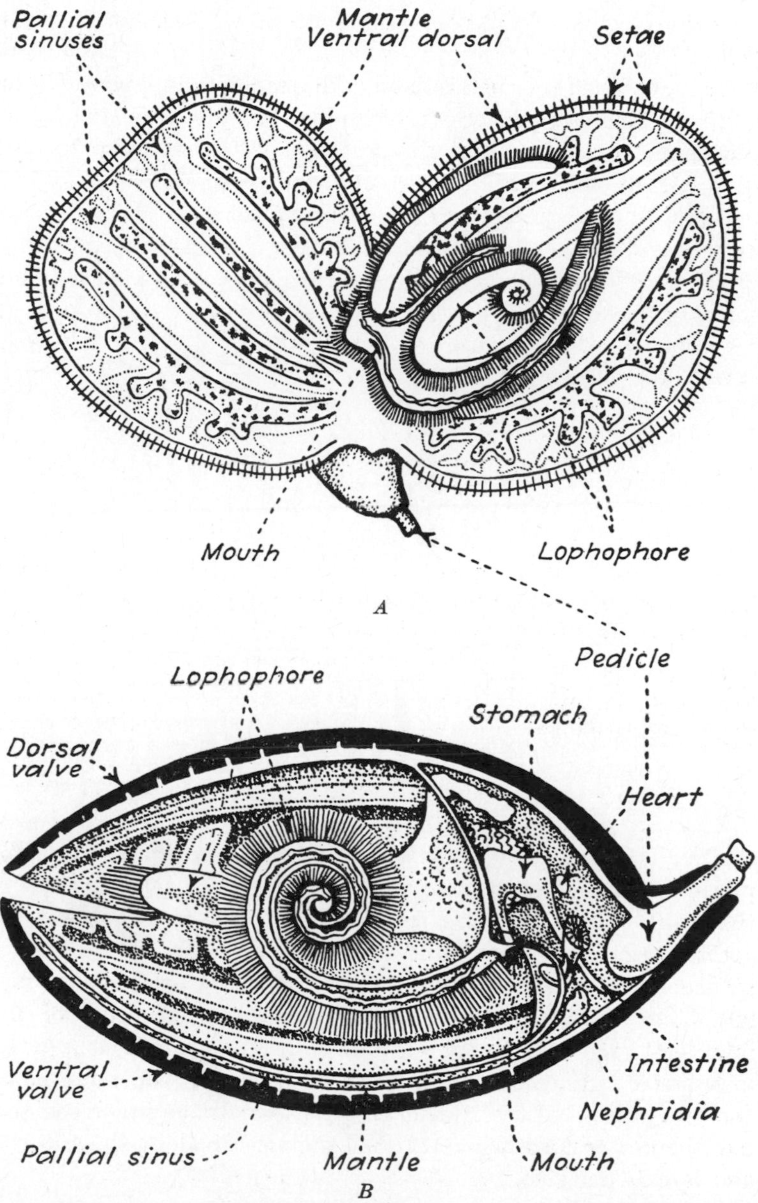

Fig. 89.—Structure of a modern brachiopod, *Magellania lenticularis*. *A*. The body removed from the shell and with the mantle lobes spread to show internal structure. *B*. Section of animal and shell along the plane of symmetry. Both figures are semidiagrammatic, with the lophophore represented as smaller proportionately than in the actual animal. (*After Parker and Haswell.*)

by spines or merely lies on the bottom without attachment (Fig. 93).

The interior of the shell is lined with a membrane, the *mantle* or *pallium*, the outer surface of which often has tiny tubular projections which extend into minute perforations in the shell (Fig. 89). The mantle is a part of the body wall and secretes the shell material. The outer part along the anterior margin is not attached to the shell, and the free edges frequently have horny bristles. The line along which the mantle becomes free from the shell is often marked by a faint depression in the shell known as

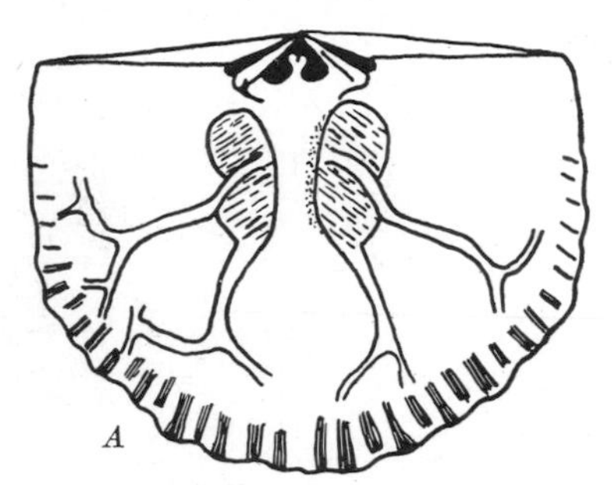

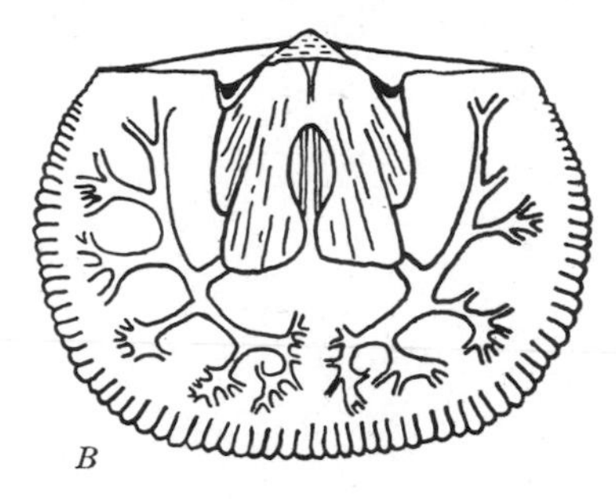

FIG. 90.—Pallial or vascular markings. *A*. Dorsal pallial markings in *Orthis rotundata*. The usual condition in the orthoid dorsal valve, of which this figure is representative, is a lateral trunk extending outward from between the posterior and anterior adductors and two anteriorly directed trunks arising on either side of the plane of symmetry at the anterior end of the anterior adductors. *B*. Ventral pallial markings in *Dinorthis* (*Plaesiomys*) *subquadrata*. The pallial trunks arise at the anterior extremities of the diductor scars. (*Both figures after Schuchert and Cooper.*)

the *pallial line*. Folding of the anterior part of the mantle produces tubular structures which are bounded on one side by the shell. These contain circulating fluids and in some cases the genital organs. Impressions of these tubes, known as *pallial sinuses* or *vascular markings*, are seen on many fossil shells (Fig. 90). The surface features, arrangement, and structure of the mantle are reflected in the various structures of the shell. The mantle enlarges the shell by increments along the margins of the two valves or by additions anywhere on the inner surface, but the greatest additions of shell matter are along the anterior and lateral margins.

The Visceral Cavity (Fig. 89).—The hollow cavity between the two lobes of the mantle (or the two valves of the shell) is divided by a transverse membranous partition into a small posterior and a large anterior region. The actual animal occupies the posterior cavity, which is therefore referred to as the *visceral cavity*. The mouth lies in the middle part of the transverse partition. Immediately posterior to it are the intestinal tract and *nephridia* or kidneys. The mouth opens into an esophagus and the latter into a stomach that narrows into a small intestine which is without an anal opening in the articulate brachiopods. In the inarticulate forms there is an anal opening situated ventrally below the

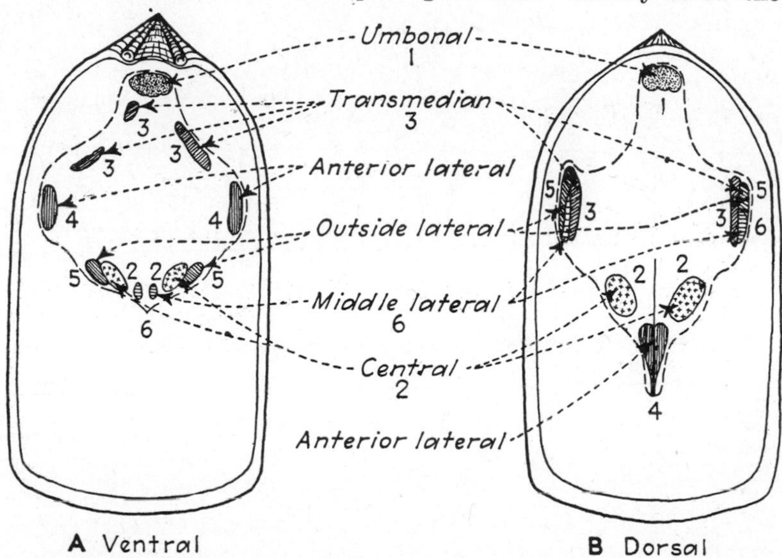

FIG. 91.—Muscle scars in inarticulate brachiopods. Simplified diagrams showing the number and arrangement of muscle scars in the common atremate, *Lingula anatina*. (*Adapted from Walcott after King.*)

mouth (*Crania*) or to the right of the mouth (*Lingula* and *Disciniscа*). The nephridia lie on each side of the intestine and serve both as excretory organs and as avenues for escape of the genital products. There is no heart, but circulation in the vascular sinuses is maintained by cilia. The nerve center is a circular ganglion surrounding the esophagus. The reproductive organs are in the lining of the body cavity, two on the dorsal and two on the ventral side, or in the pallial sinuses. The genital products are discharged into the visceral cavity and escape to the exterior through the outlet of the nephridia.

The Muscular System.—The muscles by which the shells of all brachiopods are opened and closed and by which the pedicle is adjusted lie in the visceral cavity. These muscles are attached to the interior surface of the valves and leave there various types of structures (depressions, sculptured elevated areas, etc.) known as *muscle scars*.

Shells of the Inarticulata have five pairs of muscles and one single muscle which are concerned with opening and closing the shell and with valve and pedicle adjustment (Fig. 91). The names and functions of these muscles are shown in Table 7, which explains Fig. 91.

TABLE 7.—EXPLANATORY CHART FOR FIG. 91, SHOWING THE NUMBER, NAMES, AND FUNCTIONS OF MUSCLES IN AN INARTICULATE BRACHIOPOD SHELL

Number on Fig. 91	Number of muscles	Name of muscles	Function
1	1	Adjustor, diductor, or umbonal	Separates or spreads valves by expansion
2	2	Adductors or centrals	Close shell by pulling the valves
3	2	Sliders or transmedians	Move the valves sideways
4 5 6	2 2 2	Protractors and retractors or laterals	Move valves forward and backward (longitudinally) with respect to each other

The living Articulata, or hinged shells, as represented by *Magellania*, have five pairs of muscles and a single muscle concerned with valve and pedicle movements. The two valves rotate on a definite line of turning, the *hinge-line*, and are restrained from slipping over each other sideways by teeth and sockets situated along that line. In the posterior part of the shell five *pedicle adjustors* leave five muscle scars on the valves (two on the dorsal and three on the ventral) (Fig. 92 *A*). Two pairs of diductors open the shell. These are attached at one extremity to the inner surface of the ventral valve, where the larger and more anterior pair of scars is made by the *principal diductors*, and the smaller and posterior pair by the *accessory diductors*. The latter are not always apparent on fossil shells. The other ends of the diductors are attached to a special plate, the *cardinal process*, near the posterior part of the dorsal valve. The principal diductors are attached to the anterior portion of the process, and

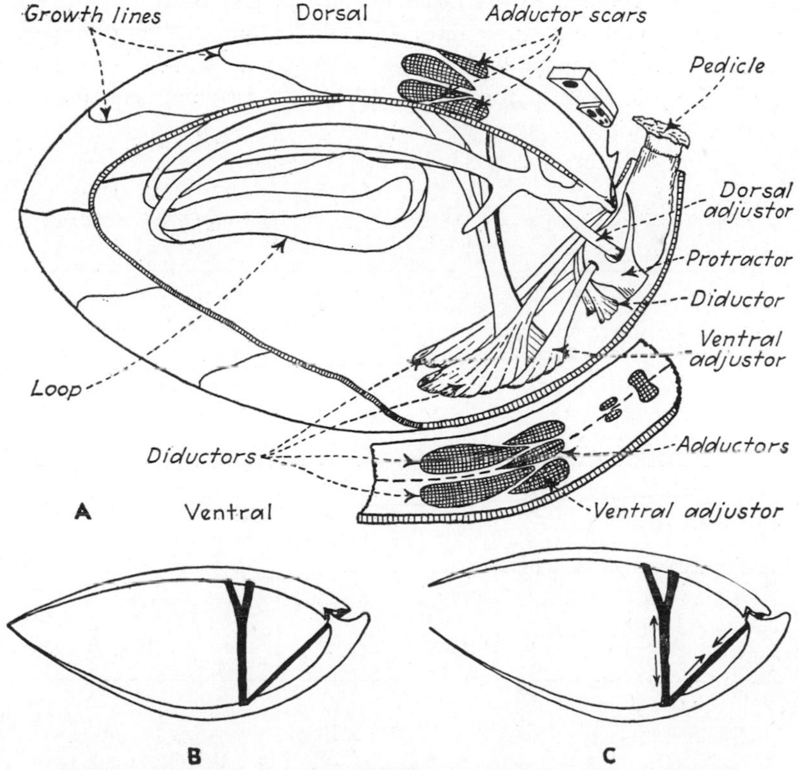

FIG. 92.—Muscular system of an articulate brachiopod. Somewhat diagrammatic drawing showing the muscular system and certain other internal structures of a modern telotrematous brachiopod (*Magellania flavescens*). *A*. The muscle scars of the dorsal valve are shown as though they could be seen through a transparent shell, and the ventral scars are shown on the diagram immediately beneath the shell. *B–C*. Diagrams showing the actions of the muscles when the valves are together and apart. (*A adapted from Gray after Hancock.*)

the accessory diductors to the posterior part. Since the base of the cardinal process is situated slightly posterior to the points of contact of the hinge structures on the two valves (Fig. 92 *C*), it is apparent that when the diductors contract the shell opens because of the lever-fulcrum principle. The long lever in this arrangement is the part of the dorsal valve anterior to the hinge teeth; the short lever is the part of the same posterior to the hinge teeth; and the teeth of the ventral valve form a fulcrum. The diductor muscles pass between the two hinge teeth. A pair of *adductors* pull the valves together and thus close the shell. These are attached to the inner surface of the ventral valve on either side of the median line, where an elongate heart-shaped double scar is made, and extend directly across the visceral cavity, splitting into four muscles before reaching the dorsal valve. Hence two pairs of muscle scars are left on the inner surface of the dorsal valve (Fig. 102 *A–B*).

TABLE 8.—EXPLANATORY CHART FOR FIG. 92, SHOWING THE NUMBER, NAMES, AND FUNCTIONS OF MUSCLES IN AN ARTICULATE BRACHIOPOD

Name of muscle	Number	Function
Adductors	2	Close the shell as the diductors relax. They are stretched when the shell is open
Principal diductors	2	Open the shell by contraction
Accessory diductors (or divaricators)	2	
Ventral adjustors	2	Adjust the pedicle
Dorsal adjustors	2	
Protractor (also a ventral adjustor)	1	

Since death and decomposition almost invariably result in the relaxation of the muscles, the shells of dead brachiopods, as well as fossil shells, are nearly always closed unless the valves have actually been separated. This situation is the reverse of that found in most pelecypods, for in the latter the mechanics of the hinge structures are such that the valves are forced apart on death.

The number, names, and functions of the various muscles in an articulate brachiopod are shown in Table 8, which is explanatory of Fig. 92.

The Brachial Cavity.—The anterior or *brachial cavity* is occupied by two coiled muscular appendages, the *arms* or *brachia,* which constitute the *lophophore.* The brachia arise on opposite sides of the mouth and extend toward the anterior margin of the shell. They are provided with nerves, closely spaced tentacles, and cilia. Along the upper side of the arm at the base of the tentacles is a ciliated groove, with the side opposite the tentacles extended into a liplike structure (Fig. 89). When occasion requires, the tentacles are retracted so as to come into contact with the edge of the lip and form a nearly closed tube. The cilia urge a current of water inward along this tube, and the small organisms that serve as food are thus carried into the mouth. The brachia function also for respiration and possess a circulatory tube.

Some brachiopods have a horseshoe-shaped lophophore; others have the brachia coiled into spirals. When the shell is open the latter may be unwound and extended outward beyond the anterior margin of the shell. In the more highly specialized brachiopods calcareous supports for the brachia are developed. These range from mere spikelike processes attached one on each side of the cardinal process to long spiral structures. All are grouped under the general term of *brachidia* (*brachidium*).

Attachment.—The earliest known brachiopods were attached to some object on the bottom either by direct cementation or by a strong, thick pedicle, and both habits are found among living species (Fig. 93). Cementation is considered a specialized mode of attachment, however, for evidence clearly indicates that the earliest brachiopods were attached by a pedicle, at least in the embryonic growth stages. Most living and fossil forms retain the pedicle for attachment throughout life, but in the Protremata and Telotremata its dimensions are commonly reduced.

The strong pedicle of the Palaeotremata and Atremata generally maintained, and in living forms maintains, the shell in a vertical position with the anterior side upward. In *Lingula*, however, attachment is relinquished in mature individuals, and the pedicle is modified for burrowing (Fig. 93 *L*). Among the Neotremata the ventral valve seems generally to have been on the underside with the pedicle emerging from a perforation in that valve. As the pedicle was shortened, the valve came nearer and nearer the object to which the shell was attached, until finally the apex of the ventral valve was cemented to the object, and the pedicle atrophied or was completely eliminated. In a few forms the ventral valve became cemented by its entire

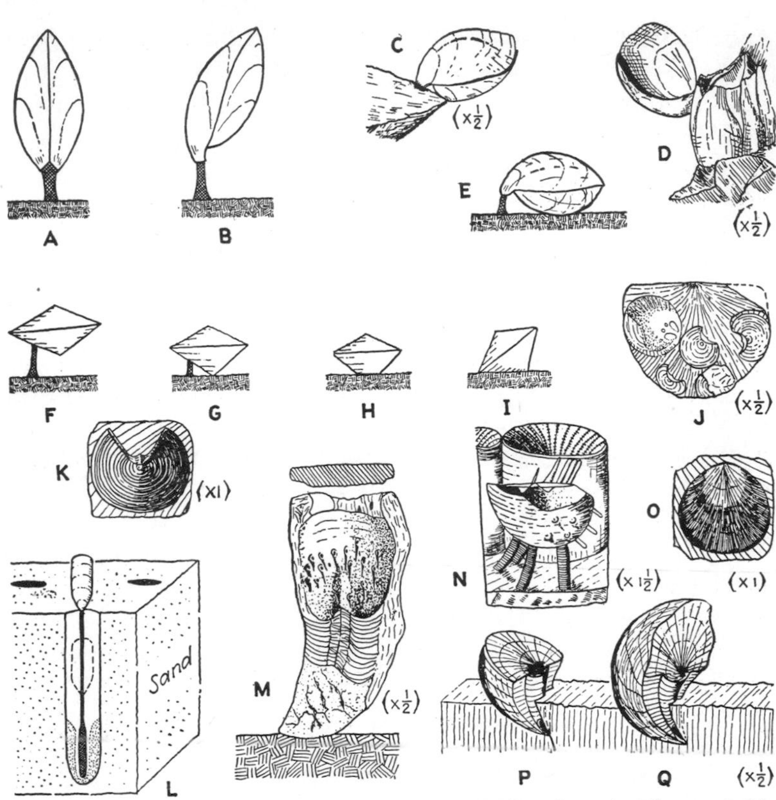

Fig. 93.—Modes of attachment among Brachiopoda. *A*. The probable living position of such simple forms as *Rustella*, etc. *B*, *E*. Common positions observed among modern terebratuloids. *C–D*. Two positions of *Terebratalia*, observed in Pacific waters. In *C* the ventral valve is up; in *D* it is down. *F–I*. Diagrammatic positions of certain neotremate brachiopods, based on living and fossil specimens. *J*. A valve of *Rafinesquina alternata* to which are attached several circular shells of *Schizocrania filosa*. *K*. The pedicle valve, natural size, seen on the extreme right of *J*. *L*. *Lingula anatina*, a modern burrowing atremate brachiopod with a long pedicle. *M*. *Richthofenia lawrenciana* from the Permian (Salt Range) of India. The conical ventral valve is cemented to the substratum, and the dorsal valve, shown in cross section, acts as a lid. The ventral valve is sectioned longitudinally to show the internal structure. *N*. *Strophalosia radicans*, the pedicle valve of a spinose brachiopod from the Devonian (Hamilton) of Michigan. The shell is attached to a corallite of *Prismatophyllum davidsoni* at several points. At the apex of the valve and also along the cardinal margin spines serve for attachment; on the convex surface of the valve large faintly annulated spines attach the valve to the substratum. *O*. Exterior view of a brachial valve of *Schizocrania filosa*, attached to the surface of *Rafinesquina alternata*. *P–Q*. Two specimens of *Clitambonites* in living position with beaks buried deeply in the substratum. *P* is a young individual that still possesses a short pedicle. The larger specimen is an adult and has lost the pedicle. (*All diagrams more or less diagrammatic and simplified. C–D after Fenton and Fenton; J–K, N–O after Hall and Clarke; M after Waagen; P–Q after Öpik.*)

surface, and every trace of pedicle opening disappeared (Fig. 93 *F–I*).

In the Protremata the ventral valve is usually above and the dorsal below. Some forms, however, show the reverse, as in *Derbya*, a genus in which the pedicle was lost and the shell was cemented to the bottom by the beak of the ventral valve. Many *Strophomena* also lost the pedicle in maturity, but instead of cementing the valve to the bottom they lay unattached. Most members of the family *Productidae* upon losing the pedicle utilized spines for anchorage. Beginning in the Permian a family of Protremata, the *Richthofenidae*, became cemented by the beak of the ventral valve, and this valve then assumed a conical shape (Fig. 93 *M*). The bottom of the valve became filled with cystose structures, some of which resemble tabulae, and took on much of the character of a cyathophylloid coral except for lacking septa. The dorsal valve meanwhile was modified to become little more than an operculum. The only living representatives of the Protremata still retain this method of fixation.

Representatives of the Telotremata tend to be attached by a pedicle with the ventral valve upward and the dorsal on the underside.

THE SHELL

General Considerations.—The embryonic shell of a brachiopod, designated the *protegulum*, consists fundamentally of three plates (Fig. 94): (1) a convex ventral plate, the *ventral* or *pedicle valve*, attached to the ventral or abdominal part of the animal; (2) a convex dorsal plate, the *dorsal* or *brachial valve*, attached to the dorsal side of the animal; and (3) a plate, known as the *prodeltidium*, which is attached to the dorsal side of the animal and ultimately fuses to the ventral plate completely to surround the pedicle. At this stage it becomes the *deltidium*. These three plates are present in the early growth stages as described, but in the mature shell they may become greatly modified, and the deltidium may be lost.

None of the terms used above for the valves is particularly fitting. Dorsal and ventral can hardly have the same meaning in different brachiopods. Brachial is used because the calcareous supports for the brachia are attached to the dorsal valve, but in those forms lacking brachidia the brachia may belong as much to one valve as to the other. Furthermore, the term pedicle, as applied to the so-called ventral valve, does very well for the Neotremata, Protremata, and Telotremata but has no significance in the Palaeotremata and Atremata, because in the latter two divisions the pedicle emerges freely through an opening shared by both valves.

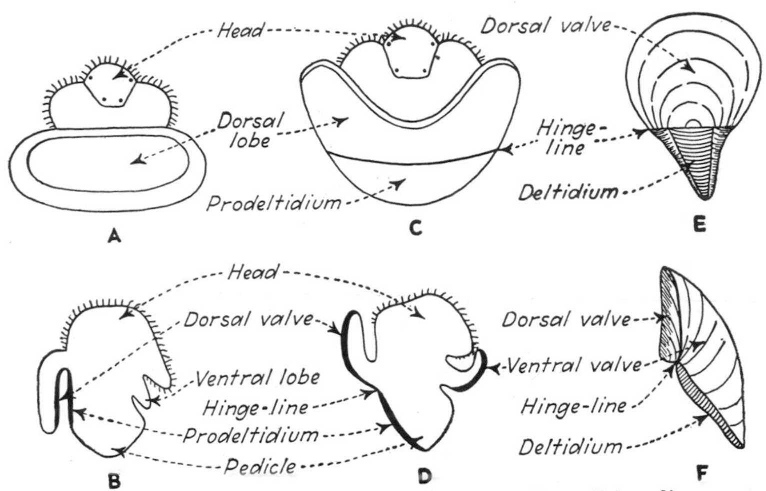

FIG. 94.—Development of a brachiopod, *Thecidium* (*Lacazella*) *mediterraneum*. *A*. A late embryonic stage, viewed dorsally. *B*. Dorsoventral longitudinal section of an embryo similar to *A*, showing the incipient development of the dorsal valve and prodeltidium. *C*. An embryo representing a later growth stage than *A*, viewed dorsally. *D*. Dorsoventral longitudinal section of *C* showing the relative positions and degree of development of the three plates of the protegulum. *E–F*. Dorsal and lateral views of an adult shell showing the relations of the valves and the deltidium, which has developed from the prodeltidium. (*A–C after Beecher from Kovalevski; D–F after Beecher.*)

The valves of a brachiopod are equilateral but of different sizes and shapes. The ventral valve is generally larger than the dorsal, and its pointed apex, the *beak*, usually projects over the rounded beak of the dorsal valve. It tends also to be somewhat more convex than the dorsal, though this condition is frequently reversed.

The shell is bilaterally symmetrical, with the plane of symmetry passing through the apices of the valves and the middle of the anterior margin (Fig. 95). The *length* of the shell is measured along the plane of symmetry, the *width* at right angles to this plane where the shell is widest, and the *thickness* in the plane roughly at right angles to the valves.

The part of the brachiopod shell adjacent to the pedicle and containing the viscera is designated *posterior;* that containing the brachia, *anterior.* Shells in the living position may have the posterior, dorsal, or ventral part up or down, but when illustrated the posterior side is usually placed upward.

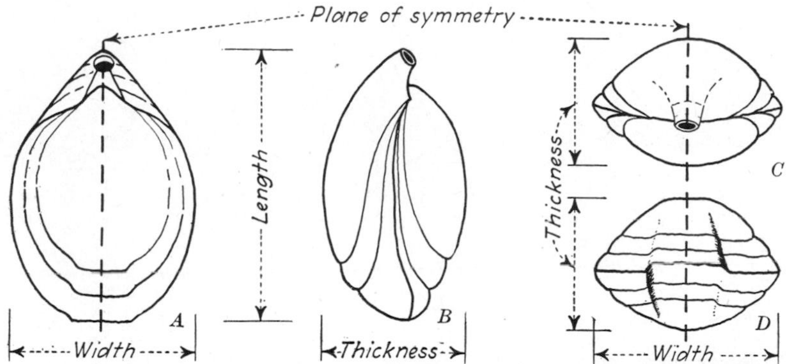

FIG. 95.—Diagrammatic figures, based on *Magellania flavescens*, a modern telotrematous brachiopod, showing position of plane of symmetry and lines along which dimensions are determined. *A.* Dorsal view showing several prominent growth lines on the dorsal valve and the circular pedicle opening near the beak of the ventral valve. *B.* Lateral view showing the relative convexity of the two valves. *C.* Hinge-line view showing nature of union of valves along the hinge line and position of pedicle opening. *D.* Anterior view showing commissure and faint fold on ventral (upper) and sinus on dorsal valves.

Shape and Size of the Shell.—The ultimate shape of the brachiopod shell (seen dorsally or ventrally) depends upon the way additions are made to the more or less triangular valves of the protegulum, and the size depends upon the species and stage of growth. If additions to the shell are made equally on the lateral and anterior margins, the mature shell will have the same general shape as the protegulum at any time during its growth. If additions are made more rapidly at some points than at others, the shape of the shell will depart more or less widely from the shape of the embryonic shell. The posterior margin of the shell is termed the *hinge* or *cardinal margin.* This margin may be less than the greatest width of the shell, equal to that width, or greater than it. In a few forms it is produced laterally for an unusual distance, and the shell is described as *alate.* The ends of the cardinal margin may be rounded or angular, with the angularity ranging from acute to obtuse. Ordinarily there is a curve in the surface of the shell anteriorly from the termination of the cardinal margin.

In most shells the ventral valve is convex, but the dorsal varies considerably as shown in Fig. 96. *Biconvex* shells are

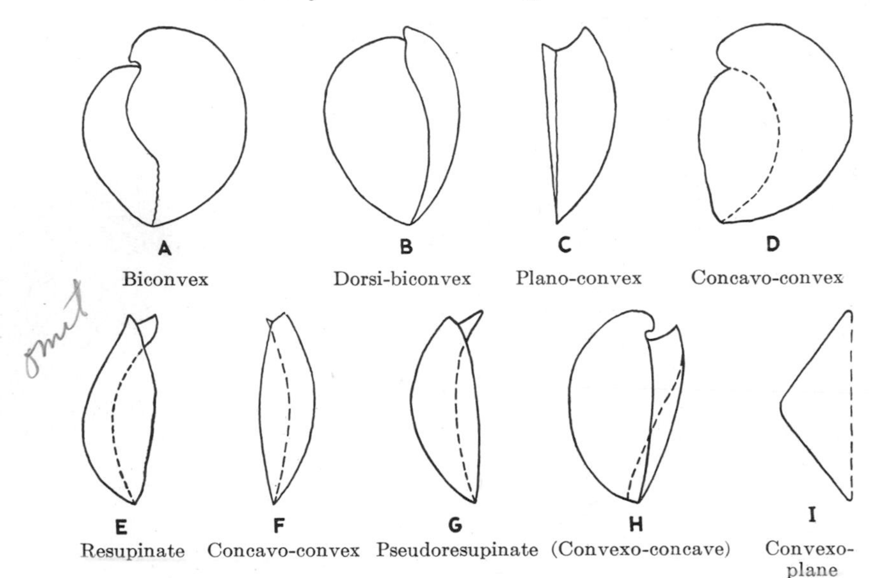

FIG. 96.—Lateral views of brachiopods to show convexity and concavity of valves. *A*. Biconvex shell represented by *Conchidium*. *B*. Dorsi-biconvex shell illustrated by *Atrypa*. *C*. Plano-convex shell common among the orthids. *D*. Concavo-convex shell, a form characteristic of the Productids. *E*. Resupinate shell well illustrated by *Strophomena*. *F*. A thin concavo-convex shell such as that found in *Rafinesquina*. *G–H*. Pseudoresupinate or convexo-concave shells. *G*. A form found in *Valcourea*. *H*. A shape characteristic of *Hebertella*. *I*. Convexo-plane shell characteristic of many conical neotremate shells which are cemented by the entire surface of the ventral valve.

All of the figures are semidiagrammatic. In all cases the left valve is dorsal; the right, ventral. Dashed lines indicate the position of the concealed valve along the plane of symmetry.

those in which both valves are convex. Forms in which the dorsal is more convex than the ventral are *dorsi-biconvex*. Shells with convex ventral valves and plane dorsal ones are described as *plano-convex;* those with convex ventrals and concave dorsals are designated *concavo-convex*. If the shell begins concavo-convex or plano-convex and then becomes reversed in maturity—the arrangement illustrated by *Strophomena* and some of its allies—the shell is described as *resupinate*. Shells which are convexo-concave, without the incipient flat stage in the dorsal valve, a condition well illustrated by many orthids such as *Valcourea*, may be designated *convexo-concave* or *pseudoresupinate*. It is to be noted that in all of the descriptive terms just used the first term refers to the dorsal valve; the second, to the ventral. This is purely arbitrary, and some authors prefer the reverse.

The dimensions of brachiopod shells vary considerably. Adult shells range from a few millimeters to as much as 8 to 12 cm. wide or long, and a large productid species, *Productus* (*Gigantella*) *giganteus*, from the Carboniferous reached 300 mm. (12 in.) in width and 225 mm. (9 in.) in length. Length and width, however, seldom exceed 25 mm. (1 in.).

Composition and Structure of Shell Material.—The shells of brachiopods are composed of *chitin*, *calcium phosphate*, *calcium carbonate*, or some combination of these materials. The dorsal and ventral lobes and other parts of the mantle, and to a lesser degree the pedicle, secrete the shell material. Additions are made chiefly along the lateral and anterior margins of the valves and on the interior surfaces in the anterior region.

Shells composed of chitinous, or horny, and calcareous materials have these substances arranged in alternating layers (Fig. 97 *A*). Many of the Palaeotremata very likely had such shells, and Atremata still possess them. The shells of most brachiopods, however, are composed almost entirely of calcite. In these the shell matter is arranged in three layers (Fig. 97 *G*). On the outside is a thin layer of chitin, known as the *periostracum*, which is rarely if ever preserved in fossils. It is similar to the black, chitinous layer found on the exterior of clam and mussel shells. Lying next to the periostracum, and forming the exterior of fossil forms, is the thin *laminated layer*, so named because it consists of thin, parallel laminae of calcite. These laminae are arranged approximately parallel with the surface of the shell. The thick inside layer of shell matter is designated the *prismatic layer* because it is composed of prisms of calcite obliquely disposed with respect to the laminae of the laminated layer with which these prisms make an acute angle anteriorly. Growth takes place to some degree around the margin of the shell but mainly over the entire inner surface, and the shell matter is secreted by the mantle proper. The prismatic layer as it thickens obliterates crenulations and other inequalities on the inner

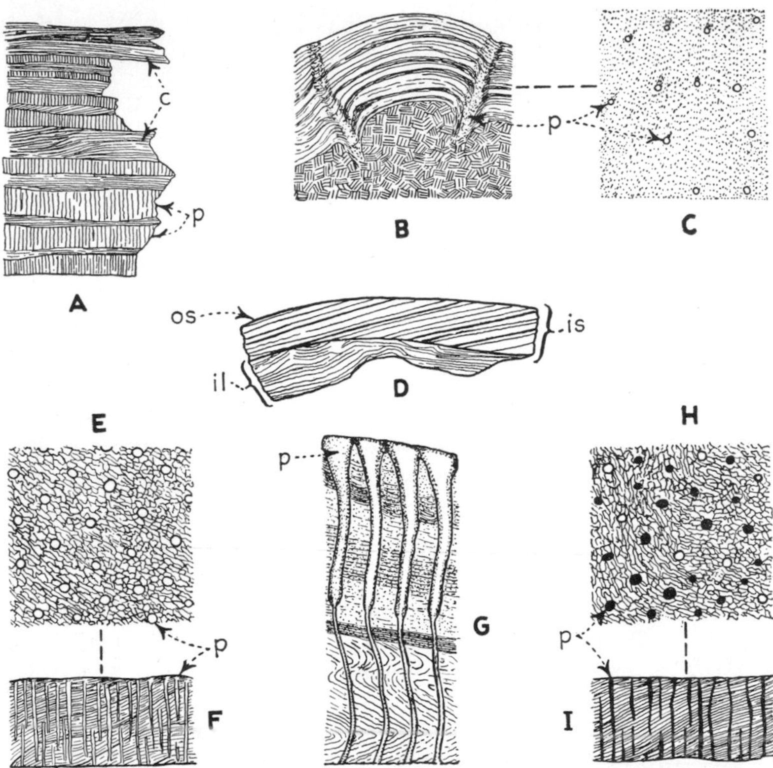

Fig. 97.—Structure of brachiopod shell matter. *A*. Transverse section of *Lingula anatina*, showing the alternating layers of corneous matter (*c*) and mineral matter (*p*), with vertical perforations. *B–C*. Transverse and tangential sections of the shell of *Strophomena aculeata* showing the minute perforations (*p*) and the laminated nature of the calcareous matter. *D*. Median, longitudinal thin section through the central part of a ventral valve of *Lingulella acutangula* showing the thin, structureless outer layer (*os*); the obliquely laminated inner layer (*is*); and the interior crinkled lamellae (*il*) produced by the thickening of the shell. *E–F*. Tangential and transverse sections of the shell of the modern *Magellania flavescens* showing the minute perforations (*p*) and the obliquely laminated calcareous matter. *G*. Highly magnified transverse section of a small portion of the shell of *Magellania australis* showing the trumpet-like punctae (*p*) and also the contraction in size in the inner (probably later) layer. *H–I*. Tangential and transverse sections of the shell of *Cyrtina hamiltonensis* showing the same features as *E–F*, with which they should be compared. The punctae are largely filled with iron oxide. (*A from Davidson, after Gratiolet; B–C after Davidson; D after Walcott; E–F after Nicholson and Lydekker; G after Davidson; H–I after Nicholson and Lydekker.*)

surface. The development of the two calcareous layers is variable.

The angle at which new material is added determines the convexity or concavity of the valves. The hinge structures determine the extent to which a shell may be opened, and if material is added to a shell at high angles there is corresponding decrease in the opening of the shell. Additional shell material may be added to the interior of the valves as growth proceeds, making these progressively thicker, particularly in the posterior or older part. On the other hand, it is possible for the valves to be reduced in thickness by resorption. Boring animals and other predaceous organisms often reduce the thickness of the valves, whereas sedentary incrusting forms such as corals, worms, bryozoans, small brachiopods, and barnacles commonly attach themselves to living or dead shells and subsequently add much bulk to them. The normal structure of the shell substance in some individuals is interrupted by injuries which have been repaired.

The valves of a brachiopod shell may be solid, or they may be perforated by small tubes or pores termed *punctae* (Fig. 97). A shell with such perforations is said to be *punctate.* Among certain genera the inner prismatic layer is perforated by minute tubuli known as *endopunctae.* These tubes extend from the mantle to the base of the laminated layer but never extend through the latter to the exterior surface. In living shells these are filled by tiny, blind tubular extensions of the mantle. Some shells have pores in the outer laminated layer, and these usually are readily visible on the unworn exterior. They do not penetrate far into the shell material and never pass completely through the prismatic layer to the interior surface. Such perforations are known as *exopunctae.* The presence of punctae may often be demonstrated by treating the surfaces of a valve with a weak solution of hydrochloric acid.

Surface Characteristics.—The shells of most primitive brachiopods are smooth on the exterior except for the concentric growth lines, and these are often barely visible. The shells of very young individuals of all species also tend to be smooth, but with increased age and added growth there is nearly always some development of ornamentation (Fig. 98).

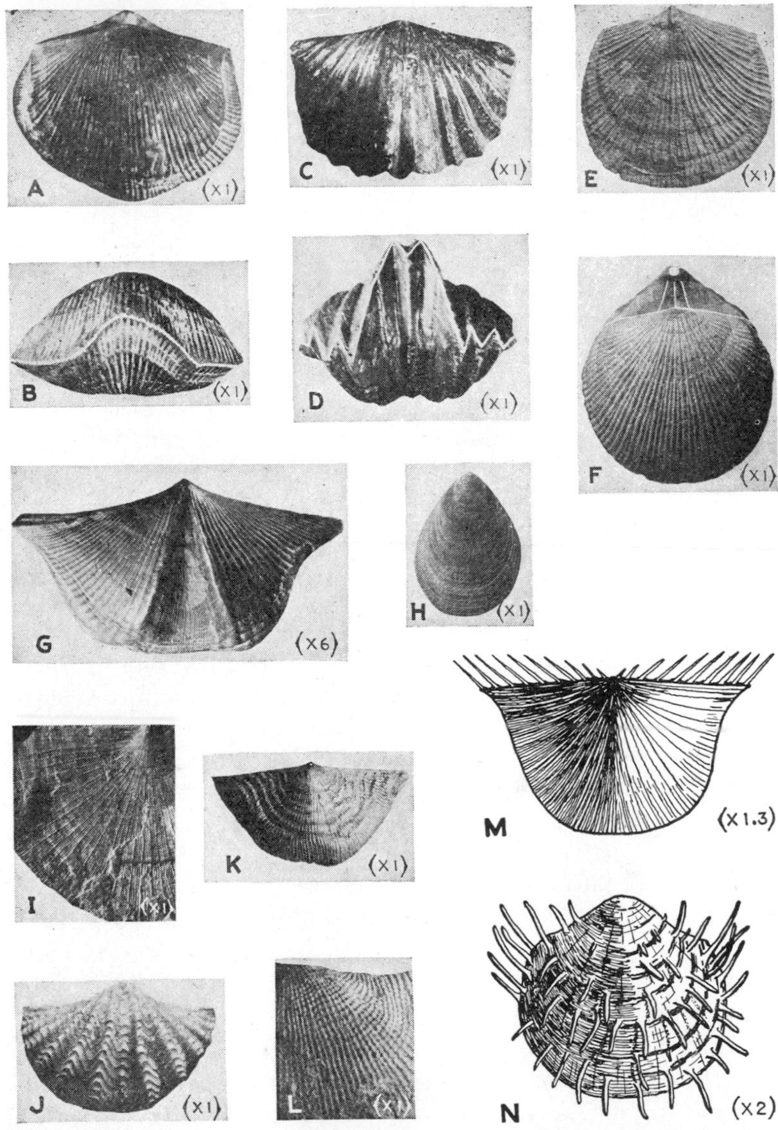

Fig. 98.—External surface ornamentation. *A–B*. Dorsal and anterior views of *Hebertella*, showing rounded radial costae on both valves, simple fold on dorsal valve, and sinus on ventral. *C–D*. Dorsal and anterior views of *Platystrophia* showing a few angular radial costae, a very sharp costate fold on the dorsal valve, and a sinus on the ventral. *E*. Ventral view of *Hemipronites* showing a series of alternating large and small radial costae and several prominent growth lines. *F*. Dorsal view of *Trigonosemus* showing prominent rounded radial costae

The rounded or pointed posterior extremity of the valve, known as the *beak,* is usually more conspicuous on the ventral valve. It is situated in the middle of the cardinal margin except in certain Neotremata. The two convex plates of the initial shell, the protegulum, are on the posterior extremity of the beaks and constitute the initial part of each valve. These initial valves usually are destroyed in fossilization. The rounded posterior portion of each valve adjacent to the beak is termed the *umbo.* Growth proceeds around the protegulum, mainly along the anterior and lateral margins of the two valves; hence growth lines tend to be disposed concentric to the beaks. By a study of the growth lines it is possible to determine the shape of the shell during all stages of its development, and such studies are of great importance in elucidating the ontogeny of a species.

Many brachiopod shells have minute ridges, known as *striations,* radiating from the beaks. These are thought to have been formed by rows of closely spaced setae on the surface of the mantle. In some of the more advanced brachiopods the mantle is crenulated or wrinkled along the anterior margin, and these corrugations are reflected on the exterior of the shell in the form of coarse radial ridges separated by prominent troughs. Such ridges are known as *plications* or *costae.* Shells possessing them are described as *plicate* or *costate.* They serve to lock firmly the anterior margins of the valves. Because of subsequent additions to the interior of the valves, costae are usually less conspicuous on the interior than on the exterior, and they may be covered entirely.

The radially disposed ridges (striations, plications, or costae) and associated troughs increase by bifurcation or by new ridges being implanted between preexisting ones. Not uncommonly,

---

and also several hinge structures. *G.* Ventral view of *Spirifer* showing prominent finely striated sinus flanked by strong, rounded, radial costae. *H.* Ventral view of *Lingulella* showing numerous growth lines. *I.* Portion of surface of *Rafinesquina* showing prominent radial striae alternating with a band of finer striations. *J.* Ventral view of *Spirifer* showing a few very prominent costae on which crenulated growth lines are conspicuous. There is also a faint sinus. *K.* Ventral view of *Leptaena* showing conspicuous growth lines crossed by radial striae. *L.* A small section of the posterior part of the ventral valve of *Dictyoclostus* showing radial striae crossed by concentric ridges, the whole having a reticulated appearance. *M.* Restoration of the ventral exterior of *Chonetes* showing the prominent spines which rise from the cardinal margin. *N.* Ventral exterior of a productid showing characteristic spines rising from the surface of the valve and usually associated with the growth lines. (*N adapted from Davidson.*)

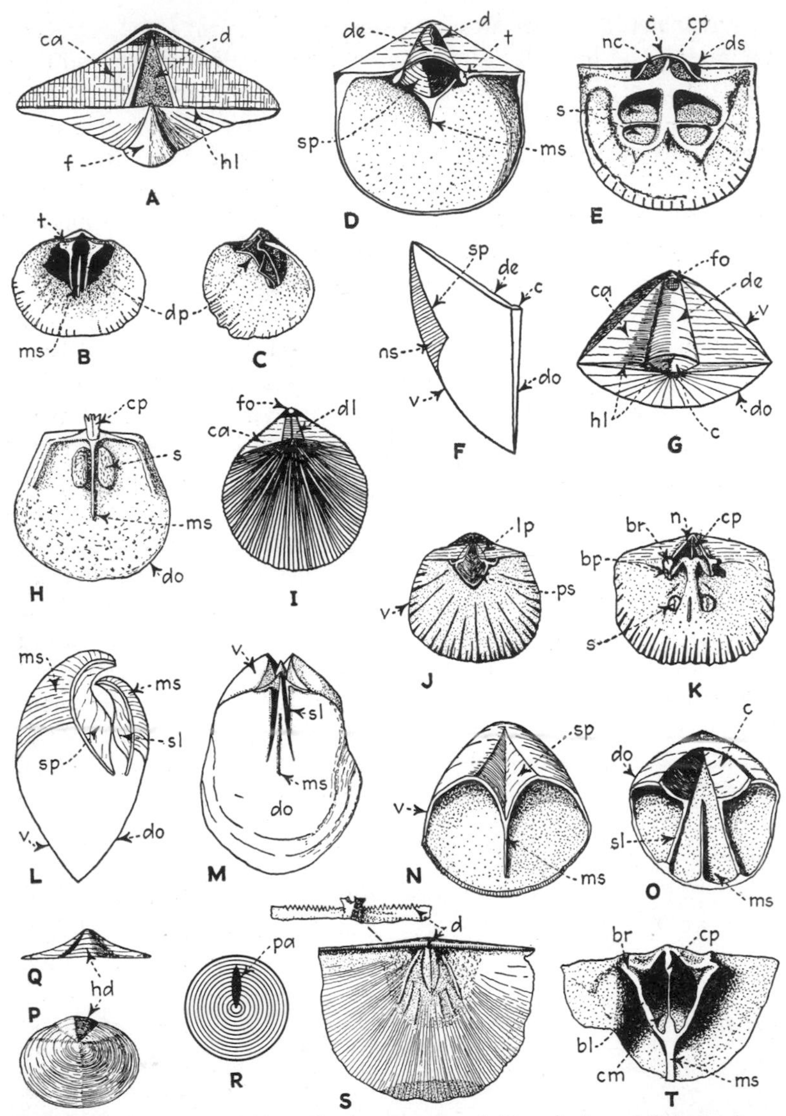

FIG. 99.—Brachiopod hinge-line structures. *A.* Dorsal view of *Spirifer* showing high cardinal area, large triangular delthyrium, and fold on dorsal exterior. *B–C.* Ventral interior of *Enteletes* showing teeth, dental plates, and very prominent median septum. *D–G.* Ventral interior, dorsal interior, longitudinal section, and hinge-line views of *Clitambonites.* *H.* Dorsal interior of *Juresania* showing prominent trifid cardinal process. *I.* Dorsal view of *Trigonosemus* showing deltidial plates and foramen. *J.* Ventral interior of *Glossorthis* showing lateral plates and pseudospondylium. *K.* Dorsal interior of *Dolerorthis* showing noto-

large ridges may alternate with smaller ones, and the former are striated in some species. If the surface of the shell has both radial ridges and concentric growth lines, or concentric striations not connected with growth lines, it will have a reticulated or checkered appearance (Fig. 98 *L*). Ornamental *spines* and *nodes* frequently arise where ridges and growth lines intersect. Spines may also develop along the hinge line or on the cardinal margin (Fig. 98 *M–N*). Brachiopod spines can usually be differentiated from the spines of other shells by their laminated structure and hollow character.

A few of the more highly developed brachiopods exhibit a large *fold* or *plica* along the plane of symmetry in one valve and a corresponding depression, the *sinus* or *sulcus*, on the other valve (Fig. 98 *A–D, G*). The fold and sinus of the early part of the shell may reverse position in the later part of the mature shell. A single or compound fold or sulcus may occur on either valve. The fold and sinus may be smooth or crenulated by striations or plications. They serve effectively as locking devices along the anterior margin, and one investigator has suggested that they may have been developed for facilitating the entrance and exit of water currents which aerated the mantle and brought in food.

Structures on the Cardinal Margin.—The line along which the valves join posteriorly and also along which they turn is designated the hinge line. It is usually a straight line contact in articulate forms but must of necessity be an imaginary line in

---

thyrium, brachiophores, and brachiophore processes. *L–M*. Longitudinal section and dorsal view of filling of *Pentamerus* showing prominent spondylium, large median septa, and well-developed crural plates. *N–O*. Magnified portion of ventral interior (*N*) and of dorsal interior (*O*) of *Conchidium* showing prominent spondylium and crural and internal plates. *P–Q*. Exterior and posterior views of *Micromitra* (*Paterina*) showing well-developed homeodeltidium (pseudodeltidium). *R*. Ventral exterior of *Orbiculoidea* showing the concentric growth lines and slitlike pedicle aperture. *S*. Ventral interior of *Stropheodonta* showing prominent denticulation along the hinge line. *T*. Dorsal interior of *Linoporella* showing a cruralium formed by the union of the brachiophore plates with the floor of the valve. (*B–C after Dunbar and Condra; J–L after Schuchert and Cooper; N–O adapted from Schuchert and Cooper; P–Q after Walcott; S after Hall and Clarke; T after Schuchert and Cooper.*)

br, brachiophore; *bl*, brachiophore plate; *bp*, brachiophore process; *c*, chilidium; *ca*, cardinal area; *cp*, cardinal process; *cr*, crural plates; *cm*, cruralium; *d*, delthyrium; *dc*, delthyrial cavity; *de*, deltidium; *dl*, deltidial plates; *dn*, denticle; *do*, dorsal; *dp*, dental plate; *ds*, dental socket; *f*, fold; *fo*, foramen; *hd*, homeodeltidium (pseudodeltidium); *hl*, hinge line; *lp*, lateral plate; *ms*, median septum; *n*, notothyrium; *nc*, notothyrial cavity; *pa*, pedicle aperture; *ps*, pseudospondylium; *s*, muscle scar; *sl*, septal plate; *sp*, spondylium; *t*, tooth.

inarticulate species. In shells of the former the hinge line is often either partially or completely minutely *denticulated* (Fig. 99 *S*). These denticulations may assist in more firmly locking the shell.

Between the hinge line and beak of many articulate shells is a plane or curved surface known as the *cardinal area*, *interarea*, or *palintrope* (Fig. 99 *A, D, I*). The area on the ventral valve is

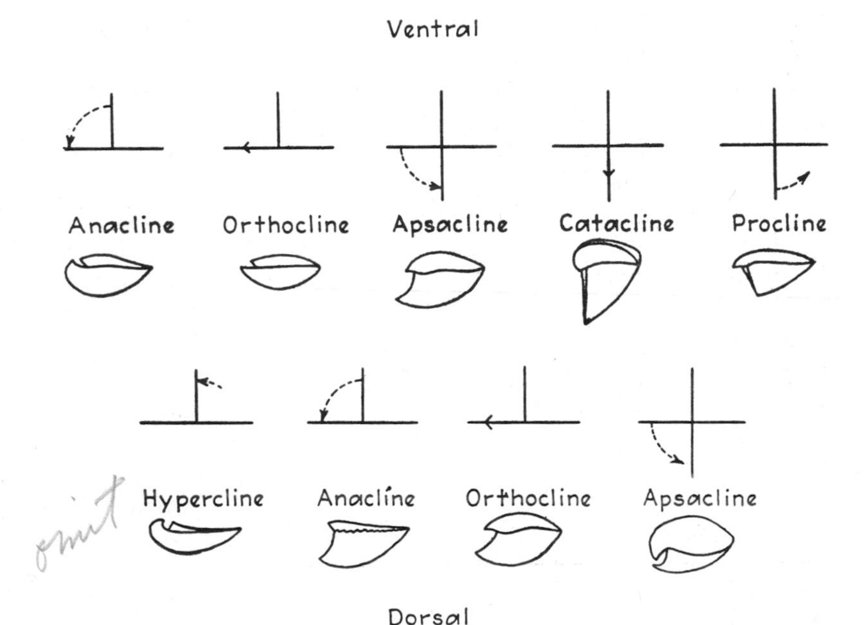

FIG. 100.—Diagrams showing the various positions of the dorsal and ventral cardinal areas or interareas to the plane of commissure. (*After Schuchert and Cooper.*)

invariably wider than that on the dorsal and is often conspicuously triangular in shape, which is in accord with the growth and enlargement of the shell. In some species it attains a width of fully half an inch. Cardinal areas usually are ornamented by growth lines parallel to the hinge line, and they may also have lines perpendicular to or slightly inclined to that line. They are characteristic of the articulate brachiopods, but similar areas may occur rarely in shells of the Inarticulata, in which case they are designated *pseudointerareas* or *pseudocardinal areas*.

The cardinal areas stand at different angles with respect to a plane, the *plane* of *commissure*, passing between the valves and including the hinge line. This angular relation is described by six different terms depending upon the inclination of the area.[1] The different types are illustrated in Fig. 100 and described in Table 9. In order to determine the position of the area, the shell is placed in such position that the plane of commissure is horizontal, and the ventral valve down.

TABLE 9.—EXPLANATORY TABLE FOR FIG. 100 DESCRIBING THE DIFFERENT POSITIONS OF THE CARDINAL AREAS WITH RESPECT TO THE PLANE OF COMMISSURE

(After Schuchert and Cooper)

Name	Valve	Position
Anacline	Ventral and dorsal	Between vertical and horizontal
Orthocline	Ventral and dorsal	Areas horizontal and parallel to the plane of commissure
Apsacline	Ventral and dorsal	Between 90 and 180 deg. from the erect vertical
Catacline	Ventral	Bent down 90 deg. from the horizontal
Procline	Ventral	Area bent more than 180 deg. from the erect vertical or more than 90 deg. from the horizontal
Hypercline	Dorsal	Area rotated in an anterior direction more than 90 deg.

While the exact purpose of the cardinal areas is not certain, they seem to have been a device for keeping the beaks apart so that the shell might be opened more widely. The beaks of each valve usually overhang their respective cardinal areas to a greater or lesser extent, with the ventral beak more prominently so. Brachiopods with narrow and small interareas may have the ventral beak overhanging to such an extent that it conceals the dorsal.

[1] SCHUCHERT, C., and COOPER, G. A., Brachiopod genera of the suborders Orthoidea and Pentameroidea, *Mem. Peabody Mus. Nat. Hist.*, vol. IV, pt. I, pp. 20–21, 1932.

The Pedicle Opening.—The opening through which the fleshy pedicle or stalk protrudes is referred to in a broad way as the *pedicle opening*. It may be a large gap between the valves, a restricted perforation shared by both valves, or a perforation limited to the ventral valve. In no known brachiopod is the pedicle opening restricted to the dorsal valve.

In the ventral valves of articulate shells a triangular opening known as the *delthyrium* perforates the middle of the cardinal area (Fig. 99 *A*). The pedicle emerges through a part or all of this opening. In the young stages the pedicle is large enough to occupy the entire perforation, but as growth continues the delthyrium enlarges, through additions to the cardinal area along the hinge line, and the pedicle no longer fills the opening. Closure of the unoccupied space proceeds along one of two lines. The ventral mantle may extend two lobes which deposit calcareous matter along the sides of the delthyrium adjacent to the hinge line in the form of a plate on each side, and these may ultimately meet and firmly unite at the hinge line along the median line of the delthyrium to form a single plate. If the two plates are distinct they are referred to as *deltidial plates* (Fig. 102 *B*); if united so as to form what appears to be a single plate, it is called a *pseudodeltidium* or *deltarium*. As a result of this method of closure, unique to the Telotremata, the pedicle is restricted to an opening immediately anterior to the ventral beak. In some instances the pedicle migrates by resorption of the shell into the beak, and then the delthyrium is completely closed by the plates. Plates, termed *lateral plates* (Fig. 99 *J*), develop in a somewhat similar manner in some Protremata.

The second method of closure of the delthyrium is confined to the Protremata. Before the brachiopod becomes fixed by the pedicle, the *prodeltidium*—one of the three fundamental plates of the protegulum—fuses with the posterior margin of the ventral valve, then spans the delthyrial opening and closes the space not occupied by the pedicle. At the same time, or subsequently, the pedicle may resorb shell matter beneath or in the beak and assume a position determined by the extent of the resorption. The plate developed in the manner described is designated the *deltidium* (Fig. 99 *D*, *G*).

In a few Telotremata the delthyrium is continued interiorly as an open tube along the dorsal side of the valve. This tube, the *syrinx*, is really a kind of open sheath for the pedicle and is well developed in *Syringothyris* (Fig. 101). Many Telotremata, and even more Protremata, have a dorsal counterpart of the ventral delthyrium. This aperture or cleft in the dorsal cardinal area is known as the *notothyrium* (Fig. 99 *K*) and is closed by a single plate, the *chilidium* (Fig. 103 *A*), which is the dorsal equivalent of the deltidium, or by two discrete plates known as *chilidial plates*.

In some of the more primitive inarticulate brachiopods there is a gap in the posterior part of the shell through which the pedicle emerges. This opening may be thought of as constituting an

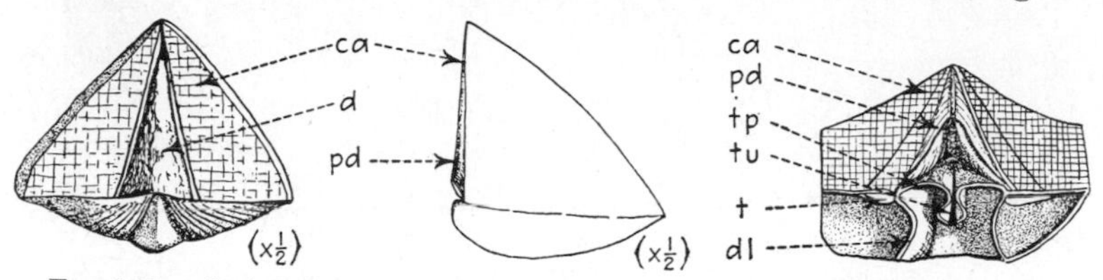

FIG. 101.—*Syringothyris*, a common Upper Devonian and Mississippian telotrematous brachiopod. *A*. Hinge-line view showing small dorsal valve and large ventral valve, which has an unusually large and high cardinal area (*ca*) and delthyrium (*d*). No covering is shown over the delthyrium. *B*. Lateral view of same specimen diagrammatically showing cardinal area (*ca*) and pseudodeltidium (*pd*). *C*. Hinge-line view of part of the ventral valve showing the cardinal area (*ca*), pseudodeltidium (*pd*), transverse plate (*tp*) and incomplete tube (*tu*) under it, teeth (*t*), and dental plates or lamellae (*dl*). (*A and C adapted from Davidson; B diagrammatic.*)

incipient delthyrium and *incipient notothyrium*. As the shell grows, additions are made about the margin of this gap, and there is deflection of the growth lines to take care of the opening, forming one structure in the ventral valve, the *homeodeltidium* (not homologous with deltidium apparently), and one in the dorsal designated by the term *pseudochilidium*. The former is well exhibited in the primitive palaeotremates *Rustella* and *Paterina* (Fig. 99 *P–Q*). In some Neotremata the pedicle opening seems to be confined to the ventral valve and to be retained at the margin of that valve for some time, but as the valve increases in size, shell matter is added in such a way that the growth lines and other shell features surround the opening without being deflected by it (Fig. 99 *R*). The pedicle opening and protegulum are then no longer at the margin but in some position near the center of the valve. The pedicle may migrate closer to the protegulum and even through to the anterior side of the valve.

During the migration, the pedicle opening is closed progressively on the posterior side by increments which constitute a plate designated the *listrium*.

Internal Skeletal Structures.—The hinge line of a brachiopod shell has already been defined as the line along which articulation

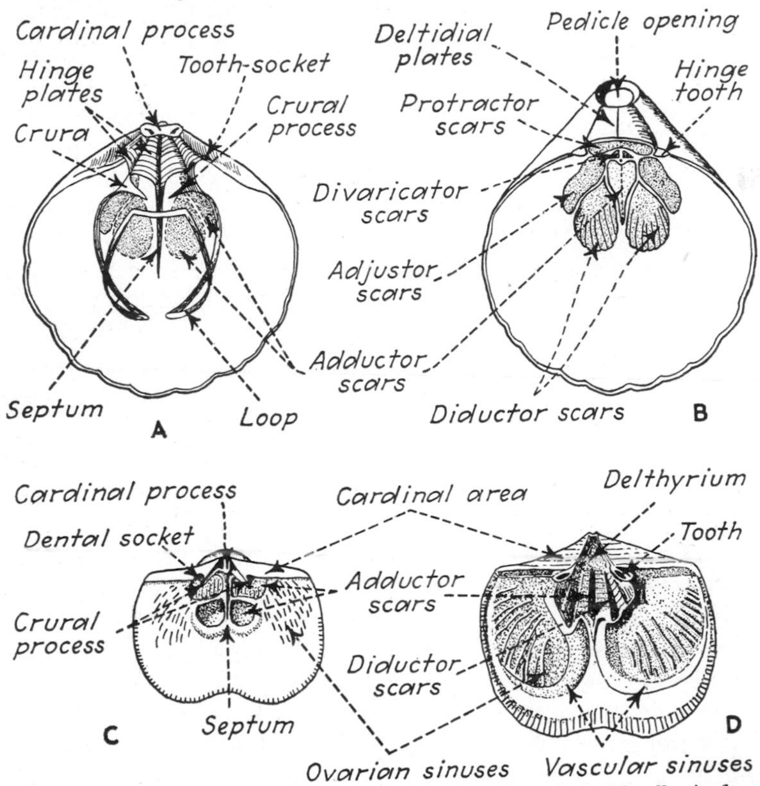

FIG. 102.—Internal structures of brachiopod shells. *A–B. Magellania flavescens*, a modern telotrematous brachiopod: *A*, view of interior of dorsal valve, with all organic matter removed; *B*, ventral interior showing various muscle scars. *C–D. Hebertella*, a very common fossil brachiopod in Upper Ordovician strata: *C. H. occidentalis*, dorsal interior. *D. H. insculpta*, ventral interior. (*A–B after Owen; C–D after Winchell and Schuchert.*)

takes place and also the line along which the valves join posteriorly. Elsewhere on the shell the junction of the valves is known as the *commissure*. In articulate shells the hinge is divided into two parts by the median pedicle opening, composed of the delthyrium and notothyrium. At the base of the delthyrium and in lateral positions are two prominent *teeth*, and at the base of the notothyrium in a corresponding position are two prominent *sockets* into which the teeth fit (Fig. 102). In some forms the teeth may be supported by thin lamellae known as *dental plates* or *dental lamellae* (Fig. 99 *B–C*). By these plates the space beneath the cardinal area or palintrope is divided into three cavities, two lateral and one middle (the *delthyrial cavity*). The teeth and sockets serve in the articulation of the shell, acting as a fulcrum as well as a device for preventing lateral motion, but in some forms they share these functions with supplementary structures, some of which become as important in articulation as the teeth and sockets themselves.

Beneath and between the margins of the notothyrium is the so-called *notothyrial cavity* (Figs. 99 *E*, *K*, 103 *A*). The floor of this cavity is often built up somewhat by extraneous shell matter. The swelling so produced is referred to as the *notothyrial platform*. On this platform in a median position is developed a ridgelike, variously modified structure, the *cardinal process*, part or all of which serves as the place of attachment for the diductor muscles (Figs. 99 *E*, *H*, *K*, *T*, 102 *A*, *C*). When the shell is closed this process fits between the hinge teeth of the ventral valve, and the latter are in their turn seated in the *dental sockets* (Fig. 99 *E*) of the dorsal valve. The diductor muscles, therefore, pass from the cardinal process between the hinge teeth to the places of attachment on the interior surface of the ventral valve. When these muscles contract, the ventral teeth and dorsal sockets act as a fulcrum, and as the posterior part of the dorsal valve is drawn inward and downward toward the hinge line the valves open along the commissure (Fig. 92 *B–C*).

Brachial Supports.—In some Protremata and all Telotremata calcified supports for the fleshy brachia are developed (Fig. 103). In the primitive protrematous orthids the brachial support consists of two parts—the *brachiophore*, composed of two structures, one on either side of the notothyrium, which bound the dental sockets; and the *brachiophore processes*, which are elongated extensions of the brachiophore. These are rarely preserved but are of great evolutionary importance. The lophophore was attached to the brachiophore processes. In some genera the brachiophores are supported dorsally by lamellae, to which the name *brachiophore plates* or *supports* is applied (Fig. 99 *K*).

Among telotrematous shells the calcified brachial support is given the name *brachidium* (Fig. 103). It varies greatly in character and has much evolutionary importance. The simplest brachidium consists of two small rodlike processes or small plates, the *crura* (Fig. 109 *C*), which are given off anteriorly from the plates bounding the dental sockets (the so-called *socket plates*). If the crura join beneath the dorsal interarea, or if they unite with the floor in the same position, the resulting process is termed a *cruralium* (Fig. 99 *T*). Crura which extend anteriorly for some distance and then join form a *loop*. This apparatus may be complex, passing through an involved metamorphosis before attaining mature development. In the most highly specialized Telotremata the crura are produced anteriorly to form a variety of spirally enrolled processes, known as *spires* or *spiralia* (Fig. 103). The two spiralia of a brachidium may remain separated, but usually they are united by the fusion of *jugal processes* developed on the inner side of the spiralia. The uniting apparatus thus resulting constitutes the *jugum* and may be quite complex. In some ancient forms branches developed on the jugum to form secondary spires which coiled within the primary ones. Such a combination is termed a *diplospire*.

A brachidium in which spiralia make up the major portion of the structure may be divided into three distinct parts—the *primary lamellae*, by which the spiralia are joined to the dorsal interarea; the jugum, by which the spiralia are joined together; and the spiralia themselves. Of the last named there are three general types (Fig. 103 *G–K*). In one the primary lamellae extend anteriorly following the lateral margin of the valve and give way to spiralia whose apices are directed toward the plane of symmetry or in a dorsal or ventral direction. This type is described as *atrypoid*. In the second group the primary lamellae extend directly anteriorly to the central part of the shell where the spiralia arise and point laterally. This is the *spiriferoid* type. The primary lamellae in the third group extend directly anteriorly for a short distance and then are deflected backward upon themselves. The spiralia begin following the deflection, and the apices are usually directed laterally. Such a brachidium belongs to the *athyroid* type. Shells with atrypoid and athyroid brachidia usually have short hinge lines; those with spiriferoid, long ones.

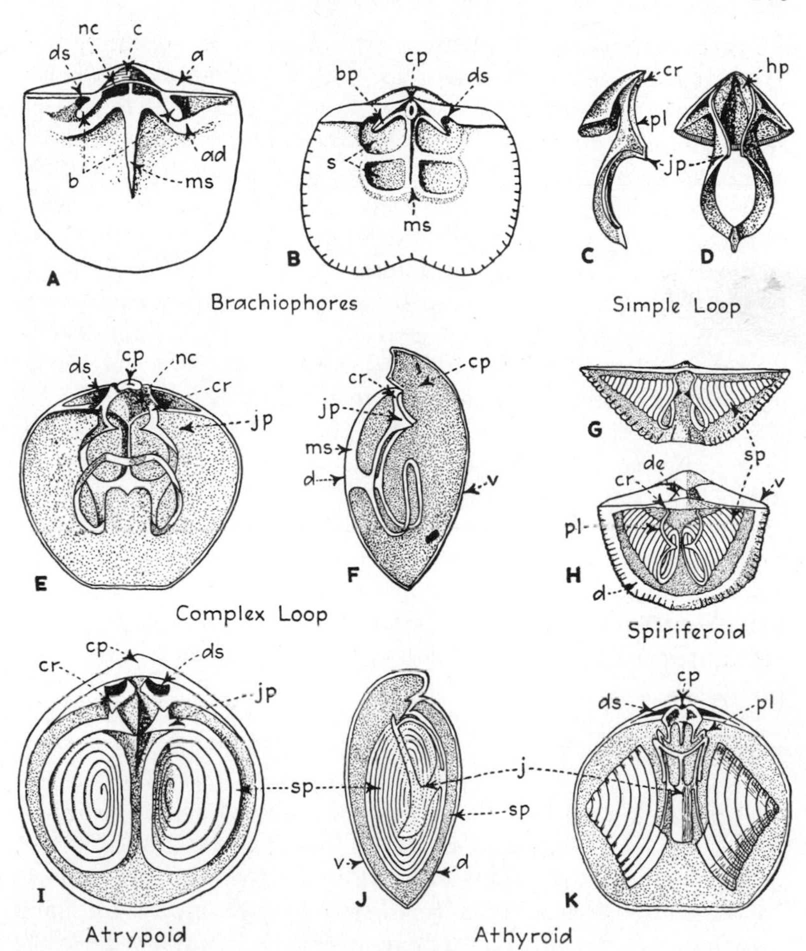

FIG. 103.—Brachidia. *A*. Dorsal interior of *Estlandia* showing well-developed brachiophores lying lateral to adventitious thickenings and chilidium roofing notothyrial cavity. *B*. Dorsal interior of *Hebertella* showing well-developed brachiophore processes (crural plates) which unite under the cardinal process. *C–D*. Lateral and dorsal views of *Centronella* showing a simple loop arising from a divided hinge plate. *E–F*. Dorsal interior and lateral view of *Magellania* showing a complex loop attached to the inside of the dorsal valve by a median septum. The jugal processes are not united. *G–H*. Interior views of *Spirifer*, with the dorsal valve broken away, showing spiriferoid spiralia with discrete jugal processes. *I*. Dorsal interior of *Atrypa*, somewhat generalized, showing atrypoid spiralia. *J–K*. Lateral view and dorsal interior of *Athyris* showing complex athyroid spiralia joined by a jugum. The posterior reflection of the primary lamellae of the brachidium is quite apparent. (*A after Schuchert and Cooper; B after Winchell and Schuchert; C–D after Hall and Clarke; E–F after Davidson; G–H after Hall and Clarke; J–K after Davidson.*)

a, cardinal area; *ad*, adventitious shell matter; *b*, brachiophore; *bp*, brachiophore process (crural plate); *c*, chilidium; *cp*, cardinal process; *cr*, crura; *d*, dorsal valve; *de*, deltidial plates; *ds*, dental socket; *hp*, hinge plate; *j*, jugum; *jp*, jugal process; *ms*, median septum; *nc*, notothyrial cavity; *pl*, primary lamella; *s*, muscle scar; *sp*, spiralium; *v*, ventral valve.

Brachial supports of all kinds are of great importance, not only for the identification of many genera and species but also because of their evolutionary significance. Unfortunately they are often lacking because of destruction during fossilization. If present, the character in some cases can be ascertained by making serial sections of the shell starting at the beak and from these constructing a three-dimensional restoration. Rarely the brachidia are silicified with the remainder of the shell calcareous. In such cases the calcareous shell can be removed by acid treatment, and the brachidial process obtained intact. Rare indeed is the case, however, in which the brachidium is not modified in one way or another as a result of fossilization.

Pallial Markings.—Parts or all of the mantle are often folded in such a way as to produce tubular extensions (*pallial sinuses*) in which are found body fluids and in some cases parts of genital organs. Such sinuses often leave *pallial markings* on the interior surfaces of the valves (Fig. 90). These markings usually have a dendritic appearance, with the smaller and more numerous branches situated laterally and anteriorly. They are of considerable importance in the definition of certain families, but it is not often that they are found well preserved.

Muscles and Muscle Scars.—The places of attachment of the various muscles are marked by pits depressed below the general interior surface of the valves, by roughened areas elevated slightly above the surface, or by areas on platforms of various kinds. These *muscle scars* and structures for attachment are of considerable importance in classification.

The term *muscle mark* is used by some authors for any mark that indicates muscular attachment; and the term *muscle track*, for the path down the valve taken by successive muscular attachments. When these terms are employed, muscle scar is then applied to a well-defined area representing the place of ultimate muscle attachment.

Brachiopod shells without definite articulation have complex sets of muscles by which the valves may be pushed apart or slipped about in respect to each other in a variety of ways. The scars of such a system are illustrated in Fig. 91.

Articulate shells possess a somewhat simpler muscular system, for the shell can only open and close. The valves are prevented from moving laterally by the various articulating devices along the hinge line and often also by crenulation of the lateral and anterior margins. The adductor muscles leave two scars on the ventral valve and four on the dorsal. The diductors leave two main scars on the ventral valve and a like number on the cardinal process. The adjustor muscles may leave small scars on both valves, and secondary diductors leave impressions though they are seldom preserved in fossil shells (Figs. 92, 102).

Supplementary processes are developed in some brachiopods for the attachment of muscles. In many Atremata (*Trimerella* and *Lingulasma*) each valve has an elevated area, known as the *platform*, to which muscles are attached (Fig. 105 *F–G*). This structure may be solid or may be a plate supported by a median septum. It elevates the place of muscle attachment above the interior surface of the valves. The ventral valve of many Protremata and Telotremata has a homologous structure in the *spondylium* (Fig. 99 *D*, *N*). This is a cuplike or spoon-shaped platform, lying immediately anterior to the delthyrium and often supported by a median septum which rises from the floor or interior surface of the valve along the plane of symmetry. Shells possessing spondylia commonly have two septa, one on either side of the plane of symmetry, rising from the floor of the ventral valve and frequently supporting a second spondylium (*Spondylium duplex*). Spondylia are present in many distantly related genera and apparently incipiently in a few Atremata. Some shells develop a callus beneath the muscles of the ventral valve and confluent with the inner lower surfaces of the dental lamellae. This structure is termed a *pseudospondylium*. It may be seen in the genus *Glossorthis* (Fig. 99 *J*). The cruralium of certain genera may have served the same function in the dorsal valve as the spondylium did in the ventral. In the dorsal valve of many articulate brachiopods a ridgelike axial thickening is developed, apparently to strengthen the valve between the adductor muscles. This thickening may take the form of a septum or partition dividing the valve into two equal parts.

CLASSIFICATION

Recent studies of the phylum in part or as a whole by numerous investigators throughout the world have produced a general classification differing somewhat from earlier efforts. The main features generally used in the classification of Brachiopoda are

1. Nature of the union of the valves (Inarticulata and Articulata).
2. Ontogeny of the shell.
3. Nature, position, and development of the pedicle opening.
4. Form and character of the brachial supports.
5. Numerous internal structures such as muscular platforms, septa, muscle scars, etc.
6. Shape and convexity of shell, and ornamentation.

The following classification is that proposed by Schuchert and Le Vene[1] in 1929, with the addition of the two artificial subdivisions Inarticulata and Articulata.

Phylum **Brachiopoda**
- *Class Inarticulata*
  - Order 1. Palaeotremata
    - Superfamily 1. Paterinacea
    - Superfamily 2. Rustellacea
    - Superfamily 3. Kutorginacea
  - Order 2. Atremata
    - Superfamily 1. Obolacea
    - Superfamily 2. Lingulacea
    - Superfamily 3. Trimerellacea
  - Order 3. Neotremata
    - Superfamily 1. Siphonotretacea
    - Superfamily 2. Acrotretacea
    - Superfamily 3. Discinacea
    - Superfamily 4. Craniacea
- *Class Articulata*
  - Order 4. Protremata
    - Superfamily 1. Orthacea
    - Superfamily 2. Clitambonacea
    - Superfamily 3. Dalmanellacea
    - Superfamily 4. Syntrophiacea
    - Superfamily 5. Pentameracea
    - Superfamily 6. Strophomenacea
  - Order 5. Telotremata
    - Superfamily 1. Rhynchonellacea
    - Superfamily 2. Atrypacea
    - Superfamily 3. Spiriferacea
    - Superfamily 4. Rostrospiracea
    - Superfamily 5. Terebratulacea

[1] SCHUCHERT, C., and LE VENE, C. M., Fossilium Catalogus, I. Animalia, Pars. 42, Brachiopoda (*Generum et Genotyporum Index et Bibliographia*), 140 pp., 1929.

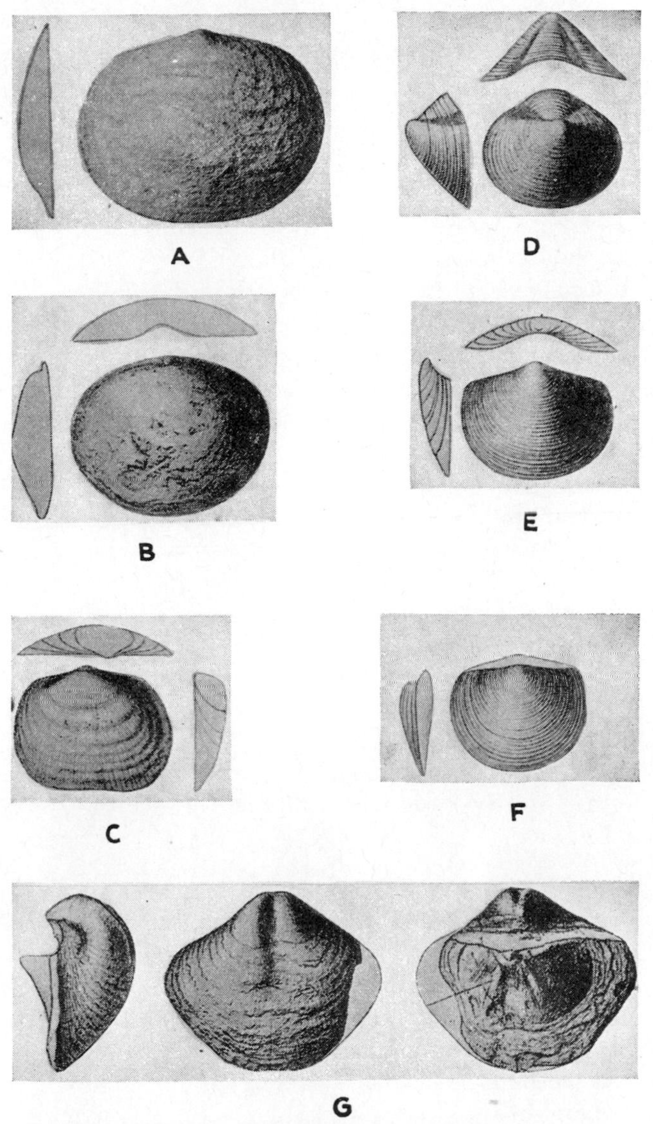

Fig. 104.—Palaeotremata. *A–C. Rustella edsoni* from the Lower Cambrian of the United States: *A*, exterior view of a compressed ventral valve; *B*, interior view of ventral valve; *C*, exterior views of a dorsal valve. *D–E. Micromitra* (*Paterina*) *bella* from the Lower Cambrian of Pennsylvania: *D*, apical, posterior, and side views of a ventral valve; *E*, summit, posterior, and side views of a dorsal valve. *F. Micromitra* (*Paterina*) *phillipsi* from the Lower Cambrian of England; top view of dorsal valve and side view of both valves. *G. Kutorgina cingulata* from the Lower Cambrian of Vermont. Side, ventral, and dorsal views of a nearly entire shell. (*A–C, G* × 1; *D–F* enlarged.) (*A–E, G after Walcott; F after Walcott from Davidson.*)

ORDER PALAEOTREMATA[1]

The members of this order of brachiopods have very primitive, inarticulate shells quite similar to the embryonic shells of later, more highly specialized forms. The pedicle emerges between the valves. The order makes its appearance in the Lower Cambrian, becomes extinct in the Ordovician, and is represented in a fossil state by three superfamilies (Fig. 104).

Superfamily Paterinacea.—This group includes the most primitive known brachiopods. These are grouped in the single family Paterinidae, and the shells are very close to the protegulum stage. The pedicle aperture is more or less closed by homeodeltidia and pseudochilidia. *Cambrian. Micromitra* (*Paterina*) illustrates the characters of the group.

Superfamily Rustellacea.—Very primitive, thick-shelled brachiopods with chitinous or calcareophosphatic shells. Homeodeltidia and psuedochilidia may be well defined. *Lower Cambrian to Ordovician. Rustella* is representative of the superfamily.

Superfamily Kutorginacea.—Progressive, thick-shelled, calcareous, atremate-like shells tending to be transverse and having rudimentary articulation, homeodeltidia, and more or less rudimentary cardinal areas. The muscle scars are prophetic of the Protremata, and some authors are of the opinion that *Kutorgina* represents the most primitive genus of the Protremata. The Kutorginacea were derived from the Rustellacea. *Cambrian.*

ORDER ATREMATA[2]

The Atremata (Fig. 105) include simple, inarticulate brachiopods with the pedicle emerging freely between the two valves, the opening being shared more or less by both valves. Growth takes place mainly along the anterior and lateral margins. The simplest forms have an unmodified pedicle opening, but in more advanced species homeodeltidia and pseudochilidia tend to restrict the pedicle to the ventral valve. Specialized forms tend to develop rudimentary articulation and muscle platforms. The

[1] Palaeotremata—Gr. *palaios*, ancient + *trema*, *trematos*, perforation; referring to the presence of a pedicle opening in the most ancient shells.

[2] Atremata—Gr. *a*, without + *trema*, *trematos*, perforation; referring to the absence of a strictly defined pedicle opening.

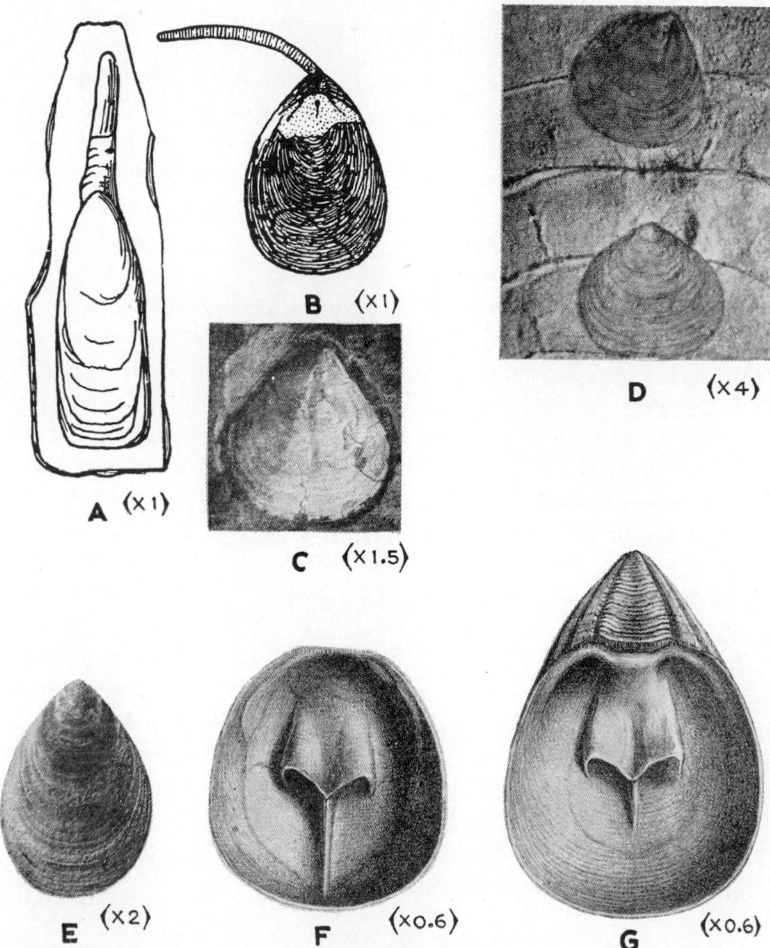

FIG. 105.—Atremata. *A. Lingula? lesueri* showing pedicle issuing from between the valves. *B. Lingula aequalis*, from the Ordovician of New York, showing the interior of a portion of the ventral valve, and the preserved pedicle. *C. Westonia aurora* from the Upper Cambrian of Wisconsin. A ventral valve. *D.* Two valves of *Obolus johni*, from the Middle Cambrian of Utah, attached to the dorsal surface of the merostome *Beckwithia typa*. *E. Lingulella ampla*, a ventral valve from the Upper Cambrian of Wisconsin. *F–G. Trimerella grandis* from the Upper Silurian (Guelph) of Canada: *F*, interior of brachial valve; *G*, interior of the pedicle valve. (*A after Davidson; B after Walcott; D after Resser; F–G after Davidson and King.*)

Neotremata, Protremata, and Telotremata arose from the Palaeotremata and Atremata. *Cambrian to Recent.*

Superfamily Obolacea.—Atremata, derived from the Rustellacea, possessing a thick, horny, or calcareophosphatic shell. Fixed throughout life by a short pedicle emerging through an unmodified opening shared by both valves. The shells are rounded or linguloid in outline. *Cambrian to Silurian. Lingulella, Westonia,* and *Obolus* (Upper Cambrian) are representative genera.

Superfamily Lingulacea.—This subdivision embraces elongate, thin-shelled, chitinous atremates which were derived from the Obolacea. They are of burrowing habit and possess a wormlike, tubular, flexible pedicle. The muscles are highly differentiated (Fig. 91). The Lingulacea have an ancient history, and genera like *Lingula* (Figs. 93 *L*, 105 *A–B*) have lived from the Ordovician to the Present, the range of the superfamily.

Superfamily Trimerellacea.—Three families, the *Neobolidae, Elkaniidae* and *Trimerellidae,* are included in this superfamily. The first two were formerly included as subfamilies under Obolidae (Obolacea).

Brachiopods of this superfamily are both progressive and divergent from the Obolidae, with posterior platforms to which some of the muscles were attached. More advanced forms have rudimentary articulation and a generally prominent ventral cardinal area that is triangular and transversely striated. The shells are thick and decidedly inequivalved. *Cambrian to Silurian. Trimerella* (Silurian) is representative of the superfamily and is an important index fossil.

Order Neotremata[1]

The Neotremata (Fig. 106) are specialized and, to a certain extent, degenerate, inarticulate brachiopods derived from the Atremata, perhaps through such a form as *Bicia.* They appear first in the Cambrian and are still found in present seas, but they seem rarely to have been either abundant or important.

The small chitinous (or rarely calcareous) shell is composed typically of flattened conical valves. The pedicle is confined to the ventral valve, emerging through a perforation or sheath or a

[1] Neotremata—Gr. *neos,* young + *trema, trematos,* perforation; referring to the character of the pedicle opening.

triangular cleft, and in maturity may be lost when the ventral valve becomes cemented to some object. The pedicle opening may be anterior or posterior to the protegulum and in some forms is partly closed by a listrium. Homeodeltidia and pseudochilidia are usually not well developed. The protegulum is semicircular or semielliptical, and since the main growth tends to be peripheral the shells are round or elliptical. *Cambrian to Recent.*

Superfamily Siphonotretacea.—Primitive thick-walled calcareous or chitinous shells with the pedicle emerging through a ventral sheath. The pedicle opening is circular, tends to be axial, and is not modified by a listrium. It may be posterior or anterior to the protegulum and may be elongate if it has migrated through the protegulum. *Cambrian to Silurian. Siphonotreta* (Ordovician to Silurian) is a characteristic genus.

Superfamily Acrotretacea.—Chitinous or calcareochitinous, more or less circular, conical, or flattened shells with a circular pedicle opening in the apex of the ventral valve. There is no listrium, but a pseudocardinal area is present. *Cambrian to Silurian. Acrotreta* (Cambrian to Ordovician) is a representative genus.

Superfamily Discinacea.—Specialized Neotremata with phosphatic shells. The pedicle slit is modified by a listrium. There are no pseudodeltidia or false cardinal areas. The shells are circular and flattened conical. *Ordovician to Recent. Schizocrania* (Ordovician to Devonian) and *Orbiculoidea* (Ordovician to Cretaceous) are typical genera.

Superfamily Craniacea.—Specialized forms with calcareous shells and without a pedicle or pedicle opening in maturity. The shells are frequently found cemented by the ventral valve (the ventral valve is unknown in many species) to other brachiopod shells. *Ordovician to Recent. Crania,* a common genus, is often cemented to other brachiopods. It has the range of the superfamily.

Order Protremata[1]

This order embraces specialized articulate brachiopods with biconvex, concavo-convex, plano-convex, and resupinate shells.

[1] Protremata—Gr. *pro,* early + *trema, trematos,* perforation; referring to the character of the pedicle opening.

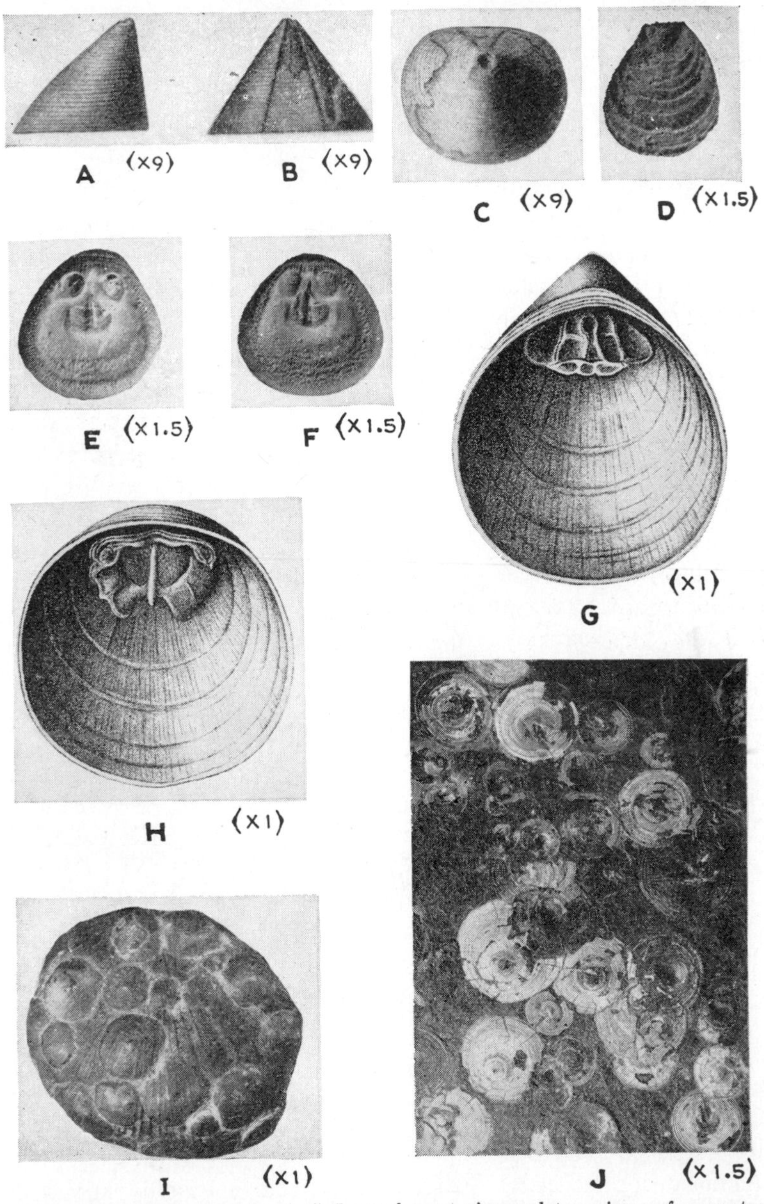

FIG. 106.—Neotremata. *A–C*. Lateral, posterior and top views of a ventral valve of *Acrotreta gemma* from the Lower Ordovician of Newfoundland. *D–F*. Ventral exterior and interiors of *Crania antiqua* from the Cretaceous. *G–H*. Ventral and dorsal interiors of *Siphonotreta unguiculata*. *I*. Ventral exterior of *Rafinesquina* covered with 20 shells of *Crania scabiosa* from the Upper Ordo-

On the calcareous shell are well-developed cardinal areas, and the surface may be smooth, striate, plicate, or costate. Growth lines may be prominent or obscure. The pedicle is restricted to the ventral valve throughout life, and the delthyrium is more or less closed by a deltidium. Chilidia, cruralia, and spondylia are frequently present. In only a few of the advanced forms do the brachia have brachial supports. In some genera the pedicle is lost, and the animal adopts other methods of fixation (hinge spines

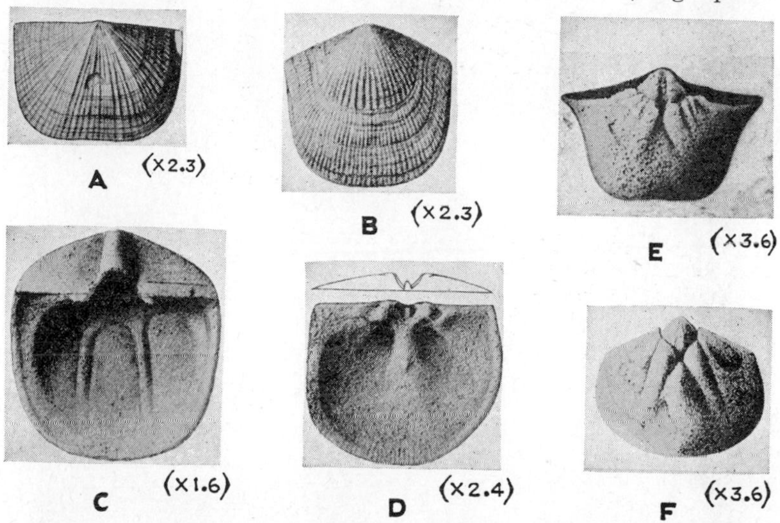

FIG. 107.—Cambrian Protremata. *A–B.* Dorsal and ventral exteriors of *Billingsella coloradoensis* from the Upper Cambrian of Texas and Idaho, respectively. *C–D.* Replicas of ventral interior and of dorsal interior of *B. coloradoensis*, probably from the Upper Cambrian of Wisconsin. *E–F.* Replicas of ventral and dorsal interiors of *Finkelnburgia* from the Upper Cambrian of Wisconsin: *E, F. osceola*; *F, F. finkelnburgia.* (*After Walcott.*)

or cementation). The order is thought to have been derived from the Palaeotremata through the Kutorginacea. It is probably the most important order of the brachiopods, though it is not represented by so many genera as the Telotremata. Protremata first appear in the Cambrian and become practically extinct by the close of the Paleozoic, with a few stragglers persisting through the Mesozoic to the Present. There are but two families extant. The order has very recently been partly monographed, and two

---

vician of Ohio. *J.* Slab of carbonaceous shale showing numerous ventral and dorsal valves of *Orbiculoidea nitida* from the Pennsylvanian of Illinois. (*A–C after Walcott; G–H after Davidson.*)

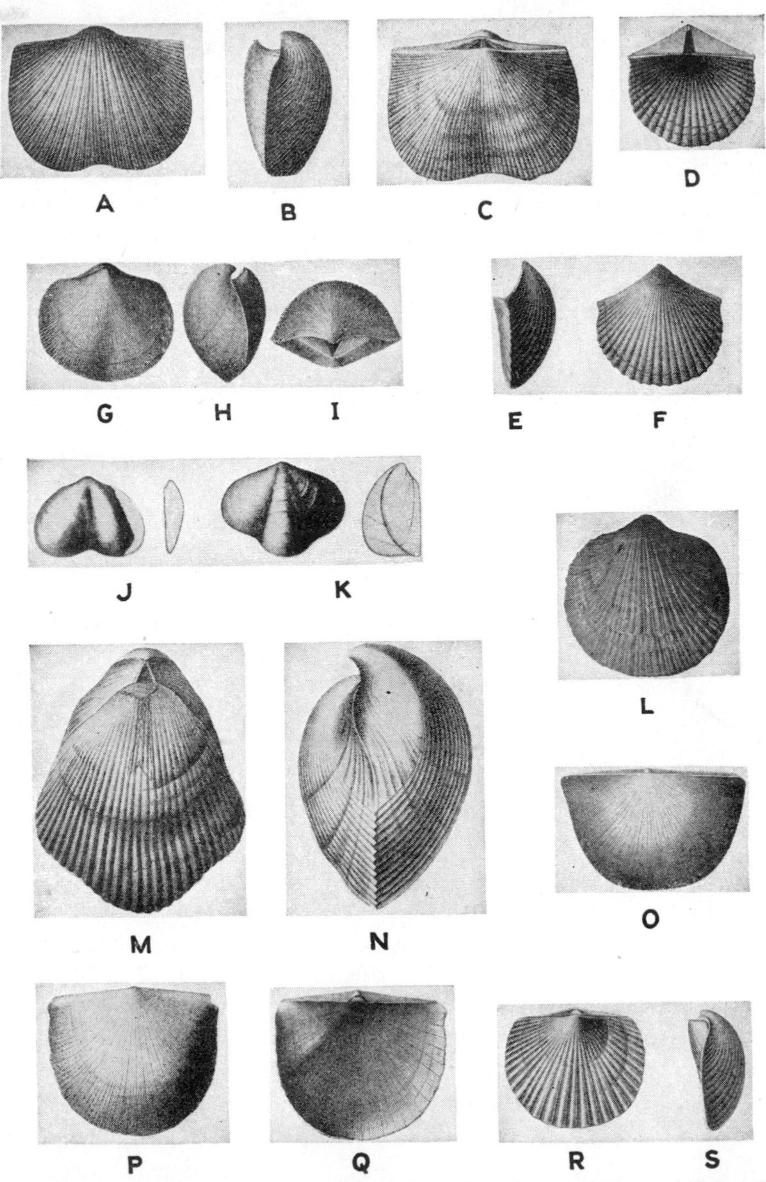

FIG. 108.—Protremata. *A–C*. Dorsal, lateral, and ventral views of *Hebertella occidentalis sinuata* from the Upper Ordovician of Ohio. *D–F*. Dorsal, lateral, and ventral views of *Hesperorthis tricenaria* from the Middle Ordovician of Wisconsin. *G–I*. Ventral, lateral, and posterior views of *Schizophoria tulliensis* from the Devonian of New York. *J–K*. Ventral and dorsal views of *Syntrophia orthia*, an early protremate from the Upper Cambrian of China. *L*. Ventral

suborders have been erected—***Orthoidea***, containing the superfamilies Orthacea, Clitambonacea, and Dalmanellacea; and *Pentameroidea*, embracing the superfamilies Syntrophiacea and Pentameracea. The superfamily Strophomenacea was not included in the study (Figs. 107, 108).

Superfamily Orthacea.—This superfamily arose as primitive orthoids in the early Cambrian and developed into a prolific group before extinction in the Devonian. The shell is always impunctate, is very rarely smooth, is generally striate or plicate, and not uncommonly is costate. The shells usually have wide hinge lines, well-developed cardinal areas (interareas) on both valves, and a simple cardinal process which is lacking in the primitive genera. Deltidia and chilidia are sporadic, pseudospondylia are common, but spondylia are rare. *Billingsella* and *Finkelnburgia* (Cambrian), and *Dinorthis, Dolerorthis, Glossorthis, Hebertella, Hesperorthis, Orthis, Platystrophia,* and *Plectorthis* are typical genera.

Superfamily Clitambonacea.—The Clitambonacea embrace a group of specialized orthoids which probably developed out of the *Billingsellidae* of the Orthacea, retaining in most cases the primitive features of the deltidia and chilidia but much enlarged. Simple spondylia or more rarely pseudospondylia are developed. The shells are impunctate. *Ordovician and Silurian. Clitambonites* is a characteristic genus (Fig. 99 *D–G*).

Superfamily Dalmanellacea.—Progressive orthoids, similar to representatives of the first two superfamilies in many respects. The superfamily is characterized by the endopunctate shell and primitively bilobed cardinal process. It is thought to have been derived from the Orthacea, appearing first in the Middle Ordovician, spreading and diversifying widely during the Silurian and Devonian, and then apparently becoming extinct during the Permian. *Dalmanella* and *Schizophoria* are representative genera (Fig. 108).

Superfamily Syntrophiacea.—Specialized Protremata derived from the Orthacea, having a lobate exterior, spondylia, and

exterior of *Dalmanella*, a common Ordovician and Silurian protremate. *M–N*. Dorsal and lateral views of *Conchidium nysius* from the Upper Silurian of Kentucky. *O*. Dorsal view of *Strophomena neglecta* from the Middle Ordovician of New York. *P–Q*. Ventral and dorsal views of *Rafinesquina alternata* from the Upper Ordovician of Ohio. *R–S*. Ventral and lateral views of *Dinorthis pectinella* from the Middle Ordovician of Kentucky. (*A–I, M–Q after Whitfield; J–K after Walcott; R–S after Emmons.*) (*J–K* × 2½; others × ½ to ⅘.)

occasionally cruralia. The cardinal process is absent or rudimentary. The fibrous shell is impunctate. *Middle Cambrian to Lower Ordovician. Syntrophia* is a typical genus (Fig. 108 *J–K*).

Superfamily Pentameracea.—The Pentameracea are specialized Protremata which appear to have had their origin in the Syntrophiacea. The shells, commonly galeate in outline, are characterized by simple or complex spondylia and by numerous structures in the posterior part of the shell. The cardinal process is usually absent, deltidia rarely occur, and chilidia are never developed. The hinge line is very narrow, interareas are small, and exteriors are smooth or costate. The shell so far as known is without endopunctae. *Middle Ordovician to close of Devonian. Pentamerus* and *Conchidium* (Silurian) are representative genera (Figs. 99 *L–O*, 108 *M–N*).

Superfamily Strophomenacea.—Progressive Protremata lacking spondylia and cruralia and nearly always possessing deltidia and chilidia throughout life. There is always a well-developed cardinal process. The pedicle, which is small, emerges usually through the apex of the ventral valve, though in some forms it is lost, and the ventral valve is then secured to the bottom by spines or by cementation, or is unattached. The shells tend to be punctate, concavo-convex, convexo-concave, or resupinate, and more advanced forms are frequently spinose. The Strophomenacea constituted a very prolific group during the Paleozoic (99 genera) but thereafter became very much less important (9 genera in the Mesozoic and 2 in the Cenozoic and Recent). *Ordovician to Recent. Rafinesquina, Strophomena, Leptaena, Chonetes,* and *Productus* are representatives of this very important superfamily. *Richthofenia* represents an aberrant genus (Figs. 93, 96, 98, 108).

Order Telotremata[1]

The Telotremata, generally considered to have developed from the Atremata, constitute a group of very highly specialized articulate brachiopods with calcareous shells provided with various kinds of brachial supports. The pedicle opening is shared by both valves in the early growth stages but is usually restricted to the ventral valve in maturity by the development of

[1] Telotremata—Gr. *telos*, last + *trema, trematos*, perforation; referring to the features of the pedicle opening.

deltidial plates. The Telotremata include more genera than any other order of brachiopods, with 189 in the Paleozoic, 162 in the Mesozoic, and 66 in the Cenozoic and Recent. The order, which ranges from Ordovician to Recent, is divided into five superfamilies—Rhynchonellacea, Atrypacea, Spiriferacea, Rostrospiracea, and Terebratulacea.

Superfamily Rhynchonellacea.—Rostrate, primitive telotremates with or without crura for the support of the brachia. The cardinal areas are generally absent, and there is often no cardinal process. The pedicle opening is just beneath the beak or rarely in a truncate ventral apex. The shells are almost always impunctate. *Ordovician to Recent. Rhynchotrema* is a typical genus (Fig. 109 *A–B*).

Superfamily Atrypacea.—The Atrypacea, formerly included in the Spiriferacea, comprise a small group of brachiopods which possess a complex brachidium with or without a jugum. The primary lamellae follow the margins of the shell, and the spiralia are directed toward the plane of symmetry. *Ordovician to Devonian. Atrypa*, one of the longest ranging genera of brachiopods, is a typical genus (Fig. 103 *I*, 109 *F–G*).

Superfamily Spiriferacea.—The Spiriferacea constitute a group of specialized telotremates which, in the mature shell, have the brachia supported by calcareous spiralia of the spiriferoid type. The shell is smooth, striate, plicate, or costate. Cardinal areas are well developed in some genera, absent in others. The superfamily appears in the Ordovician, reaches its acme during the Devonian, and becomes extinct in the Jurassic. *Spirifer* is a representative genus (Figs. 98 *G*, 99 *A*).

Superfamily Rostrospiracea.—This very recently erected superfamily includes the families of Meristellidae, Uncitidae, Rhynchospirinidae, Athyridae, Koninckinidae, and Thecospiridae. These were all formerly included in the old superfamily Spiriferacea from which, as now defined, they differ in the character of the brachidia, juga, and other internal structures. The brachidia are of the athyroid type. *Ordovician to Jurassic. Meristina, Uncites*, and *Athyris* are representative genera (Figs. 103 *J–K*, 109).

Superfamily Terebratulacea.—The Terebratulacea form a group of highly specialized telotremates with the brachia supported by calcareous loops. The loop may be unsupported by a median dorsal septum throughout life (*Terebratuloids*). The

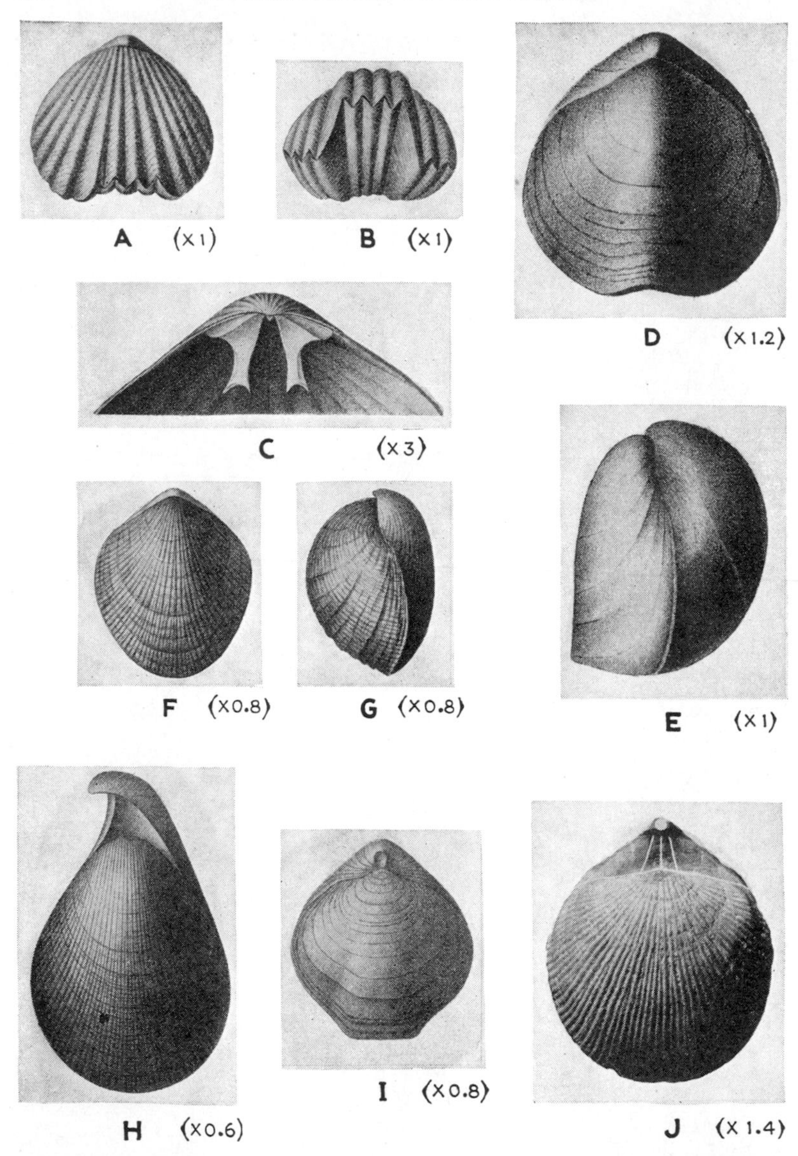

FIG. 109.—Telotremata. *A–B*. Dorsal and anterior views of *Rhynchotrema capax* from the Upper Ordovician of Ohio. *C*. Portion of dorsal interior of *Stenochisma formosa*, from the Devonian of New York, showing the minute cardinal process and the well-developed crura. *D–E*. Dorsal and lateral views of *Meristina maria* from the Silurian (Niagaran) of Indiana. *F–G*. Dorsal and lateral views of *Atrypa reticularis* from the Devonian of New York. *H*. Dorsal view of *Uncites gryphus* from the Middle Devonian of Germany. *I*. Dorsal

shells are always punctate and commonly galeate; may be smooth, striate, costate, or plicate; and usually have no cardinal areas. *Ordovician to Recent.* *Trigonosemus* and *Magellania* are representative genera (Figs. 89, 98 *F*, 109 *J*).

ONTOGENY AND EVOLUTION

The life histories of several living species of brachiopods have been determined (Fig. 94). The fertilized ovum first divides into two connected spheres, and these in turn develop into a single sphere with a multicelled wall. The latter then passes through a *gastrula* stage and from this through a *trochophore* and *cephalula* stage, at the end of which it is a larva. The presence of the trochophore stage in the ontogeny suggests that brachiopods were developed from a wormlike creature late in the Pre-Cambrian.

The larva consists of a distinct galeate *head*, a *dorsal* and a *ventral mantle lobe*, and a posterior part from which the pedicle develops. After swimming about for three or four days it attaches itself to some object on the bottom by this posterior part. The dorsal and ventral lobes are folded forward to surround the head, and the ventral and dorsal plates of the protegulum begin to form on their exterior surfaces. In the Protremata at this time the prodeltidium forms on the dorsal surface of the pedicle. The calcareous plates just described (two in the Inarticulata and Telotremata, three in the Protremata) constitute the embryonic shell or protegulum. At this stage of development the ventral and dorsal plates are semicircular or semielliptical in outline, and there are no cardinal areas. The protegulum grows into a young shell, termed *nepionic*, in which the distinctive specific characters are not yet apparent. From this point onward, specific characters develop, and the mature shell results. The latter in some cases bears close resemblance to the nepionic shell but often varies greatly from it. The adult stage is known as *ephebic*, the old stage as *gerontic*. Peculiar structures often appear in the gerontic stage that are never seen in previous stages and are frequently considered prophetic of extinction.

From the protegulum stage, divergence takes place in four directions:

---

view of *Composita subtilita* from the Pennsylvanian of Missouri. *J.* Dorsal view of *Trigonosemus palissa* from the Upper Cretaceous of Holland. (*A–B, F–G after Whitfield; C, D–E, I after Simpson; H after Roemer.*)

1. The pedicle continues to emerge freely between the valves, primitive characters are retained, cardinal areas are never or rarely developed, and chitin, calcium phosphate, or both are used as shell material. The shells grow by additions made to the lateral and anterior margins. The most primitive of these shells comprise the Palaeotremata, which are very close to the protegulum stage, and the more advanced forms, derived from the Palaeotremata, constitute the Atremata.

2. In the second group the ventral valve grows in such fashion as to envelop the pedicle, and, as a consequence, the two valves tend to assume circular outlines with the protegulum and pedicle opening in a central or subcentral position. Increments are nearly equal on all margins. No cardinal areas are needed in such shells; hence they are not present. The animals continue to use chitin and calcium phosphate for shell substance, rarely advancing to the use of calcium carbonate. These constitute the Neotremata, a group which appears to be somewhat aberrant from the Atremata in which they had their origin.

3. In the Protremata the pedicle opening is first situated on the margin of the ventral valve, and that part not used is closed by a deltidium, which appears in the embryonic shell as the prodeltidium. A definite hinge structure develops with a cardinal process, other hinge-line structures, and cardinal areas. Except in the most advanced members of the order, no supporting structures for the brachia are developed. The shell is composed of calcium carbonate. The Protremata appear to have developed out of the Palaeotremata through the Kutorginacea.

4. In the Telotremata, which seem to have developed out of the Atremata, the opening for the pedicle is shared by both valves in the early growth stages, with the dorsal valve sharing only to a slight extent. The delthyrium becomes closed by deltidial plates; and crura, loops, and spires develop for the support of the brachia. Calcareous matter is used for shell construction, and additions are made chiefly on the anterior and lateral margins of the shells. The Telotremata are the most highly specialized of the brachiopods and by far the most abundant forms in existing seas.

ECOLOGY

The brachiopods throughout their long and ancient history have always been dominantly sessile benthos, usually preferring well-oxygenated, shallow-water environments, but they lived on many bottoms with considerable range in environmental conditions. Some, like *Pentamerus*, desired bottoms free from mud; others, like *Productus*, *Strophomena*, and *Rafinesquina*, seem to have preferred bottoms receiving small quantities of mud; and forms like *Lingula* required muddy bottoms in which to burrow. Living forms have world-wide distribution and occur at all depths in all latitudes but are abundant in very few areas. Nearly three-fourths of all living forms are found between the shore line and a depth of 600 ft., and only a few forms inhabit the deeper parts of the ocean, though quite a large number live in deep water adjacent to the continental shelf. On favorable bottoms at various times during the past they lived in almost unbelievable profusion, as well illustrated by the *Pentamerus* and *Conchidium* coquinas so common in Silurian formations in many parts of the world. Under such conditions few other organisms were present. But brachiopods also lived in abundance in many different animal assemblages, as illustrated by the fossiliferous Ordovician strata of the Cincinnati region and the Pennsylvanian calcareous formations of many parts of the world. They do not seem to have been common denizens of ancient coral reefs, though they themselves are responsible for thick biostromes. Because of the fact that brachiopod shells usually remain closed after death, they are just like pebbles on the bottom and as such serve excellently as objects to which worms, bryozoans, corals, other brachiopods, mollusks, and barnacles may attach their shells. It often happens that fossil brachiopod shells are so incrusted by other organic remains that little of the surface ornamentation is visible. Spreading slowly, brachiopods often attained very wide distribution and for that reason are frequently valuable for correlation over broad areas.

GEOLOGIC HISTORY

Brachiopods attained their greatest importance in the Paleozoic and probably were at the zenith of their long career in the Ordovician and Silurian (Fig. 88). Following the Paleozoic they declined more or less gradually to the present subordinate position. All orders except the Telotremata were represented in the Lower Cambrian, with the Atremata dominant. By the close of the Upper Cambrian the Protremata assumed the leading role and continued in that position during the Ordovician and Silurian. Over 3,000 species have been described from these two latter periods. Appearing in the Ordovician, the Telotremata gradually rose in importance until in the Devonian they equaled

TABLE 10.—CHART SHOWING THE GEOLOGIC RANGE OF THE SUPERFAMILIES OF BRACHIOPODA.

	C	O	S	D	M	P	P	T	J	C	T	R
Palaeotremata												
Paterinacea	—											
Rustellacea	—	—										
Kutorginacea	—											
Atremata												
Obolacea	—	—	—									
Lingulacea		—	—	—	—	—	—	—	—	—	—	—
Trimerellacea	—	—	—									
Neotremata												
Siphonotretacea	—	—	—									
Acrotretacea	—	—	—									
Discinacea		—	—	—	—	—	—	—	—	—	—	—
Craniacea		—	—	—	—	—	—	—	—	—	—	—
Protremata												
Orthacea	—	—	—	—								
Clitambonacea		—	—									
Dalmanellacea		—	—	—	—	—	—					
Syntrophiacea	—	—										
Pentameracea		—	—	—								
Strophomenacea		—	—	—	—	—	—	—	—	—	—	—
Telotremata												
Rhynchonellacea		—	—	—	—	—	—	—	—	—	—	—
Atrypacea		—	—	—								
Spiriferacea		—	—	—	—	—	—	—	—			
Rostrospiracea		—	—	—	—	—	—	—	—			
Terebratulacea		—	—	—	—	—	—	—	—	—	—	—

and then surpassed the Protremata, but not for long, as the latter again expanded in the Mississippian and Pennsylvanian with a host of new spine-bearing genera, represented by myriads of individuals. Upon the almost complete extinction of the Protremata during the Permian, the Telotremata again assumed the dominant position and have retained it to the present. The spire bearers of the Telotremata almost vanished in the Permian, but a few stragglers survived to the Jurassic. Since the Jurassic the loop-bearing and crura-bearing genera have been dominant though they are not common in American strata. The Inarticulata, except for the brief period of time when they ruled the earliest Cambrian, have never been important and rarely abundant. The Palaeotremata became extinct sometime in the Ordovician, but the Atremata and Neotremata have persisted to the Present. The ranges of the orders and superfamilies of Brachiopoda are shown in Table 10.

NATURE OF FOSSILS

Brachiopods are often exquisitely preserved, with little or no alteration of the shell substance or structure. Many chitinous forms, particularly if in argillaceous rocks, are well preserved, and the phosphatic shells of many Cambrian species are often little altered from the condition in which they were buried. Shells which have been replaced have in many cases retained the more important structural features. Calcite, silica, and iron sulphide are the common replacing substances. Even though much of the internal structure has been destroyed during or subsequent to fossilization, most brachiopods, because of closing on death, still have the shape and surface ornamentation well exhibited in fossil forms. Solution has often completely removed the original shell, but internal and external molds generally remain to indicate the essential features of the shells which made them.

References

BEECHER, C. E.: Development of the Brachiopoda. *Amer. Jour. Sci.*, vol. 41, pp. 343–357, 1891; vol. 44, pp. 133–155, 1892.

———: Some correlations of the ontogeny and phylogeny in the Brachiopoda. *Am. Nat.*, vol. 27, pp. 599–604, 1893.

CUMINGS, E. R.: The morphogenesis of Platystrophia; a study of the evolution of a Paleozoic brachiopod. *Amer. Jour. Sci.*, vol. 15, pp. 1–48, 121–136, 1903.

DUNBAR, C. O., and CONDRA, G. E.: Brachiopods of the Pennsylvanian system of Nebraska. *Neb. Geol. Surv., Bull.* 5, 377 pp., 1932.

HALL, J., and CLARKE, J. M.: An introduction to the study of the Brachiopoda, intended for a handbook for the use of students. *New York State Geol. Surv., Ann. Rept.* 11, pp. 133–223, 1892: pt. II, *Ann. Rept.* 13, pp. 945–1137, 1894.

——— and ———: An introduction to the study of the genera of Paleozoic Brachiopoda. *N. Y. State Geol. Paleontology*, pt. 1, 367 pp., 1892; pt. 2, 394 pp., 1893.

SCHUCHERT, C.: A synopsis of American fossil Brachiopoda. *U. S. Geol. Surv., Bull.* 87, 464 pp., 1897.

——— and COOPER, G. A.: Brachiopod genera of the suborders Orthoidea and Pentameroidea. *Peabody Mus. Nat. Hist., Mems.*, vol. 4, pt. 1, 270 pp., 1932.

——— and LE VENE, C. M.: Fossilium Catalogus, I. Animalia, Pars. 42, Brachiopoda, 140 pp., 1929.

WALCOTT, C. D.: Cambrian Brachiopoda. *U. S. Geol. Surv., Mon.* 51, 2 vols., 1912.

CHAPTER IX

MOLLUSCA[1]

GENERAL CONSIDERATIONS

The Mollusca, popularly known as "mollusks," constitute a large group of invertebrate animals which are similar in fundamental biologic organization but build chitinous and calcareous shells of almost unbelievably variable architecture. Included in this great and important phylum, which is represented by over 60,000 living species and many thousands of fossil ones, are such well-known animals as oysters, mussels and clams, slugs and snails, cuttlefishes, and the notorious *Octopus*. In contrast to most other invertebrates, mollusks are of interest to man because of extensive use for food.

Since their appearance in the Cambrian, the Mollusca have deployed into most of the aquatic habitats and have even invaded the land. Judging from their wide areal distribution in the past as well as in the present, they represent one of the most successful of all animal groups. Because of the unusually wide distribution the group exhibits a great diversity of habit and bodily structure and tremendous variation in the shells. Individuals range in size from tiny adult snails scarcely a millimeter long to the giant squids of the Atlantic Ocean which span over 15 m. (50 ft.) from the tip of the tail to the end of the longest tentacle. The molluscan shell ranges in size from tiny forms less than a millimeter across to the giant 4½-m. (15-ft.) cephalopods of the Ordovician, the nearly 2-m. (6-ft.) ammonites of the Mesozoic, and the huge *Tridacna* of present seas, which weighs over 500 lb. and is large enough completely to inclose a small child.

THE ANIMAL

The term Mollusca means soft-bodied and was first applied by Aristotle to the cuttlefish of the Aegean Sea. The individual

[1] Mollusca—L. *mollusca,* a soft nut with a thin shell; referring to the bivalve shell and soft animal inclosed in the shell.

mollusk possesses an unsegmented, typically elongated, fundamentally bilaterally symmetrical body with a mouth at one end and an anal opening at the other. The *visceral mass* of the body includes the vital organs—the heart and circulatory tubes, the alimentary tract, and other organs (Fig. 110). The alimentary tract is usually a simple, straight or curved tube consisting of an *esophagus*, a median expansion or *stomach*, and an *intestine*. It terminates at opposite ends in the *mouth* and *anus*. In

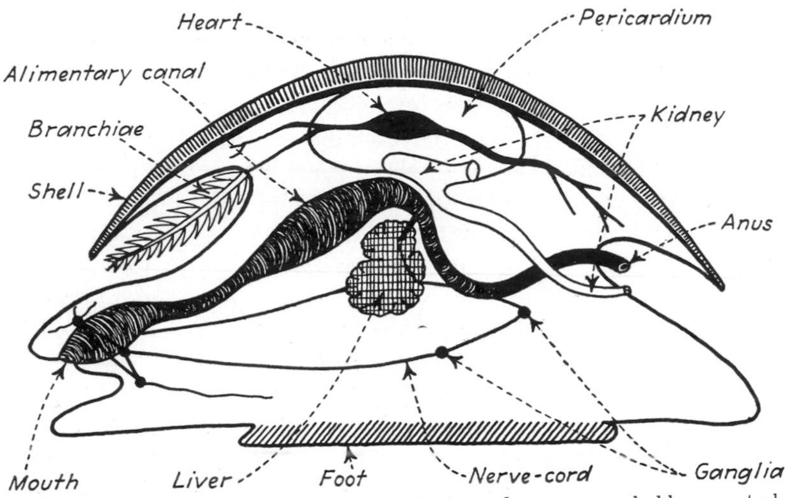

Fig. 110.—Diagram of a primitive mollusk, such as was probably ancestral to the different classes of the Mollusca. (*Slightly modified after Nicholson and Lydekker, who greatly altered a figure by Lankester.*)

certain gastropods the alimentary tract is twisted into the shape of the figure 8. The mouth is provided with glands which aid in preparing the food for the alimentary tract, and there is also a large gland known as the *liver*, which discharges into the stomach. The stomach, the intestine, and the associated organs lie within the body cavity. The circulatory system consists of a heart, situated on the dorsal side, and the necessary vessels through which the blood can move to and from the heart. The blood is colorless or red, blue, or green.

All of the mollusks except the bivalves or pelecypods have the front or anterior part of the body modified into a *head*. This usually is equipped with sensory appendages or sense organs and a mouth portion (*buccal cavity*) provided with several structures concerned with food acquisition and mastication. Beaklike jaws are present in some forms; platelike chewing structures characterize other species; and many mollusks possess a tonguelike rasp which is used as a file for cutting the food upon which the animal feeds or for boring into the shell of an unfortunate victim. This structure, known as the *radula*, has tiny chitinous teeth and lies immediately behind and below the mouth and when unusually long may be coiled in the mouth (Figs. 111, 113 *A*).

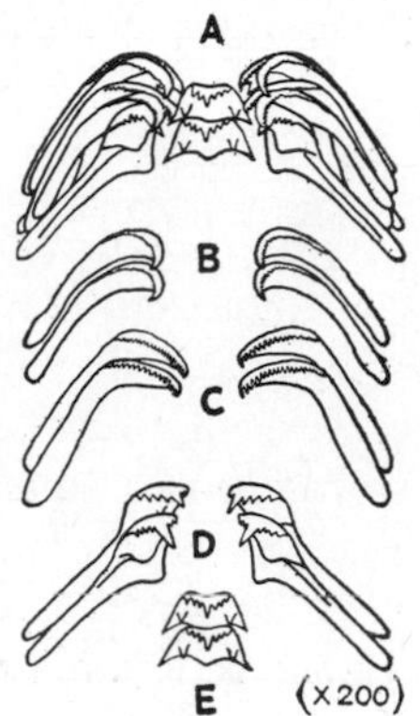

FIG. 111.—Lingual dentition of *Amnicola dalli*, a fresh-water gastropod found in the streams of Nevada. *A*. Two of the transverse rows of teeth of the odontophore, showing normal position of teeth. *B–D*. Analysis of *A*: *B*, outer laterals; *C*, first laterals; *D*, intermediate teeth; *E*, rachidian teeth. (*From Call after Beecher.*)

Except in a single group reproduction is by means of eggs, and sexes are generally distinct. The reproductive organs are usually in pairs and are situated in the walls of the body cavity. Fertilization of the eggs can take place within the body of the female, but in most cases the eggs are discharged and fertilized externally. Some mollusks prepare egg cases within which the young hatch and live for a short time. Others retain the eggs in special pouches in the mouth cavity. Species which make no preparations for the care of the young, as the oysters, produce immense numbers of eggs to assure reproduction. In all groups except the cephalopods the embryonic mollusk passes through a trochophore stage, thence into a free-swimming larva known as a *veliger*, and finally into an adult form. Because of the presence in the ontogeny of the trochophore stage, the Mollusca are thought to have developed from some wormlike ancestor during the Pre-Cambrian. The hypothetical archetypal form is illustrated in Fig. 110.

Most mollusks are short-lived, 1 to 3 or 4 years being a normal lifetime, but an extreme case of 20 years has been reported. The majority of mollusks are vagrant benthos, but some are pelagic, and a few are planktonic. They attain world-wide distribution and are known to live from 5,300 m. (17,400 ft.) below sea level to 5,400 m. (18,000 ft.) above. The gastropods were found at the greatest elevation.

THE SHELL

Most mollusks have a shell of some kind, and the shell material is commonly calcareous, though occasionally chitinous. The former material may be calcite, aragonite, or a combination of both. The shells of marine mollusks are composed of both minerals, but those of terrestrial and fresh-water habitats seem to be largely of aragonite. No general statement can adequately characterize a molluscan shell because of the great variation in size and architecture. In the simple Amphineura the shell is in the form of a dorsal shield composed of eight imbricating calcareous plates. The Pelecypoda have a bivalved shell composed of two convex calcareous valves which are generally of the same size. Scaphopods live in a hollow, tusk-shaped calcareous shell without internal structure. The shell of the Gastropoda varies from a simple unchambered calcareous cone to complexly coiled shells in which the cone is coiled about an axis in numerous ways. The cephalopod shell is essentially a slowly expanding chambered cone, which may remain straight throughout life or become coiled in a variety of ways. By far the majority of mollusks have an external shell, but a few have developed an internal one, and some have lost the shell completely (Fig. 112).

CLASSIFICATION

The Mollusca are usually divided into five classes on the basis of the character of the shell, the most obvious difference exhibited by the members of the phylum. These are

1. **Amphineura**—Chitons; "sea mice" or "coat-of-mail" shells
2. **Pelecypoda**—Bivalves; oysters, clams, mussels, etc.
3. **Scaphopoda**—Tusk shells
4. **Gastropoda**—Snails, slugs, etc.
5. **Cephalopoda**—Squids, cuttlefish, *Octopus*, *Nautilus*, etc.

Of the five classes the Amphineura and Scaphopoda are of least importance as to number, variety, or stratigraphic value. The Pelecypoda are numerous at the present and seem to have been fairly important since the early Paleozoic. The Gastropoda appear to be at their zenith at the present time but have had a rather important part among bottom faunas since the early Paleozoic. The Cephalopoda are of little present importance but were extremely abundant at certain times during the Paleo-

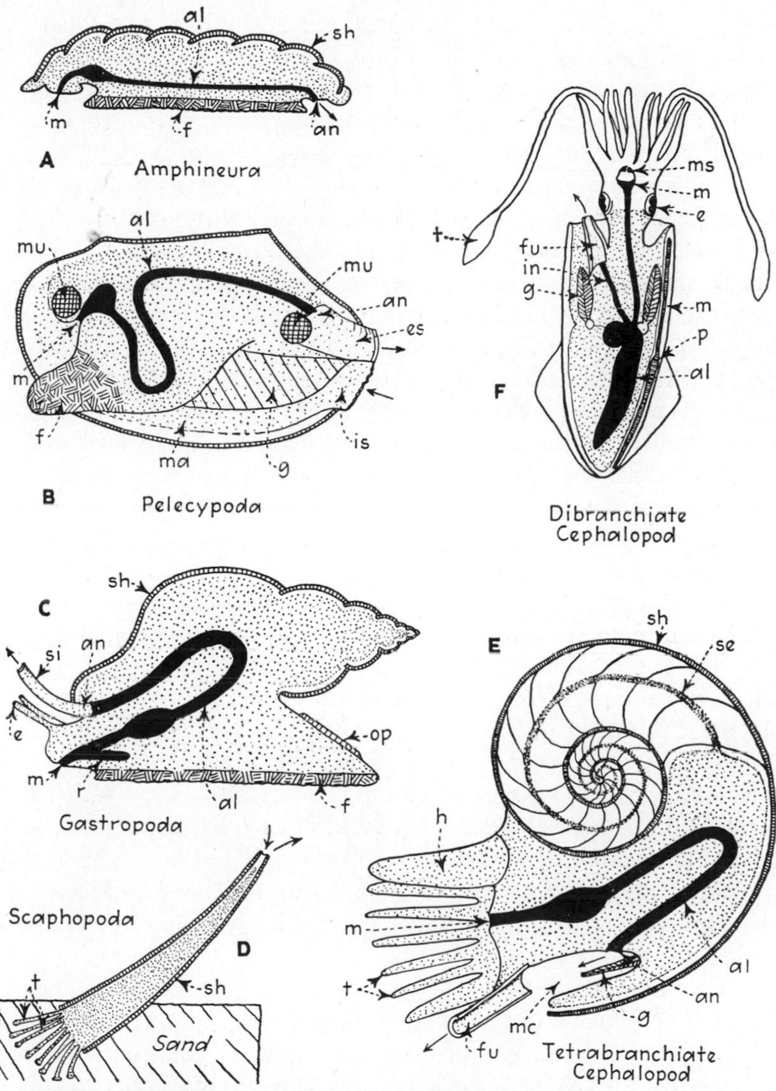

FIG. 112.—Diagrams illustrating the relation of the animal to its shell in the five classes of Mollusca. *Al*, alimentary canal; *an*, anus; *e*, eye; *es*, exhalant siphon; *f*, foot; *fu*, hyponomic funnel; *g*, gill; *h*, hood; *is*, inhalant siphon; *m*, mouth; *ma*, mantle; *mc*, mantle cavity; *ms*, horny mandibles; *mu*, muscle; *op*, operculum; *p*, pen or internal shell lying in the mantle dorsally; *r*, buccal cavity where odontophore lies; *se*, siphuncle; *sh*, shell; *si*, siphon; *t*, tentacle. (*Adapted from Figures by Parker and Haswell, Thomson, and Nicholson and Lydekker.*)

zoic and Mesozoic. Considered as a whole, the Mollusca constitute one of the most important of the invertebrate phyla. Their fossil record begins early in the Paleozoic and is unbroken from then to the present, though various groups from time to time have become extinct, and new groups have appeared.

Fossil Mollusca have received much detailed study because of the evidence for evolution recorded in the structures of the shells. Of unusual interest in this respect are the cephalopods (Ammonoidea) with complex shells. These shells when broken back from the aperture to the embryonic shell reveal step by step not only the changes and modifications that have taken place in the shell itself but, in addition, the advances and retrogressions made, over a vast period of time, by the race or phylum to which the particular species belongs. Living Mollusca have surpassed the fossil forms in the attention that they have received, since many are of commercial importance and, in addition, because they represent an ideal group for the study of ecologic relations.

Class Amphineura[1]

The Amphineura include Chitons or "sea mice" (*Polyplacophora*) and a group of wormlike creatures, known as *Aplacophora*, which possess no shell. As a group the Amphineura seem to be the most primitive of the Mollusca, although they do not appear fossilized so early as some of the more advanced classes. Some authors even go so far as to classify the Aplacophora with the primitive Archiannelida of the annelid worms, but there seems to be a more general tendency at present to consider them as primitive mollusks and to include them in the Amphineura, although it is recognized that they very likely stand close to the archetypal mollusk from which the phylum as a whole evolved.

The animal exhibits the typical bilaterally symmetrical molluscan body, with an anterior mouth, posterior anus, ventral foot adapted for creeping, and a partly or completely inclosing mantle (Figs. 112 *A*, 114 *A–B*). Internally the alimentary tract is nearly straight, and a radula is present in the poorly defined head. Gills project into a shallow mantle cavity situated on each side of the foot between the margins of that organ and the edge of

[1] Amphineura—Gr. *amphi*, both, on sides of + *neuron*, sinew; referring to the paired organs on each side of the band which connects the plates of the shell.

the mantle. Members of the Aplacophora are without a shell, but the skin is studded with tiny calcareous bodies (Fig. 113). None of the latter, however, appears to have been found in fossil form. In the Polyplacophora there is a dorsal shield

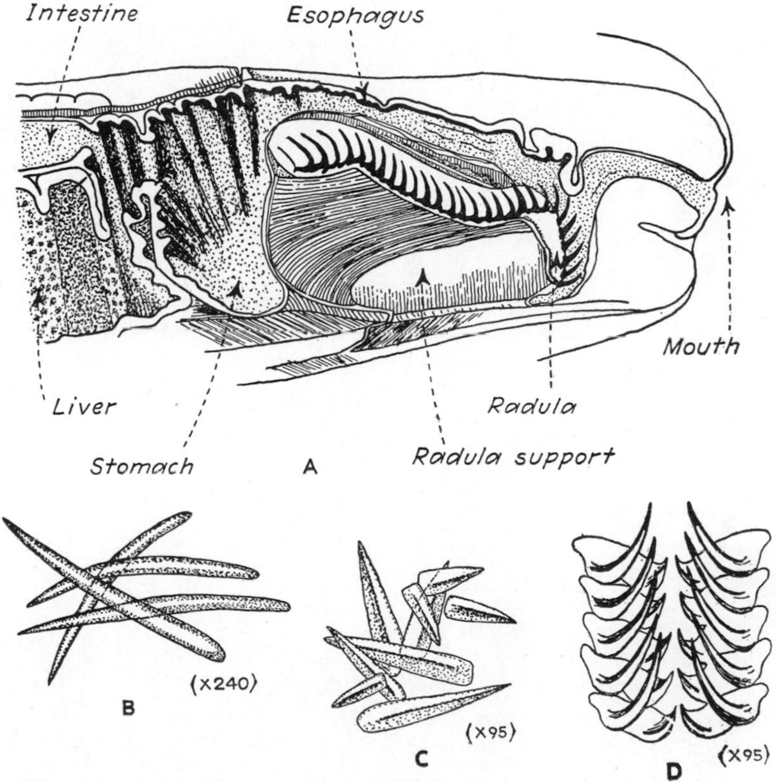

Fig. 113.—Aplacophora. *A*. Longitudinal section of the anterior part of *Limifossor talpoideus*, from Pacific waters, showing the relation of the radula to the alimentary tract. *B*. Calcareous spicules from the body of *Lophomenia spiralis*. *C*. Calcareous spicules from the body of *Chaetoderma californica*. *D*. Dorsal view of radula of *A* showing the arrangement of the teeth. (*After Heath*.)

which consists of eight imbricating calcareous plates held together by the *girdle* (Fig. 114). This girdle is a part of the mantle by which the shell is entirely surrounded and in which it is more or less extensively embedded. Its upper surface is covered by bristles, spines, or scales, which in life are responsible for the animal's resemblance to a mouse (whence the name sea mouse).

The eight *valves* of the *Chiton* shell are arranged in a single continuous series, with the anterior or *cephalic* valve and the posterior or *anal* valve always differing conspicuously from the six similar *intermediate* ones. Each valve is composed of two layers

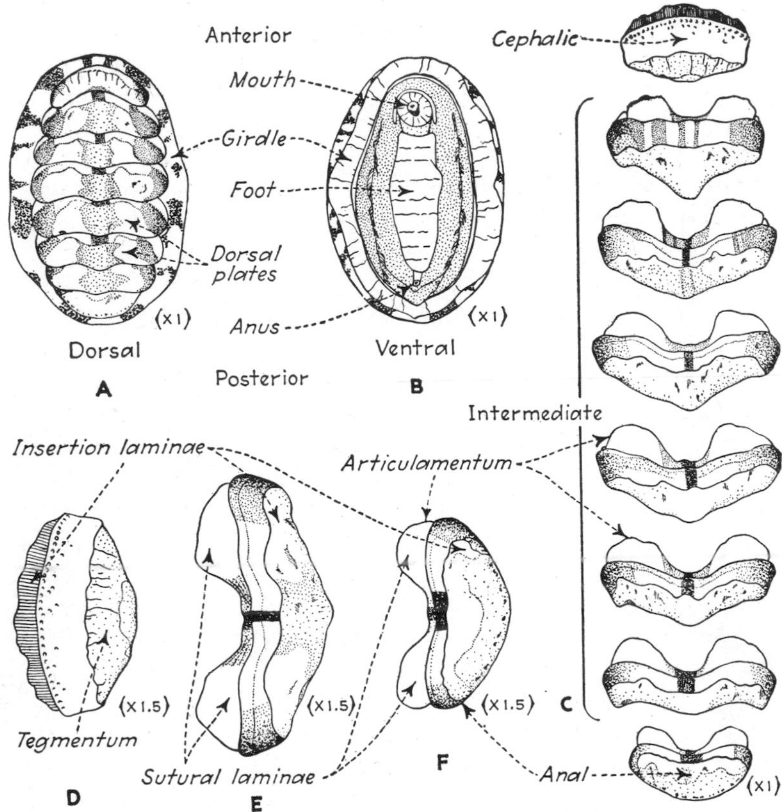

Fig. 114.—Amphineura. A modern amphineuran, *Chiton* sp. *A*. Dorsal view showing the eight imbricating plates embedded in the girdle. *B*. Ventral view showing the mouth, anus, foot, and girdle. *C*. The eight plates or valves separated to show their characteristics. *D*. The cephalic valve somewhat enlarged showing the prominent insertion lamina which is concealed in *E* and *F*. *E*. An intermediate valve, with conspicuous sutural laminae. The insertion laminae are on the underside of the valve. *F*. The anal valve.

of material: an upper consisting largely of chitin impregnated with calcium carbonate, more or less porous and having the surface sculptured; and an under layer which is nonporous in structure and composed of calcium carbonate. The upper layer of each valve, designated the *tegmentum*, owes its porous character to numerous minute holes of two sizes, known as *megalopores* and *micropores.* These are connected by tiny canals which are thought to contain fibrous or nervous tissue. The under layer of each valve, designated the *articulamentum,* is usually larger than the tegmentum; hence a certain part of it is covered above, either by the girdle or by parts of adjacent valves (Fig. 114). Extensions of the articulamentum on the anterior edge of the cephalic valve and the posterior edge of the anal valve, and also on the posterior lateral edges of the intermediate valves, are known as *insertion plates* or *laminae.* These are embedded in and concealed by the girdle. Anterior extensions of the articulamentum on the intermediate and anal valves are designated *sutural laminae.* These are covered by the valve in front; hence the valves imbricate and articulate, making it possible for the animal to enroll like a pill bug.

Amphineura are strictly marine and are represented by several hundred living species. The Chitons, ranging in length from ½ to 6 in., dwell in all depths to 4,200 m. (13,800 ft.), but they are found most abundantly on the shore between tide levels, where they adhere firmly to smooth rocks or other solid objects by means of the sucker-like foot. If torn loose, the animal slowly enrolls itself into a ball and remains thus for some time before slowly unrolling. It may also enroll upon death. The Aplacophora are not often found in shallow water and never in the littoral zone. They occur in deep water down to 2,280 m. (7,500 ft.). Some burrow in the mud, whereas others are associated with certain colonial coelenterates.

No fossil remains of Aplacophora have been described, but isolated valves of about 100 species of Polyplacophora have been reported from strata ranging in age from Ordovician to Recent. Paleozoic valves differ from later ones in lacking well-developed articulating structures or insertion and sutural laminae. The class at no time in its history appears to have been of very great importance.

CLASS PELECYPODA (LAMELLIBRANCHIA)[1]

General Considerations.—The Pelecypoda, or Lamellibranchia as they are known in the British Isles and in Europe, constitute

[1] *Pelecypoda*——Gr. *pelekus,* a hatchet + *pous, podos,* foot; referring to the resemblance of the foot to the blade of a hatchet or ax. *Lamellibranchia* —L. *lamella,* a plate + *branchiae,* gills; referring to the platelike character of the gills.

one of the larger groups of mollusks and are especially interesting because of the many different species and because members of the class illustrate so many adaptations. The class is also one of the animal groups best known to the layman because some of the members (oysters and clams) are important sources of food and also because shells of pelecypods are exploited for recovery of pearls and manufacture of buttons.

Most pelecypods are marine, but many species have become adapted to brackish or fresh waters. The body is bilaterally symmetrical and can always be distinguished from all other Mollusca by the possession of a calcareous shell of two parts or *valves*. These valves are usually alike, almost invariably articulate along a toothed hinge line, and are further joined by several transverse muscular structures. When the shell is closed the valves more or less completely surround and protect the soft parts of the animal. The organism itself is laterally compressed, has the ventral portion produced into a prominent foot, has a rudimentary development of the head, and possesses two or four symmetrical gills. The foot is sometimes modified for burrowing in the mud and sand.

Throughout their long geologic history, said to begin in the Lower Cambrian, the pelecypods have usually been vagrant benthos, often living half buried in the bottom muds or sands. A few species have developed the habit of burrowing in rocks or wood, and certain genera become permanently attached either by a tuft of threads developed on the foot or by cementation of one valve. Over 7,000 living species are known. Most marine pelecypods dwell in shallow water from low tide level to the 200-fathom line. There is a surprising variety of adaptation which in some cases is accompanied by considerable modification of body and shell structures (Fig. 118). Thousands of fossil forms are also known.

The Animal. RELATION TO SHELL.—The pelecypod is inclosed in a shell consisting of two calcareous plates or *valves* and is attached to its interior surface. In most forms when the valves are closed the animal is completely surrounded and protected by the shell. Two or more sets of transverse muscular structures are responsible for closing the valves. The visceral part of the animal is inclosed in the *mantle*. This is attached over the dorsal part of the body but hangs free on the ventral side to form the right and left lobes of the mantle (Fig. 115).

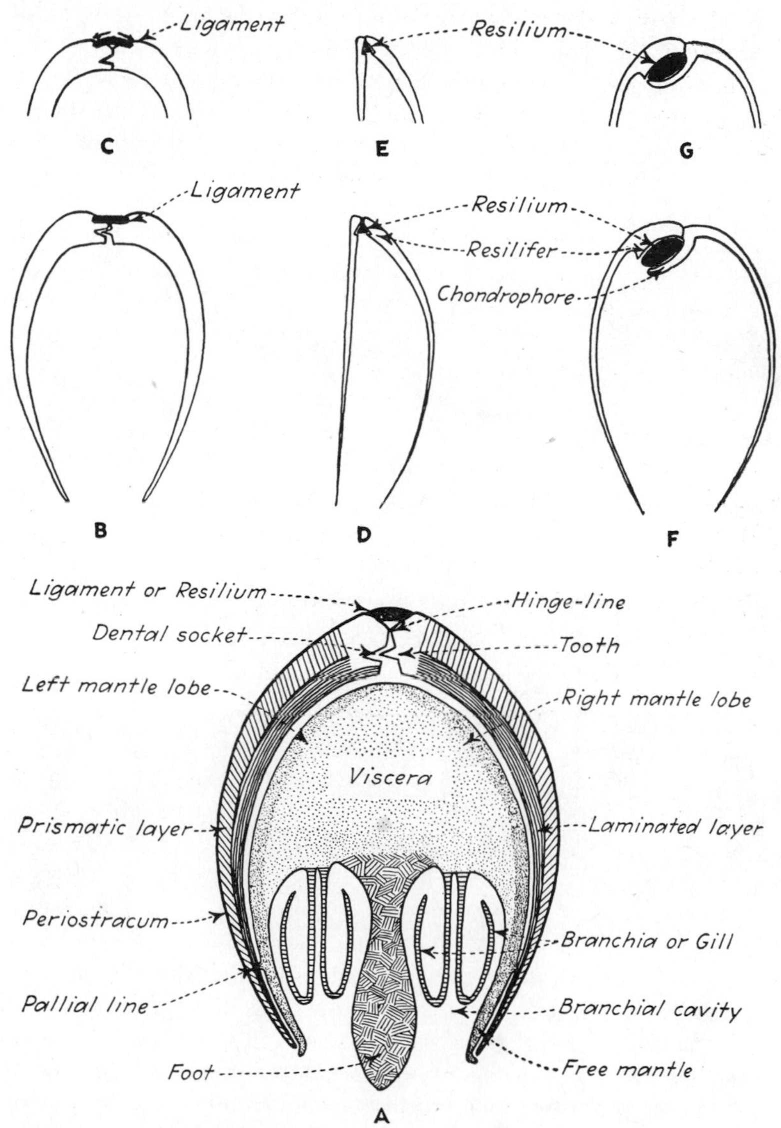

Fig. 115.—Pelecypod structures. *A*. Diagrammatic median section through animal and shell, at right angles to the plane of symmetry, showing the nature of both and their relations to each other. *B–C*. Ligament with valves apart and together, as in *Venus*. *D–E*. Resilium, with the shell open and closed, as in *Pecten*. *F–G*. Resilium, with resilifer and chondrophore, as in *Mya*.

The free edges of the mantle secrete the outer and middle layers of the shell, the additions being made along the margin. The surfaces of the mantle lobes secrete the inner or *mother-of-pearl* layer. At the place where the mantle ceases to be attached to the shell there is left on each valve a prominent depression, known as the *pallial line* (Fig. 116). Between the two mantle

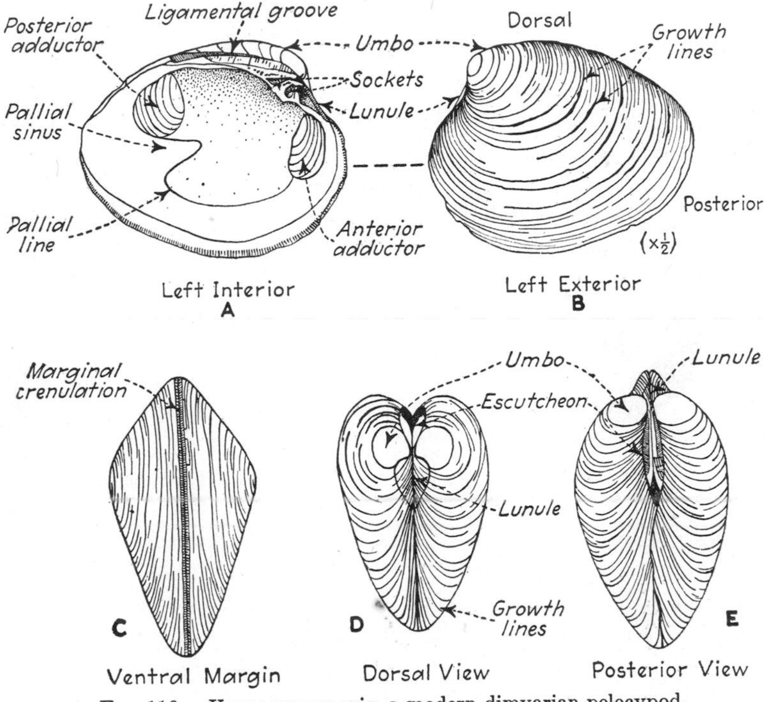

Fig. 116.—*Venus mercenaria*, a modern dimyarian pelecypod.

lobes, on the median ventral part of the animal, is the large hatchet-shaped *foot* which may be extended beyond the margin of the shell when the valves are apart. Between the foot and the mantle lobes on each side is the *gill cavity* wherein lie the ventrally projecting paired gills.

The Viscera.—The internal anatomy of the living pelecypods is relatively uniform, and there is nearly always a close correlation between the animal and the form of its shell (Fig. 112 *B*). The alimentary tract is a much coiled tube consisting of the *mouth*, *esophagus*, *stomach* (into which two digestive glands discharge), *intestine*, and *anus*. The mouth is anterior and lacks the radula so common in other mollusks. The anal opening is posterior. The animal possesses a blood circulatory system and a fairly complex nervous system and may have small ocular organs known as *eyes*. In most species the sexes are separate.

THE MUSCULAR SYSTEM.—The valves of the shell are held together internally by one or two strong *adductor* muscles which pass transversely from valve to valve. They are opened by flexible or elastic structures along the hinge line which in different species range in form from a pad to a rod or band composed of tough horny or chitinous material (Fig. 115). These structures are either external or internal. In *Venus* (Fig. 116) the structure, known as a *ligament*, is external and in the form of a flat band parallel to the hinge line. This fits into grooves in each valve and takes the form of a hemicylinder when the valves are closed as the band is then bent. In such forms as *Ostrea* the opening structure is internal and has the form of a pad, triangular in cross section, with the apex directed toward the hinge line. This structure is designated the *resilium*, and it functions as would a rubber pad caught in a nut cracker. For the reception of the resilium there is a depression or process termed the *resilifer*. The resilium may be simple, as in *Mya;* or multiple, as in *Trigonia*. Some species have both ligament and resilium. Regardless of position the opening structures are not parts of the body but uncalcified parts of the shell.

A ligament situated behind the *beak* or *umbo* of the shell is said to be *opisthodetic*, one in front *prosodetic*, and one in both positions *amphidetic*. Shells having a single adductor muscle are described as *monomyarian;* those with two, *dimyarian* (Fig. 118).

From Fig. 115 it is evident that in the closed shell of a pelecypod the adductors are contracted, and the ligament stretched or bent. Relaxation of muscles permits the valves to open. This is the reverse of the muscular system in the Brachiopoda. The dead shells of pelecypods are thus ordinarily open or separated, and closed shells are the exception. Because of this condition mud fillings of the interior of pelecypod shells are of common occurrence as fossils.

THE MANTLE.—During life all pelecypods must have a current of water bathing the gills for respiration and for bringing food to the mouth. This current enters the body through the slit between the right and left mantle lobes. Another current is needed to convey the waste products out of the body. In order that the incoming current (inhalant), carrying oxygen and food, may not mix with the outgoing one (exhalant), carrying away waste products, the edges of the mantle have been modified in a number of ways as illustrated in Fig. 118.

In the earliest and most primitive pelecypods, such as *Arca* and *Pecten*, the edges of the mantle are entirely free, but posteriorly they are folded in such a way as to produce an upper

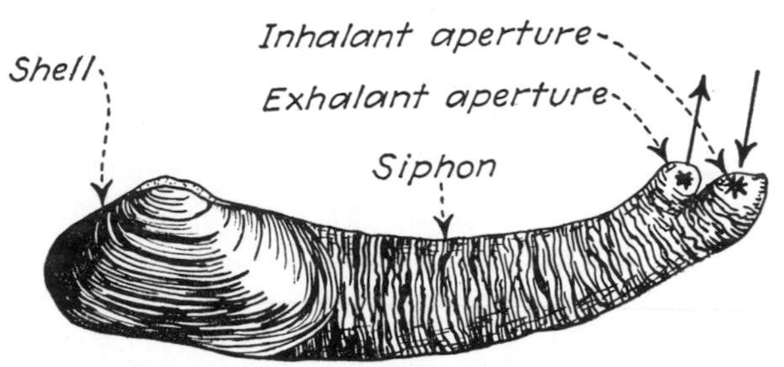

Fig. 117.—A pelecypod (*Panopaea norvegica*) showing a well-developed siphon. Water enters through the inhalant aperture (siphon) and escapes through the exhalant aperture (siphon). (*After Thomson.*)

exhalant channel separated from a lower inhalant one. The opposite edges of the mantle are not united. A slightly more advanced modification occurs in many fresh-water clams, in which the posterior edges of the mantle are united at one point, forming an incipient exhalant tube or *siphon* above. Below, the edges are separate and merely held together to restrict the entrance of the inhalant current. In the next stage the posterior edges of the mantle lobes unite at two points to form two distinct openings. These grow posteriorly into tubular siphons, the upper exhalant, the lower inhalant (Fig. 117). These siphons may grow to considerable lengths, particularly in burrowing forms in which they may be two or three times as long as the shell, and they may be separate or united to one another along one side (Fig. 118). In such siphonated forms the mantle edges in front of the siphons may unite completely except for a small ventral slit through which the foot protrudes. Such a mantle is said to be *closed*. The siphons usually can be partly or entirely retracted within the shell by muscles adapted for this purpose. These muscles are attached to the inner surfaces of the valves just below the posterior adductor, and they represent enlargement of the muscles by which the mantle is attached along the pallial line. The places of attachment form the embayment of the pallial line known as the *pallial sinus* (Fig. 116 *A*). It is possible, therefore, to determine by the absence or presence of the pallial sinus in a fossil shell whether the animal had an open mantle or siphons and also from the magnitude of the sinus whether the siphon was large or small. Siphons are best developed in forms which have the burrowing habit. Some of these are illustrated in Fig. 118.

The Branchiae (Gills).—Modern pelecypods usually have two pairs of branchiae or gills, but the number may have been different in some extinct forms. The branchiae arise from ridges on each side of the body between the mantle and foot, first as a series of filaments and later as leaflike structures formed by the union of the filaments. They exhibit considerable variety in form, arrangement, and structure and are of great importance for classification of living species (Fig. 119).

The most primitive arrangement seems to be that in which the filaments are free, short, wide, and flat. This type is known as *protobranchiate* or *aspidobranchiate*. A second type, referred to as *filibranchiate*, consists of long, slender filaments which are kept from tangling by interlocking patches of cilia or bars of connective tissue. The gills may become plaited so as to exhibit vertical folds. These are known as *pseudolamellibranchiate*. The filaments of the filibranchiate type may become connected with those adjacent to produce a perforated, leaflike variety designated *eulamellibranchiate*, and this may develop in turn into a perforated, muscular partition, termed *septibranchiate*. Largely on the basis of the gills, zoologists divide the pelecypods into the following five orders: *Protobranchia*, *Filibranchia*, *Pseudolamellibranchia*, *Eulamellibranchia*, and *Septibranchia*. Since nothing can be determined concerning gill structure in fossil shells, classification on the basis of gills cannot be used by paleontologists.

The Foot.—The foot of the pelecypod is usually not so well developed as in the gastropods. It is generally a hatchet-shaped muscular organ that may be used for locomotion. In some forms it assumes a cylindrical shape, and in the sedentary species it is essentially functionless. On the foot of some pelecypods is a gland that secretes small horny threads which are known collec-

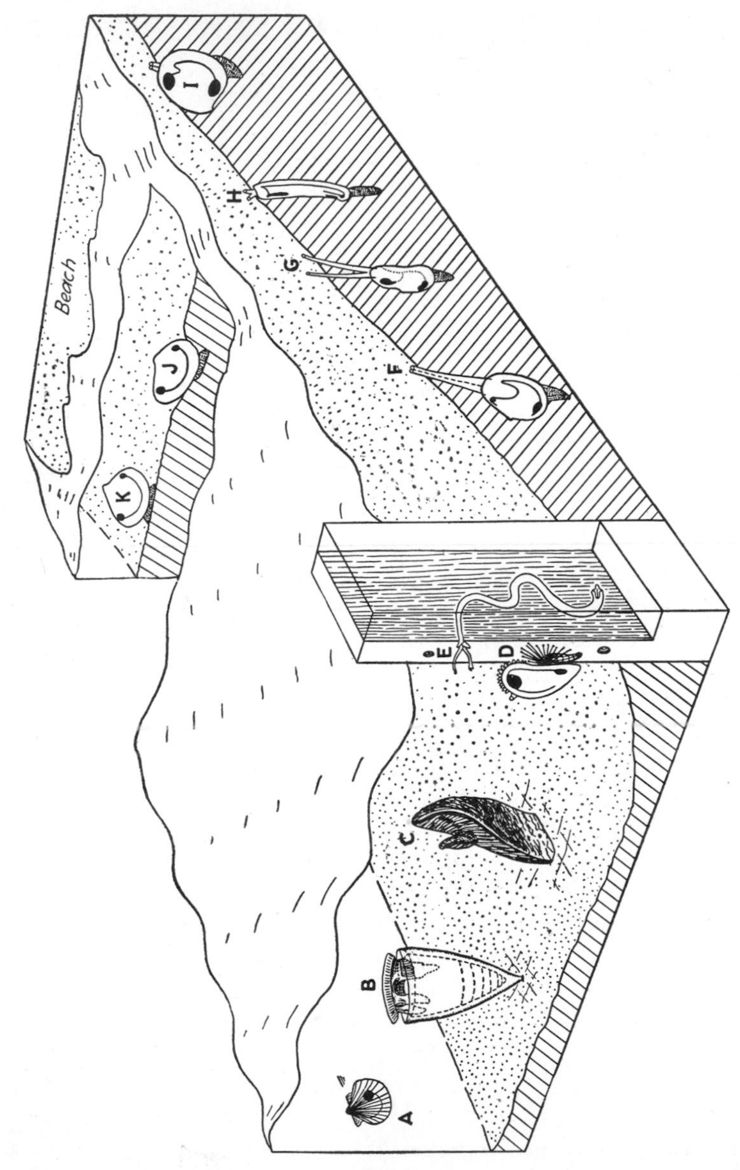

FIG. 118.—Diagrams to scale showing adaptations among the Pelecypoda. Muscles are indicated in black; the foot, by complex crosshatching; sandy bottom, by stipling; and sandy substratum, by inclined lining. *A. Pecten*, an active swimming form. *B. Hippurites*, an unusual form in which one highly

tively as the byssus (Fig. 118 *D*). The animal uses these threads to attach itself to rocks or other bodies on the bottom. Many species in the younger growth stages use this method of anchorage

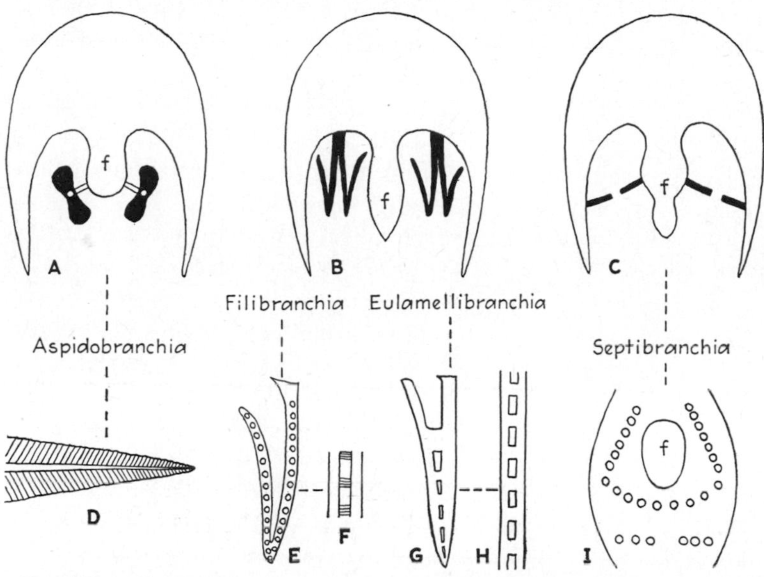

Fig. 119.—Diagrams illustrating the types of gills in Pelecypoda. *A–C*. Cross sections of the body showing the form and position of the gills (in black). *D*. Side view of part of an aspidobranchiate gill. *E*. Section of a filibranchiate gill. *F*. Diagram showing how transverse fascicles of cilia prevent the filaments from tangling. *G*. Section of a eulamellibranchiate gill showing the filaments permanently connected by transverse structures. *H*. Section showing the reticulate nature of the gill. *I*. A septibranchiate pelecypod viewed from below. (*Modified after Berry*.)

but abandon it at maturity to lead a vagrant or sedentary life. A few forms, however, as *Anomia*, become attached permanently by means of a byssus impregnated with calcite.

---

modified conical valve was attached to the bottom and the other served as a lid. *C*. *Ostrea*, the familiar oyster, attached by a small part of one slightly modified valve. A young shell is shown attached to the free valve of the larger shell. *D*. *Mytilus*, attached to the surface of a wooden pier by a byssus. *E*. *Teredo*, the shipworm, which bores into wooden piers and similar structures. The pier is sectioned vertically to show the path of the burrow. *F*. *Mya*, a burrowing form with a long siphon. *G*. *Tagelus*, a burrowing form with a long double siphon. *H*. *Ensis*, a razor-shaped burrowing pelecypod with short siphons. *I*. *Venus*, the familiar quahog, almost entirely buried in the sand. *J*. *Crassatellites*, nestling in a depression in the sand. *K*. *Nucula*, a form which crawls about over the sand. (A few of these forms may be exposed at low tide.) (*Adapted from Berry*.)

The Shell. General Considerations.—Pelecypod shells consist essentially of two equal, asymmetrical, convex calcareous plates, attached to the right and left sides of the organism and articulating along a straight or curved, toothed hinge line (Fig. 116). In forms cemented by one valve, the attached valve tends to be larger, with the smaller valve acting as a lid (Fig. 118 *B–C*). The earliest part of the valves is the pointed *beak*, which usually curves toward the anterior end of the shell. The rounded and elevated part of each valve immediately adjacent to the beak constitutes the *umbo*. The shell is bilaterally symmetrical with the plane of symmetry passing between the valves. In order to orient most pelecypod shells, the following procedure should be used: Place the shell so that the beaks are uppermost and pointing forward or away from the observer. The valve on the right is the right valve; that on the left, the left one. The front of the shell, the way the beaks are directed, is anterior. The back part of the shell, always having the pallial sinus if such is present, is posterior. If a single adductor scar is present, it will be in the posterior part of the shell. The upper or hinge-line part of the shell is dorsal; the lower, ventral. The foot is always in a ventral position.

Pelecypod and brachiopod shells resemble each other in having external, bivalved calcareous shells, but they differ radically in several other respects. A comparison of the two follows:

Brachiopoda	Pelecypoda
1. Equilateral valves	1. Inequilateral valves
2. Inequivalved	2. Equivalved
3. Valves dorsal and ventral	3. Valves right and left
4. Plane of symmetry across valves and through beaks	4. Plane of symmetry between valves and umbos
5. Pedicle opening present (except in primitive forms)	5. No pedicle or opening (in some a byssal notch or hole but in ventral margin)
6. Teeth in one valve, sockets in the opposite valve (except in the Inarticulata)	6. Teeth and sockets, if present, in each valve
7. Valves opened and closed by muscles. No ligament present	7. Valves opened by ligament or resilium at the hinge line
8. Three-layered shell—periostracum, laminated layer, prismatic layer	8. Three-layered shell—periostracum, prismatic layer, laminated or mother-of-pearl layer

The *height* of a pelecypod shell is measured along a line in the plane of symmetry from the umbo to the ventral margin (Fig. 116). The *length* is the greatest distance between the anterior and posterior margins measured in the plane of symmetry. The *thickness* is the greatest distance between valves (when shell is closed) measured at right angles to the plane of symmetry. Pelecypod shells exhibit great range in size, from minute forms less than ½ in. in length to the giant *Tridacna*, which may reach 2 or 3 ft. in length. Shape varies greatly, but the general tendency is toward a laterally compressed, anterio-posterior elongated form.

Composition and Structure of Shell Material.—The pelecypod shell is composed of three distinct layers, an outer chitinous layer and a middle and an inner calcareous one (Fig. 115 *A*). The outer layer, termed the *periostracum*, is usually thin, often absent in the adult shell, and rarely if ever preserved in fossil shells (Fig. 123 *D*). It appears to function as a covering which protects the calcareous parts of the shell from solution. The middle layer is composed of closely packed, polygonal prisms of calcium carbonate disposed perpendicularly to the surface of the shell. It is designated the *prismatic layer* and constitutes the outer layer in all fossil forms. The prisms are secreted by the free edges of the mantle lobes; hence growth takes place only on the margins of the shell. The inner layer of the shell is composed of thin laminae of calcite or aragonite, disposed roughly parallel to the surface of the mantle, and, because of the structure, is termed the *laminated layer*. It is secreted by the entire outer surface of the mantle; hence it grows continuously during the entire life of the animal, and each new lamina extends a little beyond the one last formed. Frequently the laminae are very delicate and are crumpled so that when successive laminae are exposed on the inner surface of the valves, refraction of the light rays causes iridescence. For this reason the inner layer is sometimes termed the *mother-of-pearl* layer. In many forms, however, the laminae of the inner layer are thick and are not crumpled, and the surface then has a porcelaneous character.

Certain pelecypods are of commercial importance because of the *pearls* which they sometimes form. These are small, concentrically laminated calcareous concretions secreted by the mantle in response to some type of irritation. Spherical forms are usually secreted within the mantle, whereas irregular or "blister" pearls are usually formed in the mother-of-pearl layer, as a result of abnormal secretion by the surface of the mantle. The tendency of the animal to coat any irritating object with pearly substance is utilized commercially through the introduction of small particles which the animal promptly coats with successive smooth layers of calcium carbonate.

The mineralogical composition of the calcareous shell matter varies among different species. In one group, illustrated by the oyster *Ostrea*, both prismatic and laminated layers are composed of calcite, whereas in another group the same layers are wholly of aragonite. In other forms, as in *Pinna*, the outer prismatic layer is composed of calcite, and the laminated layer of aragonite. Since aragonite is much less stable and more easily dissolved than calcite, the composition determines very largely the manner in which the shell is preserved. Hence, shells composed originally of aragonite alone are often represented in the fossil state by molds and fillings only, because of the removal by solution of the actual shell substance. Shells which have the outer layer of calcite and the inner of aragonite often show the former intact and the latter partly or entirely dissolved.

Modification in Shape of Shell.—While the majority of pelecypod shells tend to have one valve a mirror image of the other, under different environmental conditions and as a result of adaptation the two valves often assume radically different shapes and sizes. A few pelecypods attach one valve to some object on the bottom and use the other as a lid or an operculum. As a result of such attachment the shapes of the valves vary little or much depending upon the degree of modification which they have undergone (Figs. 118 *B–C*, 120). In the oysters the differences are not extreme, but in the extinct *Exogyra* and *Gryphaea* the upper valve is very distinctly different from the lower and is of much smaller dimensions. A very marked difference is exhibited by the extinct *Radiolites* and *Hippurites* in which the lower valve is a coralloid conical structure and the upper merely a lid. This development corresponds with that observed in the cemented brachiopods ranging from *Derbya* to *Richthofenia*. In some pelecypods the right valve is attached

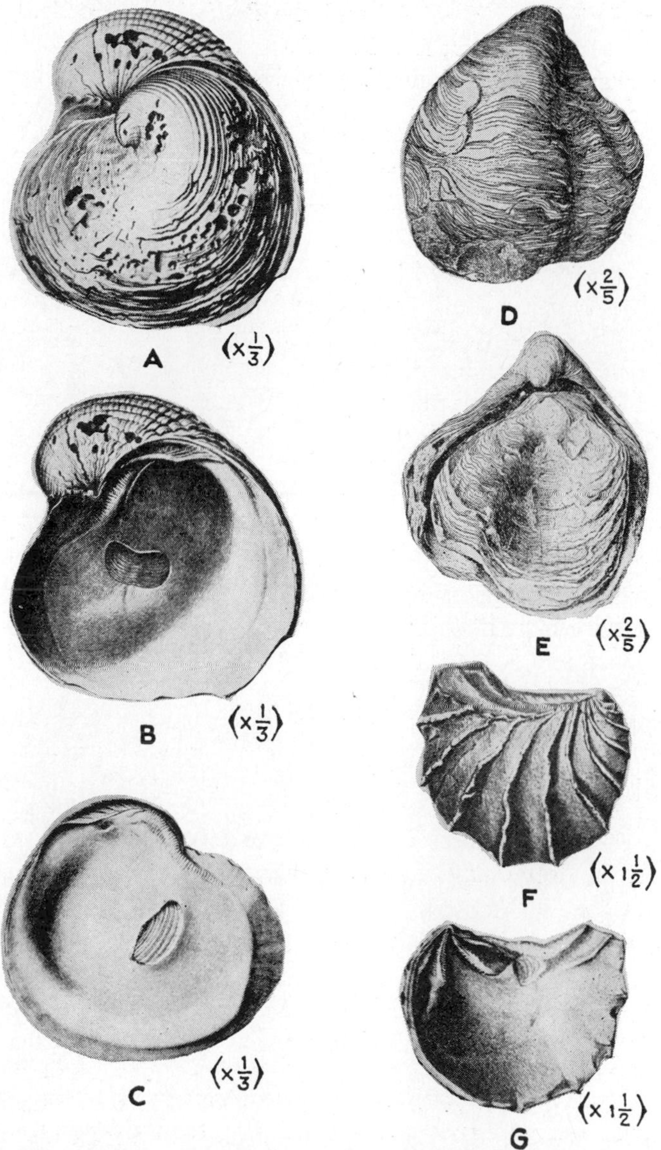

FIG. 120.—Cretaceous pelecypods. *A–C. Exogyra costata* from the Upper Cretaceous of Maryland: *A*, Exterior of right valve; *B–C*, Interiors of left and right valves, respectively. *D–E. Gryphaea corrugata tucumcarii* from the Lower Cretaceous of New Mexico. *F–G. Trigonia eufalensis*, from the Upper Cretaceous of Maryland, showing the exterior and interior of the right valve. (*A–C after Clark; D–E after Hill and Vaughan; F–G after Clark.*)

(*Pinna, Spondylus, Plicatula,* and the *Rudistids*); in others, the left (*Exogyra, Gryphaea,* and *Ostrea*).

The shape of the shell also varies greatly, depending on whether the animal swims (*Pecten*), crawls, or ploughs through the sediments on the bottom; buries itself in those sediments; or bores holes and tubes in wood or stony materials.

HINGE-LINE STRUCTURES.—The valves of most pelecypods are united to each other dorsally for a shorter or longer distance along a straight or curved hinge line. This union is effected by means of *teeth* on both valves which fit into corresponding *sockets* in the opposite valves. Shells which do not possess such locking devices are described as *edentulous.* The number and character of the teeth are of great importance in classifying fossil forms, and a detailed discussion of the systems of dentition is given in a subsequent paragraph.

Many pelecypods have an area on each valve included between the beaks and the hinge line. This has different ornamentation from the rest of the shell and is designated the *cardinal area.* In specialized shells the cardinal area becomes modified and separated into two distinct parts—an anterior heart-shaped area, the *lunule;* and a posterior, elongate, shallow depression, the *escutcheon* (Fig. 116 *D–E*). This division is effected by the forward migration of the beaks and the backward migration of the axis of rotation. Shells in which the beaks are directed toward each other are said to be *orthogyre;* those directed anteriorly or forward, as in *Venus, prosogyre;* and those directed backward, *opisthogyre.*

Posterior to the beaks in most pelecypod shells (but anteriorly also in some) is the *ligament,* and beneath or adjacent to the beaks is the *resilium,* the former external, the latter internal (Fig. 115). The ligament is a chitinous band, rod, or hemicylinder passing from one valve to the other, usually just behind the beaks, and so disposed as to be bent or stretched when the shell is closed. The lateral edges of the ligament are inserted in grooves situated in the cardinal area of each valve. These are known as *ligamental grooves.* A ligament which extends along the hinge line so that part of it is in front of the beaks and part behind is described as *amphidetic.* This is the more primitive condition. Rarely the ligament is in front of the beaks, in which case it is *prosodetic.* In the majority of shells, however, it lies behind the beaks and is designated *opisthodetic.* A hemicylindrical ligament is said to be *paravincular* and is usually opisthodetic. A ligament having the shape of a more or less flattened cord and extending from one valve to the other just beneath the beaks is *alivincular,* and such is also usually opisthodetic. A third type of ligament, known as *multivincular,* consists of a series of alivincular forms separated by short spaces. This

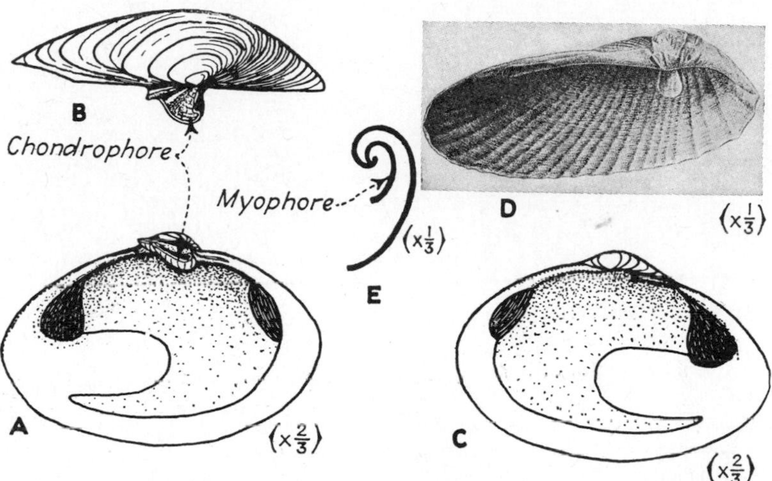

FIG. 121.—Diagrams showing chondrophore and myophore. *A.* Interior of left valve of *Mya arenaria* showing the position of the chondrophore when viewed from the side. *B.* Top view of same valve showing the position of the chondrophore in respect to the hinge line. *C.* Interior of right valve of *Mya arenaria* showing the feebly developed asthenodont dentition. The resilifer lies under the beak and is not visible. *D.* Interior of left valve of *Barnea costata,* from the Pleistocene of Maryland, showing a well-developed myophore. *E.* Diagrammatic transverse section through the beak showing how the myophore arises from under the beak. (*D after Clark.*)

type, illustrated in *Pinna* and *Arca,* may be either opisthodetic or amphidetic in position.

The resilium, a pad composed of elastic fibers, with a more or less triangular cross section, is situated with its expanded ends lodged in small pits (*resilifers*) (Fig. 115 *D–E*) on the opposing *hinge plates* (vertical plates along the hinge line containing the teeth.) In shells with very thin valves, a condition found in burrowing forms such as *Mya,* one valve may develop a resilifer and the other a spoonlike projection from inside the beak to appose it. Such a process for lodging the resilium is known as a *chondrophore,* and this may be supported by a structure termed the *clavicle* (Fig. 121). This is not to be confused with a somewhat similar process, the *myophore*, developed in some shells as an internal support for the muscles. The resilifer in some forms is strengthened by a shelly plate known as the *lithodesma*. When the shell is closed the resilium is shortened and hence is compressed, whereas the ligament if present is stretched. Relaxation of the adductor muscles permits the shell to open.

SURFACE ORNAMENTATION.—Most pelecypods have the surfaces of the valves more or less ornamented, and one of the commonest types of ornamentation is represented by the *growth lines*. These are arranged concentrically in respect to the beaks and represent increments made at the margin of the valves. The most marked growth lines usually are separated by bands of less prominent ones, the number and prominence appearing to depend largely upon the conditions of environment. In some forms it is possible to determine the age of the shell by counting the most prominent growth lines. In the majority of primitive pelecypods the ornamentation is very simple and usually consists merely of the growth lines. In the more advanced forms the surfaces of the valves are ornamented by radial structures in the form of spines, nodes, striations, and ribs. Shells having both prominent growth lines and radial ornamentation may exhibit a reticulated appearance. Some shells, such as *Tridacna*, have the entire valves crenulated into a series of large radial folds and troughs which fit into each other along the valve margins and firmly lock the shell when it is closed. On the surface of the valves, convex, ventrally extending plates rise where prominent growth lines cross the radial folds.

DENTITION.—The dorsal or cardinal margin of each valve of the pelecypod shell is reenforced by a thick vertical plate known as the *hinge plate* (Figs. 121, 122). On this are developed numerous projections, ridges, or teeth which alternate with pits or sockets. The valves are locked along the hinge line by this system of teeth and sockets, the former on one valve fitting into the latter on the other. This interlocking apparatus constitutes the *hinge* of the shell, and the term *dentition* refers to the arrangement and character of the teeth and sockets. It is thought that the first hinge teeth were derived from crenulations and ribs on the dorsal margins of the valves and developed primarily for preventing the latter from slipping over each other.

The dentition of pelecypod shells is often quite complex and confusing, and different authors are not in agreement as to the number of types that should be recognized. Regardless, however, of the character of the dentition, the teeth themselves may be divided into three groups. In the first there are one or more teeth, the *cardinal teeth*, situated immediately beneath the umbos. A second and third group of *lateral teeth* are placed on either side of the preceding. Since the different types of teeth complement each other, one is usually developed at the expense of the others; hence there are some shells which have cardinals only, some have laterals only, and some have a row of similar and equal teeth. The teeth often become modified through secondary deposits made by the mantle in the dorsal part of the shell, or supplemented by the development of radial ribs and folds, which serve to lock the valves ventrally and laterally along the shell margin.

Ten different varieties of dentition have been recognized by some investigators, while others maintain that there are but two types which can be recognized easily. There are a few shells which possess no teeth. In the following list of varieties of dentition, the first two are recognized by all workers as most distinctive and easily identified (Fig. 122).

Taxodont.—Taxodont dentition is characterized by a series of mainly similar alternating teeth and sockets. The number of each may be as many as 35. This variety of dentition seems to be primitive and has been in existence from the early Paleozoic to the present time. It is often present in the young of species which in maturity have another type of dentition. The living *Arca* has taxodont dentition.

Teleodont.—This variety represents the highest development of dentition and hinge structure among the pelecypods. The lowest and most primitive types of teleodont dentition merge into and resemble the diagenodont forms. In teleodont dentition there are a few large cardinals with or without laterals. There may also be a roughened lateral area and accessory lamellae. *Venus*, with three cardinals in the right valve and two in the left, illustrates the variety.

Schizodont.—Schizodont dentition is not well defined. It seems to have developed from the taxodont variety. Generally the teeth are of irregular and variable shapes and are more or less obscurely divided into subumbonal, pseudocardinal, and

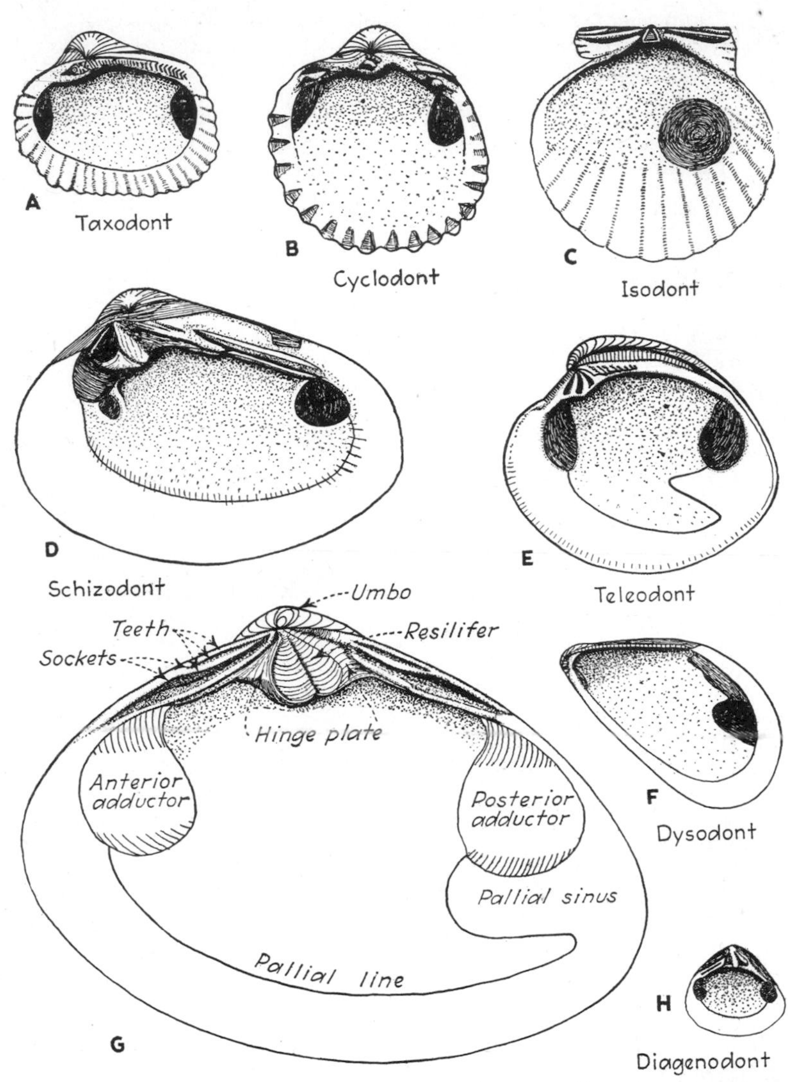

Fig. 122.—Interior views of right valves showing the different types of dentition among the pelecypods. *A. Arca.* *B. Cardium.* *C. Pecten.* *D. Unio.* *E. Venus.* *F. Mytilus.* *G.* A shell showing a well-developed hinge plate and a large resilifer. *H. Astarte.* (All shells are one-half natural size.)

posterolateral groups. This variety of dentition may be seen in considerable regularity of development in *Trigonia* and with irregularity in the fresh-water *Unio*.

Isodont.—Shells with this dentition have two teeth in each valve, so arranged that two sockets and an anterior and a posterior lateral are near the middle of the hinge line of one valve, and two teeth with one anterior and one posterior socket are present near the middle of the hinge line of the other. The teeth are more or less curved and fit into correspondingly curved sockets. In the extreme development of this relation, as in *Spondylus*, the two valves cannot be separated except by breaking the teeth. In the less extreme cases, as illustrated by *Pecten*, the teeth are almost obsolete.

Dysodont.—In dysodont dentition the teeth are very feebly developed, and it is clear that they evolved from external ornamentation across the cardinal area from the beak. This variety may be seen in *Mytilus*.

Pantodont.—Pantodont dentition seems to be a stage which possibly antedated the development of the true teleodont variety. The teeth are differentiated into cardinals and laterals, with the cardinal teeth grooved and with more than two laterals in any one group. Shells with pantodont dentition are confined to the Ordovician and Silurian. *Allodesma* and *Orthodonticus* illustrate this form of dentition.

Diagenodont.—This type of dentition consists normally of one or two laterals in any one group and three or less cardinals. *Astarte* is representative.

Cyclodont.—Cyclodont dentition is characterized by the absence of a flat hinge plate and extreme bending of the teeth. It is well exhibited in *Cardium* and *Tridacna*.

Asthenodont.—This variety of dentition is found in several groups of burrowers and borers in which the teeth have become obsolete, presumably from disuse. At any rate, the absence of teeth cannot be referred to an immediate ancestry without teeth. *Mya* and *Pholas* possess this variety of dentition. In addition the former has a chondrophore and the latter a myophore.

Anomalodont.—Anomalodont dentition is found in a group of primitive borers in which the teeth are very small or wanting. *Allorisma* represents this variety of dentition.

Paleoconcha.—There is a group of ancient pelecypods, with a single living species, *Acharax,* which have shells without teeth of any kind. This condition is expressed by the term *paleoconcha.* *Grammysia* and *Solenopsis* are well-known representatives of the group.

DENTITION FORMULAS.—A formula has been devised by Steinmann to indicate the number and character of the teeth, sockets, and other supplementary processes concerned with articulation. The following symbols are used:

R	right valve
L	left valve
1	teeth
0	sockets
C	resilium or chondrophore
l	lateral teeth
m_1m_2	laminae which receive laterals
(9)	number represents a series of nine teeth and nine sockets essentially alike
.	two taxodont rows meeting at one hinge margin and not separated by a resilium have the junction indicated by a period
1. etc.	obsolete or feeble teeth are represented by the proper *italicized* symbol used for normal teeth
x	amorphous elevations functioning as teeth

The right side of the formula is always anterior.

Using the symbols just given, the teleodont dentition of *Venus mercenaria* may be expressed $\frac{Lx01010}{Rx10101}$; hence from back to front (posterior to anterior) there is first a roughened area on each valve followed by three sockets and two teeth on the left valve which fit with two sockets and three teeth in the right valve. For *Tellina interrupta,* another form with teleodont dentition, the formula is $\frac{L11010l}{Rl01011}$; hence the left valve has a strong lateral tooth, then a cardinal, a socket, a second cardinal, a second socket, and finally a feebly developed lateral at the front, indicated by the italicized *l.* The right valve has two cardinals and two sockets, but the two laterals are reversed in position, the stronger one being anterior; the weaker, posterior. The formula for the taxodont dentition of *Glycimeris undatus* is $\frac{L10(11)\cdot(14)}{R01(11)\cdot(14)}$. The center is indicated by the period; hence there are 11 similar teeth and sockets behind the center (posterior) and 14 in front (anterior), the number in parentheses indicating the number of times that the units and zeros are repeated.

INTERNAL STRUCTURES.—Pelecypod shells are closed by one or two large adductor muscles that extend across the space between the valves. The contraction of these adductors pulls the valves together, and at the same time the ligament is stretched or bent and the resilium compressed. Hence when the shell is closed every muscle is strained, but when it is open they are relaxed. Most pelecypods have two adductors, one posterior and one anterior, and such seems to have been the case in the earliest and most primitive forms. Many advanced forms, however, have gradually modified the two until only a single muscle remains, and this is generally situated posteriorly.

The adductor muscles, where attached to the inner surfaces of the valves, leave pits or roughened areas known as *muscle scars.* If two are present, the shell is described as *dimyarian*, and the scars are designated *posterior* and *anterior adductors.* If a single scar is present, it is situated posteriorly, and the shell is *monomyarian.* The scars in most shells are much closer to the dorsal edges of the valves. In addition to the usual adductor muscle scars there are other less obvious muscle impressions of several kinds. The foot is commonly provided with *pedal muscles*, and these may leave impressions marking the places of attachment. When these muscles are well developed there are two kinds of depressions—a *protractor* scar, made by the protractor muscle which exserts the foot; and a *retractor* scar, formed by the retractor muscle which retracts the foot. Both scars are situated in the anterior part of the valves, but a second retractor may be present behind or posterior to the protractor. Siphonated shells have a muscle scar on each valve immediately below the posterior adductor. This marks the place of attachment of the retractor muscles of the siphon. Muscle scars were once considered an important character for classification, but this view has been abandoned because the two original adductors appear to have been reduced to a single muscle in several remotely related divisions.

The *pallial line* is the narrow depression, more or less parallel to the lateral and ventral margins of the valves, marking the line of attachment of the mantle. It terminates at opposite extremities in the anterior and posterior muscle scars. Siphonated shells have a posteriorly situated embayment, the *pallial sinus*, in the pallial line.

Classification.—The classification of the Pelecypoda has always been a difficult problem for paleontologists because most existing classifications are based on the soft parts of the animal. The features most used for taxonomic purposes are

1. Character of gills and associated soft parts.
2. Character of dentition, ligament and ligamental grooves, and resilium and resilifer.
3. Nature and position of the muscle scars (monomyarian and dimyarian), pallial line, and pallial sinus.
4. Shape, size, and ornamentation of the valves may be used but always with extreme caution.

Some of the features just mentioned have been used frequently in classifying pelecypods, but it is well known that while not very satisfactory, they are the best available.

The classification most extensively used by modern zoologists is based on the form and structure of the gills, and on this basis the class has been divided into five orders—Protobranchia, Filibranchia, Pseudolamellibranchia, Eulamellibranchia, and Septibranchia. The features of these orders have been discussed above in connection with the gills.

Most paleontologists prefer a classification based mainly on the nature of the dentition. Using this as a basis, the three orders of *Prionodesmacea*, *Anomalodesmacea*, and *Teleodesmacea* have been erected to include those shells which have teeth along the hinge line. An edentulous group composed largely of extinct forms, and known as *Paleoconcha*, is included in the first order. Taxodont, schizodont, isodont, and dysodont types of dentition are confined to the Prionodesmacea. It is thought that all are derivatives of a primitive original taxodont type. Anomalodont dentition characterizes the Anomalodesmacea. The Teleodesmacea have teleodont, pantodont, diagenodont, cyclodont, and asthenodont dentition. It is possible that the teleodont type may have derivative relations with some of the others. It is probable that the division of the Pelecypoda into the three orders just characterized is somewhat artificial, but it is one which can be used fairly satisfactorily by paleontologists.

Fig. 123.—Modern and fossil pelecypods. *A–B.* Exterior and interior views of the convex right valve of a modern *Pecten*. *C.* Exterior view of the right valve of a fossil *Pecten* from the Pleistocene of Italy. *D.* Exterior view of the right valve of a modern fresh-water *Unio* showing the periostracum intact over much of the surface but exfoliated near the umbo to reveal the white prismatic layer. *E–F.* Interior of left valve and exterior of right valve of a modern *Unio*.

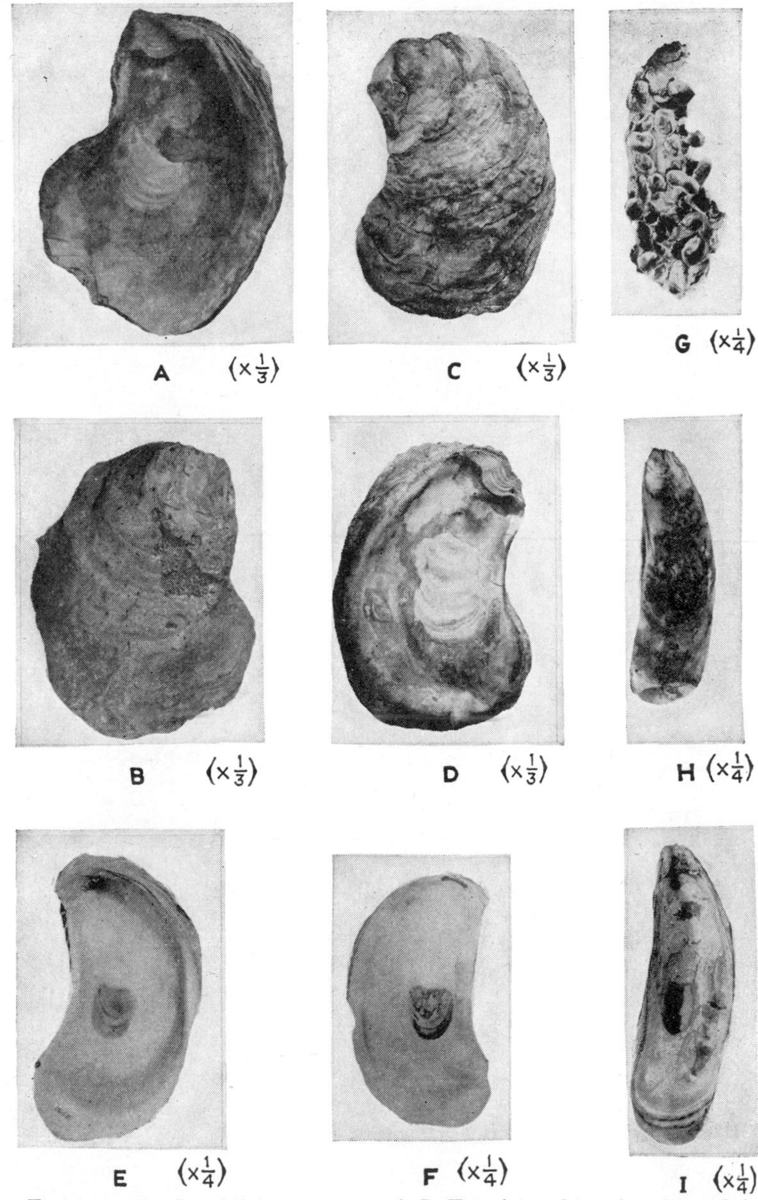

FIG. 124.—Fossil and living oysters. *A–D*. Exterior and interior views of the convex and flat valves of *Ostrea percrassa* from the Miocene of Maryland. *E–F*. Interior views of both valves of a modern *Ostrea* showing the single muscle scar and the lack of dentition. *G*. Exterior view of a narrow shell of a modern *Ostrea*

Order Prionodesmacea[1]

The Prionodesmacea include a group of pelecypods in which the mantles are generally separated or so poorly united that siphons are wanting, and the pallial sinus is either absent or but feebly developed. The cardinal area is amphidetic or obscure and rarely has an escutcheon and lunule. If the two latter features are present, the ligament is amphidetic. It is almost never opisthodetic. The early stages among living representatives of this order have taxodont dentition, but this usually becomes modified into one of the derivatives in maturity. Ten superfamilies have been erected, and these include forms ranging in age from the Ordovician to the Recent. The following genera are representative: *Arca, Cyrtodonta, Exogyra, Glycimeris, Gryphaea, Myalina, Mytilus, Nucula, Ostrea, Pecten, Trigonia, Unio,* and *Vanuxemia* (Figs. 118, 120, 122–125).

Order Anomalodesmacea[2]

Representatives of this order have the mantle lobes more or less united to form well-developed siphons, and the pallial line has a sinus. There are two unequal adductor muscles, an amphidetic or obscure and rarely distinctly divided cardinal area, and an opisthodetic ligament which generally has associated with it a resilium with chondrophore and lithodesma. The valves are generally unequal, there is no distinct hinge plate, and there are few or no teeth. The shells have various shapes, and the external ornamentation may be concentric only or concentric and radial. Some forms are attached. The order ranges from the Silurian to Recent and is subdivided into three superfamilies.

[1] Prionodesmacea—Gr. *prion,* saw + *desmos,* bond; referring to the serrated character of the hinge line.

[2] Anomalodesmacea—Gr. *anomalos,* irregular + *desmos,* bond; referring to the irregular nature of the dentition.

---

showing the surface covered with the small shells of the same genus. *H–I.* Exterior view of the flat valve and interior view of the convex valve of a modern *Ostrea,* with a narrow, elongate-shell.

Order Teleodesmacea[1]

The Teleodesmacea have eulamellibranchiate or septibranchiate gills, the mantle lobes are more or less perfectly united to form siphons, and the pallial line has a sinus. The shell is dimyarian, with the muscles essentially equal. The cardinal area, if present, is prosodetic or is amphidetic with lunule and escutcheon. The ligament is opisthodetic and paravincular, and a resilium may be present or absent. The shells have various shapes, with concentric or concentric and radial surface ornamentation, and the valves are usually equal. A distinct hinge plate is invariably present, and the dentition may be teleodont, pantodont, diagenodont, cyclodont, or asthenodont. Most members of this order belong to the vagrant benthos, but a few are sessile, and some are burrowers or borers. Nearly all are marine. There are 17 superfamilies in this order, which ranges from the Devonian to the Recent. Representative genera are *Astarte*, *Cardium*, *Crassatellites*, *Ensis*, *Hippurites*, *Mya*, *Panopaea*, *Teredo*, and *Venus* (Figs. 116–118, 121–122, 125).

Geologic History. Ontogeny and Evolution.—The fertilized pelecypod egg hatches into a free-swimming trochophore. By enlargement of the ciliated ring a collar- or bell-shaped swimming structure is developed, and the embryo is known as a *veliger*. From the veliger develops the larva characteristic of all Mollusca. The initial shell, the *prodissoconch*, appears over the mid-dorsal part of the larva and extends on each side of the median line to produce the two-valved condition. The mid-dorsal part of the shell is chitinous, but the lateral parts contain more or less calcium carbonate. The prodissoconch at this stage has a straight hinge line and two nearly equal, circular or nearly circular valves. At about this stage of growth the animal ceases to be free swimming and becomes a part of the benthos. The mantle develops, and the valves continue to enlarge through additions along the hinge line and the lateral and ventral margins. Growth usually is slight along the hinge-line area but extensive along the lateral and ventral margins, where the free edges of the mantle secrete the periostracum and the prismatic layer of the shell. The original shell along the dorsal line remains

[1] Teleodesmacea—Gr. *teleos*, perfect + *desmos*, bond; referring to the excellence of articulation or well-developed dentition.

chitinous or horny and merges with the ligament and resilium. From this simple beginning the many types of shells develop, with their different shapes, sizes, ornamentation, and dentition.

The initial shell is very thin and fragile, and as it becomes large it is essential that it become stronger. This may be

Fig. 125.—Fossil Pelecypoda. *A–B.* Interior and exterior views of *Venericardia*, a common Cretaceous and Cenozoic pelecypod. *C.* Dolomite filling of the left valve of *Cyrtodonta*, a common Middle Ordovician pelecypod, also found in the Silurian. *D. Glycimeris*, a common genus in strata from Cretaceous to Recent. *E.* Dolomite filling of the right valve of *Vanuxemia*, a common Ordovician pelecypod. *F–G. Myalina subquadrata* from the Pennsylvanian of Kansas, an index fossil of the Pennsylvanian.

effected by thickening the shell, by giving the valves greater convexity, or through the growth of radial ribs or arches as in *Tridacna* and *Cardium*. All three structures have developed in the evolution of the class. The prodissoconchs of modern pelecypods lack teeth and irregularities on the ventral margin; hence there is difficulty in preventing the valves from sliding laterally. Many early and primitive pelecypods labored under similar disadvantages. The development of teeth on the hinge line and crenulations on the ventral margins removed this difficulty. Similar forms of these locking devices are found in divisions that are not closely related.

Shells that adopted the burrowing habit tended to become elongated and to develop siphons (Fig. 118). The anterior part of such shells became greatly shortened, and the umbo took position near that end. Pelecypods living in soft muds developed thin shells, whereas those living in stiff clays, wood, or rock developed shells of circular cross section due to the animal's necessity to rotate about an axis parallel to the burrow. Those forms that acquired the habit of attaching themselves to some object by means of byssal threads became elongated posteriorly and shortened anteriorly. This method of attachment was acquired by forms living in strong currents, and the conditions favored byssal attachment to the anterior part of the shell, so that ultimately the hinge line in front of the shell almost disappeared, and the shell acquired an oval shape with the umbo on the small end of the oval and with the hinge line short and subparallel to the long axis of the shell. These features are well illustrated by the common shore clam *Mytilus edulis* (Fig. 118 *D*). In such shells as those just described the anterior adductor muscle becomes obsolete.

Pelecypods which remained free on the bottom tended to remain circular or oval in outline, as illustrated by *Venus mercenaria* (Fig. 116). Those that attached themselves by one valve, however, lost the typical bilateral symmetry of the shell, because of the great increase in thickness and size of the attached valve. The upper valve tended to develop normally but with certain modifications imposed upon it by the necessity of its serving as a lid or operculum. This fixed condition developed both among forms previously attached by a byssus and those which were originally unattached. In the former, the combination of byssal attachment and cementation of one valve led to the shells' assuming a spiral form, like that seen in *Gryphaea* and *Exogyra* (Fig. 120).

ECOLOGY.—The Pelecypoda, so far as known, are exclusively aquatic animals living in abundance in all kinds of water. The majority, however, live in marine environments, mainly on the bottom, in the bottom sediments, or attached to objects resting on the bottom. There are very few swimmers among the pelecypods. The known depth range for marine forms is from tide level to 5,300 m. (17,400 ft.), and different genera are found on the continental shelves and slopes of all seas. Over these areas, where deposition is slow, individuals of numerous species often occur in prodigious numbers and over extensive areas. One such area, situated on the south end of Dogger Bank, has an extent of 700 square miles and an estimated population of 4,500,000,000,000 clams. The oyster beds with their great populations are also well known. Among the fossil pelecypods *Exogyra cancellata* (Upper Cretaceous) has been traced with interruptions for 2,500 miles (from New Jersey to Mexico), and in one place the down-dip spread of the zone is as much as 115 miles wide.[1] The deep bottoms also have many species. These ordinarily have thin, fragile, and more or less transparent or translucent shells, which contrast strikingly with the thick, massive shells commonly observed in areas of strong wave action or of abundant predatory animals. The fresh waters of lakes and streams may also support a large population of pelecypods, some of which attain lengths of 15 cm. (6 in.) and secrete thick, massive shells (*Unio*).

Dispersal of pelecypods is effected chiefly by currents which transport the free-swimming larvae, but fish often carry parasitic forms; birds and water beetles sometimes carry the eggs from one body of water to another; and birds may also transport the actual animal and shell from one point to another with the animal clinging to the bird's legs. Bivalves have been reported to have even killed birds by fastening their shells to both of the fowl's feet, thereby preventing it from walking, swimming, or flying.

Since they are, in the main, sedentary animals, pelecypods, as a group, exhibit many interesting adaptations and specializations. The many forms which are permanently free and which are vagrant do not show the modifications so common among those which have developed the burrowing and boring habits or have attached themselves permanently by one valve. One line of specialization has been in the direction of organs useful for moving through the muds and sands on the bottom or for burrowing and boring in various materials. Most burrowing

[1] Stephenson, L. W. The zone of *Exogyra cancellata* traced twenty-five hundred miles, *Bull. Amer. Assoc. Petr. Geol.*, vol. 17, pp. 1351–1361, 1933.

forms live within a few inches of the bottom surface, but a few have developed long siphons whereby they may be buried 7 or 8 in. and still maintain a current of water through the body by means of the inhalant and exhalant siphons which are usually kept more or less at the surface (Fig. 118). The tidal zone and the shallow waters immediately adjacent may be densely populated by species of *Mya*, a burrowing genus, whose position along the shore may often be detected by the water that is squirted from the siphon as one walks near the buried shell. Certain pelecypods burrow or bore into such hard substances as wood and stone and have become adapted to such an existence. These excavations may be made by the animal directly or by acid secretions from the animal body. The rocks of many coasts are fairly riddled with holes excavated by *Pholas*, and the boring activities of *Teredo* in wooden ships and piers has caused it to be named the "shipworm."

Many species of pelecypods attach themselves permanently to objects on the bottom by cementation of one valve. Specialization and, in some cases, even degeneracy often follow assumption of this habit. In forms such as the oyster (*Ostrea*) the attached valve becomes larger and somewhat deeper. This tendency was carried to the extreme in certain Cretaceous genera (*Hippurites*, *Radiolites*). The attached valve became a cone, in which coralloid structure was developed, and the upper valve was modified into a lid which carried on its underside long teeth fitting into deep sockets in the internal calcareous framework of the lower valve (Fig. 118 *B*). These forms lived in remarkable profusion and were widely distributed in the Cretaceous of the Mediterranean and Mexican-Texas regions, living apparently in clear, shallow waters where calcareous muds were being deposited.

Burrowing pelecypods not only bring about considerable destruction of rock by dissolving and pulverizing the material, but certain forms (*Mya*) also take large quantities of sand and mud into their stomachs, and this material is certain to undergo some physical and chemical changes during its passage through the alimentary tract.

Commensalism, or the habit of sharing food without being parasitic, is commonly found among pelecypods. Some forms live in the burrows of crustaceans and worms, others live on echinoderms, and still others live embedded in the tests of Ascidians or in the tissues of sponges. Rarely a species is parasitic (*Entovalva* in holothurians). The surface of a pelecypod shell offers an excellent place for all sorts of benthonic animals to attach their shells; hence worm tubes, bryozoans, small pelecypod shells (particularly oysters), barnacles, and calcareous algae may often cover a large part of the exterior surface of the shell.

Pelecypods are known to have been an important source of food for man since a very early stage in his development, and the shell heaps accumulated by ancient man emphasize the importance of this source in early human history. Oysters, scallops, marine mussels, and marine clams have been used most often for food. Pelecypods furnish food for numerous other animals. Starfish feed over the shell beds (especially over the oyster banks) and kill their prey by more or less complete envelopment of the shell by the protruded digestive area. Many gastropods drill holes into living shells to get at the flesh within, and small pelecypod shells are swallowed by fish, crustaceans, and other animals. The shells of certain bivalves have long been exploited for the mother-of-pearl layer used for buttons, inlay work, knife handles, etc., and from ancient times the pearls of bivalves have been prized as gems. Certain pelecypods have caused man much damage. Chief among these are the boring forms well illustrated by the shipworm. These did great damage to wooden ships of olden days, and today as in the past they riddle submarine wooden structures such as piers. In four years' time (1917–1921) shipworms caused $25,000,000 damage to wooden structures in San Francisco Bay.

Stratigraphic Range.—Pelecypods made their first appearance in the Cambrian and soon after became an important element in benthonic faunas, a position which with certain interruptions they have held to the present time. Few forms are known from the Cambrian (*Glyptarca* from the Upper Cambrian being the most certain), but during the Ordovician many genera and species appeared. Large pelecypod faunas are found in Silurian and Devonian strata. Some Devonian forms lived in fresh water, and species thought to have lived in brackish waters appeared in large numbers during the late Paleozoic. During the Triassic, however, the class underwent considerable change as many ancient genera became extinct and many new genera, some of which have persisted to the present, made their appearance. Since that time the pelecypod fauna of the world has become increasingly more modern in its aspects.

The number of new families appearing in each period is as follows:

Period	Families	Period	Families
Cambrian	1	Triassic	14
Ordovician	10	Jurassic	15
Silurian	10	Cretaceous	18
Devonian	9	Eocene	15
Carboniferous	3	Miocene-Pliocene	2
Permian	1	Pleistocene-Recent	3

At certain times during the geologic past pelecypods have contributed very materially to the construction of calcareous formations. The majority of early Paleozoic forms, although adding to the inclosing sediments at the time of burial, rarely have the shell matter preserved because of removal by solution. Beginning with the Pennsylvanian, however, shell matter is more commonly preserved. In the Cretaceous, bioherms were built by such forms as *Chama* and the Rudistids; and in the Pierre shales of Colorado, the pelecypod *Lucina occidentalis ventricosa* is responsible for biohermal mounds, referred to as "tepee buttes," in the cores of which the shells are piled on each other. These mounds average about 4½ m. (15 ft.) in diameter and are of different heights. They represent places where the pelecypods lived on in spite of muddy conditions. Many genera were locally abundant during the Mesozoic, often forming considerable portions of the rocks. Such forms are *Gryphaea* and *Exogyra* from the Jurassic and Cretaceous and *Ostrea* from the Cretaceous and Tertiary. *Ostrea* still builds biostromes of great areal extent.

Character of the Fossil Record.—Most Paleozoic pelecypods in strata older than the Pennsylvanian are preserved as molds and fillings. Beginning with the Pennsylvanian, however, the shell matter is very commonly preserved. It is suggested that the pelecypods of the early Paleozoic constructed the calcareous parts of the shells very largely if not entirely of aragonite and did not change to calcite until the Pennsylvanian. The unstable aragonite was soon destroyed, whereas the more resistant calcite was partly or entirely preserved.

The shells of most dead pelecypods are open, and often the valves are spread apart or are separated. This condition, as stated above, is due to the fact that the relaxation of muscles brought about by the death of the animal permits the valves to open and to remain so. Corals, bryozoans, worms, and brachiopods are frequently found incrusting fossil pelecypod valves. Holes bored by predatory animals often indicate the manner in which the victims met death (Fig. 135 *C–D*), and repaired injuries indicate accidents of various kinds.

In general, pelecypods are not among the best index fossils, chiefly because of the fact that poor preservation frequently makes impossible accurate determination of species. Especially is this true of many Paleozoic shells. Thereafter, however, and to a limited extent in the Pennsylvanian also, the better preserved shells may be important index fossils. Among these are *Exogyra*, *Gryphaea*, *Hippurites*, *Inoceramus*, *Protocardium*, and *Radiolites* (Figs. 118, 120).

Class Gastropoda[1]

General Considerations.—The class includes such well-known forms as the land and fresh-water snails and the myriads of variously colored "conch shells" common in marine waters and on many coasts. The body, which has a distinct head and a well-developed foot, usually has a coiled, unchambered, calcareous shell which varies greatly in architecture and size.

Gastropods are dominantly aquatic mollusks. The greatest variety and the more primitive living types dwell in shallow marine waters. They have, however, adapted themselves, through certain modifications, to brackish and fresh-water environments and have also successfully invaded land habitats. Today gastropods may be found in the woods far from permanent water bodies, along lake shores and in streams, in brackish water lagoons, and in the ocean.

At the present time gastropods excel all other mollusks in variety and importance and appear to be reaching their acme of development. Over 30,000 species have been described, of which

[1] Gastropoda—Gr. *gaster*, *gastros*, stomach + *pous*, *podos*, foot; referring to the fact that the animal appears to walk on its stomach.

20,000 are Recent. Their long geologic history begins in the Lower Cambrian and extends throughout geologic time to the present.

The Animal.—The body of the gastropod is readily divisible into three principal parts—the *head*, the *foot*, and the *visceral sac*. The last part is more or less completely protected by a fold of the dorsal integument, known as the *mantle*, which is never divided into a right and left lobe as in the Pelecypoda. The body usually is distinctly asymmetrical, although original bilateral symmetry is observable in the young stages.

The head is well developed and is often provided with stalked eyes and other sensory organs. The mouth opens into the *buccal cavity* which contains a dental apparatus, of which the chief part is a chitinous band beset with transversely arranged teeth. This band, known as the *radula*, is supported on a cartilaginous cushion, the *odontophore*, and can be rotated in such a way that it becomes a very effective rasp or file. The number, arrangement, and shape of the tiny teeth are very characteristic and are of great value for taxonomic purposes (Fig. 111). The number ranges from 16 to as many as 750, 000, and there is great variation in shape. The teeth are usually arranged in two symmetrical sets, one on each side of a median tooth. In some forms there are also horny jaws (*mandibles*) in the upper part of the buccal cavity. These oppose the radula. The radula and associated dental plates are of considerable use to boring gastropods, and many fossil and recent shells show evidence of boring activities (Fig. 135 *C–E*). Common boring gastropods are *Purpura* and *Natica*. These drill holes through pelecypod and other shells for access to the soft parts of the prey, using the radula and an acid secretion from the alimentary canal.

The foot is a muscular locomotory organ developed on the ventral side of the body and posterior to the head. It is greatly modified in a few forms. In benthonic species locomotion is accomplished by rhythmic waves which cause the surface of the foot to be thrown into minute ridges and troughs. In some forms contraction of the foot enables the animal to jump. In certain pelagic gastropods, the *Heteropoda*, the foot is modified into a vertical laterally compressed fin, and in the *Pteropoda* it consists of a pair of winglike membranes near the head. Members of both groups swim by means of the modified foot.

The intestinal tract in young forms is a nearly straight tube with the mouth in an anterior position and the anus at the posterior end. Many mature gastropods, however, have the intestinal tract looped and twisted in such a way that the anal opening is situated above the mouth and the tract has the appearance of the figure 8 (Fig. 112 *C*). This distortion of the animal is also reflected in the shell.

The esophagus is surrounded by a large liver, the kidneys, and numerous glands. The heart is either one or two chambered. Circulation is accomplished by a much branched system of blood vessels, filled with colorless, red, greenish, or bluish liquid. Respiration is carried on in a few forms by the general surface of the body, but most gastropods have gills or lungs. Fundamentally the gills are paired, but owing to the distortion of the body the gill on the left side is lost in many groups. The gills are lamellar, plumelike or featherlike, and are generally situated in a *gill cavity* within the mantle. Rarely they are exposed on the back or the sides. Gastropods which live on the land have a *lung* and a *lung cavity*, and in a few species there are both lungs and gills.

In order to assure the bringing of uncontaminated water to the gills and removal of refuse discharged into the mantle cavity, some provision has to be made for a change of water. In some gastropods this is accomplished by pulsatory contraction and expansion of the mantle cavity, resulting in alternate expulsion and drawing in of water. This method is characteristic of forms possessing two gills. In many single-gilled species some part of the mantle is set apart for ingress and some part for egress, the water then entering through the main opening and being expelled at some point along the margin. In the most specialized forms the mantle is united in such a way as to produce an excurrent tube, the *siphon*, and rarely a second tubular process for the ingress of water. Gastropods possessing such modified mantles have the shells modified in adjustment to the internal structures (Fig. 126).

Reproduction usually takes place by means of eggs, but in a few genera the young are born alive and with an immature shell. The sexes are distinct in some gastropods, united in others. The male and female sexual elements are discharged through separate openings directly to the exterior or into a *cloaca*. In many forms there are cases for the reception of the eggs, and in these cases the young hatch and live for a short time. The embryonic stages are usually completed in the egg capsule, but in those forms with the primitive method of development the young are free-swimming trochophores.

A simple conical, cup- or cap-shaped calcareous shell, known as the *protoconch*, appears quite early, and the ultimate shape of the mature shell depends upon the way in which shell matter is added to the ventral margin of the protoconch. Elongation of the protoconch, with coiling about an axis in a single plane,

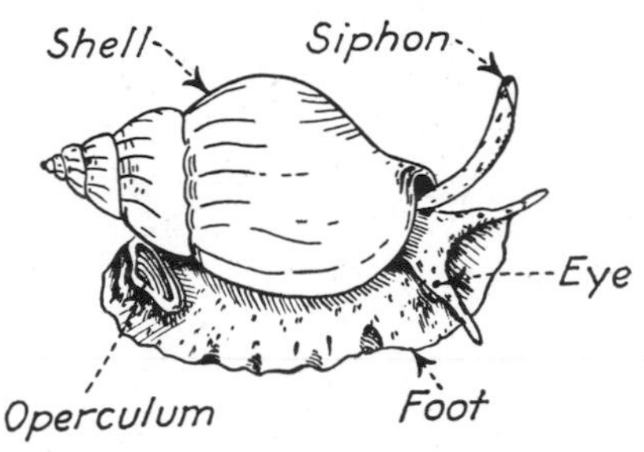

Fig. 126.—A common gastropod (*Buccinum undatum*) showing the various structures of the shell and soft body. (*After Thomson, with modifications.*)

produces a *planospiral* shell, and that condition may persist throughout life. In many forms, however, the coiling is *helicoid*, resulting in various spirally coiled shells. In all species of which the shell development is known, the final stage of the protoconch is a helicoid spire regardless of the shape of the mature shell. It does not necessarily follow, however, that this is always the case. It is possible that the cup-shaped gastropod shells of the Cambrian represent the first condition of the protoconch; the planospirals of Cambrian, Ordovician, and later periods, the second stage in shell development; and the helicoid spirals, the third stage. It is known, however, that some of the cup-shaped forms do not represent a primitive stage, as they have a helicoid protoconch.

The coiling of the shell reflects the coiling of the body of the animal, and as a consequence the anal opening is brought forward to a position below the mouth, and the intestinal tract becomes U-shaped. As the coiling becomes helicoid the anus moves upward on the right side, finally taking a position above the mouth, and the intestinal tube assumes the form of a figure 8.

The Shell.—The gastropod shell begins in the protoconch, which consists of several minute whorls or coils and is quite distinct from the remainder of the shell. Excepting for the embryonic protoconch, which is more often missing than present, the gastropod shell consists fundamentally of a simple, unchambered expanding cone, open at the larger end and usually coiled about some sort of axis.

The simplest type of shell, architecturally considered, is the uncoiled conical shell characteristic of the *limpets*. Even some

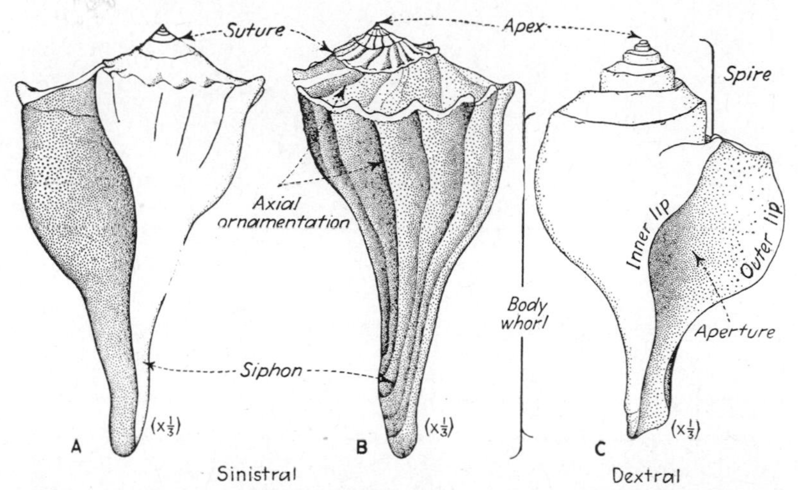

Fig. 127.—*A–B*. A left-handed, siphonated Recent gastropod (*Busycon*) showing prominent axial ornamentation and some surface ornamentation. *C*. A right-handed Recent gastropod with a somewhat shorter siphon.

of these have a helicoid protoconch (*Patella*), which indicates that they have descended from a complex ancestor. It has been suggested that the Cambrian cap-shelled gastropods were very near the ancestral molluscan type, but it is clear that later shells of the same type may represent animals with complex ontogeny, for simple conical shells appear in groups which are only remotely related. Shells in which the primary cone is coiled about an axis perpendicular to the plane of coiling are described as *planospiral*. One complete volution about the axis of coiling is known as a *whorl*, and the line of contact between adjacent whorls is designated the *suture* (Fig. 127). The suture is absent in shells which do not have the whorls in contact. All the whorls in maturely developed shells except the last comprise the *spire*. The last constitutes the *body whorl*, and it may be much larger than the whorls of the spire. In many planospiral shells the whorls are not in actual contact or are just in contact (Fig. 130 *H*). In such shells all whorls are visible, and the

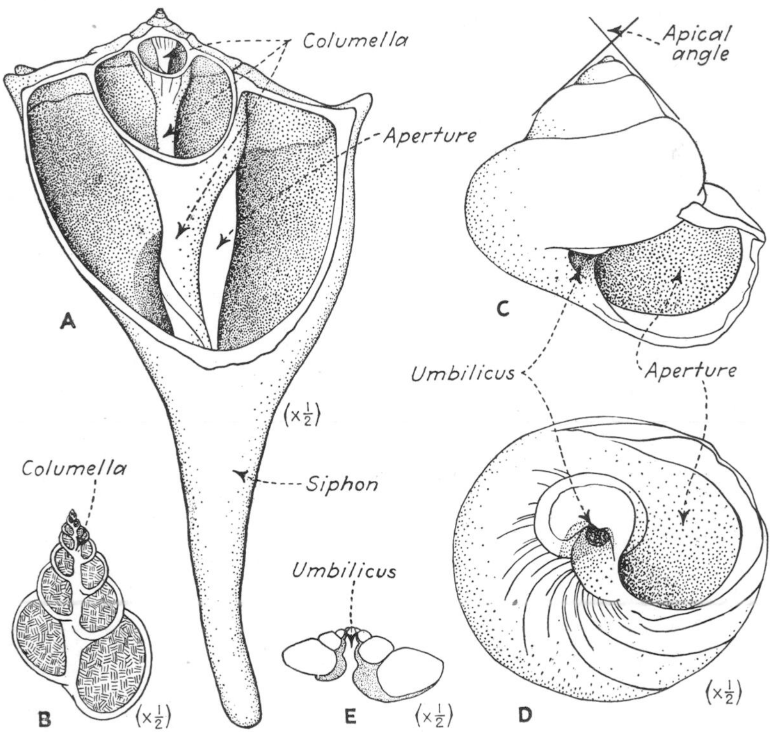

Fig. 128.—Columella and umbilicus. *A*. A modern siphonated, sinistral gastropod (*Busycon*) shell sectioned to show the twisted columella. *B*. Columellar section of *Auriptygma virgatum*, from the Pennsylvanian of Missouri, showing the prominent columella and the hollow whorls filled with sediment. *C–D*. A modern umbilicated gastropod, showing apertural and umbilical views. *E*. Vertical section of *Liospira angustata*, from the Middle Ordovician of Minnesota, showing the prominent umbilicus and the thickening of the shell along the umbilicus. (*B after Knight, with restoration of last whorl; E after Ulrich and Scofield.*)

cross section of a whorl tends to be circular or elliptical. Whorls may be in contact in the early stages but remote in maturity. In some shells the coiling is such that each succeeding whorl covers those preceding, so that only the last is visible. This type of coiling is referred to as *convolute* or *involute*, and the shell is described by the same terms. In the majority of gastropod shells the primary cone is coiled spirally around an imaginary axial cone. Such a shell has the form of a *helicoid spiral* (Figs. 130, 131). The angle included between the two slopes of the spire is the *apical angle* (Fig. 128). The shells are low or high depending on whether the apical angles are large or small. The imaginary axial cone about which coiling takes place may be so narrow that the whorls are in contact along the inner surface as well as along the ventral and dorsal surfaces; an axial pillar, the *columella,* is then formed, and the shell is *imperforate.* If the whorls are not in contact on the inner surfaces, the space between the whorls is designated the *umbilicus,* and the shell is said to be *perforate.* A true umbilicus extends to the apex of the spire, whereas a false one is confined to the space inclosed by the body whorl only (Fig. 128). In some forms the umbilicus is restricted at the opening or completely closed by a shell growth known as the *callus.* Coiling may be irregular, as in *Haliotis* and *Vermicularia* (Fig. 131), but most shells coil regularly, either *right-handed* or *left-handed,* the former termed *dextral;* the latter, *sinistral* (Fig. 127). To orient the shell it should be placed with the apex of the spire upward and rotated about the axis of coiling until the *aperture* or opening into the body whorl is visible. If the aperture is on the right side, the shell is dextral; if on the left, sinistral. Most spirally coiled shells are dextral.

The gastropod shell is secreted by the mantle and the epidermis of the visceral integument. The shell matter consists of an organic base mineralized with calcite or aragonite. When treated with a dilute solution of hydrochloric acid the organic material does not dissolve but is not of such character as to preserve the shape of the shell. There are normally three layers of calcareous matter, each of which is composed of very thin laminae which in turn are composed of microscopic prisms of calcium carbonate obliquely oriented with respect to the surface of the shell and differently oriented in each lamination. The external surface of the shell is covered by a chitinous layer, the *periostracum,* which is rarely if ever preserved in fossil shells. Extraneous shell matter is added to the internal surface in some forms.

In the simplest gastropod shells the whorls have a circular cross section, but coiled forms always show more or less modification caused by contact of the whorls. In helicoid shells the upper side of the whorl tends to become differentiated into distinct areas and to range from flat to convexly or concavely curved. The spire then presents a contour consonant with the character of the whorls. Flat upper surfaces give the spire a terraced aspect, as in *Lophospira* (Fig. 130 *I–J*), or a uniformly

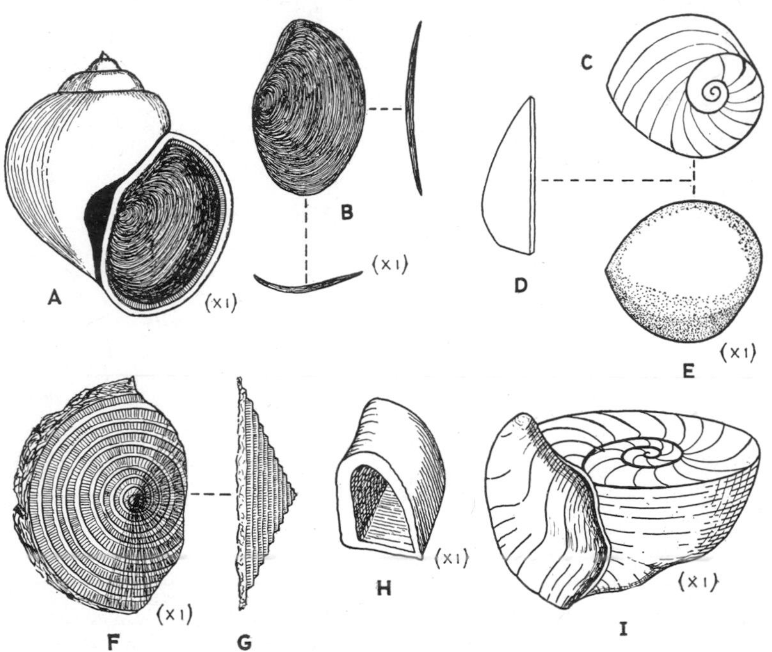

Fig. 129.—Opercula of Gastropoda. *A–B. Ampullaria cumingi*, a modern operculated gastropod: *A*, Apertural view of the complete shell, with the chitinous operculum drawn into the aperture; *B*, Exterior and longitudinal and transverse sections of the operculum showing its slightly concave character. *C–E.* Exterior, lateral, and interior views of a calcareous operculum of a modern Pacific gastropod. *F–G.* Supposed operculum of a Silurian gastropod (*Oriostoma?*) from the Niagaran of northern Indiana. *H–I. Ceratopea calceoliformis*, an operculated Lower Ordovician gastropod from Tennessee: *H*, diagram of an operculum; *I*, the operculum shown oriented in the aperture of the shell. (*F–G after Kindle and Breger; H–I after Oder.*)

inclined surface, as in *Trochus.* The body whorl is always the largest, and in some forms it is larger than the others combined. Its lower surface may be much flattened as compared to earlier whorls.

The opening of the shell is the *aperture*, which in many forms is closed by a chitinous or calcareous plate, the *operculum*, carried on the foot (Figs. 126, 129). The aperture is circular, oval, crescentic, or slitlike (Fig. 127). The marginal area surrounding it is the *peristome*. This is divided into an *inner lip* or that part of the margin adjacent to the umbilicus or columella; an *outer lip*, directly opposite; an upper part designated the *upper lip;* and a lower, the *lower lip*. An unbroken apertural margin is designated *entire;* an *interrupted* apertural margin is broken by notches on the outer margin or by a channel on the lower margin. In some forms the channel is produced into a tubelike *siphon* through which the water is conveyed from the gill cavity to the exterior by a tubular structure of the mantle. The shelly siphon may be straight or curved, and in some forms it is longer than the aperture of the shell (Fig. 127). The outer lip of the peristome may be thin or thick, curved outward (*reflected*) or inward (*inflected*), or produced into winglike or finger-like processes (Fig. 132). In many gastropods with two gills, as the *Pleurotomaridae* and *Bellerophontidae*, the outer lip is interrupted by a notch or slit for the reception of the excurrent canal of the mantle. Both the notch and the slit are progressively closed as the shell grows, with the former indicated by crenulation of the growth lines and the latter by a structure known as the *slit band* (Fig. 130 *D*). The inner lip in the closely coiled forms is modified by the wall of the last or body whorl or by a *callus*, and it may bear spiral ridges which in some forms extend to the apex (Fig. 131 *G*, *L*, *N*).

Gastropod shells range in height, the distance from the apex to the lower margin of the aperture, from less than 1½ mm. to as much as ½ m. The shape may be conical, turbinate, fusiform, cylindrical, spherical, etc. Ordinarily the shape has no more than generic value, and often remotely related shells have very similar shapes. In discussing or illustrating a shell it is common practice to place the shell with the apex upward and the aperture facing the observer. In such a position the apex is posterior; the aperture, anterior.

The *surface ornamentation* of gastropod shells varies greatly. Primitive and ancient forms have little in the way of exterior ornamentation, and it appears that the development of such was gradual and rather slow. Evidence of this evolution is often clearly shown on shells in which the ornamentation of the early whorls is simple, whereas that of the later whorls on the same shell is complex. *Color* is conspicuous on many shells and is often sufficiently varied to produce attractive designs. It is rarely preserved on fossil forms. The grosser surface ornamentation consists of striae, ridges, ribs, nodes, and spines. Ornamental features arranged transverse to the whorls, thus intersecting the suture at some angle, are termed *axial* or *transverse;* those which tend to parallel the whorls are *spiral* (Fig. 127).

The *operculum*, used for closing the aperture of the shell, is carried on the posterior part of the foot and is placed in position when the animal withdraws into the shell (Figs. 126, 129). In living forms it is smooth or variously ornamented. The initial operculum, made when the animal was small, may be central or to one side, and the additions made during growth may be concentric or spirally arranged. Many species belonging to the *Solariidae* have a conical operculum which is covered externally with many spiral laminae. Fossil opercula are rare (Fig. 129 *F–I*).

The gastropod is attached to its shell by muscles fastened to the columellar or umbilical portion of the shell. By contraction and expansion of these muscles the animal is enabled to withdraw itself into the shell or emerge therefrom. A few gastropods have so completely surrounded the shell by soft body tissue that it is no longer of use for protection and has degenerated into a small plate entirely unlike the usual shell. Rarely the shell has disappeared completely, and the animal is naked. This condition is found in the nudibranchs, in some pteropods, and among many of the air-breathing forms.

Classification.—The classification of the Gastropoda into the larger divisions is based almost entirely on the soft parts, among which those considered most important are the nervous system, respiratory organs, structure and use of the foot, reproductive organs, structure and character of the heart, and nature of the radula. It is only among the smaller divisions that the characters of the shells are considered of importance. Largely on the basis of the nervous system the class has been subdivided into two subclasses—*Streptoneura*, in which the visceral nerve commissures are crossed to resemble the figure 8; and *Euthyneura*, in which the commissures are not crossed. Naturally most of the soft parts leave no impression on the shells, but because of the long range of the families it has been possible to fit most fossil forms into what are considered proper associations.

Subclass Streptoneura[1]

The Streptoneura include gastropods of which the visceral nerve commissures are so crossed as to produce a shape resembling the figure 8. The heart is behind the single gill, the sexes are separate, and a shell is almost always present. The shell is planospiral, helicoid, or a low cone and is rarely without an operculum. In the helicoid shell the intestine is twisted from left to right, thus placing the anus above and to the right of the head, and those organs which are normally on the right side are twisted over to the left side. The right gill is the one usually present, but in a few cases both gills are present and of equal size. This is by far the largest group of gastropods, constituting over 20,000 living and fossil species. It has been subdivided into the two orders—*Aspidobranchia* and *Ctenobranchia.*

ORDER ASPIDOBRANCHIA

This order, the name of which means shield-like gills, has a nervous system and a radula of generalized type. The first fossil representatives appear in the early Paleozoic (Cambrian), and the order is still represented in existing seas. Most Paleozoic gastropods belong to the Aspidobranchia. Two suborders, *Docoglossa* and *Rhipidoglossa,* have been erected. The Docoglossa include the earliest and most ancient of fossil gastropods and range from the Cambrian to the Recent. All species are apparently marine. Representative genera are *Scenella* and *Salpingostoma* among fossil forms and *Acmaea* among living forms (Fig. 130). The Rhipidoglossa are aquatic or air-breathing gastropods with limpet-like or spiral shells and with a well-developed radula. The suborder ranges from the Cambrian to the Recent and is represented by the following genera: *Cyclonema, Eccyliopterus, Fissurella, Haliotis, Hormotoma, Lophospira, Maclurites, Pleurotomaria, Straparollus, Tegula* and *Turbo* (Figs. 130, 131).

ORDER CTENOBRANCHIA

The Ctenobranchia, so named because of the single comblike gill, constitute the largest order of gastropods. Most live in

[1] Streptoneura—Gr. *streptos,* curved + *neuron,* nerve: referring to the twisted character of the nervous system.

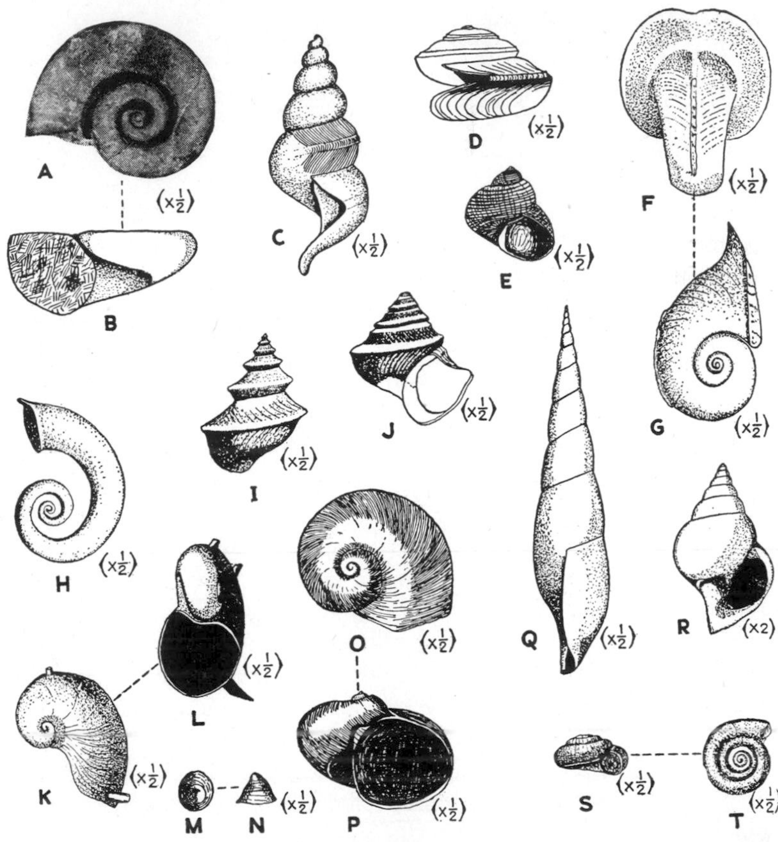

Fig. 130.—Fossil gastropods. *A–B.* Apical and apertural views of a filling of *Maclurites bigsbyi* from the Middle Ordovician of Wisconsin. *C.* Filling of external mold of *Hormotoma trentonensis*, from the Middle Ordovician of Minnesota, showing remains of the regular surface markings. *D.* View of exterior of *Eotomaria supracingulata*, from the Middle Ordovician of Illinois, showing the slit band and prominent growth lines. *E. Cyclonema humerosum* from the Upper Ordovician of Ohio. *F–G.* Filling of external mold of *Salpingostoma buelli* from the Middle Ordovician of Illinois: *F*, view showing prominent dorsal slit and faint indications of the external markings; *G*, side view showing planospiral form. *H. Eccyliopterus volutatus* from the Lower Ordovician of Vermont. *I–J.* Two specimens of *Lophospira*, a very common Ordovician gastropod. *K–L.* Two views of *Platyceras paxillifer* from the Lower Devonian of Quebec. *M–N.* Two views of *Scenella affinis* from the Middle Ordovician of Minnesota. *O–P. Diaphorostoma niagarense* from the Middle Silurian of Indiana. *Q. Subulites regularis* from the Middle Ordovician of Kentucky. *R. Auriptygma virgatum* from the Pennsylvanian of Missouri. *S–T.* Two views of *Straparollus spergenensis* from the Mississippian (Salem) of Indiana. (*C–J, M–N, Q after Ulrich and Scofield; K–L after Clarke; O–P after Hall; R after Knight; S–T after Cumings.*)

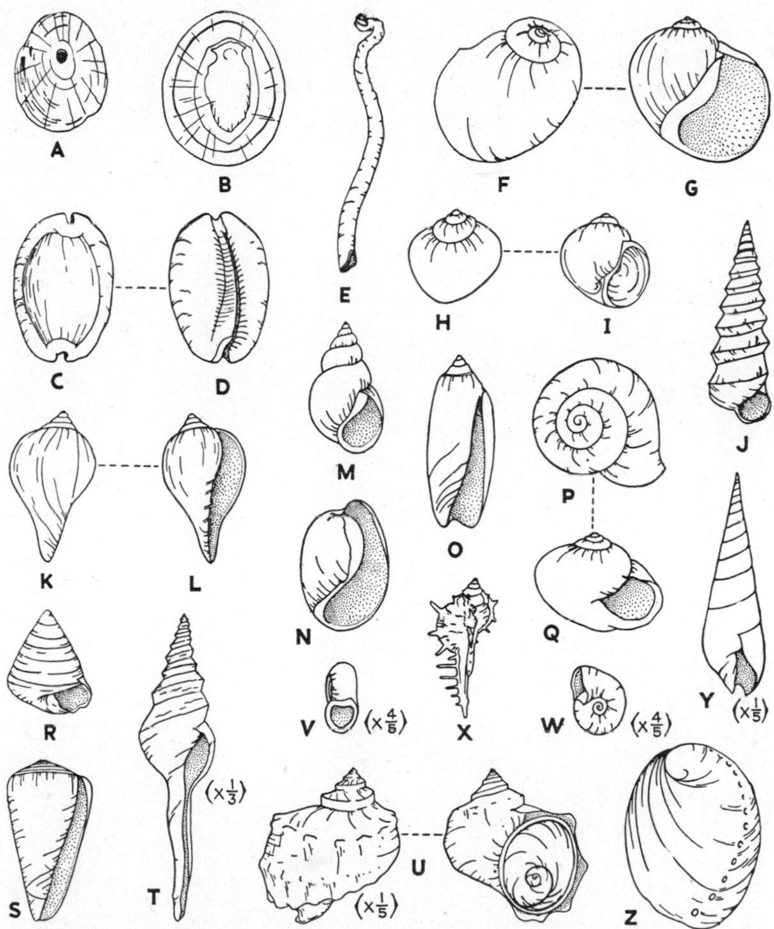

FIG. 131.—Gastropod shells. *A. Fissurella*, and *B. Lottia*, illustrating patellate shells. *C–D. Cypraea*, an oval shell. *E. Vermicularia*, a peculiarly coiled shell. *F–G. Natica*, a common boring gastropod, with a hemispherical shell. *H–I. Ampullaria*, with a globose shape and with the operculum in position. *J. Turritella*, a fossil form from the Cenozoic, with a turreted shell. *K–L. Caricella*, a pyriform shell from the Eocene of Alabama. *M. Campeloma*, a common, ovate, fresh-water form from the streams of Wisconsin. *N. Bullaria*, illustrating an unusual type of coiling. *O. Oliva*, with obovate shell. *P–Q. Helix*, with a depressed helicoid shell. *R. Tegula*, with conical form. *S. Conus*, an obconical form. *T. Fusus*, with fusiform shell. *U.* Two views of the turbinate shell of *Turbo*. One view shows the large calcareous operculum in position. *V–W.* Two views of the common lenticular shell of *Planorbis*. *X.* A spinose shell of the boring gastropod *Murex*. *Y.* The pyramidal shell of *Terebra*. *Z.* The familiar *Abalone* or *Haliotis*, an auriculate shell. (Unless indicated otherwise, magnification is ×2/5.)

marine waters, but a few inhabit fresh waters, and some are terrestrial. The shell is usually a more or less elevated spiral form. The *Heteropoda* have the foot modified into a fin, whereas the *Platypoda* have it normally developed. The order makes its appearance in the Silurian but does not seem to have been

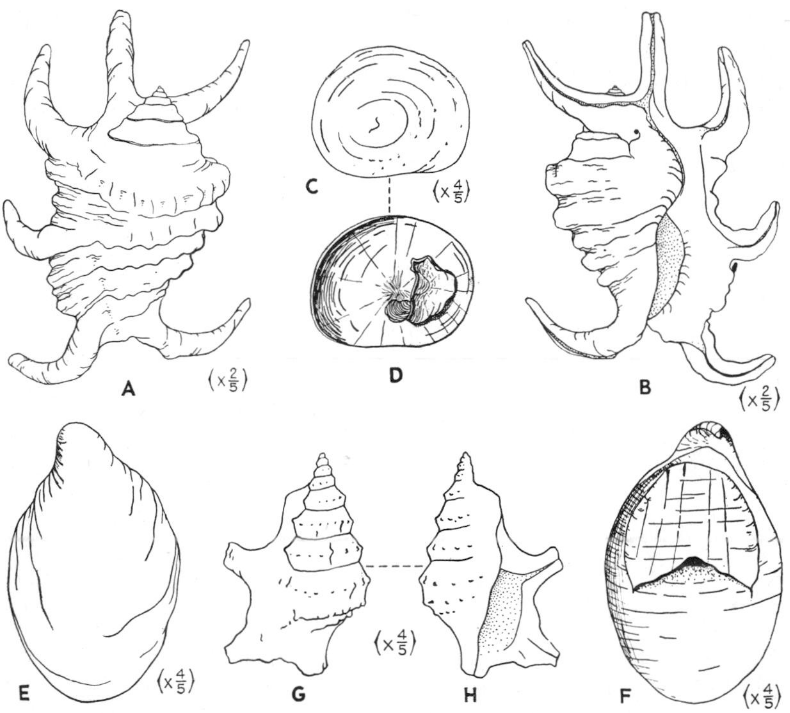

FIG. 132.—Modern gastropods with unusual structures. *A–B*. Two views of *Pterocera*, showing the tubular spinose processes developed on the outer lip and giving the shell the appearance of a crab. *C–D*. *Crucibulum*, a small, conical shell characterized by a small internal plate. *E–F*. *Crepidula* showing the prominent, flat internal plate. *G–H*. A representative of the Aporrhaidae showing the outer lip expanded into a winglike structure.

important until the Mesozoic. The following genera, most of which are still living, are representative of the Platypoda: *Ampullaria, Buccinum, Busycon, Campeloma, Caricella, Conus, Crepidula, Crucibulum, Cypraea, Diaphorostoma, Fusus, Murex, Natica, Oliva, Platyceras, Pterocera, Subulites, Terebra, Turritella*, and *Vermicularia* (Figs. 126–129, 131–132).

Subclass Euthyneura[1]

The Euthyneura comprise a group of gastropods in which the visceral nerve commissure forms a simple loop without crossing. The sexes are united, and the heart is often in front of the gill. There is generally no operculum, and the radula is commonly multiserial. The spiral or saucer-shaped shells are smaller and much less ornamented than those of the Streptoneura. In a few forms the shells are vestigial or absent altogether. The subclass ranges from the Cambrian to Recent and is usually divided into the two orders *Opisthobranchia* and *Pulmonata.*

ORDER OPISTHOBRANCHIA

This order of marine, naked or shelled gastropods is so named because of the position of the gills behind the heart. In some forms true gills are wanting. The body and nervous system usually have bilateral symmetry. Of the three recognized suborders, the *Nudibranchiata* are without a shell and hence without a known fossil record; the *Tectibranchiata* have a shell and range from the Carboniferous to Recent; and the *Pteropoda,* ranging from Cambrian to Recent, are swimming gastropods with the foot modified into winglike fins. Representatives of the pteropods form small calcareous shells which often accumulate in prodigious quantities on some sea bottoms to form "*pteropod* ooze." A fourth suborder, the *Conularida,* is commonly placed provisionally in this order. It constitutes a small group of peculiar Paleozoic shells of doubtful affinities, some of which are probably not even mollusks. *Bullaria* (*Tectibranchia*), *Hyolithes* (*Pteropoda*), and *Tentaculites* and *Conularia* (*Conularida*) are representative of the order (Figs. 131, 133).

ORDER PULMONATA

The Pulmonata, as the name suggests, are air-breathing gastropods, in which the mantle cavity has been modified into a lung. They are mainly terrestrial and fresh-water forms. The shell may be vestigial or absent. This is the second largest group of gastropods, comprising over 6,000 living and 700 fossil species. The earliest known Pulmonata lived in the Devonian, and,

[1] Euthyneura—Gr. *euthus,* straight + *neuron,* nerve; referring to the uncrossed nature of the visceral nerve commissures.

until comparatively recent geological time, fossil remains are few. The suborder *Thalassophila* ranges from the Devonian to Recent; the *Basommatophora*, from Jurassic to Recent; the *Teletremata* have no shell and hence no fossil record; and the

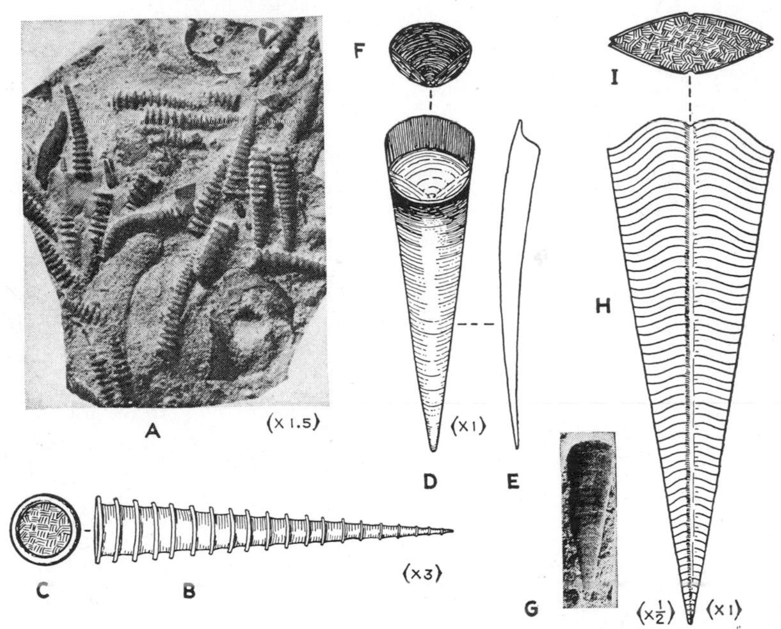

Fig. 133.—Questionable Gastropoda. *A–C. Tentaculites*, a common genus in the Ordovician, Silurian, and Devonian: *A*, photograph of a number of specimens on a small piece of shaly limestone; *B*, enlarged drawing of one of the specimens in *A*; *C*, transverse section showing hollow center filled with matrix. *D–G. Hyolithes*, a Paleozoic pteropod especially abundant in Cambrian and Ordovician strata: *D*, Restoration of a complete shell based on several specimens from the Upper Cambrian of Wisconsin, such as shown in *G*; *E*, Side view of the shell showing the slightly curved longer edge and the slightly concave shorter edge; *F*, The operculum apart from the shell; *G*, A typical specimen from the Upper Cambrian of Wisconsin. *H–I. Conularia*, a common genus found in strata from Ordovician to middle Mesozoic: *H*, View of a compressed specimen from the middle Devonian of Wisconsin; *I*, Transverse section of the shell with the interior filled with matrix. Originally the shell had a quadrate transverse section.

Stylommatophora (land snails) appear in the Carboniferous and are important today in many parts of the world. *Helix* and *Planorbis* are representative genera (Fig. 131 *P–Q*, *V–W*). The former belongs to the family Helicidae, the females of which are unique in having small calcareous darts associated with the reproductive organs (Fig. 134). So far as known none of these has ever been reported in fossil form.

Geologic History. ONTOGENY AND EVOLUTION.—The egg of the gastropod develops into a free-swimming trochophore larva. This larva, spherical and with a girdle of cilia, goes through a series of changes to become an adult organism. The first shell (*protoconch*) appears in the embryo as a simple platelike cover which becomes coiled as growth takes place around the edge and ultimately develops into the great many different types of shells. It seems likely that the ancestors of the gastropods had a cap-shaped shell in the adult stage.

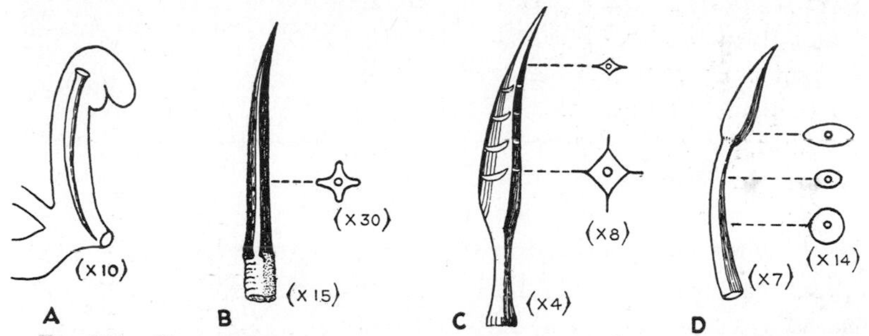

FIG. 134.—Darts. These small, calcareous darts, unique to the Helicidae, are thought by some investigators to be used by the female during mating. *A*. A dart in the dart sac. *B–D*. Darts found in species of *Helix*. (*After Ashford*.)

The oldest representatives of the class are found in the Cambrian, but it seems very likely that the class dates back to Pre-Cambrian times for its beginning. The earliest and most primitive shells tend to be smooth and are conical or planospiral (*Scenella* and *Salpingostoma*, respectively) (Fig. 130 *M–N*, *F–G*). The class very likely began in marine waters. As a whole the group exhibits a very great variety of shell types in which many interesting features are developed. Because of the lack of data concerning the soft parts, little is known about the actual evolution of the group.

ECOLOGY.—The gastropods have world-wide distribution, being found in the sea, in brackish waters, in fresh waters, and on the land. Gill-bearing forms are limited to an aquatic habitat, but pulmonate species may live in either aquatic or terrestrial habitats and may even change from one to the other. The greatest populations are found in the shallow, well-lighted marine waters of the continental shelves, but some species range to over 5,180 m. (17,000 ft.), and on the land both terrestrial and fresh-water forms have been found at elevations as great as 4,800 m. (16,000 ft.) to 5,400 m. (18,000 ft.) above sea level.

Species with strong and massive shells live in the shallower marine waters adjacent to the strand line. Some of these attach themselves to rocks and plants, and others burrow into sand and mud. The limpets and limpet-like forms adhere to rocks by means of strong muscles, and in some cases the attachment is so strong that the animal can be torn loose only with difficulty. The large *Abalone* (*Haliotis*) of the California coast is so strong that it is dangerous to attempt with the hands to tear the shell away from the rocks to which it is attached lest the fingers be caught and held fast beneath the shell. Different genera of gastropods live in different bottom environments, and gastropod assemblages often show a remarkable tenacity in the habitation of certain types of bottoms.

Most marine gastropods die if placed in fresh water, and fresh-water species suffer a similar fate when placed in saline waters. There are, however, exceptional fresh-water genera, as *Melania*, *Neritina*, *Amnula*, and *Planorbis*, which can live in brackish or salt water; and marine genera, such as *Littorina*, *Cerithium*, and *Trochus*, which can live in fresh waters. *Littorina* may be found in abundance where fresh-water streams empty into the sea.

On land pulmonate gastropods attain world-wide distribution and show great vertical range. Fresh-water forms have been found in high lakes in the Himalayas over 5,480 m. (18,000 ft.) above sea level. At lower elevations they live in lakes, rivers, ponds, swamps, hot springs, moist surfaces on cliffs, etc. Often they occur in great abundance. The gastropods which live on the land do not seem to be so tolerant of external conditions as many terrestrial invertebrates. Extremes of temperature do not appear to limit distribution so much as does lack of moisture and lime in the soil. Lack of shade and places of concealment also seem to be important. Few species are found in arid habitats, but individuals of a species may be extremely abundant under such conditions. Land snails and slugs are found in areas of considerable vegetation such as woods, pastures, hedges, among mosses and lichens, and on cliffs, rock surfaces, and in sand dunes. They sometimes burrow underground, often climb trees, and even invade houses. Over 6,000 species of land gastropods are known.

Most gastropods are herbivorous, both in the sea and on the land, feeding upon various plants, which they cut up by means of the radula. Some are unusually voracious, as many a gardener can attest. A few feed upon living and decomposed animal matter, and many genera, such as *Natica*, *Buccinum*, and *Murex* (Fig. 131), are ferocious predators, drilling holes in other mollusk shells to reach and feed upon the soft parts within. On certain coasts 88 per cent of the dead shells of the pelecypod *Spissula elliptica* had been bored into by *Natica alderi*, and mollusk shells from many Pacific and other beaches show gastropod borings. Gastropods are also preyed upon by different animals among which are crustaceans, fish, birds, and other gastropods. Usually the shell is sufficient protection, but some predators, such as certain carnivorous beetles, thrust their heads into the aperture of the shell and drag out the inhabitant. Commensalism and parasitism are not common among the gastropods. One of the best known examples of the former relation is that of *Igoceras pabulocrinus*, which cemented its shell to the tegmen of certain crinoids near the anal opening and fed on the waste products expelled (Fig. 53 *E*).

Gastropods are not of great importance to man but have played some part in human activities. Many species are hosts for parasitic organisms which are responsible for human and other animal diseases. Snails and slugs are used extensively for food in certain parts of the world and seem to have been an important part of the diet of ancient Paleolithic man, since among the ruins of his camping sites great numbers of the shells may be found. In past ages certain gastropods were exploited for the dye employed in the preparation of "Tyrian purple."

Stratigraphic Importance.—The earliest known gastropods, found in Lower Cambrian strata, are small, low-spired, or cap-shaped shells such as *Raphistoma* and *Scenella*. The pteropods *Hyolithes* and *Hyolithellus* are extremely common in some Cambrian strata. All are very simply ornamented. By Ordovician time many families were in existence, and throughout the remainder of geologic time there has been a gradual increase in the number of families as shown in the following table:

Cambrian	8	Triassic	27
Ordovician	13	Jurassic	41
Silurian	19	Cretaceous	61
Devonian	18	Tertiary	69
Carboniferous	21	Recent	71
Permian	21		

Of the 81 families only 10 are extinct. The class as a whole seems to have its maximum at the present time and constitutes the largest group of Mollusca. Of the 30,000 known species, about two-thirds breathe by means of gills; one-third, by lungs.

Paleozoic gastropods are, in general, simply ornamented and have apertures with entire peristomes. The pulmonate gastropods appeared in the Devonian; the first land snails, in the Carboniferous; and fresh-water forms are known from the Jurassic onward. It cannot be assumed that land snails preceded the fresh-water forms in biologic development.

Character of Fossils.—Paleozoic gastropods, as a rule, are not well preserved. Molds and fillings are very common, but actual shell matter is of rare occurrence until late in the era. Too often the fossil gastropods of this part of geologic time are too poorly preserved for accurate identification or description. It has been suggested that the failure of preservation is due to the fact that most early gastropods were composed of the easily destroyed aragonite and that the few forms, as *Cyclonema* and *Diaphorostoma* (Fig. 130 *E*, *O–P*), in which preservation is excellent, had calcitic shells. The shells of the Mesozoic and Cenozoic gastropods are often very well preserved, and perhaps these shells were composed of calcite.

Gastropods are thought to have been responsible for some of the trails made in the muds of ancient seas (Fig. 135). These markings have been described under various names, and the origin of some of them is very doubtful.[1] Fossil shells often show borings which may have been made by gastropods (Fig. 135 *C–E*).

Class Scaphopoda[2]

Scaphopods are small, marine, bilaterally symmetrical mollusks with an external, curved and tapering tubular shell open at each

[1] Powers, S., Gastropod trails in Pennsylvanian sandstones in Texas, *Amer. Jour. Sci.*, vol. 53, pp. 101–107, Figs. 1–3, 1922.

[2] Scaphopoda—Gr. *scaphe*, a bowl + *pous*, *podos*, foot; referring to the hollow character of the tusklike shell.

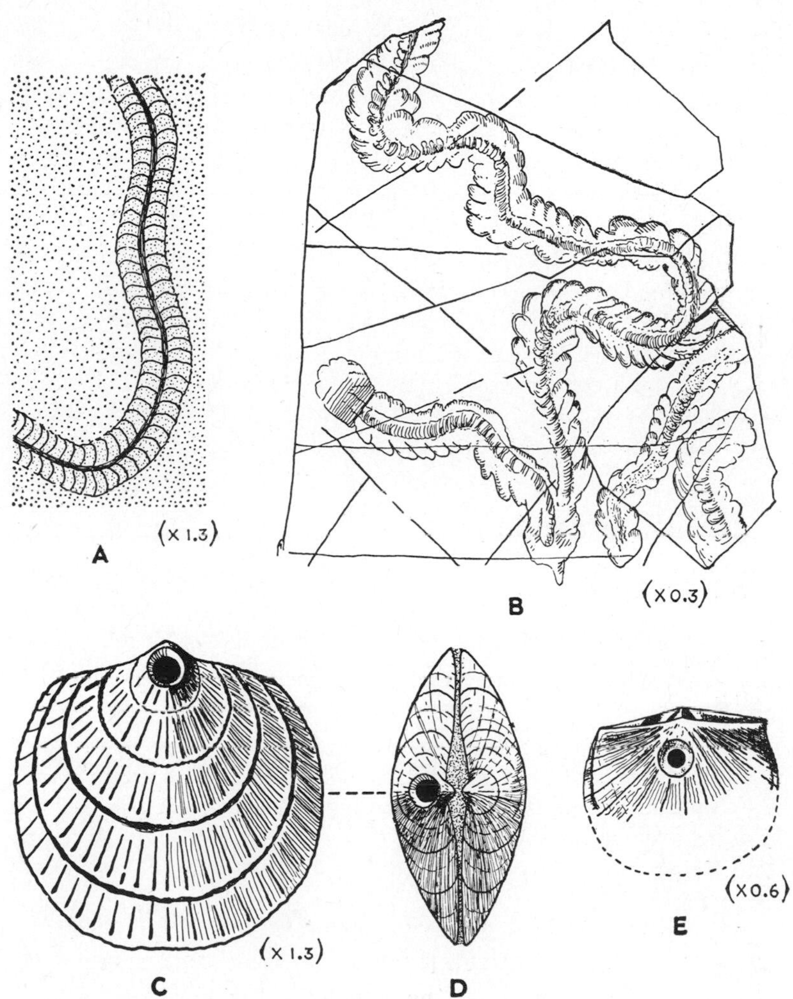

FIG. 135.—Gastropod trails and borings. *A.* Trail of the living *Purpura lapillus* made on firm sand. *B.* A supposed gastropod trail from a Pennsylvanian sandstone of Texas. *C–D.* Lateral and hinge-line views of a small *Glycimeris*, from the Miocene of Maryland, showing a prominent boring near the umbo of one valve. This boring may have been made by a gastropod, for it shows close resemblance to recent borings by the same animals. *E.* Shell of *Rafinesquina*, from the Upper Ordovician of Indiana, showing a supposed gastropod boring. (*A from Nicholson and Lydekker after Gray; B after Powers; E slightly modified after C. L. and M. A. Fenton.*)

end (Fig. 112 *D*). The animal is attached to the shell by muscles near the posterior end. Both body and shell are somewhat curved, and the concave side is dorsal. The head is vestigial, and eyes are absent. The mouth is in a cylindrical snout and is surrounded by a rosette of leaflike appendages and a cluster of numerous exsertile filaments known as *captacula*. There is a radula. The foot which protrudes from the larger or anterior end of the shell is rather long, pointed, and spadelike and is adapted for burrowing. It is adjacent to the mouth and on the ventral side. There is a single-chambered rudimentary heart, which is little more than an enlargement of a blood vessel, and there are no gills, the respiration being carried on by the general surface of the mantle. The sexes are separate, and the sexual products reach the exterior through the right kidney. The organization is clearly of a low type.

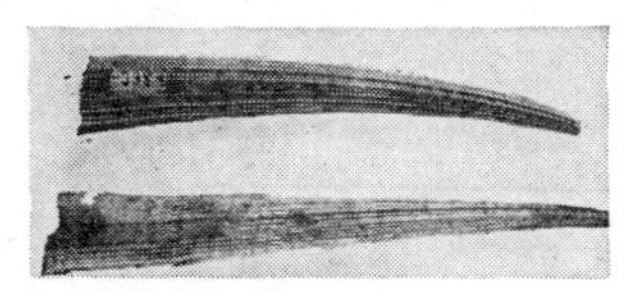

FIG. 136.—Scaphopoda. Two shells of *Dentalium elephantum* from the Pleistocene of Italy (×½).

Members of the class live mainly in fairly deep water, but they may be found also over shallow bottoms. Specimens have been obtained from depths as great as 4,570 m. (15,000 ft.), and it is probable that they live at even greater depths. During life the shell is buried obliquely in the mud with the anterior or head end down and the smaller end projecting above the surface. The animal feeds on small organisms, such as Foraminifera. These are captured by the filamentary captacula. About 200 living species are known, and about 300 fossil species have been described.

The scaphopod shell is composed of aragonite and grows by successive additions to the larger or anterior end. Frequently the shell is shortened at the smaller posterior extremity by breakage, wear, or solution. There is no operculum. Shells rarely attain a length of 15 cm. (6 in.), and the exterior surface is smooth, longitudinally striated, or annulated. The posterior end of some shells is crenulated or fissured. The scaphopod shell differs from the shells of some gastropods and all cephalopods in being open at each end and unchambered; from the calcareous tubes of tubicolar annelids in having three layers in the shell instead of two; and from *Conularia* and *Tentaculites* of the Pteropoda in being striated longitudinally.

Scaphopods appear early, probably in the Ordovician, and are still living. They are found sparingly throughout the geologic column, becoming fairly common after the Pennsylvanian, but their fossils are of little stratigraphic importance. Most species belong to the genus *Dentalium* (Fig. 136).

Class Cephalopoda[1]

General Considerations.—The Cephalopoda constitute an exclusively marine group of highly organized Mollusca. Among the members are found the largest of all living or fossil invertebrates. Over 150 genera of living cephalopods are known, of which the devilfish, cuttlefish, and the chambered *Nautilus* are the most familiar representatives. The cephalopods are an old group, appearing first in the late Cambrian, and are represented by over 10,000 fossil species. Great diminution of numbers has taken place in the more recent geologic periods.

The cephalopods agree with other mollusks in general structure and seem to have closest affinities with the Gastropoda. The visceral mass is an elongate body covered by a *mantle*. The latter secretes a chambered shell and incloses a cavity in which the breathing organs or *gills* are suspended (Fig. 112 *E–F*). The alimentary tract terminates in a well-formed head, and the mouth is provided with a pair of jaws and a radula. Cephalopods differ from all other mollusks in having the head and "foot" together so that the mouth lies in the middle of the foot and is surrounded by a circlet of *tentacles* formed from the drawn-out edges of that organ. The eyes are highly developed and in most forms are large. On the ventral side of the animal, beneath the mouth, a portion of the "foot" is modified in the form of a funnel-shaped process which connects with the gill cavity. This is the *hyponome* or *ambulatory funnel* which serves a locomotory function. Rapid expulsion of water from the gill cavity through the hyponome propels the animal backward, and this is its characteristic mode of locomotion. In living species the gill cavity contains one or two pairs of gills, and the shell in most forms is in a reduced or degenerate condition. If a shell is present, it may be internal or external and is almost always chambered. Some species have lost the shell completely.

[1] Cephalopoda—Gr. *cephale*, head + *pous*, *podos*, foot; referring to the symmetrical arrangement of the pedal tentacles about the head.

The cephalopods of existing seas represent only a small fraction of those that have lived, although it is possible that naked forms and those with internal shells are more abundant now than ever before. The few living species with external shells are but a mere remnant of a great race that filled the seas during the ages that are past. Many of the ancient forms possessed beautiful ornamentation and reached gigantic proportions for invertebrates.

The class is divided as follows:

Subclass I. **Nautiloidea**—A single living genus, *Nautilus*, represents this important group of ancient cephalopods. Living species have four gills (tetrabranchiate).

Subclass II. **Ammonoidea**—An extinct group of cephalopods which may have been tetrabranchiate. They were especially important during the Mesozoic.

Subclass III. **Coleoidea (Dibranchia)**

Order 1. **Belemnoidea**—Dibranchiate cephalopods represented by the extinct *Belemnites* and the living *Spirula*.

Order 2. **Sepioidea**—Dibranchiate cephalopods possessing 10 tentacles. Includes squids and cuttlefish.

Order 3. **Octopoda**—Dibranchiate cephalopods with eight arms or tentacles. This order includes the naked octopods and *Argonauta*, the female of which secretes an external "shell" not homologous with the shells of other groups of cephalopods (Fig. 146 *B–C*).

The Animal.—The cephalopod animal is a bilaterally symmetrical mollusk in which the main part of the foot is displaced forward to the position of the mouth and divided into a number of sucker-bearing *arms* or *tentacular lobes* (Fig. 137). The remainder of the foot is modified into a funnel for the exit of water from the mantle cavity in which the gills are located. The visceral mass of the organism is symmetrical and uncoiled. Posteriorly and ventrally the mantle incloses a large mantle cavity, into which various organs discharge. The shell may be well developed, as in *Nautilus;* rudimentary, as in the squids; or absent, as in *Octopus*. If present and well developed, it may be external or internal. In some forms there is an internal cartilaginous skeletal structure which serves to support and protect the nerve centers and to give attachment to the muscles. The mouth is provided with a pair of *chitinous jaws*, and there is an *odontophore* bearing many small, horny teeth. In most cephalopods there is a unique organ in the form of an *ink gland* which opens into the rectum through a duct. The breathing organs (*stenidia*) and the "kidneys" are either two or four in number. The nervous system is very well developed, with the main nerve ganglia clustered together around the esophagus. The sexes are separate.

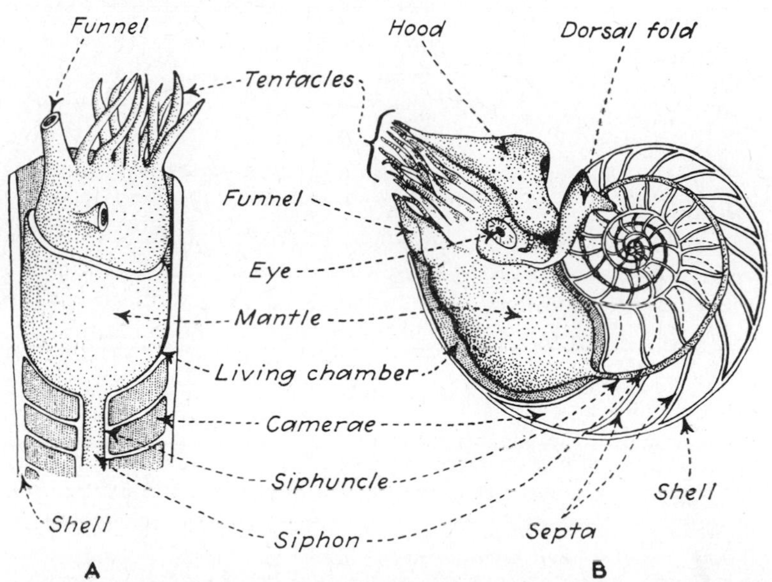

Fig. 137.—Ancient and modern cephalopods. *A*. Restoration of *Orthoceras*, a straight-shelled Paleozoic cephalopod, with the later part of the shell sectioned to show the interior as well as various animal structures. *B*. *Nautilus pompilius*, the well-known "chambered nautilus," with shell sectioned to show its interior and the relation of the living animal to it. (*A and B slightly modified after Nicholson and Lydekker.*)

Knowledge of the soft parts of cephalopods is based on the few living species with external shells, the several forms which possess internal shells, and the numerous representatives of the class which have no shell. Of the first mentioned there are but three species known, and all of these are found in the warmer waters of the Pacific Ocean. *Spirula* and the various types of squids and cuttlefish represent the second group, and *Octopus* may be taken as representative of the third.

The Shell. General Considerations.—The cephalopod shell is fundamentally a straight, curved or coiled, tapering cone, closed at the smaller end and divided by transverse partitions into chambers which are in communication with each other and with the large living chamber at the larger end of the shell. In life the body occupies the living chamber and is connected with each preceding chamber by means of a fleshy tube that reaches back to the first chamber. The body is attached to the shell by muscles (Fig. 137).

Living cephalopods with internal shells are often described as naked, and these forms have two gills; those with external shells have four gills. It is generally assumed that extinct species with external shells also had four gills, but this cannot be stated with certainty. The general architecture of such shells, however, conforms to that of the living tetrabranchiate *Nautilus*.

Composition of the Shell Material.—The shell of living cephalopods and certainly some fossil forms is composed of an outer or external layer of imbricated laminae of porcelaneous aragonite and an inner layer of thin parallel laminae of aragonite forming the mother-of-pearl layer. The exterior of the shell is superficially ornamented by color designs, and fossil shells frequently possess ornamentation in the form of nodes, ridges, and spines. The interior of the shell is often iridescent.

Structures of the Shells.—The chambers of a cephalopod are known as *camerae;* the dividing transverse partitions, as *septa;* and the perforations in the septa constitute the *siphuncle* (Fig. 138). The small tubular processes on the apex or convex side of the septa are designated *septal necks*, and when these fuse to form a single continuous tube reaching from the *protoconch*, or primary chamber of the shell, to the *living chamber*, the tube is referred to as a *siphuncular tube.* The siphuncle may be central, dorsal, or ventral. The junction of the septa with the internal surface of the shell is marked by a smooth or wrinkled line designated the *suture* (Fig. 140). This is not visible on the exterior.

Coiling.—Primitive and early cephalopods had small, conical, chambered shells, but these became greatly modified in later forms. Excepting bizarre and aberrant types, and the internal ones which show profound modification consequent to the extension of the body around the shell, the remainder of cephalopod shells fall into a progressive series of architectural types ranging from a straight, imperfectly chambered cone to closely coiled chambered shells of planospiral or helicoid nature (Fig. 139).

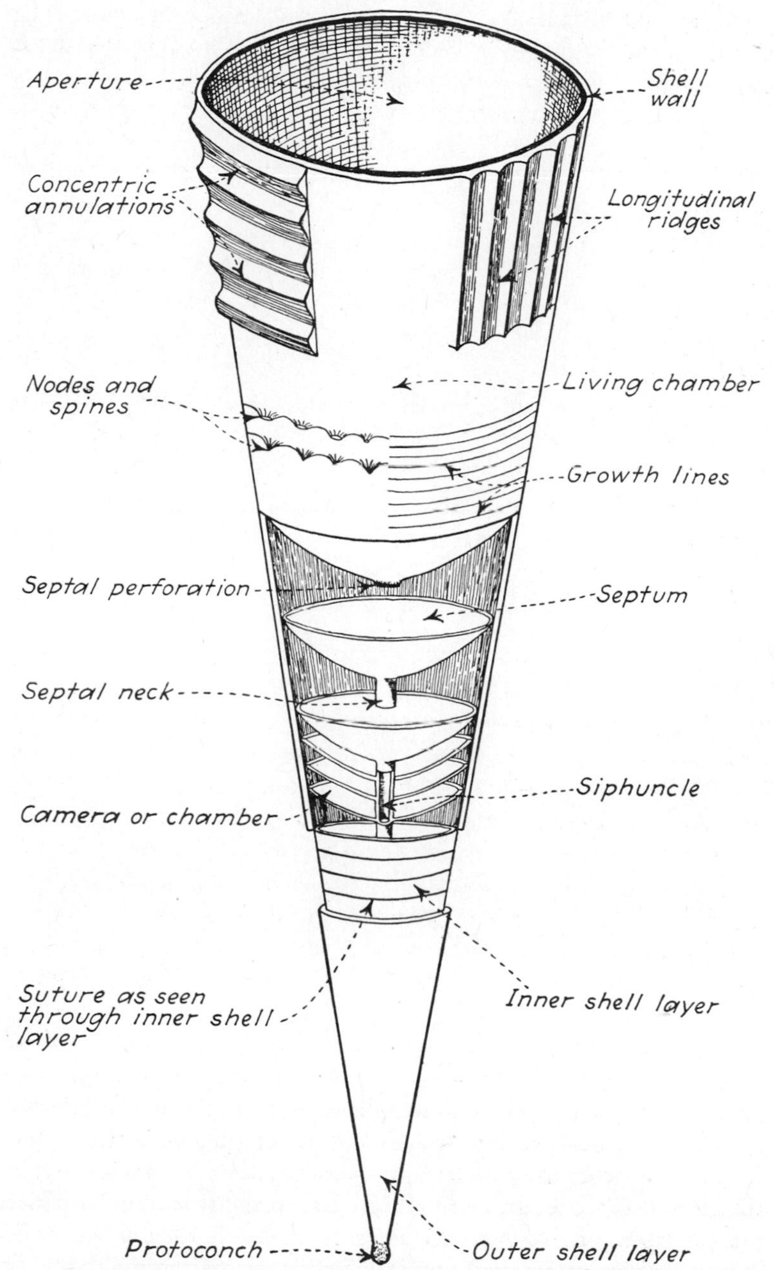

FIG. 138.—Idealized diagram of an orthoconic cephalopod variously sectioned to show numerous external features and internal structures.

Early cephalopod shells were dominantly straight or but slightly coiled, as illustrated by the orthoceratites of the early and middle Paleozoic. Among the Nautiloidea this type of shell is known as an *orthocone;* among the Ammonoidea it is designated a *bactriticone.* The first stage in coiling is illustrated

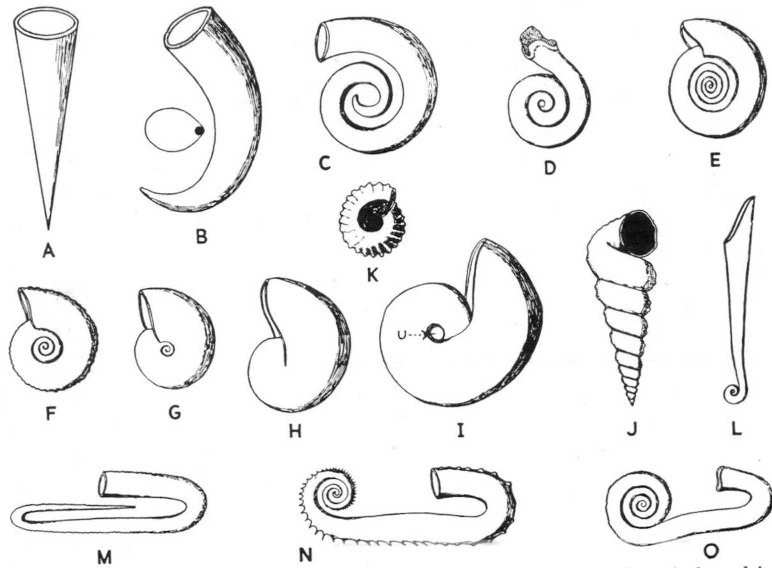

FIG. 139.—Coiling in cephalopod shells. *A.* An orthocone such as is found in *Orthoceras* and *Bactrites. B.* A cyrtocone based on *Cyrtoceras.* The position of the siphuncle is indicated in the small supplementary figure. *C.* A gyrocone, such as the shells of *Gyroceras* and *Mimoceras. D.* An ophiocone, represented by such genera as *Lituites* and *Dactylioceras. E–H.* Nautilicones and ammoniticones illustrated by *Clymenia* (*E*), *Trachyceras* (*F*), *Hoplites* (*G*), and *Nautilus* (*H*), showing progressive encroachment of last whorl on preceding whorls until the shell becomes involute (convolute) as in *H. I.* An ammoniticone with an umbilicus (*u*), illustrated by *Scaphites. J.* A torticone (turrilitįcone), which is illustrated by *Trochoceras* and *Turrilites. K.* Shows a view of the larger end of *J* looking along the axis of coiling and into the umbilicus. *L.* A modified ammoniticone showing uncoiling and straightening of the shell in maturity, based on *Baculites. M–O.* Modified ammoniticones coiled in various ways [*Hamites* (*M*), *Ancyloceras* (*N*), *Scaphites* (*O*)]. (*The diagrams are adapted from figures by numerous authors.*)

by the genus *Cyrtoceras,* of which the shell is slightly curved. This type of shell is known as a *cyrtocone* in the Nautiloidea. There is no corresponding stage among the ammonoids. The next stage is represented by those gently coiled shells in which the whorls are more or less remote from each other. Nautiloid shells of this type are designated *gyrocones;* ammonoid forms, such as certain Devonian species, are designated *mimocones* after the genus *Mimoceras.* Progressive coiling next produces a shell in which the successive whorls are in contact like a coil of rope but make little or no impress on each other. Such a shell among the nautiloids has been named an *ophiocone,* but no name has been applied to the corresponding type in the Ammonoidea. Since it is well represented in the genus *Dactylioceras,* it might well be designated a *dactyliocone.* It has sometimes been included in the rather general term *ammoniticone.* Planospiral coiling reaches its limit in the *nautilicone* and *ammoniticone.* In the earlier stages the later whorls embrace the preceding to a greater or lesser degree, and finally the last whorl covers all preceding ones to produce an *involute* or *convolute* shell. Cephalopod shells which are coiled in a helicoid spiral are known as *torticones,* and this type of coiling is not sequential to either the nautilicone or ammoniticone. Not many shells show this type of coiling. Nautiloid torticones have been called *trochocones;* and ammonoid examples, *turriliticones,* after the genera *Trochoceras* and *Turrilites* which are coiled in this fashion.

In many ancient cephalopods coiling was later succeeded by uncoiling, so that a young shell would be completely coiled, whereas an adult shell of the same species would have the later whorls straight. The beginning of uncoiling in adult life is shown in the ammonite *Scaphites* and particularly well in *Baculites* (Fig. 139 *L, O*). Degenerate coiled forms also appeared near the end of the Mesozoic, but they do not seem to follow any consistent method of coiling. Closely coiled shells bring the whorls in contact and produce an *impressed zone* on the dorsal side of each whorl. This may be a *contact furrow,* existing only while the whorls are in contact, or a *dorsal furrow,* appearing by inheritance in the young before the whorls come in contact. A *persistent dorsal furrow* is found on the free senile whorls of some shells and is a remnant of the impressed zone of the earlier stages. The *gerontic contact furrow* is that found in the old-age stage of certain distorted ammonoids.

The causes of coiling and uncoiling can only be inferred. There is no doubt that a coiled shell under ordinary environmental conditions is easier to manage than one that is long and straight. Any tendency toward coiling, therefore, would give the animal an advantage over forms with straight shells, since its shell would be less cumbersome and also less likely to be broken. If the vacated chambers in the earlier shells were filled with gas of some kind, a condition which seems altogether likely, the straight shells would have had a buoyancy that might well have made trouble for the animal, since such a shell would have a tendency to tip the animal forward on its head. Such a handicap would have been a serious one for either benthonic or swimming cephalopods. In order to obviate such a difficulty the mantle may have secreted shell matter more rapidly on the ventral side so as to aid the animal in keeping its head out of the mud or in maintaining a more nearly horizontal position. Such growth would result in a cyrtocone, and continued development would have led to the ophiocone and finally to the nautilicone. The torticone may be considered as an adaptation to bottom dwelling, since the helicoid shell seems easier to manage under variable environmental conditions. Gastropods have been very successful with this type of shell. That the buoyancy of straight shells was a problem for the animal is suggested by the secretions of calcium carbonate that some of them made in abandoned chambers, apparently for the purpose of decreasing the buoyancy. Another method of managing the shell is shown in such genera as *Ascoceras* and *Piloceras*, in which air chambers were developed over the top part of the body, in this way placing the center of gravity at some point in the body chamber (Fig. 142).

Shape and Size of the Shell.—Shapes range from slender cones, as in many orthoceratites, to robust straight forms like *Poterioceras*. Coiled forms may be more or less spherical, as many Pennsylvanian nautiloids, and may range from such a shape to highly lenticular forms like *Aganides* and *Placenticeras*. Some shells are boat shaped (*Scaphites*) or hooklike (*Hamites*). The umbilicus, the term having the same significance as in the gastropods, may be wide open, small and narrow, or absent (Fig. 139).

There is great variation in size. The largest known coiled form, *Pachydiscus septemaradensis* from the Cretaceous of Westphalia, is 2 m. (6 ft. 8 in.) in diameter. From this extreme, shells vary in dimension to tiny forms less than 25 mm. (1 in.) in diameter. Straight shells show even greater extremes in size, ranging from very small forms less than 25 mm. long to the giant *Endoceras* of the Ordovician with a maximum length of 4½ m.

(15 ft.) and a maximum diameter across the living chamber of about 30 cm. (1 ft.).

ORNAMENTATION AND COLOR MARKINGS.—Except for growth lines many cephalopod shells are smooth, a condition well shown in the living *Nautilus*, by many extinct nautiloids (especially orthoceratites), and by numerous ammonoids. Orthocones, cyrtocones, and gyrocones are often ornamented by spiral and transverse ridges and ribs or by nodes and spines similarly arranged. There seems to have been a gradual increase in ornamentation from the time the cephalopods first appeared in the Lower Cambrian to their climax in the Mesozoic. Especially rapid was the increase during the Mesozoic when many bizarre and specialized or degenerate forms evolved. The general extinction of cephalopods in the late Cretaceous eliminated all of the highly ornamented forms, sparing only the few simply ornamented types, in which the color was more conspicuous than shell structures.

The external shells still found on living cephalopods are highly colored, and it may be inferred that brilliant color was also a characteristic of many cephalopods throughout the history of the class. Color cannot often be seen on fossil specimens, but it has been found, particularly in Cretaceous shells preserved in concretions, and in a few cases the colors are well displayed. The color pattern may be present on all sides of the shell or on only a part and is in the form of annular, undulating or zigzag bands. Such markings have been reported to occur on species of *Cyrtoceras* from as far back as the Silurian of Bohemia (Barrande). Shells with uniform coloring on all sides are believed to have maintained a vertical position during life, and the animal is assumed to have crawled on the bottom or to have floated or swum in the water with the pointed extremity of the shell upward. Some shells, as *Kionoceras angulatum*, have a color pattern on the dorsal side only, and this in the form of a series of bands which zigzag across the shell. In *Geisonoceras tenuitextum* the bands are on one side only and are parallel to the long axis of the shell. It is assumed that cephalopods with dorsally ornamented shells crawled on the bottom or swam with the dorsal side of the shell always upward.

SEPTA.—The number of septa varies greatly among the different species, and the distance between adjacent septa is

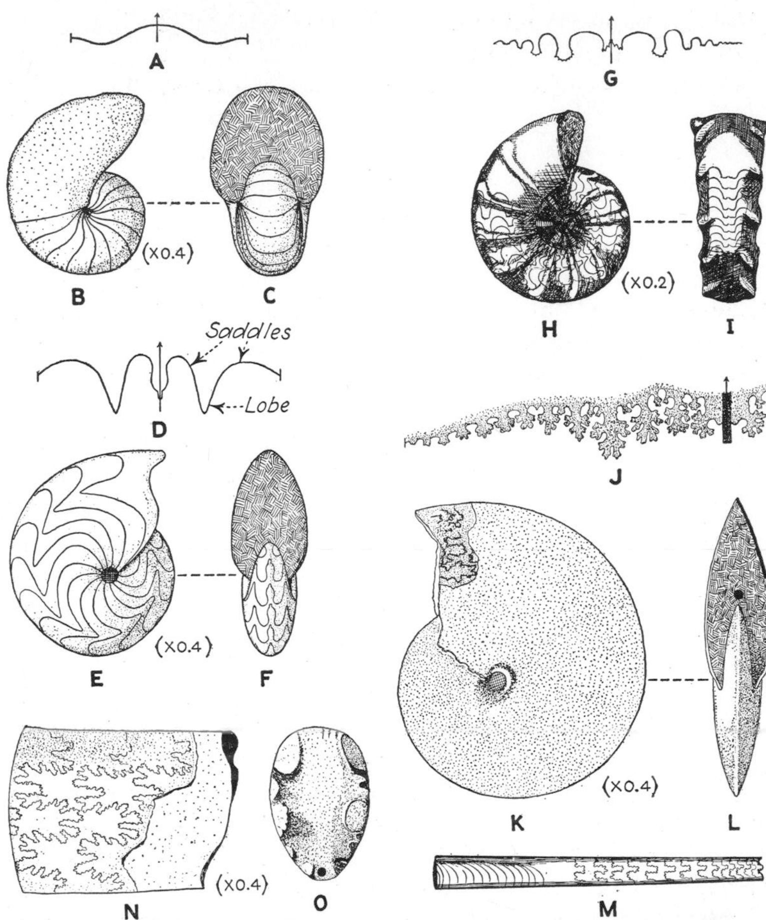

FIG. 140.—Sutures of cephalopod shells. *A–C. Nautilus undulatus* from the Cretaceous of England: *A*, a complete suture with the extremities marking the axis of coiling and the arrow at the midventral line pointing toward the aperture; *B*, *C*, side and apertural views of an internal filling of the shell showing nature of the sutures. *D–F. Aganides rotarius* from the Mississippian of the United States: *D*, a complete suture, with rounded saddles and angular lobes; *E*, *F*, side and apertural views of an internal filling of the shell showing the relation of the sutures. *G–I. Ceratites nodosus* from the Triassic of Germany: *G*, the complete visible suture (part of the suture is hidden on the dorsal side), with rounded saddles and crenulated lobes; *H*, *I*, side and back views of a filling of the shell showing the relation of the sutures. *J–L. Placenticeras lenticularis* from the Cretaceous of western United States: *J*, the left half of the complex suture; *K*, *L*, side and apertural views of a somewhat smaller shell than that represented by the suture shown in *J*. A small portion of the shell matter has been broken away revealing the sutures. *M–O. Baculites*, a common Cretaceous cephalopod in many parts of the world: *M*, *B. anceps*, from the Cretaceous of England, showing the terminal part of the shell and a few of the sutures; *N*, view of a

likewise variable, but both number and spacing are relatively constant in the same species. Septa tend to be relatively farther apart in the younger growth stages, are separated by constant intervals in maturity, and are close together in old age. In the majority of species the septa are single and concave toward the aperture of the shell and convex toward the pointed smaller part. In *Actinoceras* the septa in some species are double, and in others the camerae are divided into chamberlets by small *pseudosepta.* The last may be parallel to the regular septa or at an angle to them and are composed of two readily separable laminations. The earlier and more primitive cephalopod shells are characterized by smoothly curved, bowl-like septa which join the shell wall along a circular or elliptical suture. In the more advanced forms the septa became much crumpled along the edges, and the suture is very intricate.

SUTURES.—The suture has been defined as the line which marks the union between the septum and the interior of the wall of the shell. In the majority of straight shells, the suture is circular, but in all the coiled forms it is more or less undulating (Fig. 140). Undulations convex toward the aperture are termed *saddles;* and those that are concave, *lobes.* The lobes and saddles are *lateral,* if on the sides of the shell; *dorsal* (also *columellar* or *antisiphonal* in the Ammonoidea); and *ventral* (*siphonal* in the Ammonoidea). The main dorsal lobe in the Nautiloidea may contain a small central lobe. This is termed the *annular lobe.* The ventral lobe (Ammonoidea) is bounded on each side by the large first or superior-lateral saddle and the superior-lateral lobe in the order named. Then follow in order the inferior-lateral saddle and inferior-lateral lobe. New lobes and saddles develop near the line of involution and move therefrom both ventrally and dorsally as the whorls widen. These lobes and saddles are termed auxiliary and are numbered in order from the one of first origin. Adventitious lobes and saddles arise between the first pair of lateral lobes and the median line of the *venter* (ventral side), this being done either on the sides of the ventral lobe, by division of the outer parts of the first lateral

---

fragment showing the nature of the sutures; *O*, view of a septum showing the lobes and saddles. (*A–C after Sharpe; J–L after Meek; M after Wright; N–O after Meek.*)

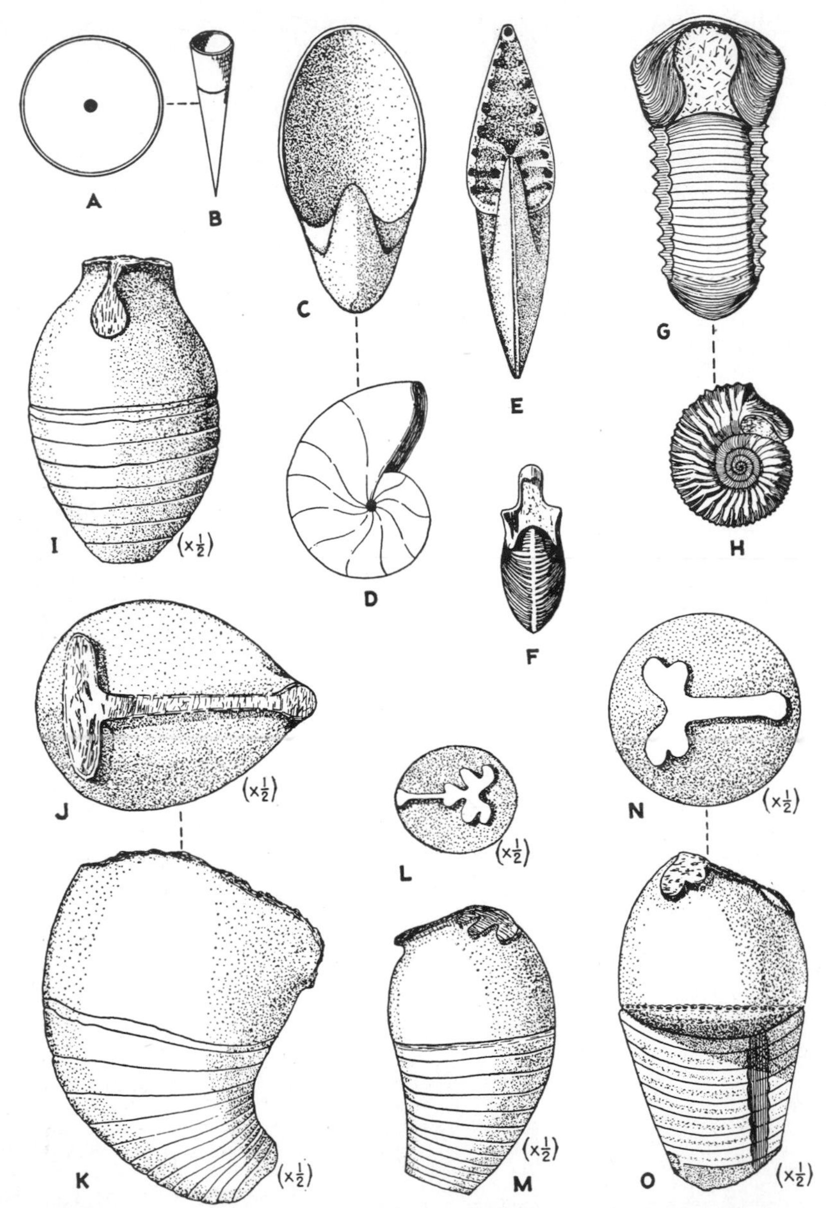

FIG. 141.—Apertures of cephalopods. *A–B. Orthoceras: A*, showing the circular aperture with the centrally located siphuncle; *B*, entire shell showing size of living chamber as compared to remainder of shell. *C–D. Nautilus pompilius: C*, showing the interrupted elliptical aperture; *D*, side view of shell showing its

saddles, or by division of the inner parts of the ventral or siphonal saddle.

There are four general types of sutures, which, in order of increasing complexity, are orthoceratite (nautiloid), goniatite, ceratite, and ammonite. It is almost a universal practice, when illustrating these types, to show them as they would appear if they were transferred to a plane surface by rotating the whorl through 360 deg., with the axis of rotation perpendicular to the plane of the suture. The edges of the diagram then mark the median dorsal line of the shell, and an arrow in the middle of the diagram pointing toward the aperture marks the position of the median ventral line. The spaces between the ends of the projected suture and the arrow represent the lateral surfaces of the whorl.

The *orthoceratite* or *nautiloid* suture is either a circle, as in *Orthoceras;* or an undulating, closed curve without distinct lobes or saddles, as in *Nautilus.* These are shown in the usual manner in Fig. 140 *A–C.* Sutures of this type are found in straight and coiled shells ranging from the Cambrian to Recent. Cephalopod shells with smooth and simple lobes and saddles appeared in the Devonian. Such sutures are termed *goniatite* and are well shown in the Mississippian *Aganides.* Shells with goniatite sutures disappear in the late Pennsylvanian or Permian. In the *ceratite* suture the saddles remain smooth, but the lobes become crumpled by secondary undulations. Shells with this type of suture make their appearance in the Permian, replacing shells with goniatite sutures, and disappear in the Triassic, giving way to the ammonite type. There is, however, a *pseudoceratite* suture present in certain Mesozoic shells. In the most complex of sutural types,

---

involute nature. *E.* Apertural view of *Placenticeras placenta,* from the Cretaceous of western United States, showing the sagittate aperture, one of the crenulated septa, and the ventrally located siphuncle. *F.* Apertural view of *Scaphites refractus* showing a modified aperture. *G–H.* Apertural and lateral views of *Stephanoceras braikenridgii* from the Jurassic showing a modified aperture. *I. Mandaloceras hawthornensis* from the Silurian (Racine) of Illinois showing a constricted aperture and several of the larger chambers. *J–K.* Apertural and side views of *Phragmoceras rex* from the Silurian of Bohemia showing a T-shaped aperture. *L–M.* Apertural and side views of *Hexameroceras* from the Silurian of Illinois: *L, H. byronense; M, H. jolietense. N–O. Gomphoceras deshayesi,* from the Silurian of Bohemia: *N,* showing an apertural view; *O,* side view showing complete living chamber and several chambers longitudinally sectioned to show the position and nature of the siphuncle. (*E after Meek; F–H after Wright; I after Foerste; J–K after Barrande; L–M after Foerste; O after Barrande.*)

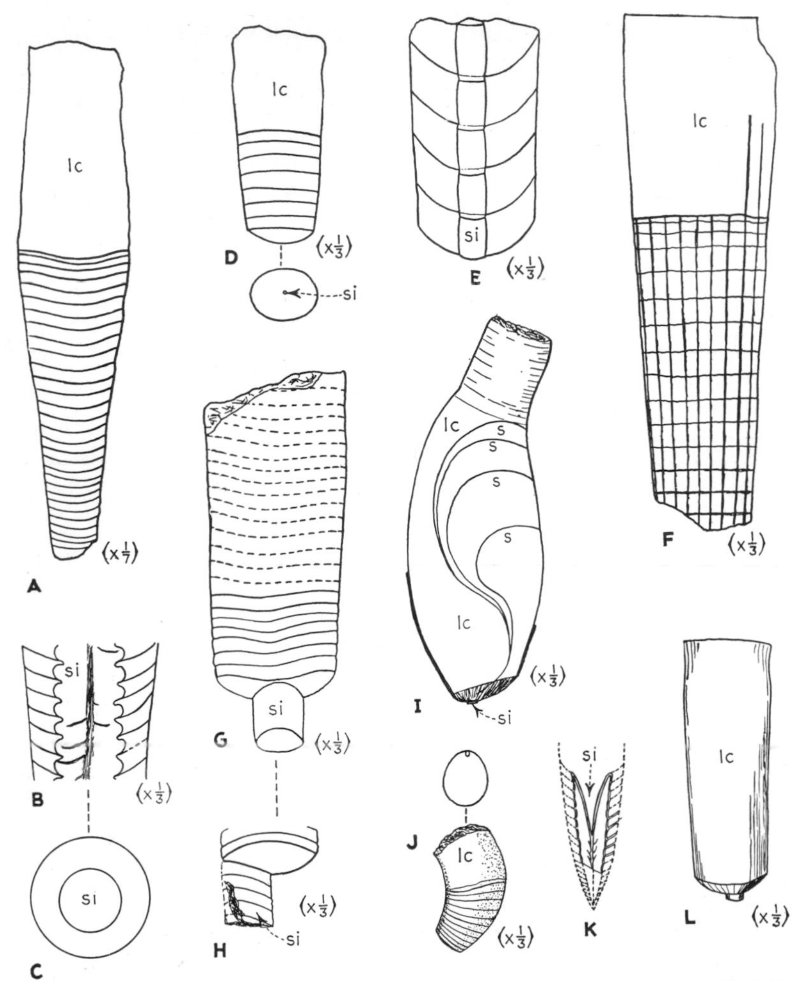

Fig. 142.—Fossil cephalopods. *A. Actinoceras beloitense* from the Middle Ordovician of Ontario. A filling of the shell showing most of the living chamber and a number of the camerae. *B–C.* Longitudinal and transverse sections of *Actinoceras centrale*, from the Middle Ordovician of New York, showing the nature of the siphuncle and the curvature of the septal necks. *D.* Filling of the shell of *Orthoceras wilmingtonense*, from the Upper Silurian of Ohio, showing most of the living chamber and a few camerae. *E.* Longitudinal section of *Orthoceras whitfieldi*, from the Silurian of Ohio, showing the nature of the siphuncle. *F. Kionoceras strix*, from the Silurian of northern Indiana, showing part of the living chamber and several camerae. *G–H. Endoceras subannulatum*, from the Middle Ordovician of Wisconsin, showing the nature of the siphuncle and its relation to the septa. *I. Ascoceras bohemicum*, from the Silurian of Bohemia, showing the living chamber restricted by the curved saddles. *J. Oncoceras pandion* from the Middle Ordovician of Wisconsin. *K.* Diagrammatic reconstruction of *Piloceras amplum* (Lower Ordovician) showing the conical nature

termed *ammonite* because of its prevalence among ammonoid shells, both lobes and saddles become minutely crenulated, in some species so intensely as to give to the suture a dendritic or mosslike appearance (Fig. 140 *J*). Shells with ammonite sutures appear first in the Triassic and disappear with the extinction of the Ammonoidea at the close of the Cretaceous.

THE SIPHUNCLE.—The siphuncle shows great variation in position, size, structure, and shape. It may be central, eccentric, ventral, or dorsal. The first three positions are common, but the last is rare. In coiled forms the siphuncle is usually in a ventral position. It is often of small diameter, commonly less than one-tenth the diameter of the shell, but it may be nearly as large as the shell, in which case the septa are reduced to narrow shelves around the periphery. The former is shown in some species of *Orthoceras* (Figs. 141, 142); the latter, in *Endoceras* (Fig. 142).

The septal necks or siphuncular funnels are usually short and incomplete and do not extend to the preceding septum. In the mature stages of certain primitive forms and in the early stages of many more advanced shells, however, they extend from one septum to the next, thereby forming an unbroken siphuncular tube which connects the living chamber with the first chamber succeeding the protoconch. Septa in which only septal necks are present are said to be *retrosiphonate*, because the necks always extend backward toward the earlier chambers of the shell. Shells in which the septa are retrosiphonate are described as *monochoanitic*. Collars may surround the siphuncular perforation on the apertural side of the septum and extend forward toward the aperture. Septa which have collars only are said to be *prosiphonate*, and shells with such septa are *chloiochoanitic;* those with both septal necks and collars are termed *transitional*, and the shell is said to be *diplochoanitic*.

Nautiloids, except for *Nothoceras* and its allies, are retrosiphonate, whereas ammonoids may exhibit one or all types in the same shell. Retrosiphonate septa are characteristic of the middle Paleozoic ammonoids, transitional ones occur in some

of the siphuncle. *L*. Filling of the living chamber of *Geisonoceras wauwatosense* from the Silurian of Wisconsin. *lc*, living chamber; *s*, saddle; *si*, siphuncle. (*A–E after Foerste and Teichert; F, L after Foerste; G–H after Whitfield; I after Barrande; J after Clarke; K after Dawson.*)

late Paleozoic species, and prosiphonate ones are found in Mesozoic forms. Most Triassic and all Jurassic and Cretaceous species exhibit all three stages—retrosiphonate in the youthful part of the shell, transitional at a later period, and prosiphonate in maturity and senility.

In some species the siphuncle is uniformly tubular between the septa, and in others inflated. In the latter case the siphuncle resembles a string of beads (Fig. 142). These interseptal expansions may be quite small, as in many orthoceratites, but they are often in the form of large disks which may extend halfway to the margin of the shell. In shells with continuous siphuncular tubes the interior of the tube in some forms is filled by a series of conical laminae, producing a cone-in-cone structure. An axial tube, the so-called *prosiphon* or *endosiphon*, perforates the apices of the cones and thus keeps the siphuncle open. Numerous other deposits may be made within the siphuncle so as nearly to fill it, but sufficient space is always left for the endosiphon.

In life the siphuncle is occupied by a fleshy, tubular prolongation of the visceral region known as the *siphon*. This fleshy tube is thought by some to represent a remnant from the early developmental stages of nautiloid evolution before the septa were fully developed and when the visceral cone of the animal was much larger. The siphon was not lost, it appears, because at times it functioned to deposit shell substance in the camerae, thereby decreasing the buoyancy of the shell, and, furthermore, at all times it served effectively to anchor the body of the animal to its shell. The latter function is an important one, since it allows the animal to be less firmly attached to the wall of the living chamber. This is a real advantage because during growth the animal needs to move forward as the apertural margins are extended and new septa are added behind.

The calcareous deposits in the empty chambers around and within the siphuncle were added by the siphon and almost certainly served to reduce the buoyancy of the shell, thereby rendering it more easily manageable in the water. In the modern *Nautilus* there seems to be no connection between the animal and the empty chambers, in spite of Verrill's statement that sea water could readily pass into and out from the chambers. While it may be possible for fluid to enter the chambers, it has not yet been demonstrated that either living or fossil cephalopods can or could regulate contents of the empty chambers by means of the siphon.

THE APERTURE.—The terminal opening of the shell may be circular, oval, chordate, or irregular (Fig. 141). The edges of the shell are almost always uneven, being somewhat convex at the sides and slightly concave at the top and bottom (dorsal and ventral). The marginal convexities which project forward are known as *crests*, and the concavities as *sinuses*. Most shells have a dorsal sinus, a lateral crest on each side, and a ventral sinus below. The ventral sinus is frequently referred to as the *hyponomic sinus*, since this part of the shell is immediately below the hyponome. The absence of a hyponomic sinus has usually been interpreted to mean that the hyponome was wanting or greatly reduced, but such a view is difficult to maintain. Shells having the ventral sinus on the arched external side are said to be *exogastric;* those, like *Phragmoceras* (Fig. 141 *J–K*), having the sinus on the concave internal side are described as *endogastric*. The former is the more common condition.

In many genera the apertural opening became more or less restricted (Fig. 141). This type of opening is conspicuous in the nautiloid families of *Oncoceratidae*, *Poterioceratidae*, *Trimeroceratidae*, and *Phragmoceratidae*. In some species of these families the aperture was reduced to a mere slit. In *Mandaloceras* the very small aperture is shaped like the letter T, with the hyponomic sinus at the base of the T. In *Phragmoceras* it was constricted laterally, leaving a rather large opening on the ventral side and a smaller one on the dorsal, with a narrow slit connecting the two openings. Such restriction of the apertural margins has been interpreted in various ways. It probably aided in keeping the animal in the shell, and since some of the shells possessing restricted openings are thought to have floated in the water with the aperture downward, it might well have served as a support below the body and thus have been a structure of great value. The vital parts of the animal were also protected by restriction of the opening. On the other hand, restriction of the aperture limited motion, almost certainly interfered with locomotion, and necessitated using food of smaller dimensions. The restriction of the aperture seems to have taken place only after the shell had attained maturity.

CHARACTERISTICS OF INTERNAL SHELLS.—Two general shapes prevail among the few internal shells found in cephalopods.

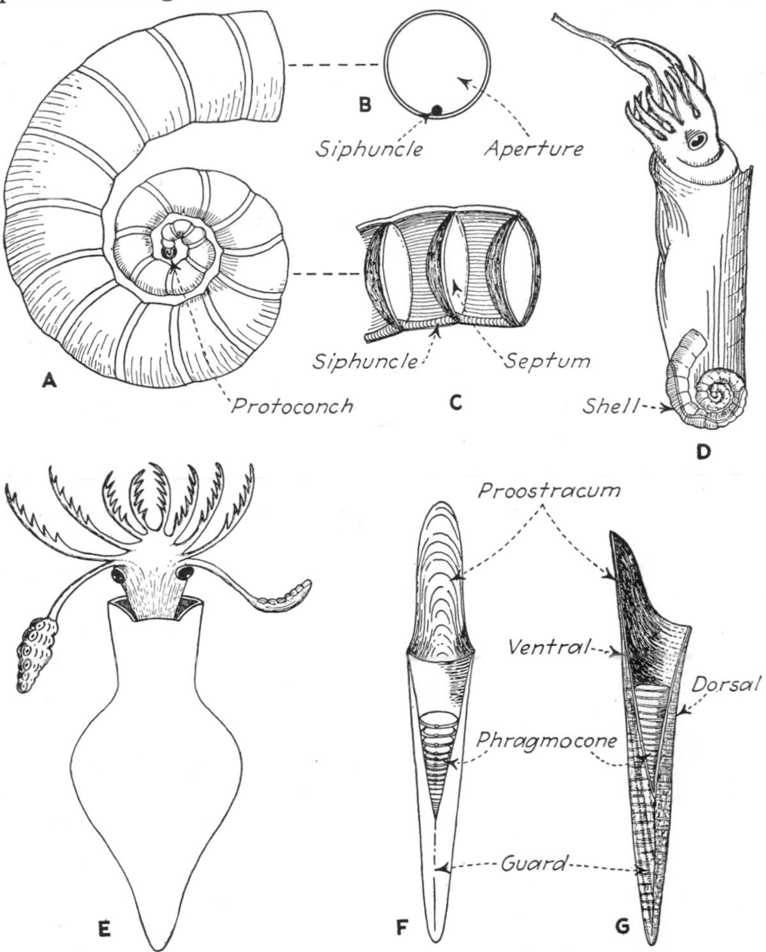

FIG. 143.—Belemnoidea. *A–C. Spirula peronii*, a modern belemnoid from the Atlantic Ocean: *A*, The complete shell, a gyrocone, which is internal as shown in *D*; *B*, Apertural view showing the position of the siphuncle; *C*, Small portion of the shell sectioned to show the septa, concave to the aperture, and the position of the siphuncle. *D. Spirula australis*, a modern species showing the position of the shell in relation to the remainder of the organism. *E*. Restoration of the animal of a belemnite. *F*. Diagram of the complete shell of *Belemnites paxillosus* from the Jurassic. *G*. Diagram of a complete belemnite shell showing the several characteristic structures. (*D. after Wright; E–G after Phillips.*)

Spirula, a genus of Belemnoidea, has a planospiral, chambered shell coiled in a gyroconical manner (Fig. 143 *A–D*). The septa are perforated by a siphuncle, as in *Nautilus*, but the initial chamber of *Spirula*, unlike that of *Nautilus*, is dilated into a sphere and is separated by a constriction from the succeeding chamber. It has passing through it a *prosiphon* which is not continuous with the siphuncle. *Spirula* also differs from *Nautilus* in the character of the aperture.

The second type of internal shell is found in *Belemnoteuthis* from the Cretaceous and *Belemnites* from the Jurassic and Cretaceous (Fig. 112 *F*). The shell of the first genus is composed of three parts—a solid apical structure of conical shape, the *guard*, within which is a straight, chambered shell, the *phragmocone*, with a small tubular siphuncle; and extending upward from the phragmocone a leaf-shaped or spatulate plate known as the *proostracum*. The phragmocone corresponds to the complete chambered shells of the nautiloids and ammonoids, and the simple sutures of the shell suggest derivation from some nautiloid ancestor. The shell of *Belemnites* (Fig. 143 *E–G*) has a large cigar-shaped guard which in very well-preserved specimens has in the larger end a small, conical, chambered phragmocone provided with a siphonal canal. The phragmocone is straight on the ventral side, curved on the dorsal. There is a proostracum extending upward from the dorsal margin. The chief difference in the two shells described above lies in the relative sizes of guard and phragmocone. *Belemnoteuthis* has a small guard and large phragmocone; *Belemnites* shows the reverse. The rare Upper Triassic genus, *Aulacoceras*, has a small guard that incloses only the apex of a phragmocone which is twice as long as the guard. There is no proostrocum. In still other internal shells the guard and phragmocone are either absent or undifferentiated, and the "shell" consists essentially of a large proostracum.

It may be suggested that an orthoceratite was the ancestor of the naked forms and, further, that in certain shelled forms the overgrowth of the mantle caused the shell to become internal and to be modified in order to meet the new conditions. *Aulacoceras* is suggested as a transitional form from *Orthoceras* to *Belemnites*, and it is further suggested that some form of *Belemnites*, through the loss of the proostracum and the accompanying enlargement of the phragmocone, led to *Spirula*. Possibly loss of guard and phragmocone and enlargement of proostracum may have produced the Sepioidea also.

Classification.—Several classifications of the Cephalopoda have been proposed. One, based on the number of gills, includes two subclasses—Tetrabranchia (Tetrabranchiata) and Dibranchia (Dibranchiata). The first subclass is composed of the orders Nautiloidea and Ammonoidea, although it is not known definitely that the ammonoids had four gills. The orders Belemnoidea, Sepioidea, and Octopoda are included in the Dibranchia.

A second classification is based mainly on the supposed time of appearance of the group. The first subclass, Protocephalopoda, includes the orders Nautiloidea and Ammonoidea and hence is equivalent to the Tetrabranchia. The second subclass, Metacephalopoda, includes the orders Octopoda and Decapoda (Sepioidea, Belemnoidea) and is equivalent to the Dibranchia.

A third classification, and the one used in this work, includes three subclasses—*Nautiloidea* (Tetrabranchia), *Ammonoidea*, and *Coleoidea* (Belemnoidea, Dibranchia). This arrangement has the advantage of not making any commitment as to the number of gills in the extinct Ammonoidea and also in not using an ordinal name for a subclass name (Coleoidea rather than Belemnoidea).

Subclass Nautiloidea

The Nautiloidea are tetrabranchiate cephalopods which secrete an external, straight, curved or coiled calcareous shell divided into chambers by simple, retrosiphonate septa. The sutures are simple and belong to the nautiloid or orthoceratite type. The gills in living forms are paired, the head is surrounded by about 90 filament-like arms, and there is generally an incomplete hyponomic funnel. The body of the animal is attached to the shell by muscles and by means of the fleshy siphon which extends backward from the living chamber through the septal perforations to, but not into, the protoconch (Fig. 137). The apex of the shell is cup or saucer shaped. Apertures as a rule have a ventral hyponomic sinus and a dorsal crest. Septal necks are usually well developed. The subclass has been divided into the following five orders: *Holochoanites*, *Mixochoanites*, *Schistochoanites*, *Orthochoanites*, and *Cyrtochoanites*. These will be considered in detail immediately following the consideration of the living nautiloids.

There are only three living species of this important subclass of cephalopods, and all belong to the single genus *Nautilus*, but over 2,500 fossil species have been described from strata ranging in age from the Cambrian to the Recent.

The Living Nautilus.—The soft parts of *Nautilus* consist of a somewhat cylindrical, baglike body which is domal at one end and tentacle bearing at the other (Fig. 137 *B*). The entire body is covered by a mantle over which is a thin cuticle of horny substance. The mouth, located in the middle of the anteriorly situated head, is surrounded by about 90 filamentous tentacles that are placed upon lobes. The basal parts of these tenacles can be retracted into fleshy sockets or sheaths. One pair on the dorsal side is fused to form a crude *hood* which covers the head of the animal when it is withdrawn into the shell. On the ventral side just beneath the tentacles is a thick, muscular, leaflike hyponome or ambulatory funnel which connects the gill cavity with the exterior (Fig. 112 *E*). It is contracted anteriorly and expanded where it enters the cavity. Water is slowly admitted into the gill cavity and then expelled. If the expulsion is violent, the animal is rapidly propelled backward. The eyes are situated on each side of the head near the bases of the lateral tentacles. The structure of the eyes is primitive and much simpler than in the Coleoidea. The mouth is equipped with a pair of powerful horny jaws or beaks with calcified points, which are placed one above the other in dorsoventral position. There are also a fleshy tongue and a radula armed with numerous rows of plates and hooks. There are two pairs of feather-like gills which are situated at the base of the hyponome on either side of the anus. On the posterior side of the body the mantle is produced into a hollow siphon which connects the body with the apex of the shell. This siphon contains blood vessels only and is surrounded by a thin sheath of horny matter. The intestinal tract is U-shaped, with an expanded gastric portion. The anal opening lies beneath the mouth toward the anterior part of the body, and just posterior to the anus is the single or double opening of the sexual organs. The nervous system consists of a large cerebral ganglion above the esophagus, a circumesophageal ring connecting the cerebral ganglion with a subesophageal ganglion, and nerve cords extending backward from the lower ganglion. There is a heart and a circulatory system. The life history of *Nautilus* is unknown, except for a few inferences that can be drawn from the study of the shells.

The animal is attached to the shell by two oval muscles situated on either side of the mantle. These muscles make shallow impressions on the shell and are connected both dorsally and ventrally by a band of fibers known as the *annulus*. A shallow impression on the shell may also be made by this structure. Posteriorly the body of the animal is held in the living chamber of the shell by the siphon.

The shell of *Nautilus* is calcareous and is composed of an external, laminated and irregularly prismatic layer and an internal mother-of-pearl layer, both of aragonite. The shell is planospirally coiled and may be involute or imperfectly involute with an umbilicus. The body of the animal resides in the large living chamber, and the remainder of the shell posteriorly is divided into small chambers or camerae. Each chamber is only a fraction of the length of the living chamber, and each represents a part of the living chamber that was partitioned off by the growth of a septum as the shell grew forward. The simple septa, which join the shell along a gently curving suture, are concave toward the aperture. They are perforated by the siphuncle, and septal necks form an interrupted or continuous siphuncular tube. This is occupied by the siphon, which ends blindly in the *caecum*. The margin of the aperture is entire, more or less oval in outline, and undulatory. There are a ventral hyponomic sinus, a dorsal sinus, and a lateral crest on each side.

The first half of the initial whorl of the shell is somewhat different from what follows. It is not closely coiled, so that there is a minute *umbilical perforation*. A similar perforation occurs in most coiled nautiloid shells, although it is often concealed by the later whorls. The first two septa are different from all succeeding ones. The first septum has no perforation or septal neck but only a curved depression, known as the *septal caecum*, against which the caecum of the siphuncle impinges. The second septum reaches back almost to the first. The terminal chamber represents the first camera succeeding the initial horny protoconch. It is spheroidal and bears a scar which is thought to mark the place of attachment of the protoconch.

ORDER HOLOCHOANITES[1]

The shell of the Holochoanites is an orthocone, cyrtocone, or gyrocone. The septal necks extend from the septum of origin to or beyond the preceding septum. The siphuncle is generally large and more or less filled with calcareous conical sheaths centrally perforated by an endosiphon. There are no calcareous fillings in the camerae. The order includes the most primitive of the nautiloids and is confined almost entirely to the Ordovician, although a few forms survive into but not beyond the Silurian. The relation of the earliest cephalopod (*Volborthella* from the Lower Cambrian) to Holochoanites has not yet been determined. *Endoceras* and *Piloceras,* both from the Ordovician, are representative genera (Fig. 142).

ORDER MIXOCHOANITES[2]

Mixochoanite shells are orthocones or cyrtocones with expanded living chambers and contracted apertures. There is a series of vacant chambers without siphuncular connection dorsal to the large living chamber. The septa are generally oblique to the axis of the shell. The siphuncle in specialized forms has short, straight septal necks in the young stages, but in the adult shell collars are built around the siphuncular perforation, a development also found in some goniatites. The order appears in the Upper Ordovician and disappears in the Silurian. *Ascoceras* is a typical genus.

ORDER SCHISTOCHOANITES[3]

The Schistochoanites include orthocones and cyrtocones in which the septal necks, usually more or less imperfect, are present on the internal side and absent or split on the outer side. The

[1] Holochoanites—Gr. *holos,* entire + *choane,* funnel; referring to the septal necks which reach from the septum of origin to or beyond the preceding septum.

[2] Mixochoanites—Gr. *mixos,* a mixing + *choane,* funnel; referring to the irregular character of the septal necks.

[3] Schistochoanites—Gr. *schizo,* cleave + *choane,* funnel; referring to the cleft frequently present in the septal necks.

order is confined to the Ordovician. *Conoceras* is a typical genus.

ORDER ORTHOCHOANITES[1]

Shells of the Orthochoanites show great range in coiling. Orthocones, cyrtocones, gyrocones, and nautilocones are common; trochocones are rare. In a few genera (*Lituites*) there is uncoiling in the adult stage. The septal necks range from tubular to slightly nummuloidal and are generally longer and straighter than in the Cyrtochoanites, and the posterior ends of the funnels are never bent sharply outward as in that group. Most of the nautiloids belong to this order, which has the longest range of any of the subclass (Ordovician to Recent). Representative genera are *Orthoceras* (Ordovician to Triassic), *Kionoceras* (Silurian to Carboniferous), *Lituites* (Ordovician), and *Nautilus* (Jurassic to Recent) (Figs. 139 *D*, 141 *A–D*, 142).

ORDER CYRTOCHOANITES[2]

The shells of this order range from orthocones to nautilocones, and many are variously ornamented with ribs, annulations, and nodes. The sutures are very simple, and the septal necks are generally short and commonly bent outward or crumpled. The siphuncle is simple, nummuloidal or complex, and the order contains all the nautiloids with beaded siphuncles. Of the 10 families 4 have shells with restricted apertures. The order ranges from the Ordovician to the Pennsylvanian. The Upper Cambrian *Plectronoceras* may belong to the order, but the relations have not been definitely determined. Representative genera are *Actinoceras* (Ordovician to Pennsylvania), *Oncoceras* (Ordovician), *Mandaloceras* (Silurian), and *Phragmoceras* (Silurian) (Figs. 141, 142).

Subclass Ammonoidea

The Ammonoidea comprise a large group of complex extinct cephalopods, about which very little concerning the soft parts is

[1] Orthochoanites—Gr. *orthos*, straight + *choane*, funnel; referring to the generally straight character of the septal necks.

[2] Cyrtochoanites—Gr. *cyrto*, bent + *choane*, funnel; referring to the fact that the septal necks are bent outward or are crumpled.

known. The shells are in the form of bactriticones, mimocones, dactyliocones, ammoniticones, and turriliticones. The septa are usually considerably crumpled, the sutures are complex, and the apertures are closed by a single horny plate—the *anaptychus*—or by two calcareous plates forming the *aptychus* (Fig. 144). The siphuncle of young forms is larger in proportion to the size of the entire shell and nearer the center than in the Nautiloidea. The earlier species have retrosiphonate shells; those from the Pennsylvanian exhibit transitional siphuncles in some forms; and Permian species are in some cases prosiphonate. Most Triassic and all Jurassic and Cretaceous genera have chloiochoanitic siphuncles. Most ammonoids do not have an umbilical perforation, and the general shape of the shells differs from that among the Nautiloidea in being thinner and more discoidal. There are also numerous straight shells among the Ammonoidea. Apertures may be modified in a few families.

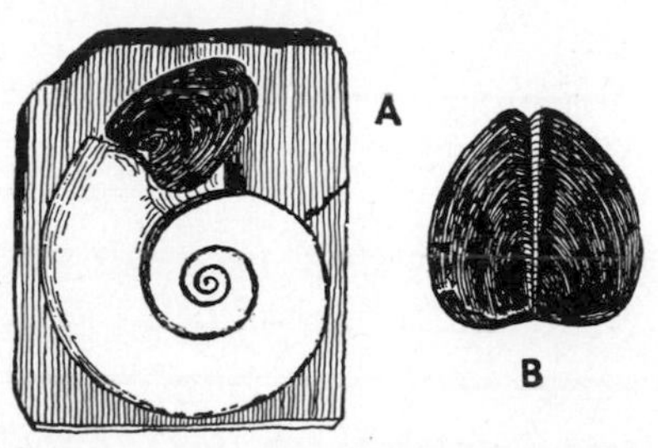

FIG. 144.—*A. Aptychus carinatus* lying in the body chamber of an ammonite. *B.* The *Aptychus* apart from the shell. (*After Wright.*)

The first representatives of the Ammonoidea appear in the Upper Silurian, and the last become extinct toward the close of the Cretaceous. Individuals are extremely numerous in the European Triassic and Jurassic and to a lesser degree in North American strata of that age, but in the Cretaceous they are extremely abundant throughout the world. Fossil ammonoids are among the most valuable of index fossils.

No permanent classification of the Ammonoidea seems yet to have been worked out. The older classification, based on the type of suture (goniatite, ceratite, and ammonite), is fundamental, but it is difficult to establish sharp lines of division because of the gradual transition of one sutural type into another. By some authors the position of the siphuncle is considered as a basis for dividing the subclass into *Intrasiphonata* (dorsal siphuncle) and *Extrasiphonata* (ventral siphuncle). The former contains the single family Clymeniidae; the latter contains the 31 other families.

ORDER INTRASIPHONATA[1]

The siphuncle in the Intrasiphonata occupies a dorsal position, the sutures are simple and more or less transitional between the nautiloids and the goniatites, and the shells are smooth or spiny ammoniticones. The single genus *Clymenia* is confined to the Devonian (Fig. 139 *E*).

ORDER EXTRASIPHONATA[2]

Nearly all ammonoid shells belong to this order, and they possess the features of the subclass as described above. The siphuncle is ventral, the sutures are complex (goniatite, ceratite, and ammonite), and the shells range through all types of coiling. The first representatives appear in the late Silurian, and the order became extinct at the end of the Cretaceous. Goniatite sutures are illustrated on *Aganides* (Mississippian); ceratite, on *Ceratites* (Triassic); ammonite, on *Placenticeras* from the Cretaceous, and *Baculites* from the Jurassic. Other representative genera are *Trachyceras* (Triassic), *Hoplites*, *Scaphites*, *Turrilites*, *Ancyloceras*, and *Hamites* (Cretaceous) (Figs. 139, 140).

Subclass Coleoidea (Dibranchia)

The Coleoidea include naked or shell-bearing cephalopods with a single pair of gills and 8 or 10 sucker-bearing arms. The hyponome forms a complete tube, and there are an ink gland and a duct. If a shell is present, it is usually internal; but if external, it is not septate. The subclass may be divided into the three orders of *Belemnoidea*, *Sepioidea*, and *Octopoda*.

ORDER BELEMNOIDEA

This order includes the most primitive members of the subclass and is the only one of paleontologic importance. The belemnoids appear suddenly in the Triassic, reach their apex in the middle of the Mesozoic, and then gradually decline to the Present with but a single species of *Spirula* remaining.

[1] Intrasiphonata—L. *intra*, within + Gr. *siphon;* referring to the dorsal position of the siphon.

[2] Extrasiphonata—L. *extra*, without + Gr. *siphon;* referring to the ventral position of the siphon.

In life they are thought to have closely resembled a modern squid or cuttlefish. The young secreted a straight or loosely coiled chambered shell which became internal through overgrowth of the mantle. Further growth differentiated the shell into the phragmocone, proostracum, and guard. The proostracum is commonly missing in fossil forms, but in one family (Belemnoteuthidae) the guard is undeveloped, and the shell is much like the pen of modern Sepioidea. In the single living species *Spirula* (Fig. 143 *A–D*) the phragmocone is a cyrtocone or gyrocone, but the shell lacks both guard and proostracum, though a Tertiary genus *Spirulirostra* had both structures. *Belemnites* (Fig. 143 *E–G*) from the Jurassic and Cretaceous is an important fossil genus.

ORDER SEPIOIDEA

The order Sepioidea includes the squids and cuttlefish and hence most living cephalopods. The shell is internal and consists essentially of a horny or calcareous spatulate *pen* which acts as a stiffening axis for the body (Figs. 112 *F*, 145). This pen may have a small, pointed *mucro* at the small end, from which the broader part of the shell extends. The pen of the Sepioidea is the cuttlebone of bird cages and is sometimes known as a *sepion* or *gladius*. Anteriorly on the pen there is a series of thin, shelly laminae which are homologous with the septa of the externally shelled cephalopods. The pen corresponds to the proostracum in the Belemnoidea. Neither guard nor phragmocone is differentiated in the sepioid shell.

The squids differ from *Nautilus* in having a single pair of gills instead of two pairs and in having 10 arms instead of a much larger number. The hyponomic funnel is a closed tube rather than an infold of the mantle. All living squids have an ink sac connected with the lower intestine near the anus. The ink is discharged into the gill cavity and thence through the hyponomic funnel to the exterior where it serves as a "smoke screen" under cover of which the animal can escape. Rarely the ink sac is preserved. The arms are provided with suckers or hooks, and two of them are much longer and more slender than the other eight. The lower surface of a sucker is cup shaped and has a central perforation, and the margins in some cases are provided with sharp teeth or horny hooks (Fig. 145 *C*). There are two horny jaws in the same relative position as in *Nautilus* (Fig. 112 *F*). The eyes are large and more complex than in

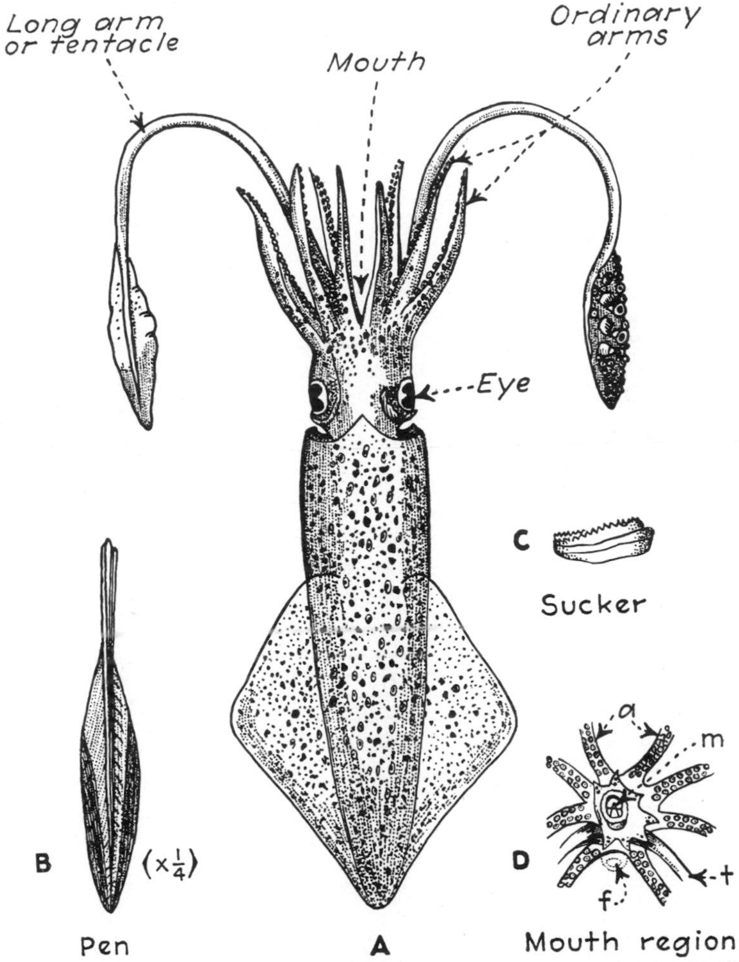

FIG. 145.—A modern cuttlefish, *Loligo*. *A*. The complete animal. *B*. The internal "skeleton" or "pen." *C*. Lateral view of one of the small suckers, showing the horny hooks surrounding the margin. *D*. View of the mouth region showing the mouth (*m*), funnel (*f*), bases of the arms (*a*) and tentacles (*t*). (*From Nicholson and Lydekker, with slight modifications; B after Woodward.*)

Nautilus, and the head is much better differentiated. The shell is either completely internal or incompletely so, as in *Spirula*.

The earliest representatives appear in the Jurassic, and during the Mesozoic the sepioids seem to have been similar to living species. The order is of no stratigraphic importance.

ORDER OCTOPODA

The Octopoda comprise the notorious octopuses or devilfish (Fig. 146). The body is shorter and rounder than in either of the preceding orders and is provided with eight sucker-bearing

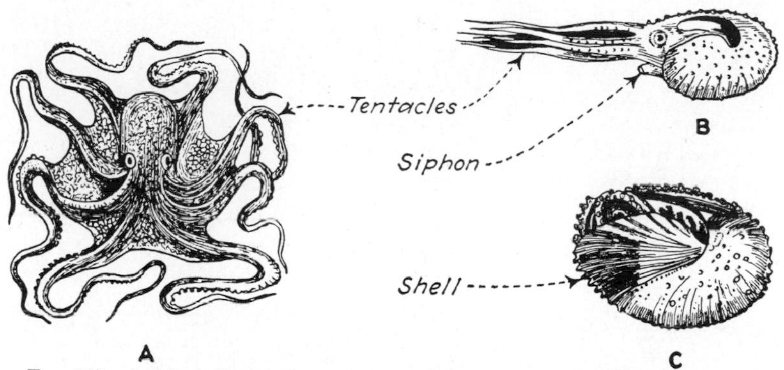

Fig. 146.—Modern Octopoda. *A. Octopus vulgaris* showing the nature of the body and the eight, sucker-bearing tentacles. *B. Argonauta argo*, the female in swimming position, with the shell which serves as a brood pouch. *C.* The animal withdrawn into the shell. (*After Wright.*)

arms or tentacles of equal length. There is no true shell among the octopods, but the two dorsal arms and the mantle of the female *Argonauta* (Fig. 146 *B–C*) secrete an unchambered, spirally coiled calcareous shell which serves as a brood pouch. This type of shell is unique among the Mollusca and is not homologous with that of other cephalopods or for that matter of any other mollusk. The earliest known fossil octopod occurs in the Upper Cretaceous.

Geologic History. Ontogeny and Evolution.—Knowledge of the life history of *Nautilus* is limited, because the animal has very rarely been taken or studied alive. The eggs are known to be extruded through the hyponome, but the subsequent history is unknown. Squids and devilfish lay their eggs either singly or in clusters on various objects projecting above the sea bottom, such as rocks, coral heads, etc. These hatch and develop into embryonic cephalopods, but little is known about them.

The cephalopods seem closest to the gastropods, which they resemble in possessing a distinct head, specialized sense organs, and a radula. They may have branched from some primitive gastropod stem, of which the foot developed so as to surround the mouth and at the same time divided to form lobes. These modifications would not have been difficult.

Lankester suggests that the archetypal mollusk had a straight intestinal tube, with an anterior mouth, a posterior anus and gills adjacent to each other, a well-developed ventral foot, and a small conical shell in dorsal position (Fig. 110). Beginning with such a simple organism certain modifications were necessary for it to become a primitive cephalopod. It is known that the anus and gills do migrate forward, as observed in primitive gastropods, thereby bringing the two structures below the mouth and toward the anterior side. Such modification would make it readily possible for the foot to surround the mouth. The shell might at the same time become narrowed at the aperture and increase in height. It may be assumed that the foot did not at first completely surround the mouth but gradually migrated so that the oral part became lobelike, with the posterior part retaining its original function of crawling. The migration of the gills and anus to a forward position gradually led to the mantle around them assuming a leaflike form and finally becoming a hyponomic funnel. The intake and expulsion of water were necessary to bring oxygen to the gills, as is still the case in many living gastropods. Rapid expulsion of the water developed the characteristic rocket-like locomotion of the cephalopods, and it appears likely that it was first developed as a by-product of the method of respiration.

The narrowing of the shell from a dorsal umbrella-like covering to an inclosing cone necessitated migration of the animal outward as it increased in size. Since the mantle of the living *Nautilus* is covered with a cartilaginous film, it may be assumed that a similar condition existed in the ancestors of the cephalopods. Calcification of this film produced a septum which cut off a small chamber in the terminal part of the shell. The septa at first were conical, as they are in the Ordovician *Endoceras,* and correspondingly a conical part of the animal body extended to the apex of the original conical shell. This visceral cone gradually became restricted through deposition of conical calcareous laminae—the primitive septa—about it, so that only a tubular extension of the body, the siphon, remained. The septa increased in width, took position directly across the shell, developed septal necks to sheath the siphon when the visceral cone disappeared, and made unnecessary further retention of the conical laminae. Coiling later developed in some shells, and there was also great increase in size. The large forms could not maintain themselves and ultimately became extinct. Crenulation on the septal margins developed in the Upper Silurian, producing the goniatite type of suture. By the Pennsylvanian this type had evolved into the more advanced ceratite suture, and the latter gave way to the ammonite suture in the late Permian. It is thought that some as yet undiscovered orthoceratites of the late Paleozoic initiated envelopment of the shell by the mantle. Ultimately the shell became completely internal, as in *Belemnites.* The naked and shell-less *Octopus* appears to belong somewhere in this evolutionary series.

The life history and the phylogeny of a cephalopod in terms of shell development, from the time when the protoconch was secreted to the time of death in maturity or senility, are often clearly shown in well-preserved shells. By starting at the aperture and breaking away the wall of the shell at the successive septa there are revealed the different stages in the racial history. As progress is made toward the apex, the septa, sutures, siphuncle, ornamentation, and character of whorls change from complexity toward simplicity. Each change corresponds to a stage not only in the shell itself but in the developmental history of the race to which it belongs, thereby illustrating the principle that "ontogeny recapitulates phylogeny." If the shell of *Placenticeras,* a Cretaceous form, is broken back as described above, there appear in succession features in its shell which were possessed by the ancestors that lived during earlier periods of geologic time. By examining the shells which lived during these earlier periods, with the knowledge of the structures that they should exhibit, it is sometimes possible to identify the probable ancestor from which a given species evolved. Thus the changes taking place in a single shell during one lifetime epitomize the changes in a race through the ages.

The embryonic shell of the cephalopod, known as the protoconch, is chitinous in *Nautilus* and hence is lost in fossil specimens, though a scar may be left in the posterior wall of the initial camera showing its place of attachment. The protoconch among the ammonoids is calcareous, of large size, ovoid or spherical in shape, and constricted where it is closed by the first septum. The postembryonic part of the shell is sometimes termed the *conch.* A shell consisting of the first few chambers added during infancy is said to be in the *nepionic* stage; additional chambers built during adolescence bring the shell to the *neanic* stage; and mature shells in which the generic characters are differentiated are said to be in the *ephebic* stage. Senile or old shells are in the *gerontic* stage and are often of great evolutionary interest, since they may skip some of the ephebic characters, revert to earlier characters, or develop a variety of new bizarre features such as spiny ornamentation, uncoiling, etc. In a single shell the various growth stages pass gradually into each other, just as the racial history very probably passed by general modifications from one stage to the next. In the genus *Placenticeras* the nepionic shell may show close resemblance to some mature Paleozoic species, the neanic shell may resemble a Triassic or Jurassic form, and the Cretaceous form is not attained until the ephebic stage has been reached.

ECOLOGY.—About 150 species of living cephalopods are known, and fully 10,000 fossil species have been described. Of the latter about two-thirds are ammonoids; one-third, nautiloids. Living cephalopods are exclusively marine, living in the warmer waters of the world, and there is no evidence to suggest that they ever lived in fresh waters. The three species of *Nautilus* are found only in the area between the Fiji Islands and the Philippines, living near the bottom in waters up to 550 m. (1,800 ft.) deep. They are believed to breed at these depths. They come into shallow water only at night. The larger squids are pelagic, spending their lives swimming at various depths, and many forms such as *Sepia* and *Loligo* do not live far from land. The ancient squids (*Belemnites, et al.*) seem to have lived in both shallow and deep waters. Squids are gregarious and swim in the open seas and shoreward waters in vast numbers, pursued by whales and fish which feed upon them. The cod fishermen of the north Atlantic are well aware of the relation between the squids and the cod and express it by the laconic "Plenty squids, plenty cod." They use the common squid of the Gulf of St. Lawrence as bait, and their catch may be more or less proportional to the quantity of squid that they can obtain. Storms sometimes destroy squids by the thousands. In July, 1929, a storm of only ordinary magnitude along the Labrador coast of Quebec washed squids ashore in Betchewan Bay in such large numbers that fishermen gathered them by boatloads. Cephalopods are commonly carnivorous, feeding upon crustaceans and small fish. Some of the octopods feed upon organic debris of the sea bottom. Whether or not extinct forms were carnivorous is unknown, but it is quite likely that some were.

Squids and devilfish are used as food by many people. In the Mediterranean region and in China and Japan they are caught in great numbers for this purpose. Indians dwelling along the Pacific coast in Canada and Alaska are said to use the devilfish for food on many occasions. A rather odd and unexpected use for cephalopods is found among the Plains Indians of Montana and Wyoming. Living over Cretaceous strata, the medicine men collect specimens of the beautifully preserved fossil ammonoids and carry them in their medicine bags as "medicine."

The ink bag present in the squids represents the first known "smoke screen" and shows the great antiquity of one of man's contrivances. Under certain conditions the fluid in the bag is extruded through the hyponome into the face of an attacking animal. The water is so blackened that the pursuer cannot see the pursued, and the latter effects its escape through the rocket-like impulse given it by the expulsion of the "ink." After the bag is emptied, however, some time is required to replenish it; hence, in the meantime, the cephalopod is in the condition of the savage who has shot away all of his arrows.

Besides having developed the first smoke screen and rocket locomotion, cephalopods have been credited with the discovery and use of a third important principle, that illustrated by the submarine, which sinks or rises through a change in content of certain chambers. Crediting this principle to the cephalopods presupposes, naturally, that they were able to replace the gas of the camerae by water, or vice versa, and thereby sink or rise. It has not been established, however, that *Nautilus* can replace the gas of its shell chambers by water, and the same statement can be made with respect to ancient forms. It is altogether possible that many cephalopods increased the specific gravity of the shell so that it was equal to that of water by partially filling the chambers with calcareous matter. With such a shell the animal could then rise or sink by simply adjusting itself to the living chamber.

The octopus or devilfish and the squids have played a somewhat exaggerated role in popular literature, and stories are current describing the horrors of attack on small ships by giant squids and octopuses. One such story pictures a giant squid dragging a small ship beneath the waves and grasping a helpless sailor in its long arms. While their reputation for ferocity is not unmerited, it is rather unlikely that serious damage has ever been done to ships of any size by them. The giant squid of the north Atlantic, *Architeuthis princeps*, with a length exceeding 15 m. (52 ft.), might conceivably damage a small boat and make conditions uncomfortable for those on board, but no recorded and authenticated report of such an event is known to exist. It is altogether possible, furthermore, that individuals swimming in marine waters might be attacked by octopuses.

The chambered *Nautilus* has been described in poetry by Oliver Wendell Holmes, and though the animal is not known to perform all of the activities credited to it by the poet, the description is worthy of quoting:

> This is the ship of pearl, which, poets feign,
> Sails the unshadowed main,—
> The venturous bark that flings
> On the sweet summer wind its purpled wings
> In gulfs enchanted, where the Siren sings,
> And coral reefs lie bare,
> Where the cold sea-maids rise to sun their streaming hair.

The same romantic picture of *Nautilus* rising to the surface of the sea, spreading out some part of its body, and sailing away across the waves appears in Pope's "Essay on Man," in the lines

> Learn of the little Nautilus to sail,
> Spread the thin oar, and catch the driving gale.

These pictures are only imaginary, for no one has ever seen a *Nautilus* perform in the fashion painted by the poets.

With such a group as the cephalopods swarming the seas from the Cambrian to the present time, it is to be expected that during such a long interval of time different members of the class would have become adapted to every marine environment during every period. All other dominant groups of animals whose history is fully known made such adaptations, and it does not seem unreasonable, therefore, to assume that during every period there were planktonic, nektonic, nektonic-planktonic, and benthonic cephalopods. Only one form of marine adaptation seems to have been omitted, that of sessile benthonic life, and even that may have been acquired by the peculiar *Nipponites* from the Upper Cretaceous of Japan. It is almost certain that the foot became adapted for swimming, thus augmenting or displacing the hyponome in that function; that it was modified for crawling on the bottom; and finally that it became vestigial in some forms. Some cephalopods seem to have learned to swim with the shell held in a horizontal position. This is suggested by the calcareous fillings in the empty chambers of *Actinoceras*. Some appear also to have held the shell in an oblique position, and still others carried the shell with the aperture downward. In some forms the shell seems to have been dragged along the bottom, while others carried the structure upon their backs. Shells with streamline contours (*Placenticeras*) were probably swimmers, whereas such clumsy forms as *Mandaloceras* or *Phragmoceras*, both of which had restricted apertures, were almost certainly nektonic-planktonic or entirely planktonic, more or less drifting with the shell in a vertical position and with the apex upward. The slender orthocones, such as *Actinoceras*, appear to have been swimmers; and *Endoceras*, with its large, partly filled siphuncle, may well have had a similar habit. It was probably easier for the latter to float than to drag its large shell over the bottom. Color bands preserved on the surface of some small cyrtocones strongly indicate that the shells were carried in a nearly vertical position.

STRATIGRAPHIC RANGE.—The oldest known cephalopod belongs to the genus *Volborthella* from the Lower Cambrian of the Baltic region. In this genus the shell is an orthocone with a central siphuncle and short, relatively straight septal necks. The next oldest genus is *Plectronoceras*, which occurs in the Upper Cambrian of northeastern China and Manchuria. The shell is a cyrtocone, with the siphuncle situated close to the concave side; and short, septal necks, with lower margins curved strongly outward, are present. *Volborthella* seems to be related to the Holochoanites, and *Plectronoceras* to the Cyrtochoanites, but typical representatives of these orders do not appear until the early Ordovician. The Cambrian genera seem to be more primitive than any of those included in the orders just mentioned, and their exact taxonomic positions are not certain.

Many genera of cephalopods appeared during the Ordovician, and by the close of the period all orders of Nautiloidea had been differentiated. The shells are orthocones, cyrtocones, gyrocones, ophiocones, and nautilicones. No trochocones seem to have been evolved. The Schistochoanites were confined to the Ordovician, and the Holochoanites and Mixochoanites became extinct in the Silurian. The Cyrtochoanites, first appearing in the Ordovician but with an ancestry almost certainly extending into the Cambrian, survive to the Carboniferous. Of all the orders present during the Ordovician only the Orthochoanites have persisted to the present, and but a single genus (*Nautilus*) represented by three species remains.

The majority of Ordovician cephalopods seem to have been straight or only slightly curved; some reached a length of 4½ m. (15 ft.). This length was never again attained by any shelled invertebrate. The large forms disappeared before Silurian time began. The nautiloids attained their greatest diversity during the later Ordovician and the Silurian. Decline set in during the Devonian and continued through the Mississippian. There was a short-lived revival in the Pennsylvanian, but the straight forms were extinct by the close of the Triassic. Five coiled nautiloids have been found in the Triassic, two of which lived into the Jurassic and one into the Tertiary. The single living genus *Nautilus* appeared in the Jurassic. The distribution of the nautiloid families is as follows:

Period	Families	Period	Families
Ordovician	19	Triassic	6
Silurian	24	Jurassic	3
Devonian	19	Cretaceous	2
Mississippian / Pennsylvanian	15	Tertiary	2
Permian	5	Present	1

The first ammonoids appeared in the late Silurian. These have goniatite sutures. There was considerable variety during the Devonian, although specimens are not generally common.

Ceratite sutures appeared in the Pennsylvanian but did not become common until the Permian. True ammonites appeared in the late Permian or early Triassic. The Paleozoic goniatites are small and smooth. The ceratites are much larger, and some are highly ornamented. The first true ammonites are smooth and rotund. Jurassic forms tend to be flattened laterally, and some are highly ornamented. Extreme ornamentation is characteristic of the Cretacous ammonites, and some reached gigantic dimensions, *Pachydiscus septemradensis* from Westphalia being a little more than 2 m. (6 ft. 8 in.) in diameter. The Ammonoidea became extinct at the close of the Cretaceous, but the cause of the extinction is unknown. The 32 families are distributed in geologic time as follows:

Silurian	1	Triassic	29
Devonian	11	Jurassic	22
Mississippian, Pennsylvanian	12	Cretaceous	18
Permian	15		

The earliest Coleoidea appeared in the Triassic in the form of *Aulacoceras*. The Belemnoidea flourished abundantly during the Jurassic but declined at the close and were represented by only two genera in the Tertiary. The single genus *Spirula* lives in present seas. The Sepioidea appeared in the Jurassic and are still abundant. Octopods appeared in the Upper Cretaceous and are common in existing seas.

From the above summary it is clear that there have been two times of great cephalopod evolution—one affecting the Nautiloidea during the Ordovician and Silurian and one concerned with the Ammonoidea during the Triassic, Jurassic, and Cretaceous. The climax for naked forms, such as squids and octopods, cannot yet be determined.

Character of Fossils.—Cephalopoda, particularly the ammonites, are among the most serviceable of index fossils, and they are probably the most satisfactory of all fossils for zoning the Mesozoic.

The earlier Paleozoic specimens are commonly preserved as molds, mud fillings, and casts and more often than not are incomplete and fragmental. Preservation of later Paleozoic forms is somewhat better, but the best preserved shells are found in Mesozoic strata. Exceptionally well-preserved specimens have the shell matter intact, and it is possible to study the evolution of the shell by breaking away the septal partitions.

Only a few nautiloid specimens possessing color patterns have been described. Ammonoids, on the other hand, often show exquisite preservation and for that reason have been intensively studied by students of evolution. Many Coleoidea are well preserved, though the proostracum is frequently missing. Impressions of the fleshy bodies of certain coleoids have been reported, but such occurrences are extremely rare. A few fossil squids have been found in which the contents of the ink sac have become carbonized. This carbonized substance occasionally has been converted into an ink and used to label fossil specimens for museum display. The dental elements and the arm hooks of certain cephalopods, though mainly chitinous, are possible of preservation, though they have not often been reported.

GEOLOGIC HISTORY OF THE MOLLUSCA

Evolution of the Phylum.—All embryonic mollusks pass through a trochophore stage similar to that found in annelid worms. It has been suggested, therefore, that the phylum probably evolved from some primitive annelid group during the later Pre-Cambrian. The primitive shell appears to have been some sort of dorsal shield. In the Amphineura this has become modified into eight articulating plates that are carried on the dorsal part of the body; in the Pelecypoda it has the form of a bivalve shell; in the Scaphopoda it has been modified into a curved, tapering, hollow cone open at both ends; in the Gastropoda the shell consists of a hollow, unchambered cone coiled in some way about an axis; and in the Cephalopoda the coiled cone is chambered. All except the dorsal shield of the Amphineura are obviously only modified forms of a simple, hollow cone.

Two classes of Mollusca sent invaders into the fresh-water habitat, and one of these invaded the land. Throughout geologic time mollusks have belonged largely to the benthos, either as vagrant or as sessile forms. Rarely they adapted themselves to swimming or floating lives. Cephalopods do not seem ever to have invaded brackish or fresh waters successfully, and living forms are physiologically intolerant of brackish water still.

The Amphineura have always been restricted to a sluggish existence on the ocean bottom. Pelecypods and scaphopods have specialized for living partly or completely buried in muds and sands. Gastropods and cephalopods have always maintained more freedom of movement, and some of the latter have become fairly good swimmers.

The earliest cephalopods are simple orthocones and cyrtocones belonging to the Nautiloidea. From these simple-sutured forms the ammonoids seem to have evolved in the middle Paleozoic. They became extinct at the close of the Cretaceous. The origin of the squids and their closest relatives is not certain. They may have evolved from some straight nautiloid stock of the late Paleozoic, perhaps a group which tended toward a somewhat more active swimming habit. Evolution among the Coleoidea has been in the direction of shell atrophy. The mantle overgrew the shell, first secreting a calcareous guard which became prolonged on one side into the proostracum. Gradually the guard and phragmocone were lost, and the shell then consisted mainly of the proostracum (as in living squids); finally this last vestige of a shell was lost, and the animal was totally without a shell structure of any kind, a situation now present in *Octopus*. In the single genus *Spirula* the shell consists entirely of the coiled phragmocone, and this is only in part internal.

Ecology.—No other group of invertebrates except the Arthropoda has ever successfully invaded the wide variety of habitats now occupied by the mollusks. The latter are found in the ocean at all depths and in nearly all latitudes, being benthonic, nektonic, nektonic-planktonic, and planktonic. Burrowers, borers, and commensal and parasitic forms have been evolved, and certain species live underground (30 to 90 cm., *i.e.*, 1 to 3 ft. below the surface) throughout most of life. The brackish-water molluscan group is not large. Some species of land mollusks have been found as far north as 73°30′ in Siberia, where the mean annual temperature is −10°F. and where the range is from 40°F. in July to −30°F. in January. Species may be frozen in ice and still live. They are found also in the Algerian desert, where the temperatures rise to 110°F.; and they have been reported from hot springs, where the waters register from 68 to 122°F. Certain species have been collected from fresh waters at elevations of about 5,480 m. (18,000 ft.) in the Himalayas. The range in pressure experienced by representatives of the phylum is from 6½ lb. at high altitudes to 4½ tons per square inch at great depths.

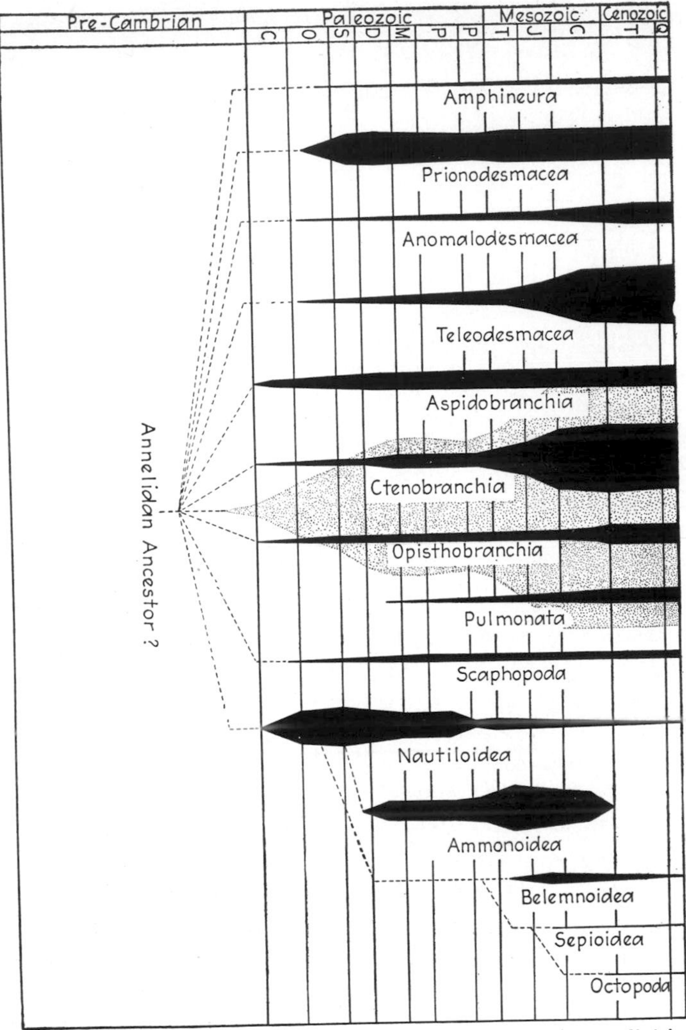

FIG. 147.—Chart showing the geologic history of the different divisions of the Mollusca, based on the number of families as given by Zittel in his "Text-Book of Paleontology." Classes Amphineura and Scaphopoda are not subdivided. Class Cephalopoda is divided into subclasses, and the subclass Coleoidea into orders. Classes Pelecypoda and Gastropoda are subdivided into the respective orders. The width of the band is proportional to the number of families present at any given time. The large central shadow gives an indication of the development of the phylum as a whole throughout geologic time.

Most mollusks are short-lived. Pulmonate gastropods are generally semiannual, though rarely they may reach an age of seven years. Marine Streptoneura live for several years, but marine nudibranchs are "annuals." Pelecypods average three or four years, but certain forms have been known to live twenty years. Cephalopods, so far as known at present, average from four to five years.

Stratigraphic Range.—Amphineura are first represented by fossils in the Ordovician, but at no time are they of much stratigraphic importance (Fig. 147). Marine pelecypods appear in the Upper Cambrian; fresh-water forms seem to have evolved as early as the Devonian; and brackish-water species occur in late Paleozoic strata. Throughout geologic time they have left an important fossil record and since the beginning of the Mesozoic have often occurred in such abundance as to form shell beds or biostromes on the sea floor. *Ostrea, Exogyra, Inoceramus, Chama,* and the various Rudistids are especially noteworthy, in this respect. Marine gastropods appear first in the Lower Cambrian, pulmonate forms developed in the Devonian, and fresh-water species are known from the Jurassic onward. The class as a whole may be approaching its zenith, having increased gradually in the number of families from the Cambrian to the Present. While often abundantly represented in fossil form, gastropods have rarely been important rock builders. The tiny shells of pteropods, however, locally constitute as much as half of some calcareous oozes found on present sea bottoms in tropical and subtropical regions. Scaphopods, though having a long geologic range (Ordovician to Recent), have little stratigraphic importance. Among the cephalopods, the Nautiloidea dominate throughout most of the Paleozoic; the Ammonoidea dominate the Mesozoic; and upon their extinction the Coleoidea take up the position of dominance and still retain it. Only locally do the Paleozoic cephalopods play any part in rock building, but during the Mesozoic the ammonoids, with their large massive shells, made considerable contributions to the calcareous sediments. The internal shells of *Belemnites* are locally of sufficient abundance to constitute an important part of a formation but more often are of sporadic occurrence.

References

Arnold, R.: The Tertiary and Quaternary pectens of California. *U. S. Geol. Surv., Prof. Paper* 47, 1906.

Barrande, J.: Cephalopodes. "Système silurien de la Bohême." Vol. 2, 1866–1877.

Bartsch, P.: Mollusca in general. *Proc. U. S. Nat. Mus.*, vols. 40, 41, etc., 1911, 1915, 1917, etc.

Berry, S. S.: Fossil chitons of western North America. *Calif. Acad. Sci.*, vol. 11, pp. 399–526, 1922.

Clarke, J. M.: The Lower Silurian Cephalopoda of Minnesota. *Geol. Surv. Minn.*, vol. 3, pt. 2, 1897.

Dall, W. H.: A new classification of the Pelecypoda. *Trans. Wagner Inst. Sci.*, Philadelphia, vol. 3, pt. 3, 1895; *Proc. U. S. Nat. Mus.*, vol. 17, No. 1032, 1895.

Foerste, A. F.: Notes on Arctic Ordovician and Silurian cephalopods. *Bull. Denison Univ.*, vol. 19, pp. 247–306, 1921.

———: Notes on American Paleozoic cephalopods. *Bull. Denison Univ.*, vol. 20, pp. 193–267, 1924.

———: Actinosiphonate, trocheroid, and other cephalopods. *Bull. Denison Univ.*, vol. 26, pp. 285–383, 1926.

———: Ordovician and Silurian cephalopods of the Hudson Bay area. *Bull. Denison Univ.*, vol. 26, pp. 1–107, 1927.

———: A restudy of some of the Ordovician and Silurian cephalopods described by Hall. *Bull. Denison Univ.*, vol. 28, pp. 173–230, 1928.

———: American Arctic and related cephalopods. *Bull. Denison Univ.*, vol. 28, pp. 1–110, 1928.

———: A restudy of American orthoconic Silurian cephalopods. *Bull. Denison Univ.*, vol. 28, pp. 296–320, 1928.

———: Black River and other cephalopods from Minnesota, Wisconsin, Michigan and Ontario. Pt. 1, *Bull. Denison Univ.*, vol. 27, pp. 47–136, 1928; pt. 2, vol. 28, pp. 1–146, 1933.

——— and Teichert, C.: The actinoceroids of east-central North America. *Bull. Denison Univ.*, vol. 25, pp. 201–296, 1930.

Grabau, A. W.: Studies of Gastropoda. *Am. Nat.*, vol. 36, pp. 917–945, 1902; vol. 37, pp. 515–539, 1903; vol. 41, pp. 607–646, 1907; *Intern. Zool. Cong.* VII, pp. 753–766, 1912.

———: Phylogeny of *Fusus* and its allies. *Smith. Misc. Coll.*, vol. 44, 157 pp., 1904.

Hyatt, A.: Genera of fossil cephalopods. *Proc. Boston Soc. Nat. Hist.*, vol. 22, pp. 253–338, 1883.

———: Pseudoceratites of the Cretaceous. *U. S. Geol. Surv., Mon.* 44, 351 pp., 1903.

——— and Smith, J. P.: Triassic cephalopod genera of America. *U. S. Geol. Surv., Prof. Paper* 40, 394 pp., 1905.

Jackson, R. T.: Phylogeny of the Pelecypoda; the Aviculidae and their allies. *Boston Soc. Nat. Hist., Mem.*, 4, pp. 277–400, 1890.

KNIGHT, J. B.: The gastropods of the St. Louis, Missouri, outlier. *Jour. Paleontology*, vol. 4, suppl., pp. 1–78, 1930; vol. 5, pp. 1–14, 177–228, 1931; vol. 6, pp. 189–202, 1932; vol. 7, pp. 30–58, 359–392, 1933; vol. 8, pp. 139–166, 433–447, 1934.

MANSFIELD, W. C.: Miocene gastropods and scaphopods from Trinidad, British West Indies. *Proc. U. S. Nat. Mus.*, vol. 66, 65 pp., 1925.

PERNER, J.: Gastropodes. Barrande's "Système silurien de centre de la Bohême." Vol. 4, 1903–1907.

PILSBRY, H. A., and SHARP, B.: Scaphopods of the San Domingo Tertiary. *Proc. Philadelphia Acad. Sci.*, pp. 465–576, 1898.

REESIDE, J. B.: Some American Jurassic ammonoids of the genera *Quenstedticeras*, *Cardioceras*, and *Amoeboceras*, family Cardioceratidae. *U. S. Geol. Surv., Prof. Paper* 118, 64 pp., 1919.

———: Cephalopods from the lower part of the Cody shale of the Oregon Basin, Wyoming. *U. S. Geol. Surv., Prof. Paper* 150, pp. 1–19; The Scaphites; an Upper Cretaceous ammonite group, pp. 21–40, 1927.

———: The cephalopods of the Eagle sandstone and related formations of the western interior of the United States. *U. S. Geol. Surv., Prof. Paper* 151, 87 pp., 1927.

RUEDEMANN, R.: The structure of some primitive cephalopods, *N. Y. State Mus., Bull.* 80, pp. 296–341, 1905.

SMITH, J. P.: The development of *Glyphioceras* and the phylogeny of the Glyphioceratidae. *Proc. Calif. Acad. Sci.*, vol. 3, pp. 105–128, 1897.

———: The Carboniferous ammonoids of America. *U. S. Geol. Surv., Mon.* 44, 211 pp., 1903.

———: Upper Triassic marine invertebrate faunas of North America. *U. S. Geol. Surv., Prof. Paper* 141, 202 pp., 1927.

———: Lower Triassic ammonoids of North America. *U. S. Geol. Surv., Prof. Paper* 167, 199 pp., 1932.

ULRICH, E. O.: Lower Silurian Lamellibranchiata of Minnesota; Lower Silurian Gastropoda of Minnesota. *Geol. Surv. Minn.*, vol. 3, pt. 2, pp. 475–628, 813–1081, 1897. (The paper on the gastropods is with W. H. Scofield.)

CHAPTER X

ARTHROPODA[1]

INTRODUCTION

The Arthropoda comprise an unusually large and varied group of highly developed invertebrates whose long geologic history reaches back almost certainly into the Pre-Cambrian. The transversely segmented, bilaterally symmetrical, wormlike body in nearly all cases is covered by a chitinous or calcareo-chitinous dorsal exoskeleton and is provided with a number of variously modified jointed, hollow appendages. Members of the phylum show a great range in size, varying from tiny insects less than 1/4 mm. in length to large trilobites over 60 cm. long, eurypterids over 150 cm. long, and the giant Japanese crab which can span 340 cm. with its claws. Fossil arthropods are abundantly represented in sedimentary rocks from the earliest Cambrian to the present time, and living forms are of great abundance in the seas, on the land, and in the air. During their long geologic history representatives of the phylum have invaded every life habitat, and they excel all other animals, with the possible exception of the vertebrates, in the success with which they have adapted themselves. A few of the more familiar members of the Arthropoda are crayfish, crabs, pill bugs, centipedes, millipedes, barnacles, spiders, scorpions, and insects. Two extinct groups, the Trilobita and Eurypterida, were important during the Paleozoic and became extinct at the end of that era.

The following classification will be used in the discussion of the phylum:

Class 1. **Crustacea**—Crabs, crayfish, trilobites
Class 2. **Onychophora**—Very primitive caterpillar-like creatures
Class 3. **Myriapoda**—Centipedes and millipedes
Class 4. **Insecta**—Flies, beetles, butterflies
Class 5. **Arachnida**—Spiders, scorpions, eurypterids

[1] Arthropoda—Gr. *arthron*, joint + *pous*, *podos*, foot; referring to the jointed or segmented character of the appendages.

THE ANIMAL AND ITS EXOSKELETON

The arthropod has an elongate, wormlike, bilaterally symmetrical, transversely segmented body. The body segments, or *somites,* may be alike or different, and in some forms two or more are fused together. The mouth and anus are at opposite extremities of the body. Each typical somite is provided with one or two pairs of hollow, segmented appendages which are made to articulate by the action of special muscles. These appendages show a wide range of modification and serve as excellent guides to the developmental history of the phylum. They function for locomotion, respiration, mastication, oviposition, swimming (paddles), grasping (claws), and as sensory organs.

There is a well-developed nervous system consisting of a cerebral ganglion above the esophagus, a nerve cord passing around either side of the esophagus, and a double chain of ganglia on the ventral side, with usually a pair to each somite. The eyes are nearly always well developed and may be simple (with one lens) or compound (with many lenses) and sessile or pedunculate.

There is an excellent circulatory system, with a heart and either lacunary or vascular distribution of the blood, which varies considerably in color. Respiration is carried on by means of external *book gills,* internal *book lungs, branchial appendages,* or *tracheae.* Those respiratory processes which are external and branched are known as *branchia,* whereas those which are internal and minutely tubular are designated tracheae. In a few forms respiration is accomplished by the general surface of the body. The more highly developed and specialized an arthropod becomes the more complex and efficient are the nervous, circulatory, and respiratory systems and sense organs and appendages.

The body of the arthropod is attached to a chitinous or calcareous exoskeleton by various muscles. The exoskeleton may be a chitinous dorsal shield (*carapace*) composed of a number of plates, a calcareous cuplike structure consisting of a series of overlapping plates (barnacles), or a bivalved shell composed of two convex calcareous plates (ostracods). A few arthropods are without any exoskeleton, but these usually have the skin hardened and strengthened by chitin. The exoskeleton of the arthropod functions as a true skeleton in that it provides places for the attachment of the muscles which move the segments of the body covering and the jointed appendages. The protection furnished by the exoskeleton has always facilitated the transition from aquatic to terrestrial life—a transition very successfully accomplished by several groups of arthropods, notably the insects.

Since the body and limbs of most arthropods are inclosed in a continuous and rigid exoskeleton, which cannot be extended or expanded, growth is possible only by periodic shedding or *molting* (*ecdysis*) of the chitinous covering. In molting, the integument separates at different points about the head, and the animal then crawls out of its old covering and is without any protection for a short period of time during which it may grow rapidly. At the termination of the growth period a new exoskeleton, which may or may not be larger than its predecessor, is secreted, and the animal again becomes incased in its rigid armor. In some arthropods growth appears to continue at a diminishing rate from youth to senility; hence the intervals between moltings increase in length with age. In the winged insects, however, growth ceases at the termination of the larval stage, and the mature insect does not molt thereafter. The majority of molting arthropods increase in size with successive molts, but some do not change dimensions, and if the food supply happens to be curtailed there may actually be shrinkage in the size of the animal. On the other hand, some parasitic Crustacea grow without molting, the external integument apparently increasing in size by interstitial growth.

The exoskeleton of the arthropod is intimately related to the soft parts of the body within—probably more so than in any other invertebrate. The animal grows by adding successive somites to the body. These are introduced in regular order from front to rear, the latest one always being added in front of an unsegmented tail or *telson region*. Simultaneously with the growth of the new somite appears the protective chitinous integument. In many of the more advanced arthropods partial fusion of adjacent skeletal segments takes place, giving rise to a head (*cephalon*), *thorax*, and *abdomen*. Fusion may even go so far as to result in a *cephalothorax* and a single abdominal plate, both showing only obscurely the original segmentation.

The Arthropoda have many features in common with the annelid worms, some of which features have been described above, and because of this similarity most investigators hold the view that the phylum had its inception in a primitive aquatic annelid sometime during the late Pre-Cambrian. Many arthropod larvae still resemble worms far more than the mature insects or other forms into which they ultimately develop and are often incorrectly referred to as "worms" by uninformed observers. The difference between larva and adult is well illustrated in the butterfly, with its larval caterpillar; the fly, with its larvae in the form of maggots; and the June beetle, which is at first a grub. On the other hand, the young grasshopper is closely similar to its parent except for the lack of wings. These structures appear only after successive moltings.

The larval stage in some cases is quite long, as among the locusts in which the larvae live for a number of years before developing into the mature locust which lives for only one year. Among the May flies and mosquitoes, in contrast, the young hatch and live in water for a short time, then crawl out, dry their bodies and unfold their wings, and fly away to live for only a few hours or at most a few days. The series of developmental changes through which many arthropods go, from the time when the egg is hatched to the appearance of the adult individual, is known as *metamorphosis*.

Developing from some aquatic annelid ancestor in the Pre-Cambrian, and apparently existing for a long period of time in the soft condition still shown by larvae, the Arthropoda were in an advanced stage of evolution by the beginning of the Paleozoic. The Crustacea, Onychophora, Myriapoda, and Arachnida had been differentiated, but the Insecta did not appear until later in the Paleozoic. The crustaceans still continue to live in the water, but the myriapods, arachnids, and many of the insects have adapted themselves to terrestrial habitats, and some of the last named have even gone so far as to modify their bodies for spending a considerable part of life in the air.

CLASSIFICATION

The Arthropoda have been variously classified, but there seems to be no general consensus of opinion as to how subclass and ordinal lines should be drawn. The following structures are the ones most commonly considered in taxonomy:

1. Nature and position of the respiratory processes.
2. Character of the segmentation of the body.
3. Number and structure of the appendages.

The classification used in this work is based largely on the segmentation of the body and the structure and number of the appendages and is as follows:

Class **Crustacea**
- Subclass **Trilobita**—Extinct trilobites
- Subclass **Branchiopoda**—Fossil and living phyllopods
- Subclass **Ostracoda**—Fossil and living ostracods
- Subclass **Copepoda**—Living copepods, none fossil
- Subclass **Cirripedia**—Fossil and living barnacles
- Subclass **Malacostraca**—Fossil and living crabs, crayfish, etc.

Class **Onychophora**—Very primitive arthropods with fossil representatives

Class **Myriapoda**
- Subclass **Progoneata**—Fossil and living millipedes
- Subclass **Opisthogoneata**—Fossil and living centipedes

Class **Insecta**
- Subclass **Pterygogenea**—Fossil and living winged insects
- Subclass **Apterygogenea**—Fossil and living wingless insects

Class **Arachnida**
- Subclass **Merostomata**—Fossil and living water-breathing arachnids
- Subclass **Embolobranchiata**—Fossil and living air-breathing arachnids

CLASS CRUSTACEA[1]

The Animal.—The Crustacea constitute a large group of aquatic arthropods which breathe by means of book gills, book lungs, or branchia. The body is incased in a chitinous or calcareo-chitinous integument which protects the animal and serves as a place of attachment for the muscles. Crustaceans are mainly carnivorous, consuming decaying organic matter. This is passed through the mouth to a large stomach, thence through a straight intestinal tube to the anal opening at the posterior extremity of the body. The anterior and posterior parts of the digestive canal are lined with a chitinous substance that is continuous with the exoskeleton; hence only the middle part of the canal is capable of secreting digestive fluids and absorbing the nutrient elements from the food. A contractile heart pumps the blood through the arteries to the surface of the body, whence it returns through veins or open sinuses to the heart. If gills are present, the blood passes through them on the return path. The sexes are separate, and reproduction is ordinarily oviparous. Most of the lower Crustacea hatch from the eggs into a free-

[1] Crustacea—L. *crusta*, crust; referring to the crustlike character of the chitinous integument of most crustaceans.

swimming larval condition known as the *nauplius stage*. At this stage of development the animal has an unsegmented body, a single median eye, and three pairs of appendages (Fig. 148). By successive molts, followed by successive slight modifications, the animal adds new somites to the body and attains maturity. In the more advanced Crustacea the nauplius stage is passed in the egg, and when the young leaves the egg it has the form of the adult although it is much smaller in size.

Most crustaceans have the appendages considerably modified for various functions. The first pair are bent rods which bear

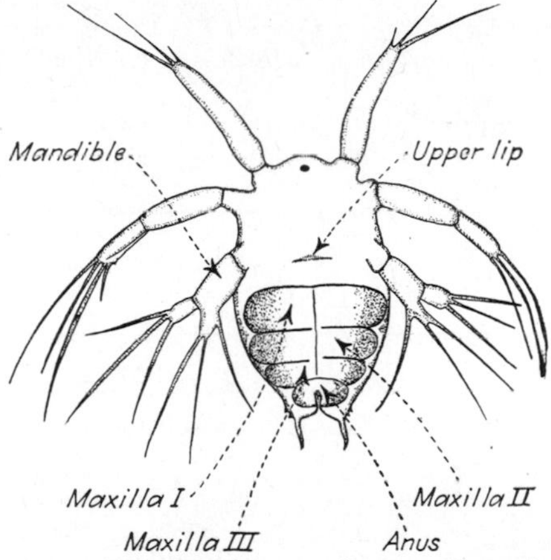

FIG. 148.—Larval stage of *Euphausia*, a modern marine malacostracan. This larva is a typical nauplius. (*After Metschnikoff.*)

small chitinous setae at their tips. They are known as *antennules* and seem to have a *tactile* function. The second pair is composed of very delicate, hook-shaped structures known as *antennae*. These serve as sensory organs. The third pair of appendages is commonly modified into strongly chitinized teeth which aid in mastication. These are designated the *mandibles*. The fourth and fifth pairs, referred to as *first* and *second maxillae*, follow the mandibles and together form a sort of lower lip. All of the appendages so far described spring from the cephalic part of the body. Succeeding appendages, modified for locomotion, respiration, or both, rise directly from the thoracic and abdominal segments. Each appendage has a basal *protopodite* which branches to form the outer *exopodite* and the inner *endopodite*.

The exopodite functions for swimming and respiration; the endopodite, for crawling. In some forms the exopodite is greatly reduced or wanting altogether (Figs. 149, 151).

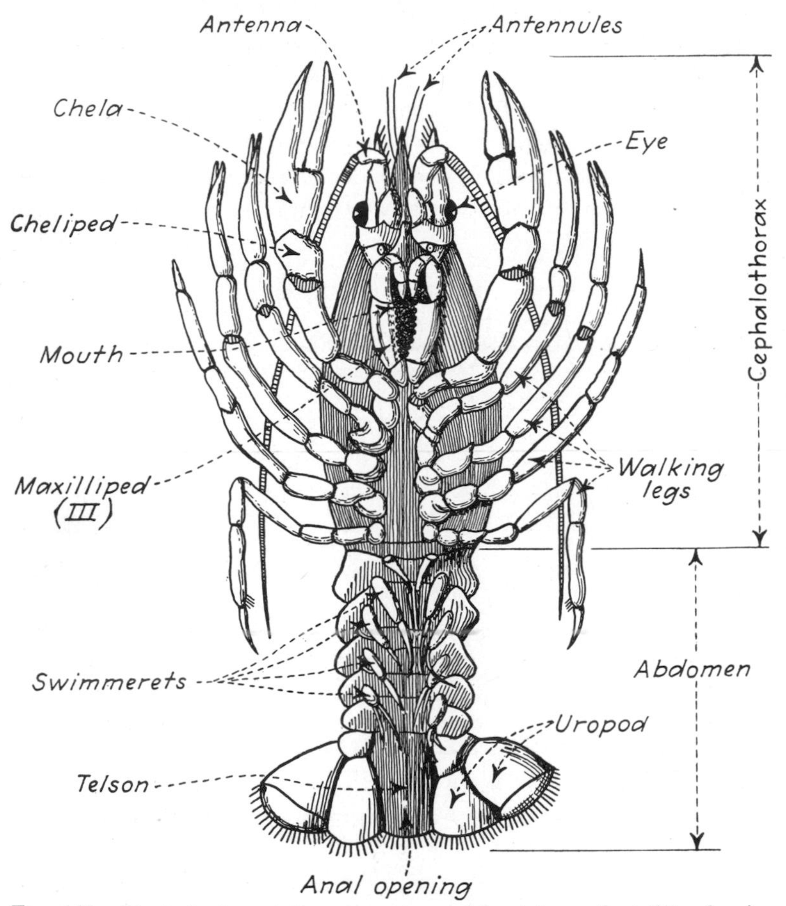

Fig. 149.—Ventral view of the common crayfish, *Astacus fluviatilis*, showing the different appendages. (*After Nicholson and Lydekker.*)

The number of free or separate body segments varies widely. In the earliest representatives of the class the number exceeds 40, but in the later more advanced forms it is much smaller. Evolution in the group has tended to reduce the number of somites through fusion.

The Exoskeleton.—The exoskeleton of crustaceans is composed either wholly of chitin or of that substance impregnated by calcium carbonate or calcium phosphate. It is usually divided into three distinct parts—*cephalic, thoracic,* and *abdominal* or *pygidial,* but in some forms the exoskeleton instead of being segmented consists of two calcareous valves (Ostracoda), four separate plates (Phyllocarida), or numerous small calcareous plates (Cirripedia).

In many of the more advanced Crustacea the cephalic and thoracic segments of the body have become fused into a cephalothorax, which is unsegmented and covered by a single dorsal plate known as the carapace. This is divisible, along a transverse cervical groove, into an anterior part, the head, and a posterior part, the thorax. In such forms the abdominal segments are separate and imbricate so that the posterior part of the exoskeleton is flexible. In the extinct trilobites the abdominal segments of the body were covered by a single segmented or smooth plate, the *pygidium.*

Subclass Trilobita[1]

General Considerations.—The Trilobita constitute an extinct group of exclusively Paleozoic arthropods which had the body divided into a variable number of segments and completely incased in a chitinous integument. The parts of the exoskeleton where no movement took place were thickened and hardened with calcium carbonate. Elsewhere the exoskeleton was thin and flexible. The thinner places very likely acted as joints where the exoskeleton could separate easily into its constituent parts during molting. The average trilobite was a small creature, usually around 50 to 75 mm. in length (2 to 3 in.) but ranging from tiny forms less than 10 mm. long to giants 675 mm. (27 in.) long (*Terataspis*).

The trilobites were entirely marine organisms, for their remains are always found in association with corals, crinoids, brachiopods, cephalopods, and other salt-water forms. They are thought to have belonged largely to the vagrant benthos, and many were very likely carnivorous. Some may have been scavengers on the ancient sea bottoms. Appearing as highly developed forms in the earliest Cambrian, they rapidly rose to a dominant position among the invertebrates and during the Cambrian and Ordovi-

[1] Trilobita—L. *tri,* three + *lobus,* lobe; referring to the transversely as well as the longitudinally trilobate character of the exoskeleton.

cian probably held the ruling position until the cephalopods attained their acme of development in the Ordovician. Thereafter the trilobites declined gradually to the close of the Paleozoic, when they became extinct. They attained world-wide distribution and are of great value as index fossils for intercontinental correlation.

The Exoskeleton.—In life the trilobite animal, about which very little is known, was completely incased in a chitinous integument which was strengthened in places by calcium carbonate. This protective exoskeleton consisted of a thick *dorsal shield;* a

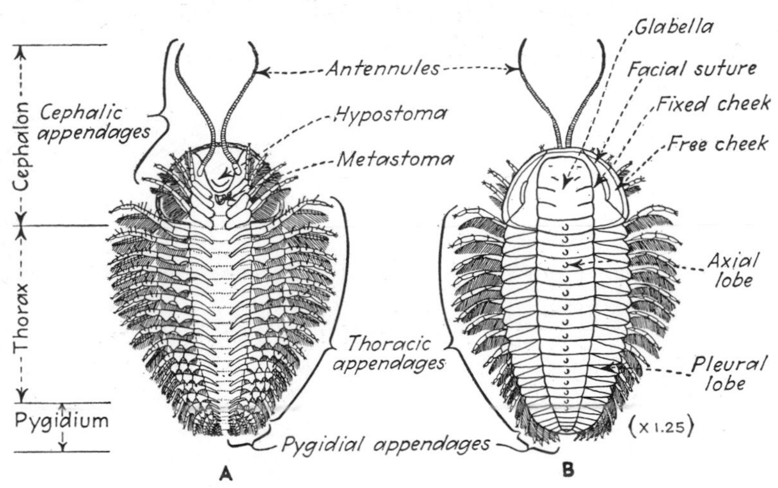

Fig. 150.—Ventral and dorsal views of a completely restored *Triarthrus becki* from the Ordovician of New York. (*After Beecher, with certain modifications suggested by Raymond.*)

small, ventral liplike structure, the *labrum* or *hypostoma;* a very thin *ventral membrane;* and the hollow *body appendages* (Figs. 150, 151).

The dorsal shield in most forms is divided transversely into three prominent lobes by two longitudinal *dorsal furrows* (Fig. 152). The central lobe is designated *axial;* the two flanking lobes, *pleural.* These are responsible for the trilobate appearance of the exoskeleton. Longitudinally the dorsal shield is divided into three distinct parts—the head or *cephalon,* the flexible middle part or *thorax,* and the abdomen or *pygidium.* Each of these exhibits the typical transverse trilobation with an axial lobe or ridge and the two lateral lobes. The *cephalic shield* (or cephalon) consists of three pieces—a median segmented or smooth ridge known as the *glabella*, which is flanked by but continuous with the two depressed *fixed cheeks;* and two lateral *free cheeks*, or lateral plates, which join the fixed cheeks along the *facial suture.* If *eyes* are present on the dorsal surface of the cephalon, they are situated on the free cheeks. The thorax is composed of a series of

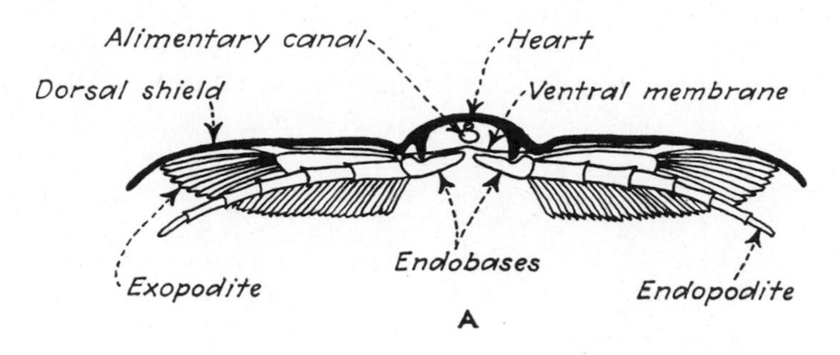

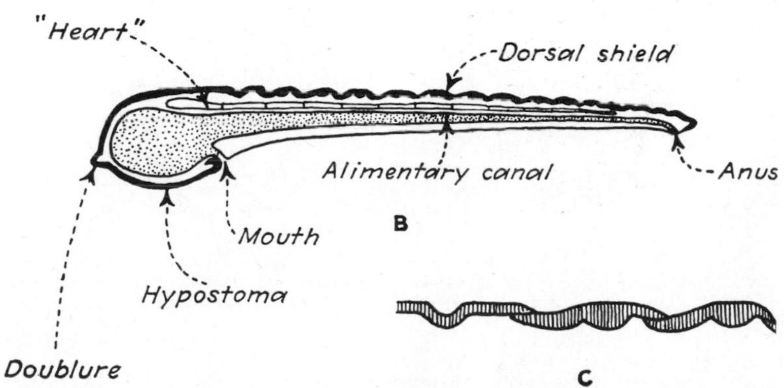

FIG. 151.—Structure of the trilobite *Ceraurus pleurexanthemus*. *A*. Transverse section of the thorax. *B*. Longitudinal section along the axial ridge. *C*. Diagram showing the posterior part of the cephalon and the first two thoracic segments, with their typical imbricating relations. (*Adapted from Raymond.*)

imbricating segments united by thin chitinous joints. Each segment is divisible into an axial and two pleural parts, but these are firmly united into a single plate so that in life movement took place only between segments. The pygidium is a segmented or smooth plate, formed from the fusion of a number of posterior segments. In some forms it is produced into a prominent posterior spine known as the *telson* (Figs. 152, 154).

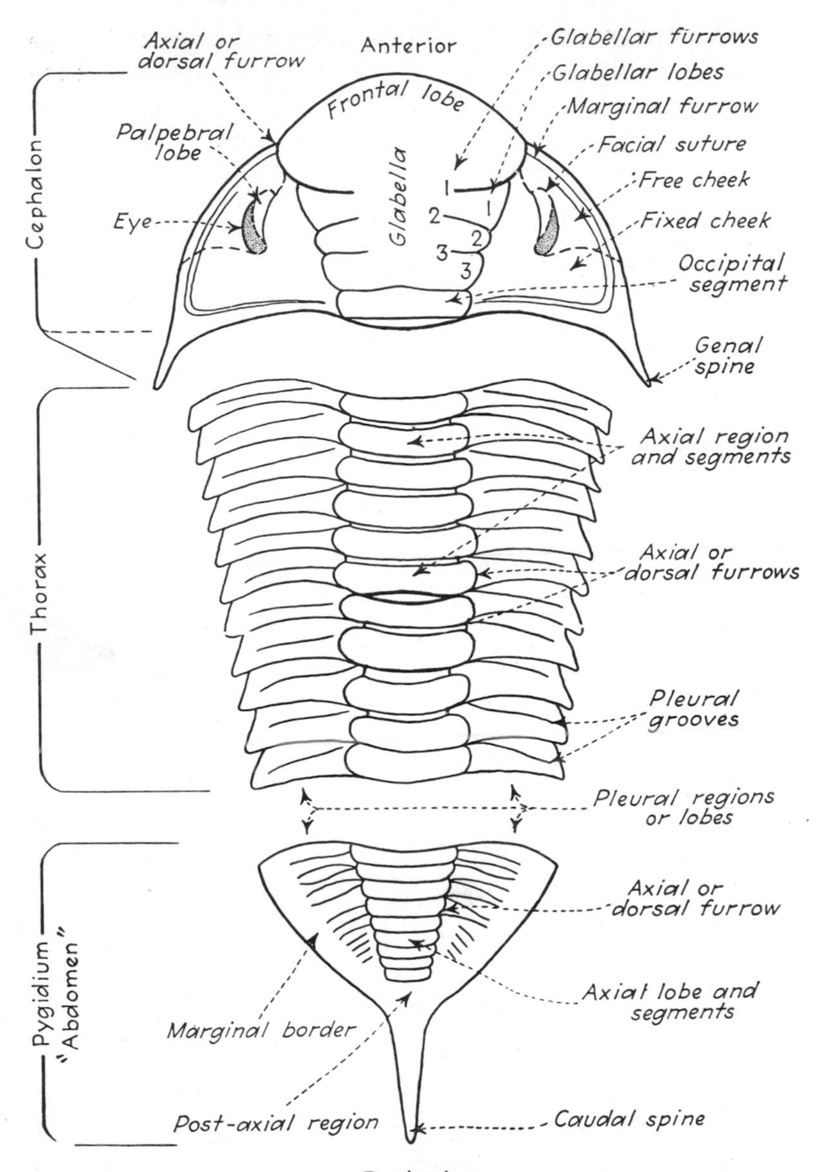

FIG. 152.—Diagram of the dorsal view of a trilobite (*Dalmanites*) showing the various structures. (*Adapted from Weller.*)

Very few fossil trilobites show the ventral part of the creature; hence knowledge respecting the appendages is lacking for most genera (Fig. 150). In all forms of which the ventral side has been seen there are five pairs of appendages on the ventral side of the cephalon. All of these are similar in appearance except those of the anterior pair, which are modified into antennules. Each thoracic and pygidial segment is provided with a pair of biramous limbs, regardless of whether the dorsal shield segments are separate or fused.

THE CEPHALON.—The cephalon or cephalic shield is a more or less rigid plate formed from the fusion of the five to seven anterior cephalic segments. It is generally somewhat arched and may be strengthened further by the three secondary arches continuous with the trilobate structure of the entire dorsal shield. The shape of the complete cephalon ranges from semicircular to triangular. The posterior margin is usually nearly straight or but slightly curved. The angle included between the posterior and lateral margins is known as the *genal angle*, and it may be prolonged posteriorly into a *genal spine*. The angle may be acute or obtuse, and the spine short and broad or long and pointed (Fig. 152).

The glabella represents the anterior part of the axial lobe and may be segmented or smooth. The transverse *glabellar furrows* divide the glabella longitudinally into a variable number (two to five) of *glabellar lobes*, the anterior one of which is commonly the larger and more prominent. These are designated *frontal*, *first*, *second*, *third*, and *occipital* or *neck* lobes. The posterior furrow, which divides the occipital lobe from the remainder of the glabella, is referred to as the *occipital furrow*. In certain species it extends laterally on to the fixed cheeks. There is some evidence to justify the statement that the five lobes of the glabella represent the five anterior somites of the trilobite ancestor, which became covered by the plates that later fused to form the glabella.

The development of the furrows and the shapes of the lobes are subject to great variation. In some forms the glabella constitutes the major part of the cephalon, whereas in others it is quite small. It may be only a fraction of the cephalon in length, or it may extend to or slightly beyond the anterior border. The furrows may be quite distinct, indistinct, or even absent entirely, and they may extend entirely across the glabellar ridge or be confined to notches on the sides. Rarely they join, and then they separate lobes from the sides of the glabella. The occipital furrow is almost always quite well defined and remains so even after the others have become indistinct.

The glabella is flanked laterally by the two fixed cheeks, from which it is set off by the longitudinal furrows. It is also separated from the frontal margin of the cephalon by a part of the *marginal furrow*.

The two fixed cheeks together with the glabella constitute the *cranidium*. The fixed cheeks may be large or small depending chiefly on the position of the facial suture. In the genus *Conocoryphe* they comprise more than half of the cranidium, whereas in *Albertella* they are quite small (Fig. 155). The longitudinal furrows are well defined in some genera (*Calymene*) (Fig. 156 *C*), faint in others (*Isotelus*) (Fig. 155 *H*), and almost invisible in still others (*Bumastus*) (Fig. 155 *I*). The fixed cheeks include the genal angles and spines if the facial suture cuts the lateral margin of the cephalon; they lack these features if the suture cuts the posterior margin. Along the lateral margin of each fixed cheek, approximately in middle position, is an elevated area, the *palpebral lobe*. This may be connected with the frontal lobe of the glabella, and it lies upward and inward from the eye which, if present, is situated on the adjacent inner margin of the free cheek.

The two free cheeks lie on either side of the cranidium, from which they are separated by the facial suture. A free cheek includes the genal angle or spine if the facial suture terminates at the posterior margin of the cephalon. It lacks the genal angle or spine if the suture terminates along the lateral margin. Anteriorly the sutures may unite or may terminate along the anterior border without union. The free cheeks always bear the eyes which are situated along the inner margin just beneath the palpebral lobe. Separation of the free and fixed cheeks along the facial suture is usually very easy, as in *Ogygopsis* (Fig. 155 *G*); but may not be possible, as in *Olenellus* (Fig. 154 *C*). In the latter genus the two cheeks are so firmly united that no suture is determinable. It is considered probable that the facial sutures functioned as places of separation of the exoskeleton in the periodic molting.

The position of the facial suture determines the relative dimensions of the free and fixed cheeks, and the position of its posterior termination is a feature of taxonomic importance in that it separates what are considered two distinct lines of trilobite evolution. Those trilobites in which the facial suture terminates at the posterior margin in such a position that the genal angle or spine is borne on the free cheek are described as *opisthoparian* (Fig. 155). Those in which the suture terminates at the lateral margin, and hence with the genal angle or spine on the fixed cheek, are said to be *proparian* (Fig. 156). The ratio between the dimensions of the free and fixed cheeks is of some value in

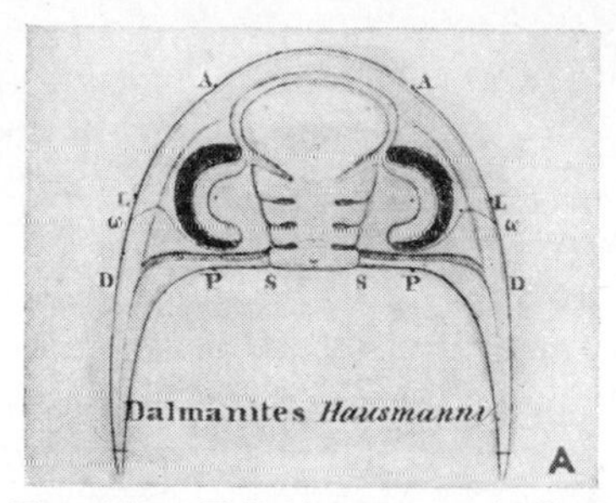

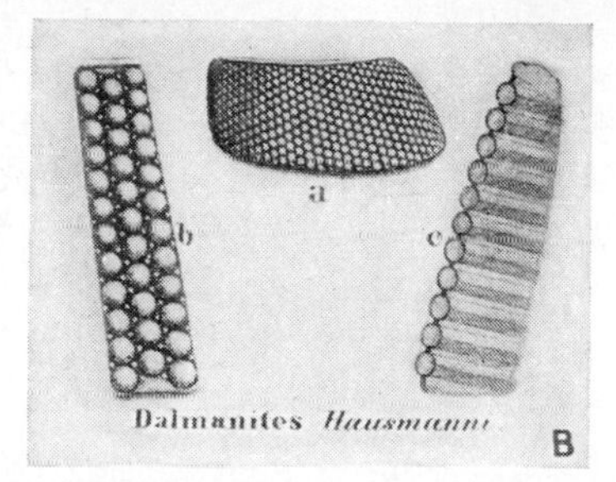

FIG. 153.—Trilobite eyes. *A*. Cephalon of *Dalmanites hausmanni* showing the positions of the eyes (in black) at the inner margin of the free cheeks. *B*. The eye of *D. hausmanni: a*, complete eye, with the lenses preserved; *b*, three vertical rows of lenses, each lens of which is surrounded by six small granules disposed in a hexagonal manner; *c*, vertical section along one of the vertical rows. (*After Barrande, with slight modifications.*)

determining rank, but it is not a decisive criterion and must be applied with caution. In some of the most ancient forms the ratio approximates unity, but in later and presumably more advanced genera, the fixed cheeks have been reduced to a narrow border around the glabella, and the ratio is several times unity.

The visual organs (*eyes*) of the trilobites are usually complex structures and vary greatly in size, position, and character (Fig. 153). Certain trilobites (*Eoharpes, Terataspis*) have visual organs on simple elevations on the fixed cheeks and at the ends of eye lines (Fig. 155 *N*), but these may be secondary structures rather than true eyes. Ordinarily the eyes are on the summits of small elevations, on upward deflections of the free cheeks at the palpebral lobe, or on stalks that rise from the surface of the free cheeks. The eye surface is usually convex outward; hence the trilobite had a wide range of vision. Those forms with stalked eyes no doubt had them in such a position because the environment in which they lived made that requirement. A very unusual eye is present in the Ordovician genus *Aeglina.* It is unusually large and is situated on the lateral margin of the cephalon. The eye surface is in the form of a hemisphere; hence at all times it was possible for the animal to see what was going on in every direction along or above the bottom. In many primitive trilobites, such as *Nevadia* and *Wanneria,* the eyes are situated on the ends of eye ridges that extend posteriorly over the free cheeks from the frontal lobe of the glabella. A few trilobites appear to have lacked eyes, and in some two small compound eyes are present on the ventral hypostoma.

Trilobite eyes are compound and of two kinds. In one group the entire eye is covered with a transparent chitinous covering known as the *cornea.* This covering may be perfectly smooth and give no indication of the compound character of the eye beneath it, or it may be granular, thereby reflecting the underlying eye facets. Eyes of this character are said to be *holochroal* and are those found on most trilobites. The second type of eye, described as *schizochroal,* has a separate cornea for each individual eye facet. A cornea may be round or polygonal. The facets of a trilobite eye range in size from less than $1/10$ mm. to as much as $1/2$ mm. and in number from 14 to 600 among the schizochroal eyes to over 15,000 in some holochroal types. In most instances the facets are regularly arranged with the greatest economy of space (Fig. 153).

The border of the cephalon is commonly set apart from the remainder of the shield, with which it is continuous, by the marginal furrow. Along the outer margin the integument is turned under to form the *doublure* (Fig. 158). The underlip or hypostoma is a subfrontal plate lying just anterior to the mouth. It sometimes bears a pair of small compound eyes. A rostral plate, known as the *epistoma,* is present in some forms above the hypostoma. The antennules originate at the lateral margins of the hypostoma. A third ventral plate, the *metastoma,* is situated immediately posterior to the mouth (Fig. 150 *A*). The mouth faces posteriorly, which is in harmony with the fact that the food was brought from that direction.

THE THORAX.—The thoracic or middle part of the trilobite exoskeleton consists of a number of trilobed segments which articulate with each other and thereby allow enrollment (Fig. 151 *B–C*). The number of segments ranges from 2 in *Agnostus* (Fig. 156 *G*) to 44 in the Cambrian *Paedeumias robsonensis*. Transversely the segments are divisible into a central or axial lobe and two pleural lobes, the latter often being produced posteriorly into spines and referred to as pleurae. Although distinctly divided on the dorsal surface by the two longitudinal furrows on each side of the axial lobe, the three parts of the thoracic segments are firmly united. Each thoracic segment has a frontal extension or flange which is inserted beneath the

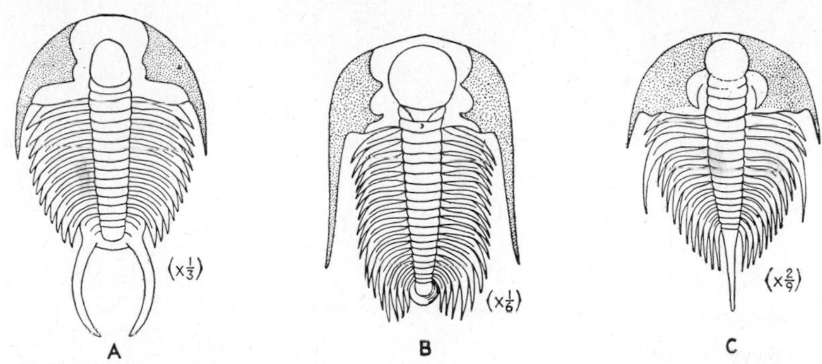

FIG. 154.—Cambrian trilobites. *A. Crepicephalus* from the Upper Cambrian of Alabama. *B. Paradoxides* from the Middle Cambrian of Massachusetts. *C. Olenellus* from the Lower Cambrian of Vermont. The free cheeks are indicated by stippling. The position of the facial sutures in *C* is uncertain. (*After Walcott.*)

posterior margin of the segment immediately in front. These flanges permit the segments to articulate with each other and also protect the thorax of the animal when the exoskeleton is enrolled. Each thoracic segment has a furrow on the posterior margin, and the pleurae may have additional furrows.

There appears to be a relation between the size of the pygidium and the number of thoracic segments. Forms with relatively large pygidia tend to have few segments [*e.g.*, *Agnostus* (2) and *Eodiscus* (3)], whereas genera with relatively small pygidia have a large number of segments [*e.g.*, *Paradoxides* (16–20) (Fig. 154 *B*) and *Eoharpes* (29) (Fig. 155 *N*)]. Since the evolutionary trend seems to have been toward reduction of thoracic segments and increase in the number fused together to make the pygidium, it is suggested that such forms as *Agnostus* and *Eodiscus* (Fig. 156 *H*) are advanced types of trilobites rather than primitive ones, as they have usually been considered. The pleural portions of the thoracic segments are thought to have originated as spines on the axial parts. During the growth of the thorax, new segments were always added between the last segment of the thorax and the pygidium.

THE PYGIDIUM.—The pygidium constitutes the posterior third of the exoskeleton and has been referred to as the *abdomen*, a designation of doubtful application, and *caudal shield*. It is a single transversely trilobate plate composed of a variable number (2 to 29) of segments firmly fused together. These may or may not be distinct. The pygidium may resemble or differ greatly from the cephalon in shape and may equal it in size or be larger or smaller. *Olenellus* had no pygidium at all, or at least none has ever been found on the species referred to this genus.

The axial lobe may extend the entire length of the pygidium, as in *Calymene;* may range to only a small fraction of it, as in *Goldius* (Fig. 155 *J*); or may merge so completely with the remainder of the pygidium that its identity as a distinct structure is lost, as in *Bumastus*. The segmentation of the axial lobe may be conspicuous, indistinct, or absent, and it is more often absent than present on the pleural lobes. The border of the pygidium may be continuously smooth or frilled with spines (Fig. 155 *B*). There is usually a marginal furrow adjacent to the border, and the latter is reflexed to form a doublure which is often of considerable width.

THE VENTRAL SIDE.—The ventral side of a trilobite, except for the part covered by the doublure and the plates around the mouth, seems to have been unprotected and covered only by a soft epidermis or membrane. There is an axial groove extending from the posterior extremity of the animal to the mouth (Figs. 150, 151). This is bordered on each side by the appendages. The forms of the appendages are known in but few trilobites, probably because they were not preserved or else because they were on the underside of the animal when it was buried and hence are usually not visible. In the few cases where they have been discovered much arduous labor and painstaking care were necessary to excavate the rock in which they were embedded. Figure 150 shows such a form. Ventral structures are now known in *Calymene*, *Ceraurus*, *Isotelus*, *Neolenus*, *Triarthrus*, and imperfectly in a few other genera, but as further collecting is carried on it seems likely that similar structures in other genera will come to light. From known specimens, it has been found that there are five pairs of appendages on the cephalon. The anterior pair is in the form of antennules which are directed forward in all cases except in *Cryptolithus*, in which they are directed backward along the ventral side. The other four pairs are postoral and are considerably modified for mastication. These four pairs of appendages, as well as all that follow posteriorly, consist of a basal protopodite and two branches springing therefrom—an outer exopodite and an inner endopodite (Fig. 151). The exopodite consists of a long basal joint followed by many smaller joints, or it is a single, broad, flat joint and bears a row of closely spaced bristles or setae on its posterior edge. The exopodite is believed to have functioned for respiration and swimming. The endopodite usually has six joints and was used for walking. On all protopodites small projections, known as *endobases*, are directed inward toward the axial groove. On the four pairs of cephalic appendages these are modified for cutting food and are designated *gnathobases*.

Dimensions.—Trilobites range in length from less than 10 to as much as 675 mm. (27 in.). Among the giants are *Terataspis grandis* from the Devonian (675 mm.), *Isotelus gigas* from the Ordovician (450 mm.), *Paradoxides harlani* from the Cambrian (450 mm.), and *Dalmanites myrmecophorus* and *Homalonotus major*, both from the Devonian (375 mm.). The average length is about 25 mm. (1 in.), and the width is usually about half the length.

Classification.—The following features have been utilized in subdividing the Trilobita into orders and families:

1. Ontogeny as revealed in evolutionary series.
2. Nature and position of the facial suture.
3. Absence or presence of eyes, and their structure.
4. Number of thoracic segments.
5. Ability to enroll.
6. Shape and margin of the pygidium.
7. Shape and character of the glabella.

None of these features, except those connected with ontogeny, seems to be stable enough for taxonomic purposes. All of the rest can be modified readily to meet changing conditions of environment.

Beecher's classic studies led him to the conclusion that the trend and orientation of the facial suture and its position with respect to the genal angle, together with the position of the free cheeks and the nature of the eyes, afforded a fundamental basis for classification. He therefore subdivided the Trilobita into three orders—Hypoparia, Opisthoparia, and Proparia. In the *Hypoparia* he placed those trilobites in which the free cheeks form a continuous marginal ventral plate on the cephalon, extending in some forms on to the dorsal side at the genal angles. The facial suture ranges from marginal to submarginal. The *Opisthoparia* have the free cheeks limited to the dorsal side of the cephalon and including the genal angle. In the *Proparia* the free cheeks are also dorsal, the facial suture terminates on the lateral margins, and the fixed cheeks include the genal angles.

It was Beecher's view that the free cheeks were at first beneath the cephalon with the facial suture marginal and that there were only eye lines and *ocelli* or eye cells rather than true eyes. This condition represents the hypoparian stage. The facial suture then migrated from the margin on to the upper surface of the cephalon; the free cheeks came to include part of the upper surface together with the genal angles; and the eyes, at first marginal, moved inward toward the facial suture on the dorsal surface of the free cheeks. Trilobites with these features had reached the opisthoparian stage. Finally, according to Beecher, the posterior margin of the free cheeks progressed laterally and then anteriorly until the facial suture came to cut the postero-lateral border of the cephalon, and the genal angle became a part of the fixed cheek. This condition is the most advanced among the trilobites and represents the proparian stage. The weakness of the first order, the Hypoparia, lies in the assumption that the group is the most primitive and is ancestral to the others. The question has been raised as to whether hypoparians might not have developed from each of the other two orders.

The recent discovery that members of the hypoparian family Agnostidae had an ancestor with a proparian free cheek and that the Cryptolithidae had an ancestor with an opisthoparian cheek naturally casts a great deal of doubt on the validity of the Hypoparia as an order. It seems best, therefore, to use only the

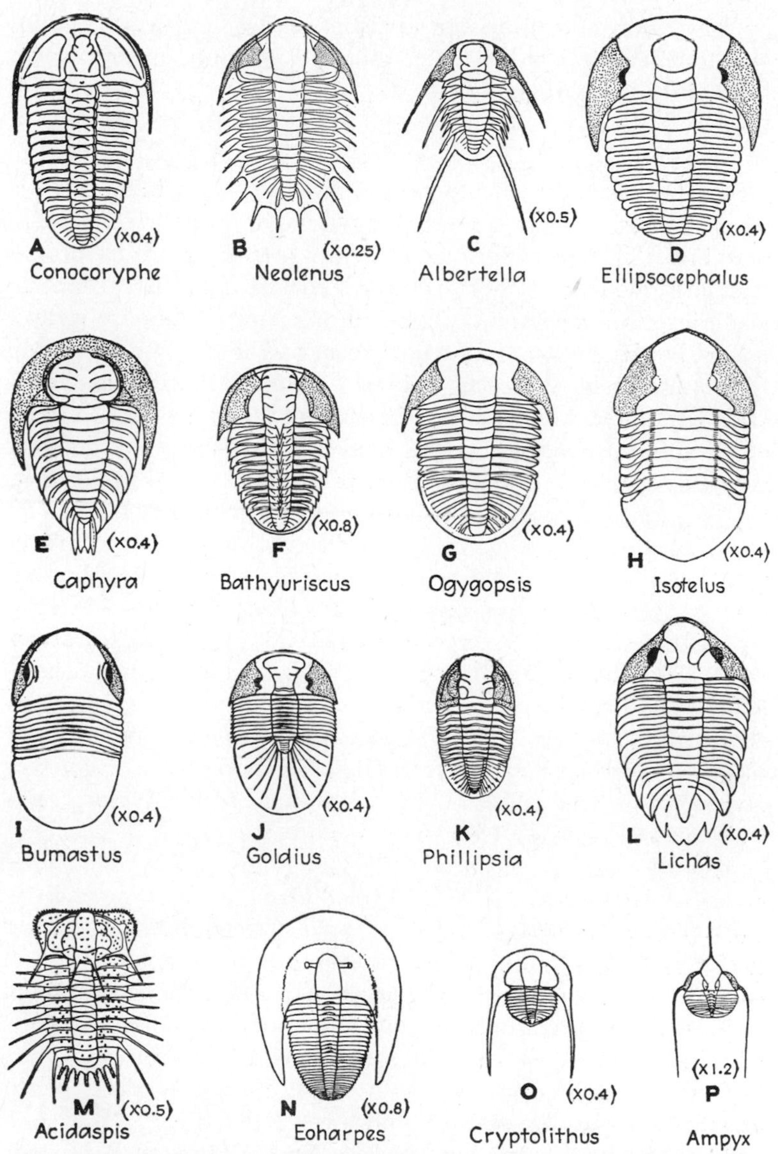

FIG. 155.—Opisthoparian trilobites. The free cheeks are dotted in except where the facial suture is marginal or submarginal or where it is not indicated, as in *Acidaspis*. (*Diagrams based on figures by the following authors: A, D–E, J, L–P after Barrande; B–C after Walcott; H, K after Nicholson and Lydekker.*)

opisthoparian and proparian divisions of Beecher's classification and to refer his hypoparian families to positions in one or the other of the two orders.

ORDER OPISTHOPARIA[1]

The Opisthoparia include those trilobites in which the free cheeks are usually not connected and always bear the genal angle or spine. The facial sutures, except in certain specialized forms once assigned to the Hypoparia, extend forward from the posterior margin of the cephalon and ordinarily cut the anterolateral border of the cephalon separately, though in a few forms they unite in front of the glabella. Eyes, if present, are compound and holochroal and are situated on the free cheeks. Some of the specialized genera once included in the Hypoparia have no eyes, though a few do have eye lines or ocelli. The majority of the trilobites, especially from the Cambrian, belong to the Opisthoparia. Twenty-one families have been erected, among which are the Harpedidae, Trinucleidae, and Raphiophoridae once included in the Hypoparia.

Opisthoparian trilobites are present in the earliest strata of the Lower Cambrian and are the last to survive to the time of extinction in the Permian. Representative genera are *Acidaspis*, *Albertella*, *Ampyx*, *Bathyuriscus*, *Bumastus*, *Caphyra*, *Conocoryphe*, *Crepicephalus*, *Cryptolithus*, *Ellipsocephalus*, *Eoharpes*, *Isotelus*, *Lichas*, *Neolenus*, *Olenellus*, *Paradoxides*, *Phillipsia*, and *Triarthrus* (Figs. 150, 154, 155).

ORDER PROPARIA[2]

Proparian trilobites have the facial sutures intersecting the posterolateral margins of the cephalon so that the genal angles or spines are borne on the fixed cheeks. The anterior terminations of the sutures may either intersect the anterior or anterolateral margins or unite in front of the glabella. The eyes are holochroal in three of the families, schizochroal in one, and absent in the other three. Of the seven families the Agnostidae, Eodiscidae, and Shumardiidae were once included in the Hypoparia.

[1] Opisthoparia—Gr. *opisthe*, behind + *pareia*, cheek piece; referring to the position of the facial suture.

[2] Proparia—Gr. *pro*, before + *pareia*, cheek piece; referring to the position of the facial suture.

The order makes its appearance in the Cambrian and becomes extinct in the Carboniferous. Representative genera are *Agnostus, Eodiscus, Shumardia, Encrinurus, Calymene, Homalonotus, Cheirurus, Phacops,* and *Dalmanites* (Fig. 156).

Ontogeny and Evolution.—The trilobites are assumed to have laid eggs, but this has never been established definitely, although certain ovoidal bodies associated with trilobite remains have been

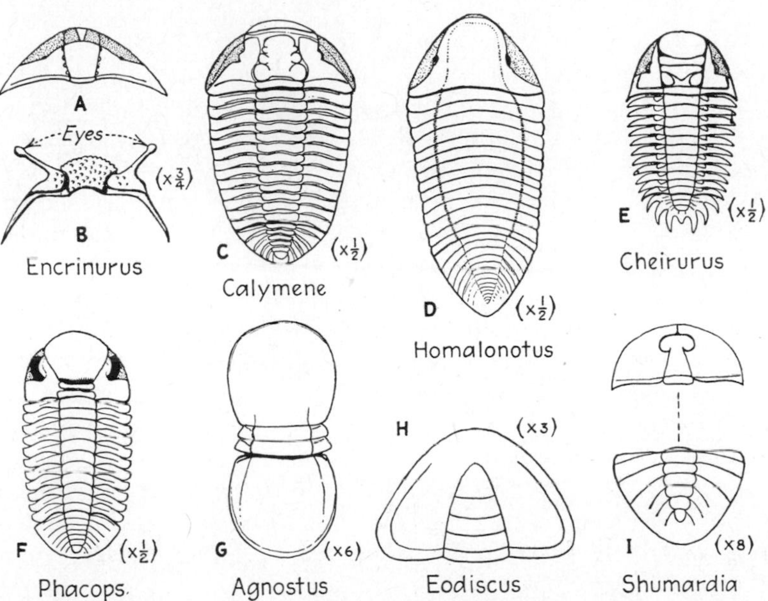

FIG. 156.—Diagrams illustrating genera representative of the families of proparian trilobites. (*Adapted from figures by the following authors: A, H after Beecher; B after Weller; C, E–G after Barrande; D after Hall; I after Billings.*)

so interpreted. The earliest known growth stage is represented by minute horny disks, which are circular or ovate in outline and about 1 mm. in diameter. These are thought to represent the young trilobite just after it had been hatched and have been so identified because they constitute the initial stage in a series of exoskeletons which represent the successive molts of a given species. This young trilobite, which has been termed the *protaspis* (Fig. 157), is thought to have been free swimming and to have resembled the nauplius stage of the more primitive living crustaceans. Like the nauplius it is assumed to have had three pairs of appendages—one pair directed forward as antennules;

and two pairs, biramous in structure, functioning for locomotion and respiration. Nothing is known of the actual soft parts or appendages of the protaspis, and it is expecting almost too much to hope that such will ever be found; hence all statements made about them must be considered as assumptions only.

The earliest known protaspis consists of a single dorsal plate provided with genal spines and a very prominent glabella. No organs of vision have been observed, although they may have been present. The shield shows segmentation and is divisible into cephalic and pygidial parts. The cephalon usually has five segments, the same number found in many adult trilobites; and

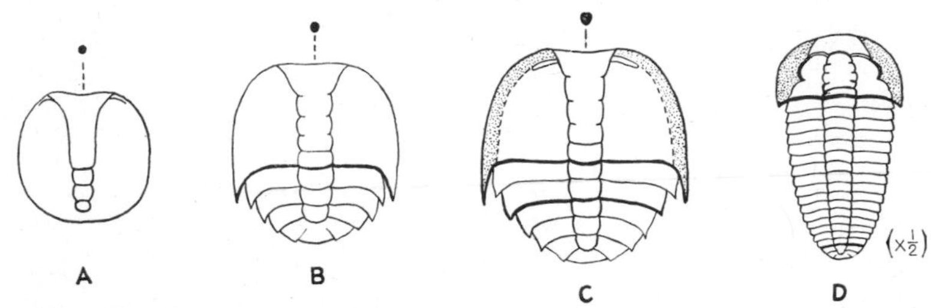

FIG. 157.—Development of *Sao hirsuta*. *A*. Earliest or protaspis stage with cephalon and pygidium undifferentiated. *B*. Later stage, with clearly defined cephalon. *C*. Stage with two free thoracic segments and narrow free cheeks. *D*. Adult, with 16 free thoracic segments. The free cheeks are indicated by stippling. (*After Barrande and Beecher.*)

the pygidial part, which is usually very small, has only a few. With progressive moltings the animal grows to maturity; the cephalon and pygidium are separated more and more as new thoracic segments are inserted, always immediately anterior to the pygidium; and the animal gradually develops the numerous structural features which are present only after maturity is attained. As the animal increases in size and takes on new characteristics the body becomes elongated, the pygidium tends to become larger through the addition of segments at the frontal margin, the glabella assumes the form typical of the adult, the facial suture finds its proper position, and the free cheeks take on the characteristics of mature life. Since the trilobite differs greatly from one growth stage to the next, any stage may have great stratigraphic importance as well as evolutionary significance. A great amount of work has been done on the evolution of the trilobites, but the results are too detailed for this discussion.

Ecology.—Little is known directly about the bionomics of living trilobites, but much can be inferred from their faunal relations, their method of preservation, and their various body structures. In a group of invertebrates as large as the Trilobita it is to be expected that there must have been many adaptations to every marine environment. If trilobites ever lived in fresh waters or upon the land, they either left no record of that existence, or the forms which lived in those habitats have not yet been recognized as trilobites. In the sea there must have been benthonic forms adapted to both muddy and solid bottoms, and there were almost certainly other forms which lived on the strand line where they wandered over the surface and burrowed in the sand much as do some modern crabs. Still other species appear to have been pelagic. Among fossil trilobites occur variously modified species which seem to have been adapted to all of the environments just mentioned.

Although the food of trilobites is not known with absolute certainty, it is known that living on the same bottoms were protozoans, sponges, coelenterates, bryozoans, brachiopods, and mollusks. From these some trilobites selected their food, and others very likely were scavengers, cleaning up organic debris that was included in the muds through which they ploughed and burrowed. It seems probable, further, that some trilobites, like certain modern crustaceans, were herbivorous, feeding on the seaweeds and other simple plants of the early Paleozoic seas. Certain types of trilobites lived in great numbers on Paleozoic reefs, and in reef environments that have been studied fully the same genera rarely occur both on the reef and on the bottoms of the interreef lagoons.

The ancient trilobites almost certainly served as food for a number of animals. Among the enemies were the giant cephalopods, eurypterids, ostracoderms, true fishes (only in the later Paleozoic), and perhaps even cannibalistic members of their own tribe. It seems more than a mere coincidence that immediately following the advent of the true fishes in the Devonian the seas were swept almost bare of trilobites, particularly those forms thought to have been denizens of the open water or of clear-water bottoms.

The original development of the dorsal protection was possibly a response to an unfavorable environment, and it has been suggested also that the development of spines was called out by environmental conditions. Some investigators are of the opinion that the ancestral trilobites were without an exoskeleton and that naked forms attacked each other, since there do not appear to have been other enemies. Such attacks eliminated those forms that were weaker and forced others to develop a protective armor. The armor appears to have served well until the fish migrated into the seas in the late Silurian and during the Devonian. This migration seems to have been an event of dire importance to the trilobite race and to have heralded the beginning of the end, for after the appearance of true fishes trilobites are uncommon. The nektonic forms probably were the first to go, falling an easy prey to the new enemy, that moved rapidly through the water with mouth wide open capturing the swimming trilobites by the thousands. There were probably bottom-browsing forms among the fish, which rooted and ploughed through the muds of the bottoms in search of food just as modern carp still do. To such fishes the mud-dwelling trilobites must have fallen an easy prey. Many trilobites enrolled, thereby protecting themselves, but this practice ironically enough instead of saving the animal may actually have aided the fish in capturing and swallowing it.

The ability to enroll seems to have been acquired in the Ordovician, for no Cambrian species are known to have had the habit. In enrollment the pygidium was apposed to the cephalon in such a way as to cover the entire ventral surface, in the manner of an armadillo. The doublures adjusted themselves to fit each other and were so perfectly apposed that no animal could reach the ventral part of the trilobite. It is thought that enrolling was developed as a protective device against animals, though this is an assumption and has not been proved.

Trilobites, like many other crustaceans, molted periodically. It is not known how often this took place, but it may have been seasonal or dependent upon the food supply. In the youthful stage of growth there were possibly several moltings in one season. As a consequence of molting there were produced on the sea bottom far more exoskeletons than actual individuals; hence, in general, trilobite remains in rocks are almost certainly more abundant than were the individuals which were responsible for them. The many free cheeks, cranidia, thoracic segments, and pygidia found scattered sporadically through sedimentary rocks should probably be regarded in large part as fragments of molts rather than as parts of exoskeletons in which the animals were present at the time of death and burial. This seems only logical when it is pointed out that the molts were no doubt of low specific gravity, with large surface area in relation to volume, and hence could be transported long distances by slowly moving waters of low competency. In this way the remains might well have been buried far from the places where the animals lived or died and in localities where trilobites could never have lived. Entire specimens indicate that the animal was within the exoskeleton at the time of burial and, further, that it probably lived and died in the place of burial.

Stratigraphic Range.—Trilobites are present in the Lower Cambrian, and by the close of that period over 100 genera and nearly 1,000 species had been evolved. Many of these genera became extinct before the opening of the Ordovician, and the character of their exoskeletons indicates clearly that they had traveled long on the road of evolution. New forms continued to appear at a rapid rate during the Ordovician, and by the close 1,200 species belonging to 125 genera had been evolved; but very soon thereafter decline set in, and only 600 species belonging to 40 genera are known from Silurian strata. During the Devonian the decline became even more marked, and though there are 40 genera known from that period, the number of species has decreased to 200. From the beginning of the Upper Devonian to the close of the Paleozoic, when the subclass died out, family after family became extinct, and only a single family with very few representatives remained in the Permian. No new families appeared after the Ordovician, and it is clear that the Trilobita reached their zenith during that period and the late part of the Cambrian.

In spite of wide adaptation, protective covering, and large representation the Trilobita rapidly declined after reaching their zenith in the Upper Cambrian and Ordovician. Numerous reasons for this decline have been suggested. Perhaps cannibalistic relatives started the decline, and it was continued first by the giant cephalopods which arose in the Ordovician, later by the Ostracoderms which arose in Middle Ordovician, and finally and perhaps with the most fatal results by the hordes of fishes of various kinds which invaded the seas during the Devonian.

After the Devonian trilobites are rare, and the last scattered survivors appear in the Permian. Finally, with a long geologic history shrouded in the almost impenetrable beginnings of life in the Pre-Cambrian, the trilobite race may well have been approaching natural death because of old age, and in such a case all of the unfavorable elements of the environment conspired only to hasten the end.

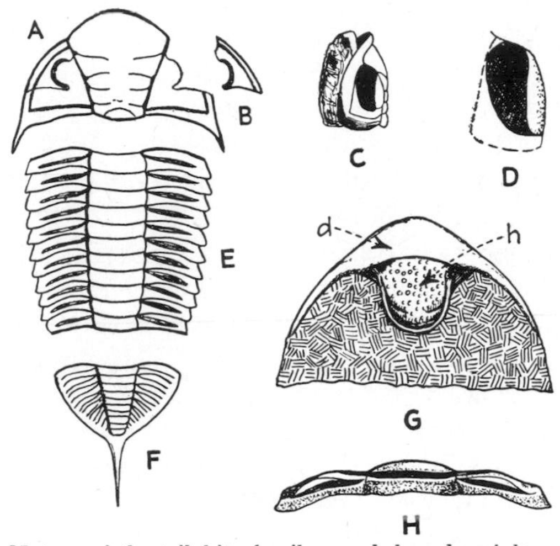

FIG. 158.—Nature of the trilobite fossil record, based mainly on specimens of *Dalmanitina socialis*. *A*. Cephalon, with left free cheek in place and right one (*B*) separated. *C*. Lateral view of a cephalon of *D. hawlei* showing the position of the eye. *D*. A magnified view of the eye showing its relation to the palpebral lobe. *E*. Complete thorax separated from the cephalon and pygidium. *F*. Complete pygidium with prominent spine. *G*. Ventral view of the anterior margin of the cephalon showing the doublure (*d*) and hypostoma (*h*). *H*. A single thoracic segment. (*Adapted from Barrande.*)

Fossil trilobites have world-wide distribution and often are excellent index fossils. Such cosmopolitan genera as *Agnostus*, *Paradoxides*, *Cryptolithus*, *Bumastus*, *Proetus*, *Calymene*, *Phacops*, and *Dalmanites* are very useful for intercontinental correlation, and more restricted genera are equally valuable for local correlations. Some formations contain large numbers of well-preserved remains, but usually they are not common.

Nature of the Fossil Record.—A complete trilobite exoskeleton is one of the rarest of fossils and when found is very likely to be more or less altered by fossilization. More often the entire dorsal shield may be preserved without the ventral part of the organism visible. In some cases the appendages may be buried in the stone, but in most instances they are wanting altogether. The usual finds are separate cephalons, cranidia, free cheeks, separated thoracic segments, pygidia, and hypostomatas (Fig. 158). The larger part of such remains very likely represents fragments of molted exoskeletons. Ovoidal bodies, interpreted by some investigators as trilobite eggs, have been reported, and various types of trails have likewise been attributed to trilobites.

Trilobite remains are commonly preserved as chitinous plates or, if the original skeletal substance has been destroyed, as molds and casts. In some cases the original structure and substance of the eyes are preserved, and in rare cases the actual integument is so well preserved that the markings on the surface can still be seen. Recently some very unusual, crablike fossils have been interpreted as possible ancient trilobites which possessed no exoskeleton.

Subclass Branchiopoda[1]

General Considerations.—The Branchiopoda constitute the most primitive group of living crustaceans, though they have had a long geologic history reaching back to the Lower Cambrian. Some forms are naked; others have a chitinous or calcareo-chitinous carapace or a calcareous bivalved shell. The body segments vary in number, and the appendages are generally leaf-like and lobed rather than leglike. A pair of feelers (*caudal furcae*) are present in some species on the posterior extremity of the abdomen. There is considerable diversity of appearance among the branchiopods, and if only the exoskeletons were considered, it would appear that unlike organisms were being grouped together. The essential features of the exoskeleton are shown in Fig. 159. Branchiopods occur in great abundance and are widely distributed in fresh, brackish, and extremely salty waters. It seems probable that they had similar distribution during the past, though their fossil representatives are not abundant.

Classification.—The Branchiopoda are usually subdivided into four orders—*Anostraca*, *Notostraca*, *Conchostraca*, and *Cladocera*.

[1] Branchiopoda—Gr. *branchia*, gills + *pous*, *podos*, foot; referring to the breathing organs carried on certain of the appendages.

The first three orders constitute the so-called *Phyllopoda* and range from the Cambrian to the present time. The Cladocera comprise the water fleas and are not known fossil before the Pleistocene.

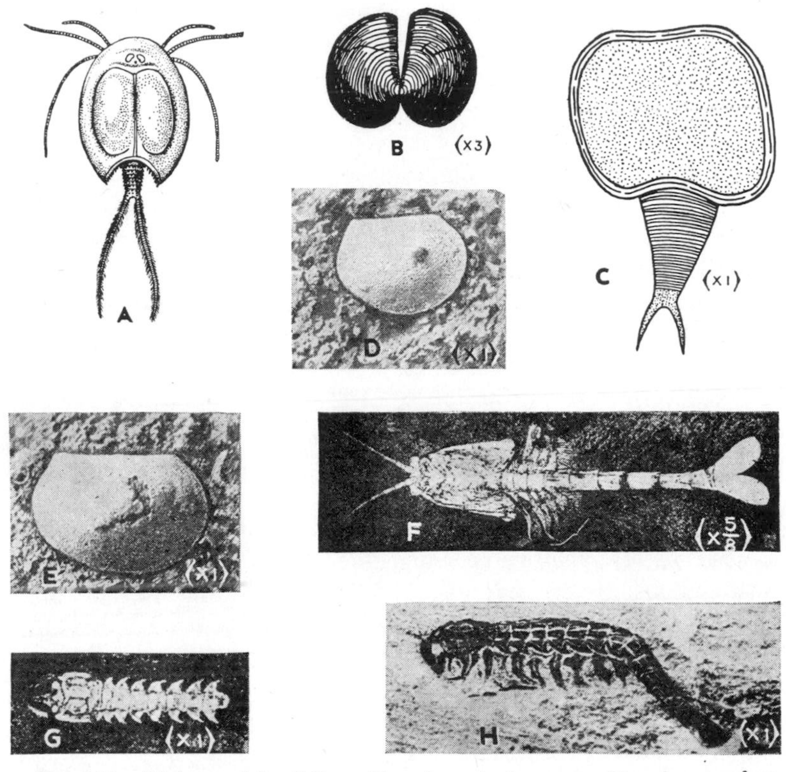

Fig. 159.—Living and fossil Branchiopoda. *A. Apus cancriformis*, a modern branchiopod, somewhat enlarged. *B. Estheria ovata*, from the Triassic, showing the two valves. *C. Protocaris marshi*, a very ancient branchiopod from the Lower Cambrian of Vermont. *D–E. Walcottella*, from the Middle Cambrian of Colorado: *D*, left valve of *W. breviuscula*, slightly less than natural size; *E*. left valve of *W. leperditoides*, slightly less than natural size; *F*, *Waptia fieldensis* from the Middle Cambrian of British Columbia. *G–H. Yohoia tenuis*, two specimens from the Middle Cambrian of British Columbia. (*A after Nicholson and Lydekker; B. after Jones; C after Walcott; D–E after Ulrich and Bassler; F–H after Walcott.*)

ORDER ANOSTRACA[1]

The Anostraca lack a carapace and have a distinct head provided with stalked eyes. The furca has unsegmented branches

[1] Anostraca—Gr. *an*, without + *ostracon*, shell of a testacean; referring to the lack of a shell or carapace.

that are rodlike or flattened. The thorax has 11 to 19 pairs of appendages. The order is represented by one or more (depending on the writer) genera from the Cambrian, two doubtful genera from the Carboniferous, and one genus (*Artemia*) from the Eocene. The last genus accords well with the structures of modern species. The great gap in the fossil representatives may be due to a very incomplete geologic record or to incorrect reference of the various genera. Two living families have representatives inhabiting salt lakes and brine pools. *Opabina*, from the Middle Cambrian Burgess shale, may be taken as a fossil representative of the order. It is the only one of Walcott's original genera which has been generally retained in the Anostraca. *Yohoia* (Fig. 159 *G–H*) probably should be made the type of a new Anostracan family rather than placed in any existing family.

ORDER NOTOSTRACA[1]

The Notostraca have the dorsal shield or carapace extending over the anterior segments and possess paired sessile eyes, a large number of appendages, and multiarticulate furcae. The order made its appearance in the Lower Cambrian and is still represented in the existing oceans. Several Ordovician genera (*Technophorus, Ischyrina*) may belong to the order, but too little is known about them to permit a positive statement. *Waptia* and *Burgessia*, from the Middle Cambrian, are fossil representatives, and *Apus* may be considered as representative of living forms (Fig. 159).

ORDER CONCHOSTRACA[2]

A bivalved carapace, sessile eyes, and 10 to 27 pairs of appendages characterize the Conchostraca. The antennae are biramous and are used for swimming. The caudal furcae have clawlike branches, and the abdomen is not bent as in the Ostracoda and Cladocera. Fossil representatives have been found in strata ranging in age from the Cambrian to the present time. They are usually small and consist of the bivalved carapace, which is often

[1] Notostraca—Gr. *noton*, back + *ostracon*, shell of a testacean; referring to the character of the shell or carapace and its position.

[2] Conchostraca—Gr. *kongche*, L. *concha*, shell + *ostracon*, shell of a testacean; referring to the character of the carapace.

difficult to differentiate from ostracod and certain small molluscan shells. *Walcottella* (Cambrian) and *Estheria* (Devonian to Recent) are typical genera (Fig. 159).

ORDER CLADOCERA[1]

The Cladocera comprise the common water fleas, which are widely distributed in existing water bodies. There is a tiny bivalved shell which incloses the body but generally leaves the head exposed. The paired eyes are sessile, and there are four to six pairs of body limbs. No fossil representatives are known unless egg cases, found in the glacial deposits of Germany, and a doubtful specimen from the Carboniferous of Europe, belong here.

Subclass Ostracoda[2]

General Considerations.—Ostracods are small, bivalved Crustacea which are found inhabiting all waters but are most abundant in marine habitats. They range in size from tiny forms less than 1 mm. in length to large specimens which measure over 20 mm., and next to the copepods are the most abundant Crustacea in modern seas. They move in vast swarms, either swimming at or near the surface or creeping over the bottom, and appear to prefer shallow waters where they can pursue their scavenging habits. An interesting fact in connection with their food is that they will quickly remove all flesh from any skeletal structure placed in their midst.

The body of the animal is contained within a bivalved horny or calcareous shell or carapace, to which it is attached by means of adductor muscles that close the valves (Fig. 160). The place of attachment of these muscles may be marked by a tubercle, a pit or a number of small spots and is often visible from the exterior of the shell. The body is smaller than the shell and is only faintly segmented. There are seven pairs of appendages as follows: first and second antennae, one pair of mandibles, two pairs of maxillae, and two pairs of slender legs. The rudimentary abdomen terminates in a single or bifurcated spine, which is used mainly for clearing out foreign matter that comes

[1] Cladocera—Gr. *clados*, a branch + *keras*, a horn; referring to the branched antennae.

[2] Ostracoda—Gr. *ostracodes*, testaceous; referring to the shelled character of the animal.

between the valves. There are commonly a small median eye and a pair of large lateral eyes. The positions of the paired eyes are indicated on the exterior of some carapaces by *eye tubercles* or ocular spots.

The sexes are separate, but the shells of the two are alike except for size. In the genus *Candona* the male shell is the

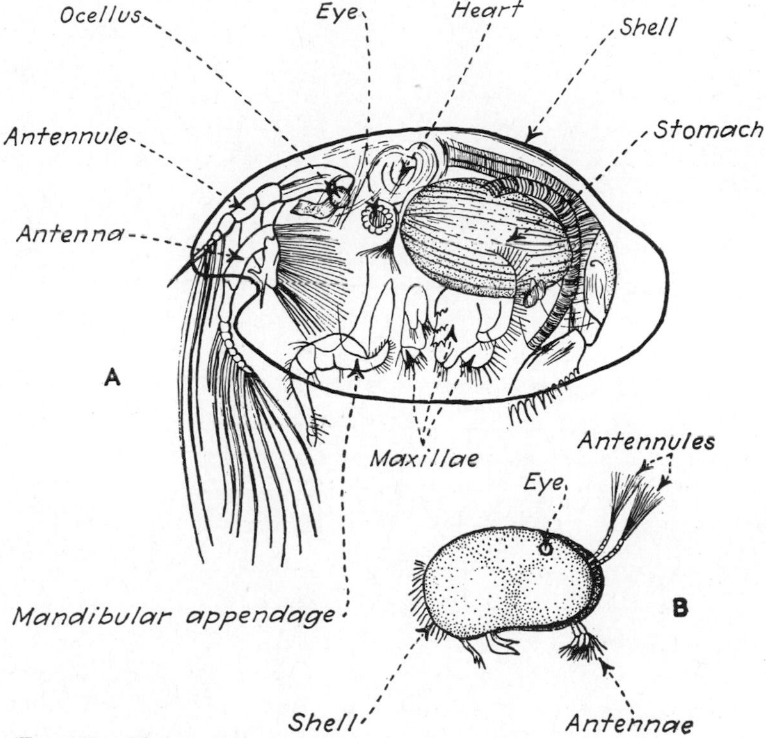

Fig. 160.—Modern Ostracoda. *A. Cypridina messinensis*, viewed from the side and greatly enlarged, with one-half of the shell removed to show the various parts of the body. *B. Cypris fusca*, viewed from the side, with the two valves slightly displaced. (*After Nicholson and Lydekker.*)

larger, whereas in *Cypris* the reverse is true. Some of the Paleozoic Beyrichidae have an inflated posterior part or a swollen pouch in that position. This expansion has been designated the *brood pouch*, and shells having such structures are assumed to have belonged to the female of the species (Fig. 161 *H*).

The Carapace or Shell.—The typical ostracod shell consists of a right and a left valve which articulate along the dorsal edge and

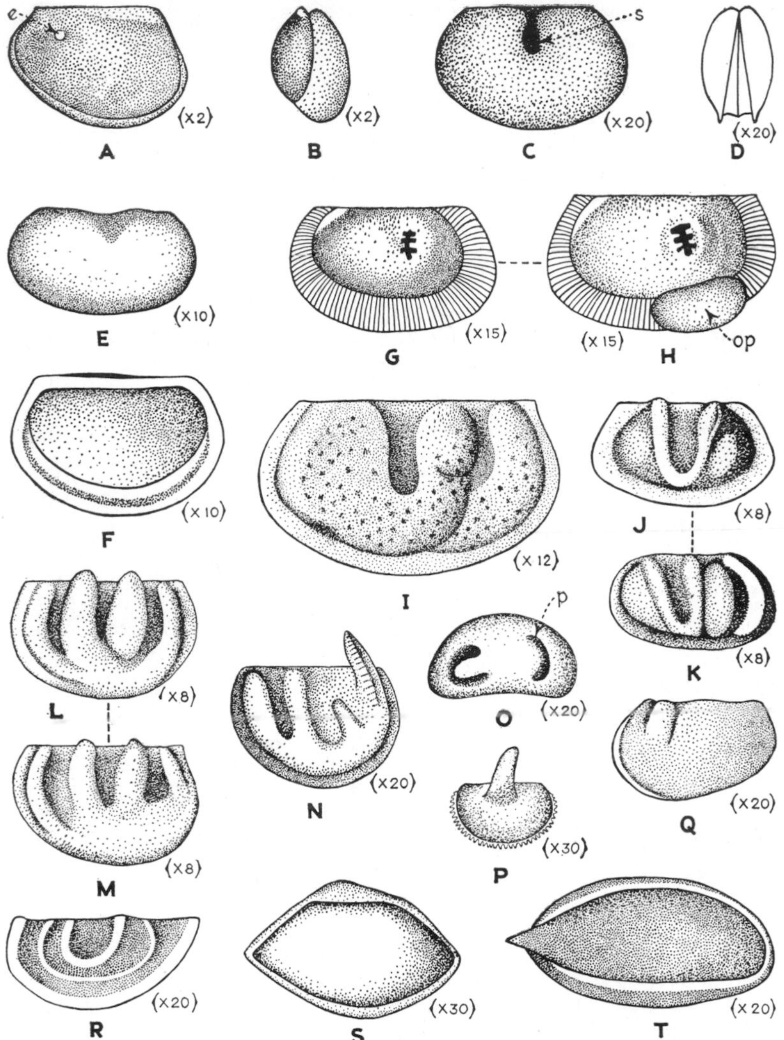

FIG. 161.—Fossil Ostracoda. *A–B. Leperditia fabulites* from the Middle Ordovician of Minnesota: *A*, left side of an entire carapace showing the eyespot (*e*) and the characteristic overlapping of the larger right valve; *B*, posterior view. *C–D. Euprimitia sanctipauli* from the Middle Ordovician of Minnesota. Right valve and end view of entire carapace. *E–F. Leperditella inflata*, from the Middle Ordovician of Kentucky, showing exterior and interior views of two left valves. *G–H. Chilobolbina dentifera*, from the Ordovician of Esthonia, showing the male and female forms, respectively. *I.* Male left valve of *Zygobeyrichia ventripunctata* from the Silurian (Keyser) of West Virginia. *J–K. Zygosella vallata* from the Silurian (Clinton) of West Virginia, a male left valve; and *Z. macra* from the same horizon in Virginia, a female left valve, showing the narrow,

meet or overlap along the ventral, dorsal, or entire margin. The valves are pulled together by a subcentral adductor muscle which frequently leaves a scar of some kind (tubercle, pit, or spots) on their inner surfaces. The shell is compact in structure and, though commonly from ½ to 4 mm. in length, reaches 10 mm. in the living deep-sea *Gigantocypris* and more than 25 mm. in some doubtful Paleozoic forms of the family Leperditiidae. The outer surface of the valves may be smooth and glossy or granulose, pitted, striate, or reticulate. In addition to these ornamental features, the valves of many fossil forms are strongly lobed, sulcate, or nodose, and variations in the number, position, and relation of these features are of stratigraphic significance. Since they represent external manifestations of internal anatomical structures of various types, and since students of living ostracods base their classification on soft parts, this lobation and sulcation are of considerable taxonomic value.

Stratigraphic Range.—The earliest ostracods appeared in the Lower Ordovician and belong to the Leperditiidae (Fig. 161 *A–B*). The numerous species which have been reported from the Cambrian, according to the most recent researches, belong to the Branchiopoda and may be true Conchostraca (Fig. 159 *D–E*). Since their appearance the ostracods have been abundant and at times have been important contributors to rock formation. The Paleozoic Ostracoda have been studied extensively, but Mesozoic species are not so well known, though it has been shown that a large ostracod fauna extended into the Tertiary. By using the following criteria for identification, ostracods may serve very satisfactorily for correlation purposes:

1. Differences in size, outline, convexity of valves, and location of greatest thickness.
2. Nature of the hinge.
3. Modifications of the hinge.

---

ridgelike brood pouch paralleling the posterior border. *L–M*. *Drepanellina clarki*, from the Silurian (Clinton) of Maryland, showing male and female left valves, respectively. *N*. *Ceratopsis chambersi*, left valve from the Middle Ordovician of Minnesota. *O*. *Thlipsura v-scripta discreta*, a left valve from the Silurian of the island of Gotland. *P*. *Aechmina bovina*, a left valve from the Silurian (Wenlock) of England. *Q*. *Kloedenella obliqua*, right valve from the Silurian of Maryland. *R*. *Strepula concentrica*, a right valve from the Silurian of England. *S*. *Bairdia beedei*, a complete carapace from the Carboniferous of Kansas. *T*. *Krausella inaequalis*, right side of a complete carapace from the Middle Ordovician of Illinois. *e*, eyespot; *op*, brood pouch; *p*, pit; *s*, sulcus. (*All figures redrawn from Ulrich and Bassler.*)

4. Overlap of the edges of the valves.
5. Surface features of the valves.
6. Lobation of the valves.
7. Character of the surface ornamentation.
8. Presence or absence of brood pouch.

Representatives of the families of Ostracoda are illustrated in Fig. 161.

Subclass Copepoda[1]

The Copepoda lack a distinct carapace. There are typically six pairs of biramous appendages and a caudal furca. The antennae and antennules are usually well developed. The order is abundantly represented in modern seas, but no fossil forms are known.

Subclass Cirripedia[2]

General Considerations.—The Cirripedia or barnacles constitute a group of greatly modified crustaceans which closely resemble certain mollusks in some particulars. Because of this close resemblance the subclass was referred to the Mollusca until 1830, when study of the life history showed them to be true arthropods.

The body is inclosed in a membranous mantle which in many forms is covered by a number of calcareous plates. It is attached by the anterior extremity of the head and is either obscurely segmented or unsegmented. The posterior part of the body has not more than six pairs of biramous appendages, and these may be absent altogether. The egg of the Cirripedia hatches into a *nauplius* which passes through a succession of molts before acquiring a bivalved shell like that of the ostracods. This larva then attaches itself to some object on the bottom by the anterior end and grows into an adult individual.

The barnacles are exclusively marine and seem always to have been so. Most species live in shallow water, but some are known

[1] Copepoda—Gr. *cope*, an oar + *pous*, *podos*, foot; referring to the oarlike legs or appendages.

[2] Cirripedia—L. *cirrus*, a curl + *pes*, *pedis*, foot; referring to the appearance of the appendages as they protrude beyond the upper edge of the cuplike shell.

to extend to depths as great as 3,650 m. (12,000 ft.). Many living forms have no shell, and this condition very likely also prevailed in ancient species, though no fossils have been found to prove such an assumption. Those provided with calcareous shells attach themselves to any object on the bottom, and rocky coasts which are not too strongly swept by waves are often literally plastered with the shells of the acorn barnacles. These have a shell composed of from 4 to 10 calcareous plates more or less fused together along the sides and bottom to form a truncated cone (Fig. 162 *D*). The opening into the hollow shell is covered by two pairs of plates, the *terga* (*tergum*) and *scuta* (*scutum*). These four plates are hinged and when retracted protect the animal within from drying out when the shell is exposed at low tide. The goose barnacle, reputed in medieval times to have changed into a certain kind of goose, is attached by a flexible stalk which may be covered with small plates, and the body is also covered by a variable number of small plates which are never fused together (Fig. 162). Some species live attached to floating or stranded wood, crabs, shells, and corals, whereas others lead a parasitic life on or within animals. Barnacles are a nuisance on ship bottoms, where they build such extensive masses that they impede the ship's progress through the water and hence have to be scraped or chopped off from time to time.

Geologic History.—The Cirripedia apparently represent an ancient group of crustaceans which became specialized through the adoption of the sessile habit. In fact they might even be termed degenerate. The animals became hermaphroditic, developed a number of protective plates, simplified certain parts of the body, and lost other parts. They seem to have descended from some ancestral branchiopod. They appeared in the Ordovician, though questionable specimens from the Cambrian have been referred to the order, and occur sporadically throughout the geologic column to the Present. They are at no time of any stratigraphic importance, though they were abundant in the Mesozoic and have continued so up to the present time.

Scalpellum and *Loricula*, belonging to the Lepadidae (Cretaceous to Recent), or goose barnacles, and *Balanus*, representing the Balanidae (Devonian (?), Cretaceous to Recent), or acorn barnacles, are typical genera (Fig. 162).

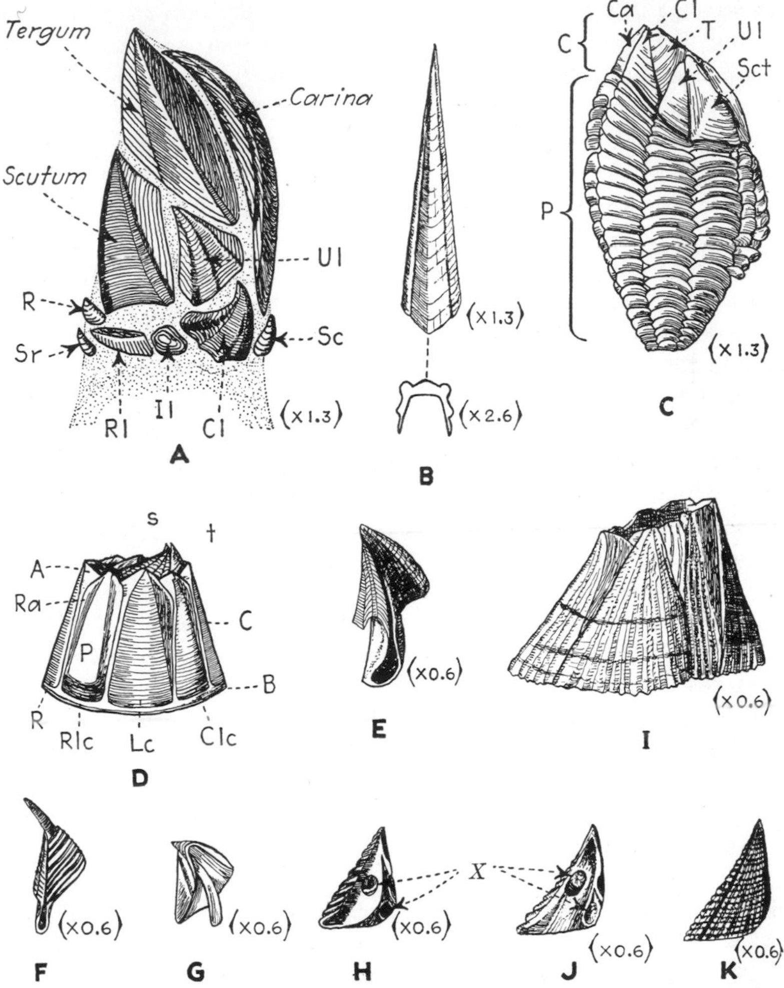

FIG. 162.—Modern and fossil Cirripedia. *A*. Capitulum of *Scalpellum fossulum*, a pedunculated cirripede from the Upper Cretaceous of England. The peduncle is shown by stippling. *B*. Dorsal view of the carina from *A*. *C*. *Loricula darwini*, a pedunculate form found attached to an ammonite from the Cretaceous of England. *D*. Diagram of the shell of the modern *Balanus*, a sessile barnacle. *E*. Tergum of *B. concavus* from the Tertiary of England. *F–G*. Exterior and internal views of the tergum of *Balanus*. *H*. Internal view of the scutum of *Balanus* showing the muscle scars (*X*). *I*. Shell of *B. concavus* from the Tertiary of England. *J–K*. Internal and exterior views of the scutum of *I*.

A, alae; *B*, basis; *C*, capitulum; *Ca*, carina; *Cl*, carino-latus; *Clc*, carino-lateral compartment; *Il*, infra-median latus; *P*, peduncle; *Pa*, paries; *R*, rostrum; *Ra*, radii; *Rl*, rostral latus; *Rlc*, rostro-lateral compartment; *Sc*, sub-carina; *Sct*, Scutum; *Sr*, subrostrum; *T*, tergum; *Ul*, upper latus; *X*, muscle scars. (*A–B*, *D–K after Darwin; C after Woodward.*)

Subclass Malacostraca[1]

General Considerations.—The Malacostraca comprise a great host of diverse forms among which are such familiar modern crustaceans as crabs, crayfish, lobsters, shrimps, etc. Since representatives of the subclass are only rarely well preserved as fossils, most paleontologists have paid very little attention to them.

The Malacostraca constitute an important source of food for man, and every year millions of individuals are taken. They are also the great scavengers of the sea bottom, eating everything of organic character irrespective of the degree of decomposition. Many have a "gastric mill" in the intestinal tract in which shells that have been swallowed are broken into bits or ground into powder. Some of the larger species break open shells with their claws in order to obtain the animals inside. Under favorable conditions all organic matter on certain bottoms passes through the alimentary tracts of some of the Malacostraca and suffers both mechanical and chemical alteration during the passage.

Living members of the subclass have 14 or 15 body segments posterior to the head. In addition to the appendages on the head, there are eight pairs of thoracic appendages and six pairs on the abdomen (Fig. 149). Paired eyes are generally present and are frequently stalked. The newly born individual has progressed beyond the nauplius stage and is frequently quite similar in appearance to its parents except for size.

Geologic History and Classification.—While members of the Malacostraca are extremely abundant in modern seas and have probably been so since the middle of the Mesozoic, they are rarely preserved as fossils in any abundance, so that fossil specimens are more in the nature of curiosities than usable objects. Solnhofen, Bavaria, is one of the few places where well-preserved individuals have been found, along with many other surprising fossils in the famous lithographic limestone quarried there. This limestone was deposited as a lime mud between Jurassic bioherms.

The Malacostraca have been divided into two groups—the primitive *Leptostraca* and the more highly specialized *Eumala-*

[1] Malacostraca—Gr. *malacos*, soft + *ostracon*, shell of a testacean; referring to the soft-shelled character of many of the members of the subclass.

costraca. In the former the carapace, if present, is either sharply folded or bivalved, and all of the thoracic segments are distinct. All forms are small, have wide distribution in existing marine waters, have been in existence since the Cambrian, and were very likely evolved in the Pre-Cambrian. The *Eumalacostraca* have an abdomen with six segments all of which may bear appendages. There are eight segments in the thorax and a like number of thoracic appendages. The appendages are rarely alike and have the appearance of legs. Most of the members of this division range from the beginning of the Mesozoic to the Present. The fossil record is so incomplete that instead of discussing it a brief outline is given below, together with a similar outline of the more primitive Leptostraca.

Series 1. **Leptostraca**

Division *A*. **Phyllocarida**—Body with seven segments, the last of which is without appendages. Carapace present, with an articulating rostral plate. First four pairs of appendages biramous, last two pairs reduced. (Middle Cambrian to Recent.)

Order 1. Nebaliacea—A heterogeneous group of living and fossil phyllocarids. *Hymenocaris* (Middle Cambrian) and *Echinocaris* (Devonian) are typical fossil genera, and *Nebalia* is a modern form (Fig. 163).

Series 2. **Eumalacostraca**

Division *A*. **Syncarida**—In this division the carapace is lacking, and the first thoracic segment is fused with the head. (Carboniferous to Recent.)

Order 1. Anaspidacea—An order found in Carboniferous and Permian strata and now extinct except for a fresh-water form living in Australia and Tasmania. *Palaeocaris* (Pennsylvanian) is representative of the fossil genera and *Anaspis* is the lone living genus (Fig. 163).

Division *B*. **Peracarida**—Small, mainly marine forms in which the test, if present, consists of four free thoracic segments and a carapace (Carboniferous to Recent.) *Anthrapalaemon* (Pennsylvanian) is a fossil representative (Fig. 163).

Order 1. Cumacea—No known fossils.

Order 2. Tanaidacea—No known fossils.

Order 3. Mysidacea (Prawns)—Carboniferous to Recent.

Order 4. Isopoda—Terrestrial pill bugs and their marine relatives. (Devonian to Recent.) *Cyclosphaeroma* (Jurassic) and *Sphaeroma* (Recent) are representatives (Fig. 163).

Order 5. Amphipoda (sand hoppers and sand fleas). (Tertiary to Recent.)

Division *C*. **Eucarida**—In this division the carapace covers a cephalothorax, and the eyes are stalked.

Order 1. Euphausiacea—No known fossils (Fig. 148).

Order 2. Decapoda—Most of the existing crustaceans belong in this order. In the suborder Natantia the abdominal appendages are well developed for swimming, but in the Reptantia they are small, and the first pair of legs are usually enlarged and provided with

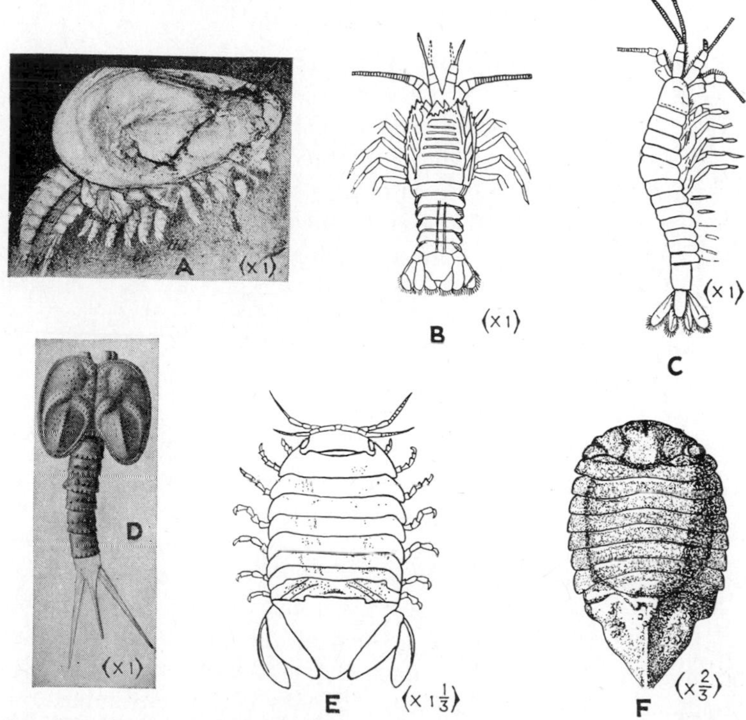

FIG. 163.—Recent and fossil Malacostraca. *A. Hymenocaris perfecta*, from the Middle Cambrian of British Columbia, showing a side view of the right valve and the form of the valve, abdomen, and various appendages. *B*. Dorsal view of *Anthrapalaemon gracilis* from the Pennsylvanian of Illinois. *C. Palaeocaris typus* from the Pennsylvanian of Illinois. *D. Echinocaris socialis* from the Upper Devonian (Chemung) of Pennsylvania. *E. Sphaeroma gigas*, a Recent isopod from Kerguelen Island in the Indian Ocean. *F. Cyclosphaeroma trilobatum*, a fossil isopod from the Jurassic of England. (*A after Walcott; B–C after Meek and Worthen; D after Beecher; E–F after Woodward.*)

pincer claws. Both suborders range from the Triassic to the Recent. The Reptantia include the following:

Palinura—Triassic to Recent.

Astacura (Lobsters and Crayfish)—Jurassic to Recent (*Astacus*, Fig. 149).

Anomura (Hermit Crabs)—Cretaceous to Recent.

Brachyura (Crabs)—Jurassic to Recent.

Division *D*. **Hoplocarida**—Small carapace and at least four free thoracic segments. The abdomen is large and ends in a tail fan.

Order 1. Stomatopoda—A relatively small group ranging from the Carboniferous to Recent. *Sculda* from the Jurassic is a typical genus.

Class Onychophora[1]

General Considerations.—The class Onychophora includes only the aberrant arthropod *Peripatus*, with its several subgenera; and a family of fossil forms (Aysheaidae) from the Middle Cambrian. *Peripatus* differs widely from all other arthropods in certain important features of organization but is very much like them in others. The same statement may be made concerning its relations to the annelid worms. In some respects it is transitional between the Arthropoda and the Annelida. The most recent students of the class are inclined to remove it from the Arthropoda and include it with the annelid worms in a new phylum of the animal kingdom. Some investigators have suggested that the fossil representatives of the class are mere relics of a large assemblage of closely related organisms which lived during the later Pre-Cambrian and early Paleozoic but which have left only a very incomplete record of their existence.

The body of *Peripatus* closely resembles that of the caterpillar, being cylindrical and unsegmented. It has a distinct head and a number of pairs of short, stumpy appendages (14 to 42 depending on the species). The surface of the body is thrown into minute transverse wrinkles and is covered with numerous conical papillae, each of which is capped with a tiny chitinous spine. The head bears two prominent antennae, a pair of eyes, a pair of jaws, and two short processes known as *oral papillae*. A jaw is situated on either side of the mouth and consists of two curved, sickle-like, pointed chitinous plates, the inner of which is toothed on its posterior concave edge. The mouth is surrounded by a circular lip. The *legs* are not jointed but consist of a conical proximal part and a small distal part known as the *foot*, the latter terminating in a pair of small horny claws. Rows of papillae give the legs a ringed appearance.

The modern members of the Onychophora are structurally very much like the expected ancestor of both the arthropods

[1] Onychophora—Gr. *onyx*, *onychos*, a claw + *pherein*, to bear; referring to the pair of claws in which each foot terminates.

and the annelid worms and give much weight to the view that the Arthropoda were evolved from some primitive annelid ancestor. When a fossil onychophoroid was found, therefore, in the Middle Cambrian Burgess shale it was immediately hailed as confirmation of the ancient lineage of the class. It is interesting to note, however, that the Cambrian onychophoroids were marine, whereas modern representatives are all terrestrial, living in damp places under bark or stones.

Since there are no hard parts except tiny chitinous jaws which might be preserved, it is not surprising that there is such a meager fossil record. Only under unusually favorable conditions as those which prevailed during the Middle Cambrian in British Columbia could a perishable body like that of an onychophoroid be preserved. It is possible, however, that some of the minute chitinous jaws which are now being found and described in rather large numbers may be all that remains of certain representatives of the class.

Classification.—The Onychophora are included in the Arthropoda with the full realization that they may constitute a division of animals which should have the same rank as the Arthropoda and Annelida and which, furthermore, should possibly be placed intermediate between them, but the present disposition is the most convenient until more is known about the fossil representatives of the class.

The Onychophora are divided by some students into two orders—the *Protonychophora,* including the ancient fossil forms of the Middle Cambrian family, Aysheaidae (Fig. 39); and the *Euonychophora,* represented by the single living family Peripatidae.

Class Myriapoda[1]

General Considerations.—The Myriapoda comprise a group of tracheate arthropods with a distinct head provided with jaws and bearing a single pair of antennae. There is an elongate, wormlike trunk composed of a number of similar segments each of which is provided with one or two pairs of jointed, leglike appendages. The head bears a pair of eyes and three pairs of jaws. The skin is stiffened with chitin (Fig. 164).

[1] Myriapoda—Gr. *myrios,* numberless + *pous, podos;* referring to the large number of legs possessed by certain members of this class.

Classification.—The class is usually divided into the *Progoneata,* in which the genital apertures are situated near the

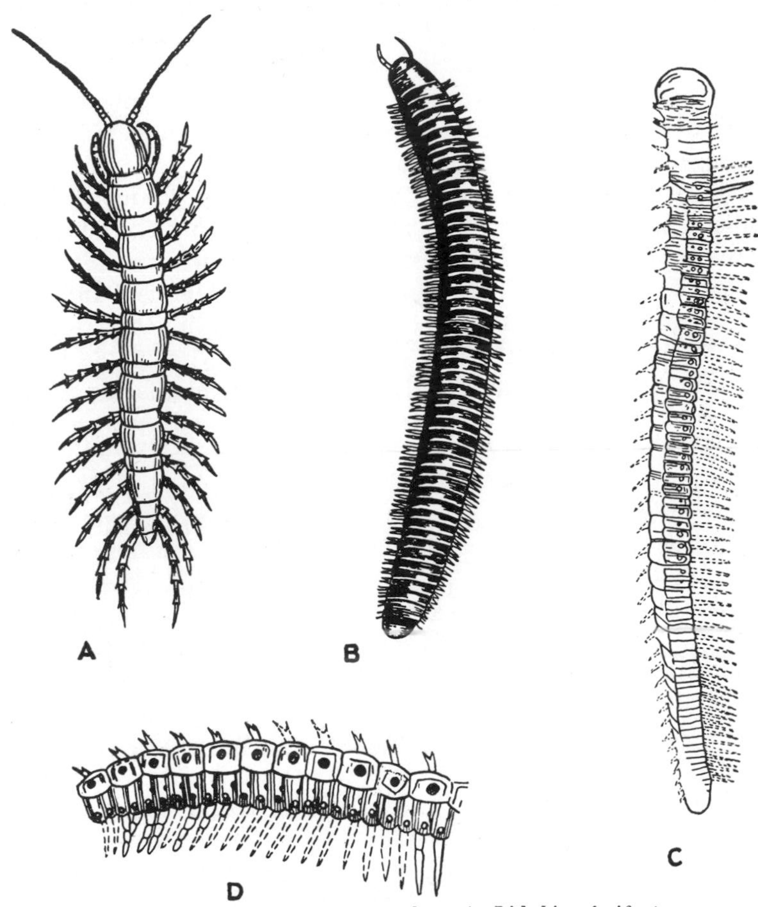

FIG. 164.—Living and fossil Myriapoda. *A. Lithobius forificatus,* a recent centipede somewhat enlarged and viewed dorsally. *B. Iulus maximus,* a modern millipede. *C–D. Euphoberia armigera,* a fossil millipede from the Pennsylvanian of Illinois: *C,* an entire specimen, with the head. The small dorsal spines and larger ventral legs are dotted in because they are not well preserved in the actual specimen; *D,* portion of an individual showing the two kinds of segments. The dark spots on the dorsal plates are pits left in the matrix by spines. (*A–B after Nicholson and Lydekker; C–D after Meek and Worthen.*)

anterior extremity of the body; and the *Opisthogoneata,* with the openings in a posterior position. Since the fossil record of this class is very incomplete, it is deemed sufficient to give only a very brief outline of the various divisions. Fossil myriapods are known from the Devonian to the present time, but the more ancient forms cannot be grouped in the same orders as living representatives of the class (Fig. 164). They are usually included in orders the members of which are all extinct.

Subclass **Progoneata**
- Order 1. **Pauropoda**—No known fossils.
- Order 2. **Diplopoda** (Millipedes)—Body composed of a large number of double segments each of which, except for the first three, bears two pairs of appendages. (Devonian to Recent.) (Fig. 164 *B–D*.)
- Order 3. **Symphala**—No known fossils.

Subclass **Opisthogoneata**
- Order 1. **Chilopoda** (Centipedes)—Body composed of numerous segments. There are four pairs of jaws. Each foot has a single claw (Carboniferous to Recent.) (Fig. 164 *A*.)

Class Insecta[1]

General Considerations.—The typical insect is a six-legged, air-breathing arthropod whose body consists of three distinct regions—head, thorax, and abdomen. The head is devoid of external segmentation, nearly always carries a pair of compound eyes, and has four pairs of modified appendages. The anterior pair is in the form of antennae; the next pair are mandibles; and the last two pairs are maxillae. The jaws are differently modified in the various orders. The eye is composed of many individual facets, of which there are 4,000 in the housefly and 28,000 in the dragonfly, and it is often a very conspicuous part of the head. The eyes function mainly to distinguish between still and moving bodies. The thorax is composed of three segments, each of which bears a pair of jointed legs, and the second and third usually bear wings on the dorsal surface in the adult stage. There may be one or two pairs of wings, or the insect may be wingless. The abdomen has a varying number of segments (7 to 11) and is devoid of appendages in the adult condition. The animal lacks a liver, has salivary glands, and possesses an elongated tubular heart which is divided into eight chambers and is situated in the abdomen. The typical insect is an air breather, and the respiratory organs take the form of breathing tubes or tracheae through which air is conveyed to

[1] Insecta—L. *in*, into + *secare*, to cut; referring to the strongly segmented character of the insect body.

all parts of the body. The nervous system and sense organs are very complex in most insects. The sexes are separate, and development of an individual usually proceeds through a definite series of growth stages beginning with the egg and ending with the winged stage. The successive stages are egg, *larval*, *pupal*, and *imagoal*, and *adult*. The egg is deposited in a suitable place and after a period of time hatches into the wormlike larva. This larva continues to grow, usually consuming a large amount of food in the meantime. It finally incases itself in some sort

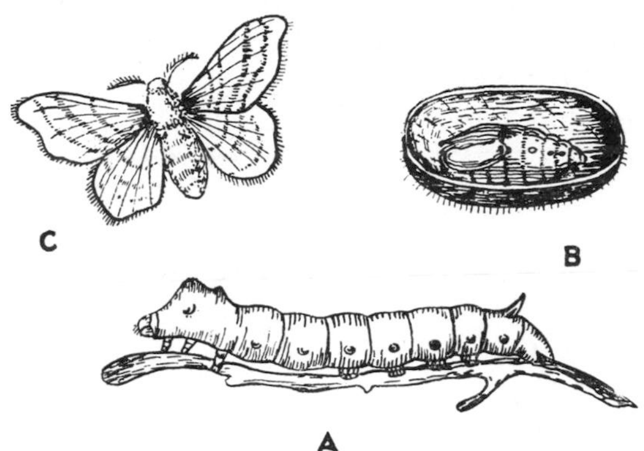

FIG. 165.—Life history of the silk moth, *Bombyx mori*. *A*. Caterpillar. *B*. Pupa and pupal case or cocoon, the latter cut open to show the interior. *C*. Imago. (*After Thomson.*)

of capsular structure and during a resting period undergoes a metamorphosis in which the typical insect characters develop from the larva. This period of rest is known as the pupal stage and gives way, when the young insect emerges from its pupal case, to the imagoal, which in turn passes into the adult stage of growth. Some of these stages may be omitted in certain forms (Fig. 165).

When the young are hatched from the egg stage they may be essentially like their parents (*e.g.*, cockroaches and grasshoppers), except for the wings which develop after a few molts. In the larval stage the young insect resembles a worm (*e.g.*, the caterpillar of the butterfly or the maggot of the housefly), and this stage may be passed in the ground, in water, in wood, in flesh, or on vegetation. The length of the larval stage may be long or short, depending on the species. At its completion the larva incases itself in a chitinous or woven capsule (cocoon of the "silkworm") and there undergoes the metamorphosis which transforms it into a typical adult. This pupal stage of metamorphosis may be quite extended, as in the case of the 17-year locust; or quite short, as in many flies, where it is almost entirely dispensed with. In temperate climates the pupal stage usually begins in the fall on the approach of cold weather and ends with the approach of warm weather in the spring. Some species, like the striped potato beetle, have several successions of larval-pupal-imagoal generations in a single summer. In the mosquito the larvae are free-swimming aquatic organisms.

Many insects have larval forms that bore into wood, and timbers that are left out of doors may, within a few years, be honeycombed with small tubes cut by them. Many a person has been dismayed to find clothes in his closet perforated by small holes that were cut by the larvae of the moth. Carpets and rugs on the floors of dark rooms may be totally destroyed by the same larvae.

It costs the people of the earth millions of dollars annually to keep their insect enemies under control, and many governments are doing their utmost to prevent importation of harmful insects by imposing quarantines and other restrictive measures. Some of the most extensive damage is done by ants which enter houses and tunnel through the timbers, in some cases reducing the woodwork to a mere shell. Other very destructive insects are the cotton boll weevil and the chinch bug.

The reproductive ability of insects is enormous. The common housefly, for example, if it could multiply without destruction and if there were an adequate food supply, could bury the surface features of the earth in a very short time with its progeny. Of the animals inhabiting the earth at the present time none is more numerous and more varied than the insects. In one form or another they are adapted to eat nearly everything organic and to live anywhere; and were it not for the fact that they serve as food for numerous animals, it would not be long before they would make the earth uninhabitable for other animals. Birds probably constitute the most dangerous enemy that the insects have. It has often been stated that man's most serious competitors for mastery of the earth are the Insecta. He makes constant war upon them in some form or another to prevent them from destroying his dwellings, the clothes that he wears, and the food that he eats. Orchards must be sprayed periodically so that the larvae of certain insects will not destroy the fruit or eat the leaves; tobacco and potato vines, as well as many other plants, must be sprayed regularly to destroy beetles and, a short time later, their larvae. Imaginative writers like to picture the earth inhabited by cyclopean insects with powers thousands of times those of men, but nature seems to have decreed that insects must forever remain small, for there does not appear to be an evolutionary trend toward gigantism among living forms.

About 500,000 species of insects have been described, and it has been estimated that between 2,000,000 and 10,000,000 are living at present on the earth. They live in every habitat in all regions, from the cold of the polar latitudes to the tropics, and wherever found there are always forms that make life miserable for other animals. In Labrador the black flies of the "bush" at times are so abundant and vicious that without protection one cannot long endure them, and in the swamps of the same region mosquitoes make life a burden for any animal entering their domain. Many insects are responsible for the carrying of dangerous diseases, either as hosts for the organisms which are responsible for the ailment or as actual carriers from the source of infection.

Classification.—The taxonomy of a group as varied and numerous as the Insecta is full of difficult problems, and hence there is no general consensus of opinion as to what the major divisions should comprise. The classification that follows is that of Handlirsch. Extinct orders are indicated by an asterisk.

Subclass 1. **Pterygogenea**—Insects normally winged in the adult stage, secondarily wingless, with faceted eyes and 9 or 10 abdominal segments. (Devonian to Recent.)

*Order 1. **Palaeodictyoptera**—Many of the ancient fossil insects are placed in this extinct order, which is supposed to have given rise to the majority of extinct Paleozoic orders, and the latter in turn are ancestral to modern groups. Members of the order had two pairs of wings of unequal size and similar form. The venation of the wings was primitive, and the wings could not be folded backward over the abdomen. In some cases (*e.g.*, *Stenodictya*) there was a rudimentary third pair of wings on the first thoracic segment. The order includes 120 species, assigned to 23 families, and it is very probable that only a small fraction of the ancient forms have been unearthed. About three-fourths of the known fossil forms have come from Europe, the remainder from the United

States and Canada. The order is exclusively Paleozoic, ranging from the beginning of the Pennsylvanian through the Permian (Fig. 166 *d.*)

*Order 2. **Mixotermitoidea**—An aberrant offshoot of the above order represented by two genera of Pennsylvanian age.

*Order 3. **Reculoidea**—An aberrant group of the Palaeodictyoptera represented by the single genus *Recula* from the coal measures of Saxony.

*Order 4. **Protorthoptera**—An ancient group of locust-like insects which appear to be intermediate between the Palaeodictyoptera and the living Orthoptera proper. About 90 species from strata of Pennsylvanian and Permian age are known.

Order 5. **Orthoptera**—A modern group including the grasshoppers, locusts, katydids, and crickets. There do not appear to be any fossil representatives before the Jurassic.

Order 6. **Phasmoidea**—A modern group of insects including the familiar walking sticks and leaf insects. (Jurassic to Recent.)

Order 7. **Dermaptera**—A modern group including the familiar ear-wigs. Fossil forms are known from the Tertiary to Recent.

Order 8. **Diploglossata**—This order includes the parasitical family Hemimeridae, living in Africa, and has no known fossil representatives.

Order 9. **Thysanoptera**—Middle Eocene to Recent.

*Order 10. **Protoblattoidea**—An exclusively Paleozoic order intermediate between the Palaeodictyoptera and the Blattoidea and Mantoidea. The more primitive members of this order are very similar to those of the Protorthoptera. (Carboniferous and Permian.)

Order 11. **Blattoidea**—A modern group of insects including the cockroaches. This order includes the majority of Paleozoic insects. Over 300 species are known from North America, and a still larger number from Europe. About 80 Jurassic species have been described, some 40 are known from the Tertiary, and there are over 1,200 living species. A number of the specialized orders of the late Paleozoic (also confined to that geologic time) are thought to have evolved from this generalized stock. (Pennsylvanian to Recent.)

Order 12. **Mantoidea**—This living order includes the interesting soothsayers or praying insects and has fossil representatives as far back as the Upper Permian.

Order 13. **Isoptera**—The Isoptera comprise the termites or white ants and make their appearance in the Eocene. About 350 living species are known.

Order 14. **Corrodentia**—This order includes the living book lice and is known from a few fossils preserved in Oligocene and Miocene amber.

Order 15. **Mallophaga**—Parasitic bird lice, unknown in the fossil state.

Order 16. **Siphunculata**—Modern ectoparasitical Insecta unknown in the fossil state.

Order 17. **Coleoptera**—The Coleoptera or beetles are well represented in modern insect faunas and have numerous fossil representatives, the earliest of which appear in the Upper Jurassic. About 350 species are known from the Mesozoic, some of which belong to modern families; nearly 2,300 species from the Tertiary; and over 200,000 from the present assemblage.

Order 18. **Hymenoptera**—This order comprises the familiar ants, bees, and wasps and makes its appearance in the Jurassic. About 300 species are known from Tertiary strata, and over 10,000 modern species have been described.

*Order 19. **Hadentomoidea**—This order comprises a single genus *Hadentomum*, which is limited to the Carboniferous and may be transitional to the next order.

Order 20. **Embioidea**—A small group of tiny and feeble insects which appear to represent the remainder of a once flourishing stock. A few fossil forms have been found in the Baltic amber (Lower Oligocene) and in the Florissant Miocene beds of Colorado.

*Order 21. **Sypharopteroidea**—An extinct order erected to include the single genus *Sypharoptera* from the Pennsylvanian. It probably represents a highly specialized aberrant offshoot from the Palaeodictyoptera.

*Order 22. **Hapalopteroidea**—An extinct group of Carboniferous insects which probably represent a specialized derivative from the Palaeodictyoptera.

Order 23. **Perlaria**—A group of amphibious insects first represented by fossils in the Permian and in later periods to the Present.

*Order 24. **Protephemeroidea**—This order includes the single Upper Carboniferous genus *Triplosoba*, which is considered as a connecting link between the ancient Paleaodictyoptera and the true Ephemeridae or May flies, included in the next order.

Order 25. **Plectoptera**—A modern group comprising the delicate amphibious May flies. The first fossil forms are known from Permian strata, and about 300 species of modern May flies are known. These are thought to represent the remnants of a dying race.

*Order 26. **Protodonata**—An extinct order of very large insects which appeared in the Pennsylvanian and became extinct in the Triassic. They are thought to be transitional between the Palaeodictyoptera and the true Odonata or dragonflies.

Order 27. **Odonata**—A modern group including the familiar dragonflies. True Odonata appear first in the Lower Jurassic and are represented by about 2,500 living species.

Order 28. **Megaloptera**—This order comprises the modern alder flies and has a long geologic history which reaches back to the Lower Triassic.

Order 29. **Raphidioidea**—A small order including the modern snake flies. The first fossil representatives are known from the Lower Oligocene, although the group is probably of Pre-Tertiary origin.

Order 30. **Neuroptera**—An order of insects including lacewing flies and ant lions which is first represented by fossil forms in the Lower Jurassic. There are only a few Mesozoic species, about 30 Cenozoic species, and some 1,300 Recent forms.

*Order 31. **Megasecoptera**—An extinct order of insects probably derived from the Palaeodictyoptera and ancestral to the Panorpatae. The order is exclusively Paleozoic. (Carboniferous and Permian.)

Order 32. **Panorpatae**—The Panorpatae, including the scorpion flies and now apparently dying out, are abundantly represented in the Jurassic of Europe, and about 100 living species are known.

Order 33. **Trichoptera**—This order includes the caddisflies and appears in the Lower Jurassic. In addition to a few Mesozoic species some 200 Tertiary and 1,400 Recent species are known. In some formations (Indusial limestone of Auvergne) the cases of certain trichopterous larvae are extremely abundant.

Order 34. **Lepidoptera**—The butterflies and moths which constitute this order are among the best known and most beautiful of insect groups. The earliest remains are found in the Jurassic, and only a few Mesozoic species are known. About 85 species have been described from the Tertiary. Modern forms, on the other hand, aggregate some 60,000 species.

Order 35. **Diptera**—A very large group of insects comprising nearly 44,000 Recent species, 1,550 Tertiary species, and something over 30 Mesozoic forms. The earliest fossil representatives appear in the Lower Jurassic. Common flies belong to this order.

Order 36. **Suctoria**—The fleas constitute a small group of living insects, which have only a single fossil representative, *i.e.*, the genus *Palaeopsylla* from the Lower Oligocene amber of the Baltic region.

*Order 37. **Protohemiptera**—An extinct group, represented by the single genus *Eugereon* from the Lower Permian. This is thought to be a connecting link between the Palaeodictyoptera on the one hand and the Homoptera and Hemiptera on the other.

*Order 38. **Palaeohemiptera**—A provisional extinct group including fossil forms from the Permian and Lower Jurassic.

Order 39. **Hemiptera**—The terrestrial and aquatic bugs comprise this order, which has Mesozoic representatives that in most cases cannot be classified with modern families. The Tertiary species, on the other hand, are much like Recent ones.

Order 40. **Homoptera**—This order includes the plant lice, wax bugs, and harvest flies. It is represented in Mesozoic strata by 50 species; in the Tertiary, by about 200; and in modern faunas, by nearly 10,000. The earliest fossil forms appear in the Jurassic.

Subclass 2. **Apterygogenea**—Wingless insects with the abdomen having 6 to 12 segments. There is no metamorphosis.

Order 1. **Thysanura**—A small group of apterygote insects ranging from the Lower Oligocene to Recent.

Order 2. **Campodeoidea**—The members of this order are similar to those of the preceding. The range is from the Lower Oligocene to Recent, and the genus *Campodea* is a representative living form.

Order 3. **Collembola**—The springtails comprise some 450 Recent species, and there are about 70 from the Lower Oligocene amber of the Baltic.

Order 4. **Protura**—Small subterraneous insects without antennae and eyes. They are unknown in the fossil state.

Geologic History.—The earliest known fossil insects occur in Pennsylvanian strata, and they appear to have been fairly

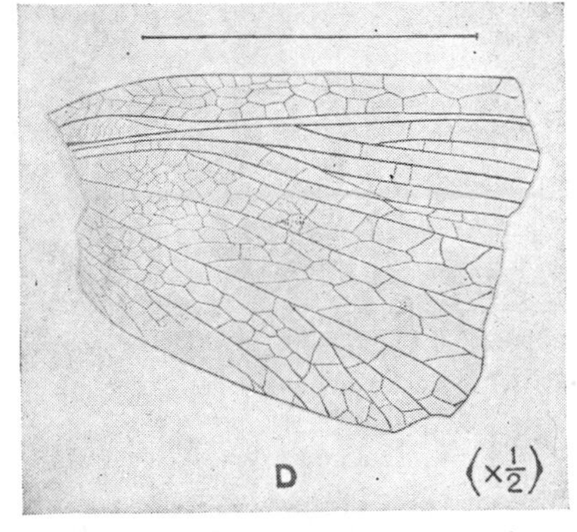

Fig. 166.—Fossil insects. *A*. A fossil butterfly (*Prodryas persephone*) from the Miocene shales of Florissant, Colo. *B*. *Spaniodera ambulans*, a fossil representative of the Protorthoptera, from the Pennsylvanian of Mazon Creek, Ill. *C*. A fossil beetle, *Anthonomus arctus*, from the Miocene shales of Florissant, Colo. *D*. Part of a wing of *Hypermegethes schucherti*, a fossil representative of the Palaeodictyoptera, from the Pennsylvanian of Mazon Creek, Ill. (*A after Scudder; B after Handlirsch; C from Scudder after Blake; D after Handlirsch.*)

abundant in the coal-forming swamps (Fig. 166). The insects of the Paleozoic are entirely extinct, and most of them belonged to orders which are no longer in existence. A few have been placed in orders which have living representatives. A single order, the Palaeodictyoptera, is found in the Lower Pennsylvanian and persists to the close of the Permian. It appears to have been ancestral to a number of late Paleozoic orders and, through them, to the several later orders. There are 12 orders in the Upper Pennsylvanian and 10 in the Permian. Only 4 orders are represented in the Triassic—a situation which may be due to the lack of preservation, failure to discover preserved remains, or actual absence of living forms. Seventeen orders are present in the Jurassic, but only 6 are found in the Cretaceous, and all of these were also present in the preceding period. In the Tertiary there are 27 orders, and of these 16 are also present in the Jurassic; hence 10 Jurassic orders cross the Cretaceous without representation, a situation which is almost certainly due to the lack of discovered remains. At the present time there are 31 living orders of which 1 extends back to the Pennsylvanian and 4 to the Permian. The wingless insects are not known earlier than the Tertiary. The ranges of the various orders are shown in Table 11.

It is generally agreed that the geologic record of the Insecta is very incomplete because of the great difficulties of preservation. Fossil insects are rarely preserved in marine deposits, and they could not be preserved in most continental deposits. If they are preserved in any degree of abundance, the inclosing deposits show unusual conditions of sedimentation. The majority of ancient insects now found in a fossilized condition were covered with silt or some other type of fine-grained sediment before they could decompose, or else they were hermetically sealed in gums which later became amber. Insect remains have been found in coal, lignite, peat, amber, volcanic ash, and various muds and silts.

One of the best known American localities is at Florissant, Colo., where an ancient fresh-water lake received deposits of volcanic ash. This ash in falling carried down insects and other organisms and buried them in the deposits of the lake. Terrestrial and water-dwelling forms are found mixed together, a mixture which could never have existed during life. A second locality from which numerous Pennsylvanian insects have been obtained is Mazon Creek in northern Illinois. Here they are preserved in small concretions in the argillaceous sandstones. At Solnhofen, Bavaria, insects were entombed in the fine calcare-

TABLE 11.—CHART SHOWING THE GEOLOGIC RANGE OF THE VARIOUS ORDERS OF INSECTA

(Based on the Classification in Zittel's "Text-Book of Palaeontology," vol. 1, Macmillan & Co., Ltd., 1927.)

Orders	Mississippian	Pennsylvanian	Permian	Triassic	Jurassic	Cretaceous	Tertiary	Quaternary
Class I. **Pterygogenea**								
1. Palaeodictyoptera	—	—	- -					
2. Mixotermitoidea		— -						
3. Reculoidea		—						
4. Protorthoptera		—	—	- -				
5. Orthoptera				- -	—	- -	—	—
6. Phasmoidea					- —	- -	—	—
7. Dermaptera						- - —	—	—
8. Diploglossata							- -	—
9. Thysanoptera						- - —	—	—
10. Protoblattoidea		—	-					
11. Blattoidea		—	—	—	—	—	—	—
12. Mantoidea			—	- -	—	- -	—	—
13. Isoptera						- -	—	—
14. Corrodentia						- -	—	—
15. Mallophaga							- -	—
16. Siphunculata							- -	—
17. Coleoptera			- -	—	—	—	—	—
18. Hymenoptera				- -	—	—	—	—
19. Hadentomoidea		—	—					
20. Embioidea			- -	- -	- -	- -	—	—
21. Sypharopteroidea		—						
22. Hapalopteroidea		—						
23. Perlaria			—	- -	—	- -	—	—
24. Protephemeroidea		—	- -					
25. Plectoptera			—	- -	—	- -	—	—
26. Protodonata		—	—	—				
27. Odonata				- -	—	—	—	—
28. Megaloptera			—	- -	- -	- -	—	—
29. Raphidioidea			—	- -	- -	- -	—	—
30. Neuroptera			—	- -	- -	- -	—	—
31. Megasecoptera		—	- -					
32. Panorpatae					—	- -	—	—
33. Trichoptera					—	—	—	—
34. Lepidoptera					—	- -	—	—
35. Diptera					—	- -	—	—
36. Suctoria						- -	—	—
37. Protohemiptera			- -					
38. Palaeohemiptera			—	- -	—			
39. Hemiptera				- -	—	- -	—	—
40. Homoptera				- -	—	—	—	—
Class II. **Apterygogenea**								
1. Thysanura			- -	- -	- -	- -	—	—
2. Campodeoidea						- -	—	—
3. Collembola						- -	—	—
4. Protura							- -	—

ous muds that accumulated on the bottoms of the lagoons between Jurassic coral bioherms. One of the richest of all fossil-insect localities is in the Baltic region of East Prussia, where thousands of specimens are preserved in Lower Oligocene amber. Some of these insects are so exquisitely preserved that seen through the transparent amber it seems as though they had been buried only yesterday. A few other famous localities are in the Pennsylvanian of Commentry, France, and Saarbrücken in southwestern Rhenish Prussia; in the Permian of Kansas and New South Wales; in the Triassic of Queensland; in the Eocene Green River shales of western United States; in the Miocene of Oeningen in Baden; and in the Pleistocene clays in Switzerland, Germany, and Ontario and in peat of the same age in France and England.

Fossil-insect remains vary greatly in character. In certain localities the animals are preserved almost as they were in life. Impressions of the body and of the delicate venation of the wings, or thin carbonaceous films representing these structures, are of fairly common occurrence in certain fine-grained sediments. Tracks of supposed insects, and also creatures believed to be aquatic larvae (of an alder fly), have been reported from the Triassic of Connecticut. Rarely the pupal cases of certain larvae have been reported.

Class Arachnida[1]

General Considerations.—The Arachnida comprise a highly advanced group of arthropods among which are such familiar forms as scorpions, mites and ticks, and spiders. One large group of aquatic members, the Eurypterida and allies, are extinct, though *Limulus*, the king crab, is a living descendant.

The body of an arachnid is divisible into two distinct sections—an anterior part or *cephalothorax* and a posterior part or *abdomen*. The division of the two lies behind the sixth pair of appendages. The segments of the former section are usually coalesced; those of the latter are free or fused. There are no true antennae, the corresponding appendages of the arachnids being designated *chelicerae*. There are six pairs of appendages on the cephalothorax. The first pair are chelicerae; the second, *pedipalps;*

[1] Arachnida—Gr. *arachne*, spider; referring to the spiders which constitute one of the large subdivisions of the class.

and the third to sixth pairs, legs. None is biramous, and those around the mouth are not greatly modified as jaws, but all have gnathobases similar to those in the Trilobita. They are used for crushing food.

The abdomen is divided into a posterior and anterior region in the scorpions, is less clearly divided in the eurypterids, and is consolidated in the spiders and limuli. All body segmentation is obsolete in living mites and ticks. On some forms there is a posterior terminal spine.

The Arachnida represent a distinct line of evolution which began almost certainly during the Pre-Cambrian in some primitive crustacean stock. The group very early acquired a definite structural plan which has persisted throughout its long geologic history. Although they resemble the Insecta in many respects, the arachnids are much more diversified though far less numerous and of more ancient derivation. Respiration is carried on in various ways. The ancient aquatic forms and the modern *Limulus* have book gills, the scorpions breathe by means of book lungs, and the later terrestrial arachnids are equipped with air tubes or tracheae similar to those of the Insecta.

Reproduction is by means of eggs in some forms, but in others (*e.g.*, scorpions, mites, etc.) the eggs are never laid, and the young are hatched within the body of the mother. In either case the embryonic arachnid has reached a mature stage by the time that it is hatched or born and differs little from its parents except in size. Consequently there are no larval stages comparable to those in the Insecta and no nauplius stage or other free-swimming larval stage such as that found in the Crustacea.

The Exoskeleton.—The arachnid body, and likewise the exoskeleton, is typically exemplified in the ancient scorpion *Palaeophonus* (Fig. 167). It is divided into three regions—prosoma, mesosoma, and metasoma. The *prosoma* is the cephalothoracic portion, and to it are attached the six pairs of appendages. Posteriorly there are six segments, which consist of dorsal pieces—the *terga*—and ventral pieces—the *sterna*—united laterally by soft skin. These constitute the *mesosoma.* The first segment bears on the underside the genital opening, which is closed by an operculum; the second carries a pair of comblike appendages, known as the *pectines,* which are tactile organs; and the third to the sixth segments have broad, flat sternal plates, which are perforated by oblique slits along the lateral margin. These perforations are known as *stigmata* and admit air into the tracheae. The seventh to twelfth segments constitute the *metasoma* (also designated *postabdomen* or *tail*). The first segment of this series is wide like the preceding ones but differs from them in having the tergum and sternum more or less united and in lacking stigmata. It is therefore grouped with the succeeding ringlike segments, though it is

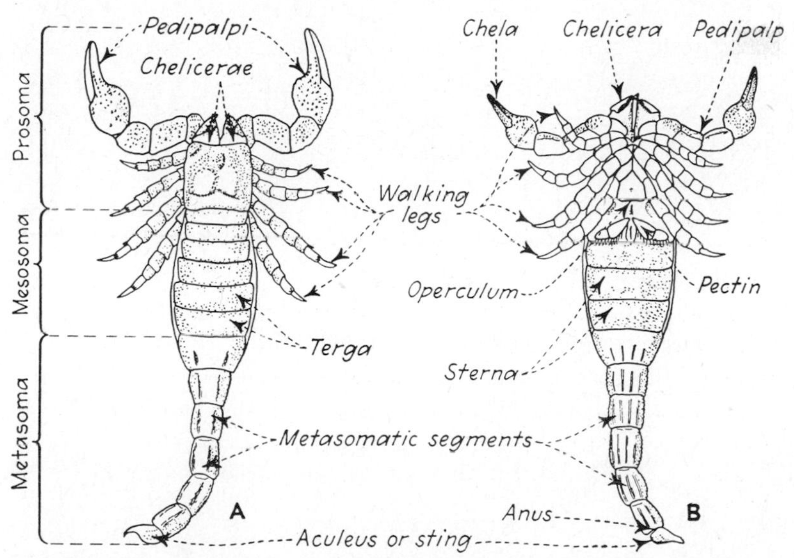

FIG. 167.—Restorations of an ancient Upper Silurian scorpion (*Palaeophonus*). *A*. Dorsal view of *P. nuntius*. *B*. Ventral aspect of *P. caledonicus* showing the space for the genital operculum, the pair of pectines, and the absence of stigmata. (*From Clarke and Ruedemann after Pocock.*)

somewhat larger. The last or twelfth segment has a spinelike appendage which is a stinging structure. It is composed of an expanded base—the *vesicle*—which contains a poisonous fluid; and a pointed extremity—the *aculeus*. In the Eurypterida this appendage is a long, spinelike process.

The carapace covering the prosoma bears two large median eyes and a number of simple eyes at the lateral edges of the frontal margin. The appendages from the front backward are one pair of chelicerae, corresponding to the antennae of the Crustacea; one pair of large *chelae* or pedipalps terminated by claws; and four pairs of seven-jointed appendages terminating in three small claws. The bases of the first three pairs of appendages are arranged about the mouth. Between the last two leg bases is a small sternum.

The oldest Arachnida seem to have been marine. The terrestrial habitat does not appear to have been invaded until the late Ordovician or during the Silurian. Since the Carboniferous, terrestrial forms have constituted the principal group of arachnids. Gaskall[1] has advanced the view that some member of the Arachnida is ancestral to the vertebrates, and Patten[2] later presented further evidence for the view. It has not, however, attained very wide acceptance.

Classification.—The Arachnida are divided into two subclasses—*Merostomata,* a water-breathing division; and *Embolobranchiata,* an air-breathing group. The former were the more primitive, lived in an aquatic habitat, and breathed by means of gills; whereas the latter replaced the lungs by tracheae and developed other necessary structures for life on the land.

Subclass Merostomata[3]

General Considerations.—The Merostomata comprise an ancient race which makes its appearance in the Cambrian and has survived to the present. Most of the species, however, became extinct toward the close of the Paleozoic; and in present seas *Limulus,* the king crab, is the sole survivor. The largest of the arachnids belong to this subclass, which for this reason has sometimes been called *Gigantostraca* (gigantic shell). Individuals with a length of nearly 3 m. (10 ft.) have been described.

There are six pairs of ambulatory appendages about the mouth except in the most primitive group. The first pair of these are chelicerae, and the other five pairs function for locomotion and mastication. The prosoma is depressed and generally bears on its dorsal surface a pair of median ocelli and a pair of laterally situated, kidney-shaped compound eyes. Respiration is accomplished by book gills which are in the nature of lamellar branchiae borne on all but one of the metasomatic segments. The body

[1] GASKALL, W. H., "The Origin of the Vertebrates," 1908.

[2] PATTEN, W., "The Evolution of the Vertebrates and Their Kin," 1912.

[3] Merostomata—Gr. *meros,* part + *stoma, stomatos,* body; referring to the division of the body into distinct parts.

is large, and in many species the metasoma terminates in a long spine or telson.

The Merostomata are the more ancient of the two subclasses, and the earliest representatives are thought to be near the ancestral stock from which the Arachnida originated. Whether or not the scorpions and spiders evolved from the merostomes cannot be stated definitely, but the morphological structures common to all suggest that such may have been the case or else that all originated from a common stock.

The Merostomata have been subdivided into the four orders of *Xiphosura*, *Synxiphosura*, *Eurypterida*, and *Limulava*.

ORDER XIPHOSURA[1]

The Xiphosura are the primitive and ancient forms of horseshoe crabs. They have a trilobed exoskeleton, consisting of a large horseshoe-shaped carapace which covers the cephalothorax and a distinct abdomen which terminates in a prominent telson. The compound eyes, if present, are lateral, and the ocelli are near the center in front. The abdomen has from 7 to 10 segments which dorsally are free or coalesced, and the 6 anterior ones are provided with lamellar appendages (gills) on the ventral side. The essential exoskeletal features of the modern *Limulus* are illustrated in Fig. 168.

The earliest fossil representatives of the Xiphosura appear in the Devonian, and the order is represented in modern seas by several species of *Limulus*. Fossil Xiphosura are found in the Devonian (*Belinurus*), Pennsylvanian (*Belinurus*, *Cyclus*, and *Prestwichia*), Permian (*Prolimulus*), and Triassic to Recent (*Limulus*) (Fig. 169).

Limulus, the sole survivor of the Merostomata, is found from Maine to the Gulf of Mexico and from Sumatra to Japan—in both regions in coastal waters. It is a bottom dweller, ploughing through the muds of the sea bottom seeking food. This consists of worms and other small animals. Life in such an environment has brought about the development of plates on the joints of the hind legs; the fusion of the segments of the body and of the exoskeleton, thereby making the latter stronger (especially the carapace); and possibly the development of the telson. The

[1] Xiphosura—Gr. *xiphos*, sword + *oura*, tail; referring to the swordlike telson.

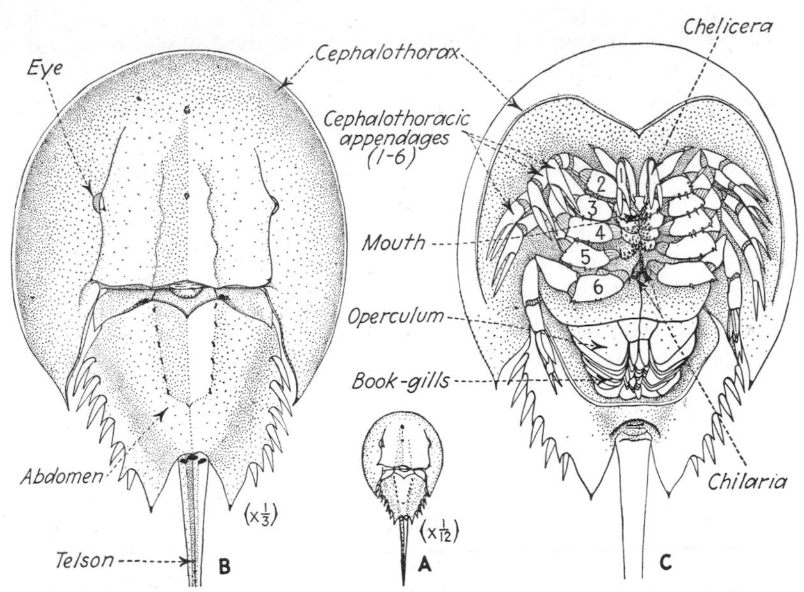

FIG. 168.—*Limulus polyphemus*, a modern king crab from the Atlantic Ocean and a representative of the Xiphosura. *A*. Entire animal viewed dorsally. *B*. Dorsal view of chitinous exoskeleton showing cephalothorax and abdomen and part of prominent caudal spine or telson. *C*. Ventral view showing the various appendages

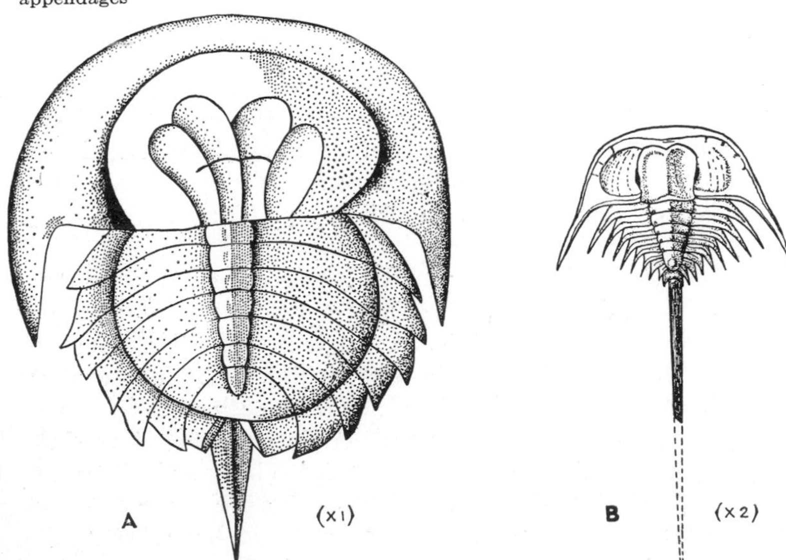

FIG. 169.—Fossil Xiphosura. *A. Prestwichia rotundata* from the Carboniferous of England. *B. Belinurus reginae* from the Carboniferous of Ireland. (*A after Nicholson and Lydekker; B after Woodward.*)

telson is used to assist in ploughing through the mud, the animal sticking it into the bottom materials and using it as a lever; and also in regaining its normal position when accidentally turned on its back. The operculum over the genital opening was developed in response to a need for covering the gills so that they could not be fouled with mud.

ORDER SYNXIPHOSURA[1]

The Synxiphosura are an extinct arachnid group which flourished during the earlier part of the Paleozoic. The cephalo-

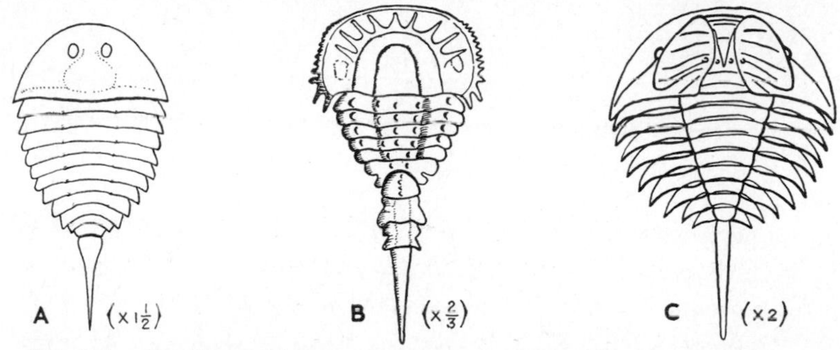

FIG. 170—Fossil Synxiphosura. *A*. Generalized diagram of the dorsal view of an aglaspid, based on the holotype of "*Aglaspis*" *eatoni* Whitfield and several other specimens from the Upper Cambrian of Wisconsin. Restoration was made under the supervision of G. O. Raasch. The shield consists of the cephalothorax, 11 simple abdominal segments, and a prominent telson segment. *B*. *Hemiaspis limuloides* from the Silurian of England. *C*. *Neolimulus falcatus* from the Upper Silurian of England. (*B–C after Woodward*.)

thorax and carapace are semicircular, with a more or less distinct median longitudinal axis, though dorsal furrows are not pronounced. Compound eyes are generally present, but there are no ocelli except in *Neolimulus* (Fig. 170 *C*). There is no evidence of a facial suture, as in the trilobites; but there is a transversely trilobate abdomen composed of free segments. The pleurae are flat and terminate laterally in flat projections or spines. The last abdominal segment is prolonged into a prominent telson. In the case of the Cambrian forms, at least, walking legs are present on the abdominal segments. In addition, there are

[1] Synxiphosura—Gr. *syn*, with + *xiphos*, sword + *oura*, tail; referring to the presence of a pointed, swordlike telson.

antennae instead of chelicerae, there are no swimming legs, and the animals are considered to have been marine.[1]

Aglaspis and several undescribed genera from the Upper Cambrian of Wisconsin strongly resemble trilobites, especially the Lower Cambrian *Olenellus*, in their external appearance. They lack, however, such typical trilobite structures as facial sutures; pygidium; eyes, such as those found on trilobites; and a distinct thorax. The resemblance strongly suggests that the Synxiphosura and Trilobita had a common ancestor. Other genera are *Neolimulus* from the Baltic Silurian, *Hemiaspis* from the Silurian of Scotland, *Bunodella* from the Silurian of New Brunswick, and *Pseudoniscus* from the Silurian of Esthonia and New York (Fig. 170).

ORDER EURYPTERIDA[2]

The Eurypterida are primitive and extremely interesting arachnids and include the largest of known arthropods. The elongate body was covered by a thin, chitinous integument ornamented with tubercles or fine, scalelike markings. The cephalothorax, which is comparatively small, bears a pair of medium ocelli and two large, crescentic, lateral eyes (Fig. 171). There are six pairs of appendages which vary in character in the different genera. The abdomen consists of 13 segments of which the anterior 6 belong to the mesosoma and, except for the first which carries the genital operculum, bear pairs of broad, leaflike appendages which probably served a respiratory function. These may correspond to the operculum and book gills of *Limulus* (Fig. 168). The metasoma consists of six free, annular, gradually tapering segments without appendages and a long telson.

The largest known arthropods are in this order, and *Pterygotus* and *Stylonurus* are known to have been between 2 and 3 m. long (Fig. 172). All known species were aquatic, but whether in marine, brackish, or fresh water is a moot question. That they lived on the bottom in the main is clear, but the development of two large, paddle-like appendages strongly suggests a

[1] Data furnished by G. O. Raasch, who is engaged in a monographic study of the Upper Cambrian Merostomata.

[2] Eurypterida—Gr. *eurys*, broad + *pteron*, wing; referring to the broad, winglike appendages, which are developed by the modification of one or more of the pairs of appendages.

swimming habit. Grabau and O'Connell have suggested that the eurypterids lived in fresh-water habitats and have marshaled the facts supporting an origin in streams, whence they were carried to the open sea or into brackish or salty lagoons to be buried in marine or lagoonal deposits. The distribution of the fossil remains in sedimentary rocks suggests that they were not dwellers in normally marine waters, except possibly in the early history of the race.

Known growth stages show that when the young eurypterid was hatched it was similar to the adult except that it had a

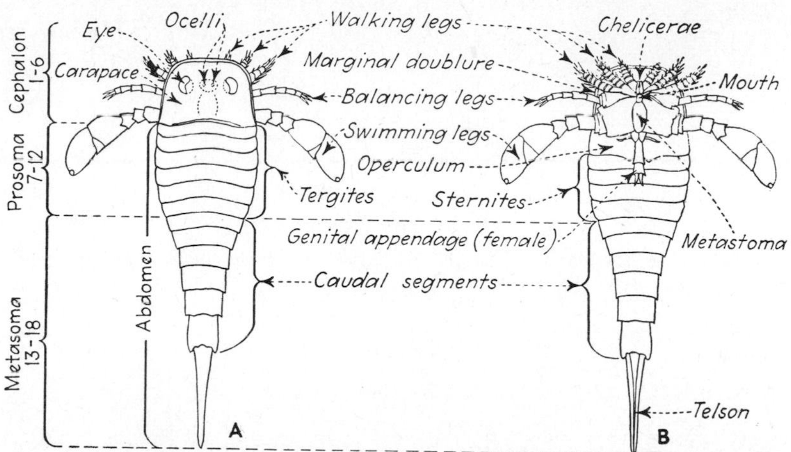

FIG. 171.—Diagram showing ventral and dorsal aspects of an Eurypterid, with the chief structures labeled. (*After Clarke and Ruedemann.*)

relatively larger carapace, larger eyes, fewer segments in the body, and a less marked difference between the mesosoma and metasoma.

The oldest known eurypterid is *Strabops* from the Upper Cambrian of Missouri (Fig. 172 *B*). It has a small prosoma. The mesosoma and metasoma together have 12 segments and a telson and are not differentiated from each other. The eyes are small and relatively farther back than in the later eurypterids. The animal is about 63 mm. (2.25 in.) long and strongly resembles the individuals of the later more advanced forms. No other eurypterids are known until the late Ordovician, but they undoubtedly were in existence and remain to be discovered. This paucity of remains accords with the idea of a fresh-water habitat. The Eurypterida appear to have attained their zenith in the Silurian and Devonian, as judged by the abundance of fossil remains, and became extinct in the Permian. Since most fossil eurypterids have been found in strata showing exceptional conditions of environment, it probably should be assumed that the finds do not give an accurate picture of their abundance.

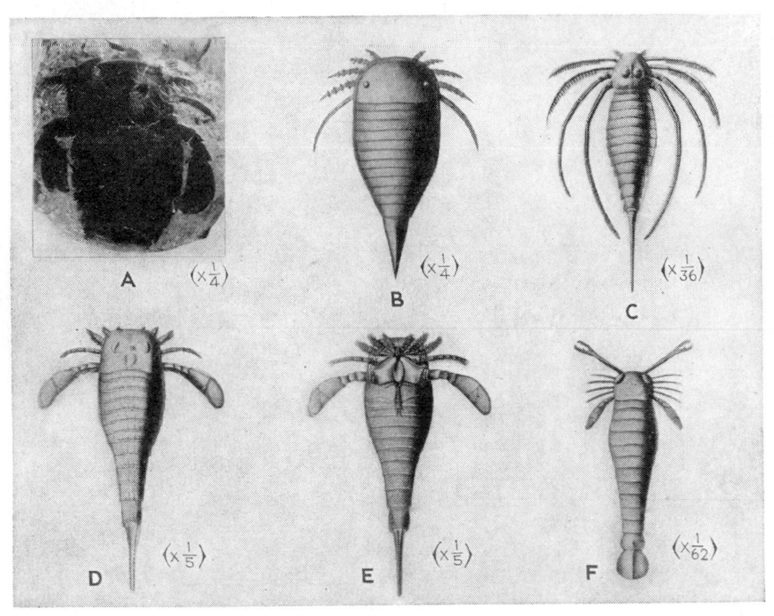

FIG. 172.—Eurypterida. *A*. A fossil eurypterid (*Eurypterus*) showing the general method of fossilization. The swimming appendages are specially conspicuous. *B*. *Strabops thatcheri*, the oldest known eurypterid restored, from the Upper Cambrian of Missouri. *C*. *Stylonurus excelsior*, a giant eurypterid restored, from the Devonian of New York. *D–E*. Dorsal and ventral views of *Eurypterus remipes* from the Upper Silurian of New York. *F*. Dorsal view of a restoration of *Pterygotus buffaloensis*, a giant eurypterid from the Upper Silurian of New York. (*B–F after Clarke and Ruedemann.*)

It is generally held that the Eurypterida were sluggish bottom dwellers or poor swimmers. They are thought to have spent the principal part of life living more or less buried in the bottom muds or crawling sluggishly about over them. The presence of swimming appendages in some forms, however, shows that the swimming habit was developed to some extent. All were probably carnivorous, and the giant forms may well have been dangerous predators. The general absence of eurypterid remains in marine deposits suggests that they were confined to rather narrow environments, and there is much to be said for the view that they lived in streams and lakes on the land or possibly in coastal lagoons.

Eurypterus (Ordovician to Pennsylvanian), *Pterygotus* (Ordovician to Devonian), and *Stylonurus* (Ordovician to Carboniferous) are representative genera (Fig. 172).

ORDER LIMULAVA

The Limulava are a small group of marine arachnids from the Middle Cambrian. There is an elongate body, a prosoma with lateral or marginal eyes, and five pairs of appendages some of which are biramous. The postcephalic part of the body consists of 12 segments, of which the anterior 9 bear branchial appendages. The last segment has a central spatulate process which is combined with lateral structures known as *swimmerets* to form a strong, caudal, fanlike fin. The second and third segments are without appendages. There is some doubt as to whether this order should be assigned to the Merostomata, because of the presence of biramous appendages and the compound caudal swimming organ. It may be that the organisms here included are transitional between the primitive eurypterids and trilobites. The best known genus is *Sidneyia* from the Middle Cambrian of British Columbia (Fig. 173).

FIG. 173.—An ancient merostome (*Sidneyia inexpectans*) from the Middle Cambrian of British Columbia. (*After Walcott.*) (Slightly less than one-half natural size.)

Subclass Embolobranchiata[1]

General Considerations.—The Embolobranchiata comprise the air-breathing arachnids among which are such familiar forms as spiders, scorpions, mites, and ticks. So far as known all are

[1] Embolobranchiata—Gr. *embolos*, anything pointed + *branchia*, gills; referring to the character of the respiratory organs.

terrestrial, breathing by means of book lungs and tracheae. The scorpions, which have already been described in considerable detail, are the most primitive representatives of the subclass and probably are nearest the ancestral stock in general appearance, whereas the ticks seem to be the most highly specialized.

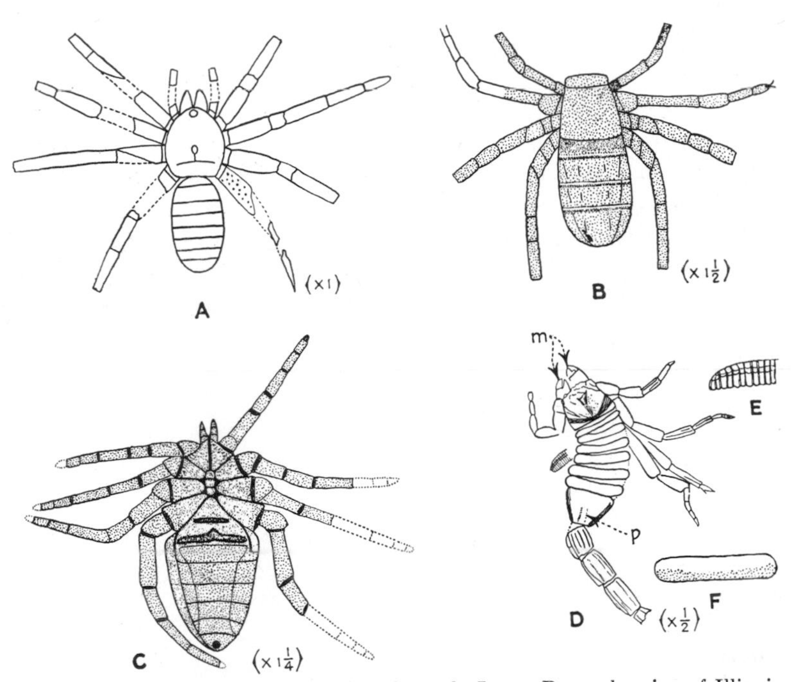

Fig. 174.—Fossil Embolobranchiata from the Lower Pennsylvanian of Illinois. *A. Arthrolycosa antiqua. B. Polyochera punctulata. C. Architarbus rotundatus. D–F. Eoscorpius carbonarius:* *D*, Fragmental specimen, with one of the "combs" lying detached from the body; *E*, Comb enlarged; *F*, One of the body segments enlarged to show the surface granules (*m*, mandibles somewhat crushed and distorted; *p*, small pits). (*A–C after restorations by Petrunkevitch; D–F, after Meek and Worthen.*)

The members of the Embolobranchiata may represent the first animals ever to assume a terrestrial life, and the changes necessary would have been easy, since only slight modification of the respiratory apparatus had to be made. The book gills could develop a covering, thereby being converted into book lungs, and the branchia could be modified into tracheae in the same manner. The chitinous covering favored migration to the land, since its presence lessened evaporation. The earliest forms known to have gone to the land are *Palaeophonus* (Fig. 167) from the European Silurian and *Proscorpius* from the Silurian of New York. These ancient forms resemble eurypterids in some respects and are unlike modern scorpions. The first true scorpions did not appear until the Carboniferous in *Eoscorpius* (Fig. 174 *D*).

Members of the Embolobranchiata have at least three preoral segments in the adult stage. There are a pair of short chelicerae in preoral position and five pairs of postoral appendages (Fig. 167). The head is fused with at least one thoracic segment. The abdomen is typically composed of 12 segments, the last of which contains the anus.

Classification.—Since the fossil record of the Embolobranchiata is a very incomplete one, it will suffice to give in outline the orders, with their better known representatives and their known geologic range. The classification is that of Petrunkevitch.

Order 1. **Scorpionida** (Scorpions)—The telson is modified to form a poison gland and sting. The first scorpions appeared in the Silurian, reached their zenith in the Upper Paleozoic, and are still living. (Figs. 167, 174 *D*.)

Order 2. **Pedipalpida** (Whip Scorpions)—Carboniferous to Recent.

Order 3. **Palpigradi**—No known fossils.

Order 4. **Kustarachnida**—An extinct order confined to the Carboniferous.

Order 5. **Solpugida**—Carboniferous to Recent.

Order 6. **Ricinulei** (Podogonida)—Carboniferous to Recent (Fig. 174 *B*).

Order 7. **Pseudoscorpionida** (Book Scorpions)—Lower Oligocene to Recent.

Order 8. **Araneida** (Araneae)—These are the spiders, which are represented by fossils from the Carboniferous to Recent (Fig. 174 *A*).

Order 9. **Anthracomarti**—An exclusively Paleozoic group which appears to be limited to the Carboniferous.

Order 10. **Haptopoda**—Includes the lone genus *Plesiosiro* from the Carboniferous of England.

Order 11. **Phalangiotarbi**—An extinct order limited to the Carboniferous (Fig. 174 *C*).

Order 12. **Phalangida** (Daddy Longlegs)—Carboniferous to Recent.

Order 13. **Acarina** (Mites, Ticks, Etc.)—Oligocene to Recent.

GEOLOGIC HISTORY OF THE ARTHROPODA

Evolution.—The Arthropoda are now generally believed to have evolved during the late Pre-Cambrian from some group of primitive, aquatic annelid worms. Through their subsequent evolution they have retained the annelid structure of the nervous system, the mode of growth of the body segments, and the dis-

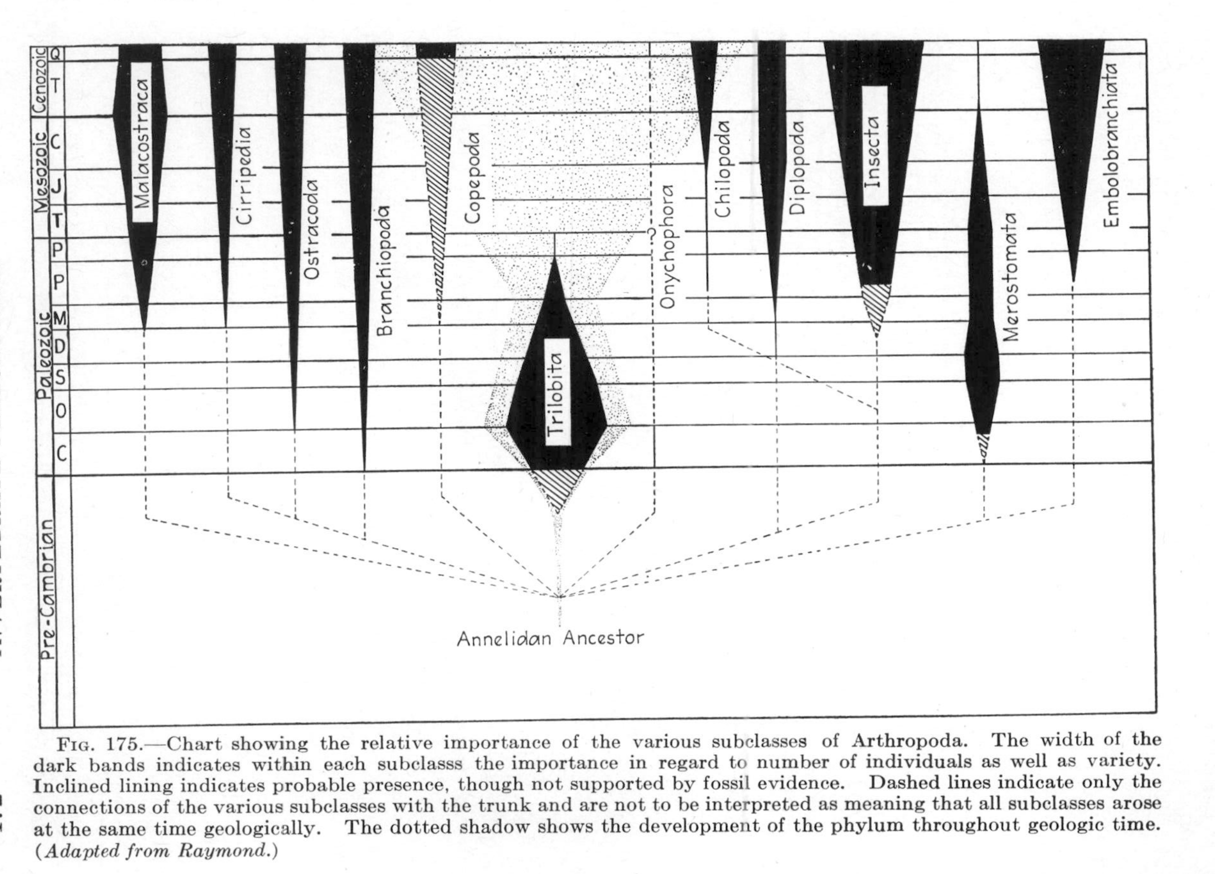

FIG. 175.—Chart showing the relative importance of the various subclasses of Arthropoda. The width of the dark bands indicates within each subclasss the importance in regard to number of individuals as well as variety. Inclined lining indicates probable presence, though not supported by fossil evidence. Dashed lines indicate only the connections of the various subclasses with the trunk and are not to be interpreted as meaning that all subclasses arose at the same time geologically. The dotted shadow shows the development of the phylum throughout geologic time. (*Adapted from Raymond.*)

tinctive elongated and segmented body proper. The beginning of the Cambrian saw them at a high level of development, with a long history behind them, about which nothing is known except by inference. At the earliest known periods of their history it is clear that they had already spread through a wide range of environmental conditions, and numerous divisions of the phylum appear to have originated at about the same time (Fig. 175). The remote ancestors must certainly be sought in Pre-Cambrian strata, and it remains to be shown whether the phylum as now defined had its origin in a single stock or in several closely related ones. The latter possibility seems a little more likely.

The Trilobita, Branchiopoda, and Arachnida are thought to have developed independently from the primitive arthropod group which is supposed to have been in existence in the late Pre-Cambrian. It does not seem likely that the Trilobita were ancestral to any subsequent group of arthropods, though this statement is by no means proved. The Crustacea are thought to have arisen out of the Branchiopoda, and the Arachnida appear to go back for their beginning to some primitive arthropod of the late Pre-Cambrian. The Onychophora, Myriapoda, and Insecta apparently belong to a single line of evolution which had its inception in the same Pre-Cambrian ancestor as the Arachnida. Because of so many gaps in the fossil record the markedly different subdivisions of the Arthropoda have not yet been joined together genetically in any sort of generally accepted relationship, and it seems unlikely that such a union will be established until more information is available.

During its evolution, beginning with the primitive annelid worms from which it is supposed to have been derived, the phylum Arthropoda shows certain progressive modifications. Some of these are outlined below:

1. Development of a chitinous covering over a part of the body or over the whole, with articulation at points where flexibility and movement were required.
2. Retention of the worm appendages (parapodia) and incasement in hollow, jointed, chitinous coverings.
3. Fusion and telescoping of some of the anterior segments of the body to form a head; a similar fusion of the posterior segments to form an abdomen; and finally the subdivision of the body and exoskeleton into cephalon, thorax, and abdomen. This brought about a concentration of the ganglia of the segments to form a brain. Further fusion of the segments ultimately

resulted in but two rigid exoskeletal plates—the cephalothorax (carapace) and the abdomen. Throughout the entire phylum, regardless of the group, there seems always to have been a tendency to eliminate free segments by fusion with others.

4. The modification of the appendages, originally similar in character, for a great variety of special functions, and the elimination of them on some segments.

5. Change in the respiratory process from gills to book gills to book lungs and from branchiae to tracheae, thereby allowing a change from water breathing to air breathing and making possible invasion of the land.

6. Development of wings on the dorsal surface of the thorax, making possible invasion of the air.

Ecology.—In a group represented by such a wide variety and prodigious number of individuals, it is to be expected that arthropods of one kind or another will be found in every known life habitat from the deepest ocean bottom to the highest mountain top and from the poles to the equator and that a like distribution obtained during past periods. Whether conditions be cold, temperate, or torrid; whether it be dry, moist, or very humid; and whether it be on the land, in the soil, in fresh water, brackish water, salt water, or in the air, representatives of the phylum are sure to be present in abundance and variety. No other group of animals probably has ever attained the latitude of adaptation shown by the Arthropoda.

The Crustacea have been called the "insects of the sea," and quite appropriately so, for the present oceans and seas are literally teeming with their countless numbers. But they are almost as abundant in fresh waters, where they are forced to compete with the insects as well as with other creatures, and scarcely a pool, ditch, stream, pond, or lake can be found which does not have its assemblage of crustaceans. On land they are not so common, but a few species have become adapted to a terrestrial habitat. Some of the Crustacea, notably the crabs and lobsters, have for a long time been used as food by man. It is in the economy of nature, however, where the Crustacea, especially the amphipods, isopods, ostracods, and copepods, stand supreme. The first three are scavengers feeding on all sorts of organic refuse and in turn serving as food for many larger marine animals such as fish. They live mainly in the shallower waters of the sea. The copepods, which feed on diatoms and other microscopic plankton, are themselves planktonic and are sometimes present in such numbers as to discolor the surface waters of the ocean for miles and thereby guide the fishermen and whalers to the best fishing grounds. In the early Paleozoic seas the extinct trilobites, along with the ancient ostracods, must have played a very important part in the scavenging of decomposing organic remains on the sea bottom. The ancient arachnids were also in many cases scavengers, and their work along with others of the arthropods must have been very important in keeping the ocean bottoms in a habitable condition.

The Insecta are typically terrestrial arthropods and are adapted for a life on, within, or above the land surface. Their relations with the plants form an entrancing story. They not only acquire food from and also find shelter in living plants, but they eat living and lifeless vegetation. They find sustenance in the dung of animals as well as in their decaying bodies. To a large degree scavenging insects are very beneficial in facilitating rapid decomposition and removal of decaying organic substances of all kinds. Aquatic insects are found mainly in fresh waters. There are almost no insects on the open sea and only a few in the shallower coastal waters. Some insects are cannibals; others are predators; and still others are parasitic, both ectoparasitic and endoparasitic. A few live with their relatives and feed at their expense. Social life reaches amazing success among certain insects, and the gregarious habit seems to be fairly typical of the class as a whole.

Stratigraphic Range.—The general relations and stratigraphic range of the larger subdivisions of the Arthropoda are shown in Fig. 175. The Trilobita appear in the Lower Cambrian but were almost certainly evolved during the Pre-Cambrian. They flourish in the early Paleozoic but after the Devonian decline rapidly to extinction in the Permian. The Branchiopoda appear also at the beginning of the Paleozoic. The Ostracoda are first known in the early Ordovician and after a slight zenith in the early and middle Paleozoic continue to the Recent without much change. The Cirripedia do not appear until the Ordovician and continue to the present, perhaps with slight increase in varieties, although this is by no means certain. The Malacostraca arise soon after the beginning of the Cambrian, almost immediately expand into a large group, and continue throughout geologic time to the Present, always a fairly important group. The myriapods appear in the Silurian as millipedes, are joined by the centipedes in the Upper Carboniferous, and continue to the Present. The Insecta appear abruptly at the beginning of the Pennsylvanian, immediately develop into a large group, and continue as such to the present time. The difficulty of preservation is very likely in part responsible for the great discrepancy between the few thousands of fossil species as compared with the half million living species. The Arachnida seem to have evolved in part during the Pre-Cambrian, for the representatives of the class found in the Lower Cambrian are complex creatures. The Merostomata expand during the early and middle Paleozoic but become extinct by the close of the Permian except for the lone genus *Limulus*, which comes through to the Present. The spiders, scorpions, mites, and ticks comprise a group of arachnids which appear in the Silurian but do not immediately expand, rather developing gradually to the important position which they hold among existing arachnid faunas.

Many fossil arthropods are of great use as index fossils, especially those which attain wide geographic distribution and are frequently preserved, but a great many more, because of the incompletely known fossil record, are of little paleontologic value except from the biological point of view. In spite of the tremendous number of individuals which must have lived during the geologic past there is a real paucity of well-preserved arthropod remains when the phylum as a whole is considered.

Nature of the Fossil Record.—Since the majority of the exoskeletons of arthropods are composed of chitin, and relatively few of calcareous matter, most fossil remains are in the form of impressions, molds and casts, and thin carbonaceous films representing what remains of the decomposed chitin (Fig. 172 *A*). The calcareous structures stand an excellent chance of preservation, although in many cases they also have been destroyed during fossilization. Larval cases of certain forms have been reported, and tracks of various types have been attributed to certain arthropods, but these are always doubtful references. Perhaps the most satisfactory fossils are those preserved in amber. Many of these remain little changed from their original condition, even with respect to color and ornamentation, and furnish a most complete picture of ancient arthropod assemblages of certain kinds. Perhaps as spectacular, and certainly as satisfactory, as any fossil remains are the beautifully preserved arthropods which have been recovered from the Middle Cambrian shales of British Columbia. Actual organic material is not generally preserved, but the anatomical features are shown in almost unbelievable detail. So varied is this assemblage that many of the specimens have not yet been placed in their proper taxonomic relations, because they appear to belong to large groups or races which have long ago become extinct. This great discovery, which has revolutionized views formerly held concerning the life of the late Pre-Cambrian, has pushed the beginnings of the Arthropoda far back into the Pre-Cambrian and has demonstrated the complexity of the phylum even as early as the Lower Cambrian.

References

ALEXANDER, C. I.: Shell structure of the ostracode genus *Cytheropteron* and fossil species from the Cretaceous of Texas. *Jour. Paleontology*, vol. 7, pp. 181–214, 1933; Ostracoda from the Midway of Texas, vol. 8, pp. 206–236, 1934.

BASSLER, R. S., and KELLETT, B.: Bibliographic index of Paleozoic Ostracoda. *Geol. Soc. Amer., Spec. Paper* 1, 500 pp., 1934.

BEECHER, C. E.: "Studies in Evolution." 638 pp., 1901.

CARPENTER, F. M., RAYMOND, P. E., and PETRUNKEVITCH, A.: The evolution of the class Insecta. *Amer. Jour. Sci.*, vol. 21, pp. 531–539, 1931.

CLARKE, J. M. and RUEDEMANN, R.: The Eurypterida of New York, *N. Y. State Mus., Mem.* 14, 2 vols., 1912.

COCKERELL, F. D. A.: The fossil fauna and flora of the Florissant (Colorado) shales. *Colo. Univ. Stud.*, vol. 3, pp. 157–175, 1916. (See other papers by this author treating of fossil insects.)

HANDLIRSCH, A.: Die fossilen Insekten, Leipzig; Revision of American Paleozoic insects. *Proc. U. S. Nat. Mus.*, vol. 29, 661–820, 1906–1908.

KELLETT, B.: Ostracodes of the Upper Pennsylvanian and Lower Permian strata of Kansas. *Jour. Paleontology*, vol. 7, pp. 59–108, 1933; vol. 8, pp. 120–138, 1934.

O'CONNELL, M.: The habitat of the Eurypterida, *Buffalo Soc. Nat. Hist., Bull.* 11, 217 pp., 1915.

PETRUNKEVITCH, A.: A monograph of the terrestrial Paleozoic Arachnida of North America. *Trans. Conn. Acad. Arts Sci.*, vol. 18, pp. 1–137, 1913.

RATHBUN, M. J.: Decapod crustaceans from the Panama region. *U. S. Nat. Mus., Bull.* 103, pp. 123–184, 1918. (Other papers treating of the crustaceans are in the same publication.)

———: Fossil Crustacea of the Atlantic and Gulf Coastal Plain. *Geol. Soc. Amer., Spec. Paper* 2, 160 pp., 1935.

Raymond, P. E.: Beecher's classification of trilobites after twenty years. *Amer. Jour. Sci.*, vol. 43, pp. 196–210, 1917.

———: The appendages, anatomy, and relationships of trilobites. *Mem. Conn. Acad. Arts Sci.*, vol. 7, 169 pp., 1920.

Reed, F. R. C.: Lower Paleozoic trilobites of the Girvan district. *Palaeontogr. Soc.*, 1903–1906.

Scudder, S. H.: Paleozoic cockroaches, *Boston Soc. Nat. Hist.*, *Mem.* 3, pp. 23–134, 1879.

———: Systematic review of our present knowledge of fossil insects, including myriapods and arachnids. *U. S. Geol. Surv.*, *Bull.* 31, 128 pp., 1886.

———: Index to the known fossil insects of the world including myriapods and arachnids. *U. S. Geol. Surv.*, *Bull.* 71, 744 pp., 1891.

Tillyard, R. J.: The evolution of the class Insecta. *Amer. Jour. Sci.*, vol. 23, pp. 529–539, 1923–1934. (This author has some dozen papers on Permian insects from Kansas published in this same journal, beginning in 1924.)

Ulrich, E. O.: Ordovician trilobites of the family Telephidae, etc. *Proc. U. S. Nat. Mus.*, vol. 76, 101 pp., 1930.

——— and Bassler, R. S.: Paleozoic ostracoda, their morphology, and occurrence. Silurian vol., *Md. Geol. Surv.*, pp. 271–391, 1923.

——— and ———: Cambrian bivalved Crustacea of the order Conchostraca. *Proc. U. S. Nat. Mus.*, vol. 78, 130 pp., 1931.

——— and Resser, C. E.: The Cambrian of the Upper Mississippi Valley. Pt. 1, Trilobita; Dikelocephalinae and Osceolinae. *Bull. Public Mus. City of Milwaukee*, vol. 12, pp. 1–122, 1930; pt. 2, Saukiinae, pp. 123–206, 1933.

Walcott, C. D.: Cambrian trilobites. *Smith. Misc. Coll.*, vols. 53, 57, 64, 67, 1908–1918.

INDEX

Bold-face names refer to phyla; *italicized* names are generic, specific or varietal; **bold-face** numerals refer to pages containing illustrations; *italic* numerals refer to pages containing tables.

A

Abactinal, 155
Abalone, **353**, 358
Abdomen, of an arthropod, 408, **412**, **416**, 422, 459, **464**
  of an eurypterid, **467**
Abdominal region, 413
Aboral, definition of, 155
  side of echinoid, **200**, **202**, **211**
Abyss, 13
Abyssal life zone, 11, **12**, 13
Acanthin, 49
Acanthocephala, 140
Acanthograptus, **91**, 92
Acanthograptus granti, **91**
Acanthopores, 228, **236**, 237, **238**
Acarina, 471
Accessory adductors, 257
Accessory diductors, 256, *258*
Acerose sponge spicule in foraminiferal shell, 40, **42**, **43**
Acetabulum, 200
Acharax, 328
Acidaspis, **425**, 426
Acmaea, 351
Acorn barnacle, 441
Acroporidae, 112
Acrotreta, 287, **288**
Acrotreta gemma, **288**
Acrotretacea, 282, 287, *298*
Actinal, 155
Actinaria, 109
Actinarian affinities of *Mackenzia*, 80
Actinoceras, 373, **376**, 386, 397
Actinoceras beloitense, **376**
Actinoceras centrale, **376**
Actinostroma, **86**, 87
Actinostroma tenuifilatum, **86**
Actinostromidae, 84
Actinozoa, 95
Aculeus, **461**
Adambulacral plates, 179, **193**, **194**
Adambulacralia, **191**
Adambulacrum, **191**, **193**
Adaptation, of pelecypods, **316**
Adductor muscles, *256*, **257**, *258*, 313, 436, 439
Adductor scars, **257**, **276**
Adhesive cells, 121
Adjustor scar, **276**
Adjustors, *256*, *258*
Adult, 450
Adventitious lobes, 373
Adventitious saddles, 373
Aechmina bovina, **438**
Aegean Sea, cuttlefish from, 301
Aeglina, 420
Aganides, 370, **372**, 375, 388
Aganides rotarius, **372**
Agassiz, 21
Agassizocrinus, **187**, 188
Agassizocrinus dactyliformis, **187**
Agglutinated protozoan tests, 39, 40, **42**, **43**
Agglutinated worm tubes, 131
Aglaspid, **465**
Aglaspis, **465**, 466
"*Aglaspis*" *eatoni*, **465**
Agnostidae, 424, 426
Agnostus, 421, **427**, 432
Air-breathing arachnid, 462, 469
Air habitat, 10, **11**
Alabama, fossil medusae from, **95**
Alar septum, 102, **104**
Alate shell, 263
Albertella, 418, **425**, 426
Alcyonidae, 113, 114
Alcyonaria, 78, 100, 109, 110, 112, **114**, 116, 120, 125
  geologic range of, **123**
Alcyonarian spicules, 78, **113**, **114**
Alder flies, 454, 459
Alexander, C. F., 477
Alimentary canal, **305**, **415**
  of a mollusk, **302**, **305**
  of a trilobite, **415**
Alivincular ligament, 323
Allagecrinus, 182
Allodesma, 327
Allorisma, 327
Altered fossil remains, 15
Alternation of generations, 29, **37**, 76, 77, 80
Amalgamata, **236**, 239
Amber, fossils in, 32
Ambitus, **198**, 201, 208

Amblysiphonella, **62,** 70
Ambulacral areas, 150, 161
Ambulacral grooves, **162, 166,** 173, **192**
Ambulacral plates, 177, 179, 180, 193, **194**
Ambulacral pores, 202
Ambulacral system, in *Bothriocidaris archaica*, **203**
in Echinoidea, **203**
in *Eucidaris tribuloides*, **203**
in *Goniocidaris caniculata*, **203**
in *Lepidesthes colletti*, **203**
in *Lovenechinus missouriensis*, **203**
in *Maccoya burlingtonensis*, **203**
in *Melonechinus multiporus*, **203**
in *Micraster cor-anguineum*, **203**
in *Oligoporus danae*, **203**
in *Palaeechinus elegans*, **203**
in *Strongylocentrotus dröbachiensis*, **203**
Ambulacral water vessel, **198**
Ambulacralia, **191**
Ambulacrum, 150, 151, **166,** 168, **169, 193, 194, 200,** 201, **202**
Ambulatory appendages, 462
Ambulatory funnel, 363, 383
Amiskwia, **130,** 140
Amiskwia sagittiformis, **130**
Ammodiscus, **42**
Ammonite, **387**
suture of, **372,** 375, 377, 387
Ammoniticone, **368,** *369*
Ammonoidea, 306, 364, **368, 372,** 373, **374,** 377, 382, 386, 399, **402,** 403
Ammonoids, fossil, **368, 372, 374,** 387
Amnicola dalli, **303**
Amnula, 358
Amoeba, **2,** 3, 7, **33**
Amoebaea, 32, **33,** 47
Amoeboid cells, 55
Amoeboid protozoans, 47
Amphibian, 8
Amphictene auricoma, **134**
Amphidetic ligament, 313, 322
Amphineura, 304, **305,** 306, **307, 308,** 400, **402,** 403
distribution of, **402**
Amphipoda, 444, 474
Amphoridea, *163*, 164
Amplexopora, **238,** 239
Amplexopora septosa, **238**
Ampulla, **151,** 175, **198**
Ampullaria, **348, 353,** 354
Ampullaria cumingi, **348**
Ampyx, **425,** 426
Anacline interarea, **272,** *273*
Anal aperture, 27
Anal opening, of arthropod, **412**
of cystoid, **162**
Anal plates, **178,** 179
Anal proboscis, 175, **178,** 180
Anal teeth, 214
Anal tube, 175, 180
Anal valve, of amphineuran, **308**
of blastoid calyx, **169**
Analysis of crinoid calyx, **178, 186, 187**
Anaptychus, 387
Anasca, 244
Anaspidacea, 444
Anaspis, 444
Anatomy, of Arthropoda, 407
of barnacles, 440
of Brachiopoda, 252
of Bryozoa, 223
of Cephalopoda, 364
of Coelenterata, 73
of Crinoidea, 173
of Crustacea, 410
of Echinoderma, 150
of Echinoidea, 197
of Eurypterida, 466
of Gastropoda, 342
of Insecta, 449
of Malacostraca, 443
of Mollusca, 301, 310
of Myriapoda, 447
of Porifera, 52
of Protozoa, 27, 28
of Synxiphosura, 465
of worms, 129
of Xiphosura, 463
Ancestral mollusk, 302
Ancestrula, 224, **225, 226**
Ancestry, of Arthropoda, **472**
of Echinoderma, 155, 215
of Echinoidea, 206
of Hexacoralla, 108
of Mollusca, **402**
Anchor, **212**
Anchor plates, **212**
Ancient bioherms, 126
Ancient climates, 20, 23
Ancient environments, 20
Ancient geography, 23
Ancient reefs, 126, 157
Ancyloceras, **368,** 388
Animal kingdom, classification of, **6,** 7
definition of, 2
divisions of, **6,** 7, 8
Animal tree, 5, **6**
Animals and plants, diagram showing relations of, **2**
Annelida, 8, 129, **134,** 141, 145, 446, 447
Annular lobe, 373
Annulata, 8, 129, **134,** 141
Annulations, **367**
Annulus, 384
Anomalocystites, 164
Anomalodesmacea, 330, 333, **402**
Anomalodont dentition, 327
Anomia, 317
Anomocladina, 66

Anomura, **445**
Anostraca, 433, 434
Ant, 454
Ant lion, 454
Antarctica, fossils from, 23
Antenna, 411, **412**, 436, **437**
Antennule, 411, **412, 414, 437**
Anterior adductor, **312, 326,** 329
Anterior lateral muscle, **255**
Anterior position, 263
Antetheca, **44**
Anthonomus arctus, **456**
Anthozoa, 79, 95, 124, 125, 128, 221
  anatomy of, 95
Anthozoan exoskeletal structures, **96**
Anthracomarti, 471
Anthrapalaemon gracilis, 444, **445**
Anticosti, fossils from, 23, **86,** 117, 126, 184
Antipitharia, 109, 112
Antisiphonal lobes, 373
Antisiphonal saddles, 373
Anus, of an amphineuran, **308**
  of an arthropod, **415, 461**
  of an asteroid, **192, 193**
  of a blastoid, **169**
  of a bryozoan, **222, 223, 244**
  of *Dipleurula*, **216**
  of an echinoderm, **152**
  of an echinoid, **198, 200**
  of an edrioasteroid, **166**
  of a holothuroid, **212**
  of a mollusk, **302, 305,** 313, 347, 348
  of a trochophore, **141**
  of a worm, **136**
Apertura, **246**
Aperture, of a bryozoan, 225, **240**
  of a cephalopod, **367, 374,** 379, **380**
  of a foraminiferal test, 40, **42, 44**
Apex of shell, 345
Apical angle, **346,** 347
Apical plate, **141,** 224
Apical system, of *Centrechinus setosus*, **204**
  of *Cidaris affinis*, **204**
  of Echinoidea, 202, **204**
  of *Eucidaris tribuloides*, **204**
  of starfish, **193**
  of *Strongylocentrotus dröbachiensis*, **204**
Apiocrinus, **188, 189**
Apiocrinus parkinsoni, **189**
Apiocrinus roissyanus, **189**
Aplacophora, 306, **307,** 309
  calcareous spicules of, **307**
Apophysis, **205**
Aporita, *163*, **165**
Aporosa, **110**
Aporrhaidae, **354**
Apsacline interarea, **272,** *273*
Apterygogenea, 410, 455, *458*
Aptychus, **387**
Aptychus carinatus, **387**
Apus, **434,** 435
Apus cancriformis, **434**
Aquatic arthropods, 410
Aquatic bugs, 455
Aquatic insects, 475
Aquatic larvae of alder fly, 459
Aqueous habitat, **11**
Arabella, **132**
Arachnida, 406, 409, 410, 459, 462, 463, 473, 476
Arachnids, 410
Aragonite, use of, in shells, 320
Araneae, 471
Araneida, 471
Arbellites, **132**
Arbellites cornutus, **132,** 133
Arborescent test, **42,** 43
Arca, 314, 323, 325, **326,** 333
Archaeocidaris, **205,** 211
Archaeocidaris wortheni, **205**
Archaeocyathinae, 66, **68,** 110, 122–125
  geologic range of, **123**
Archaeocyathus, **68,** 70
Archaeocyathus profundus, **68**
Archetypal mollusk, **302,** 306, 392
Archiannelida, **141,** 146, 406
Archichaetopoda, 142
Archimedes, 241, **242,** 243
Architarbus rotundatus, **470**
Architecture, of cephalopod shell, **368**
  of gastropod shell, **353, 354**
Architeuthis princeps, 396
Arenaceous tests, 46
Arenicola marina, **136**
Arenicolites chemungensis, **136**
Argonauta, 364, **391**
Argonauta argo, **391**
Aristocystites, 151, **161, 162,** 163, 164, **216**
Aristocystites bohemicus, **161, 162**
Aristotle, 301
Aristotle's lantern, 156, **198, 206**
Arms, of an asteroid, **192**
  of a brachiopod, 258
  of a cephalopod, 364, **390**
  of a crinoid, **174,** 175, 179
  of an echinoderm, 156, 161
Arnold, R., 404
Arrow-worms, 140
Artemia, 435
Arthrolycosa antiqua, **470**
Arthrophycus, 137
Arthropoda, 8, 145, 147, 406, 446, 447, 473, 477
  chart showing importance of, **472**
  exoskeleton of, 407
  larva of, 409
  nature of animal of, 407
  nervous system of, 407
Arthropora simplex, **240**
Articulamentum, **308,** 309

Articulata, of the Brachiopoda, 252, 256, 257, 282
of the Crinoidea, *184*, 188, **189**
Artificial replica, **17,** 18
Ascidian, commensal organisms in, 339
Ascoceras, 370, **376,** 385
Ascoceras bohemicum, **376**
Ascon sponge, **54,** 55
Ascones, 62
Ascophora, 244, 245
Ascopore, **244, 246**
Asexual reproduction, 56, 76
Aspidobranchia, 315, **317,** 351, **402**
Aspidobranchiate gills, 315, **317**
Astacura, 445
Astacus, **412,** 445
Astacus fluviatilis, **412**
Astarte, **326,** 327, 334
Asterias, **192,** 193
Asterias forbesii, **192**
Asteroblastus, 171, 172
Asteroid arm, **191**
Asteroid test, **193**
Asteroidea, 149, **152,** 191, **192,** 193, **194,** 198
Asthenodont dentition, 323, 327
Astraeidae, 110
Astraeospongia, 58, 60, **64,** 70
Astrorhiza (ae), 39, 85, **86**
Astylospongia, **64,** 65, 70
Athyridae, 293
Athyris, **279,** 293
spiralia of, **279**
Athyroid spiralium, 278, **279**
Atikokania lawsoni, 70
Atremata, **248,** 252, **255,** 259, 281, 282, 284–286, 292, 298
Atrypa, **134, 264, 279, 285,** 293, **294**
Atrypa reticularis, **294**
Atrypacea, 282, 293, **298**
Atrypoid spiralium, 278, **279**
Attachment, of brachiopods, 259, **260**
of cystoids, **152,** 163
of echinoderms, **152,** 153
of mollusks, **316**
Aulacoceras, 381, 399
Aulonia, **49**
Aulopora, **118,** 121
Aulopora serpens, **118**
Auloporidae, 117, 121
Auluroidea, 149, **191,** 193, 194, 196
arm structure of, **191**
Auricle, **205**
Auriculate shell, **353**
Auriptygma virgatum, **346, 352**
Autopore, 113, **114**
Autozooid, **114**
Auvergne, fossils from, 455
Auxiliary lobes, 373
Avicularium, **222,** 227, **228, 244, 246**
Axial furrow, **416**
Axial lobe, **414, 416**
Axial ornamentation, **345,** 350
Axial segment, **416**
Axillary plate, 179
Axonolipa, 90, 92
Axonophora, 90, 92, 93
Axopodium, 48
Aysheaia, **130,** 145
Aysheaia pedunculata, **130**
Aysheaidae, 446, 447

B

Bactrites, **368**
Bactriticone, **368**
Baculites, **368,** 369, **372,** 388
Baculites anceps, **372**
Bairdia beedei, **438**
Balancing legs, **467**
Balanidae, 441
Balanus, 441, **442**
Balanus concavus, **442**
Ballstone reefs in England, 126
Baltic region, fossils from, 397, 455, 459
Banffia, 146
Barnacles, 406, 407, 410, 440, **442**
Barnea costata, **415**
Barrande, J., 404
Barrois, C., 46
Barroisia, 62, **63**
Bartsch, P., 404
Barycrinus, **174**
Basal cyst, **93**
Basal disk, 214
Basal plates, 99, 167, **169, 174,** 177, **178, 189, 193**
Base, 200, **201**
Basis, **442**
Basket starfish, 196
Basommatophora, 356
Bassler, R. S., 127, 133, 166, 221, 249, 477, 478
Bather, F. A., 215, 219
Bathropyramis, **49**
Bathyal life zone, 11, **12**
Bathyuriscus, **425,** 426
Batostoma, 239, 245
Batostomella spinulosa, **236**
Bavaria, reefs of Solnhofen, 95, 143, 443, 457
Beaded siphuncle, 386
Beak, 262, 269, 313
Beatricia, 85, **86,** 87
Beatricia undulata, **86**
Beatricoid structure, 84, 85
Beckwitchia typa, **285**
Bee, 454, 458
Beebe, W., 4
Beecher, C. E., 70, 299, 424, 477
Beetles, 406, 453, **456**

Belemnites, 364, **380,** 389, 393, 394, 403
Belemnites paxillosus, **380**
Belemnoidea, 364, **380,** 382, 388, 389, 399, **402**
Belemnoteuthidae, 389
Belemnoteuthis, 380
Belgium, bioherms in, 126
Belinurus, 463, **464**
Belinurus regina, **464**
Bellerophontidae, 349
Benthos, **12,** 13
Bermuda, atolls of, 135, 144
Berry, S. S., 404
Bertiella, 133, 144
Betchewan Bay, squids in, 395
Beyrichidae, 437
Bicia, 286
Biconvex shells, **264**
Billingsella, **289,** 291
Billingsella coloradoensis, **289**
Billingsellidae, 291
Biloculina, **42,** 43, 45
Biloculine test, **42**
Biocoenose, 22
Biogenetic law, 45
Biologic affinities of graptolites, 90
Bioherm, **86,** 87, 100, 107, 117, 119, 122, 125, 135, 218, 245, 340, 443, 459
  at Solnhofen, Bavaria, 443
  in Swabian Alps, 70
Biology, definition of, 1
Biostrome, 119, 125, 126, 297, 340, 403
Biramous appendages, 142, 417
Bird lice, 453
Birds, 8
Biserial arm, **174,** 180
Biserial arrangement, of chambers, 41, 42, **43**
  of hydrothecae, 88
Biserial plate, 163, 202
Bivalve shell, 304, 433
Bivium, 166, 191, **200,** 201
Black corals, 112
Black flies, 452
Black shale, 21
Blastoid, **152,** 156, 157, 163, **169**
Blastoidea, 149, 151, **152,** 156, 157, 159, 163, 167, **169**
  geologic history of, **217**
Blattoidea, 453, *458*
Blister pearls, formation of, 320
Blood, circulation of, in mollusks, 313
  of mollusks, 302, 343
Body appendages, 414
Body wall, structure of, in Coelenterata, 73
    in Foraminifera, 44
    in sponges, 53
Body whorl, **345,** 346
Bohemia, fossils from, 114
Bombyx mori, **450**
Book-gills, 407, 410, **464**
Book lice, 453
Book-lungs, 407, 410, 470
Book scorpions, 471
Borden group, bioherms in, 183
Boring gastropods, 353
Boring organisms, 137, 267
Borings, 19, 137, **361**
Botany, definition of, 1
Bothriocidaris, 199, **203,** 206, 208
Bothriocidaris archaica, **203**
Bothriocidaris globosus, **208**
Bothriocidaroida, *207*, 208
Box crinoids, 185
Brace, **205**
Brachia, 156, 175, 179, 258
Brachial cavity, 258
Brachial plate, 177, **178,** 179
Brachial supports, 277
Brachial valve, 261
Brachidium, 259, 278, **279**
Brachiole, 156, **162, 169,** 171
Brachiopod, compared with pelecypod, 318
  development of, **262**
  shell of, internal structure of, **270, 276**
    length of, 263
    shape of, 263, **264**
    size of, 265
    structure of, **266, 270**
    surface ornamentation of, **268**
Brachiophore, 251, **270, 276,** 277, **279**
Brachiophore plates, **270,** 277
Brachiophore process, **270,** 277, 279
Brachiophore support, 277
Brachiopoda, 8, 147, 250, **253,** 268, **276, 283, 285, 289, 290, 294,** 313
  attachment of, **260**
  ecology of, 251
  geologic history of, **248**
  modern representatives of, **253**
Brachyura, 445
Brackish-water mollusks, 403
Brady, W. B., 50
Branchia, 131, 198, 311, 407, 410
  of mollusk, **302,** 315
  of pelecypod, **311,** 315
  of worms, 131, **134,** 136, 141
Branchial appendages, 407
Branchial cavity, **311**
Branching stars, 196
Branchiopoda, 410, 433, 434, 439, 472, 473, 475
Brittany, fossils from, 46, 70
Brittle star, 149, 154, 158, 194, 196
Brongiart, A., 22
Brood pouch, 437, **438**
Brooksella, **95**
Brooksella alternata, **95**
Brown body. 224
Bryograptus, 92, **93**

Bryograptus lapworthi, **93**
Brunswick, fossils from, 135
Bryozoa, 8, 147, 220, **232, 234, 236, 238, 242, 246**
on coral reefs, 245
development of zoarium of, **226**
embryo of, **225**
geologic history of, **248**
as micro-fossils, 221
modern representatives of, **222**
Buccal cavity, 302, **305,** 342, 395
Buccinum, **344,** 354, 359
Buccinum undatum, **344**
Budding, methods of, in Coelenterata, 77, **112**
in sponges, 56
Bugula avicularia, **222**
Bullaria, **353,** 355
Bumastus, 418, 422, 425, 426, 432
Bunodella, 466
Burgess shale, fossils from, 131, 140, 144, 146, 435, 447
Burgessia, 435
Burlington, Iowa, crinoids at, 182
Burrowing organisms, **136,** 137
Burrowing pelecypods, **316,** 338
Burrowing worms, **136,** 137
Burrows, 19, **136**
Busycon, **345, 346,** 354
Butterflies, 406, 409, 450, 455, **456**
Byssus, **316,** 317

C

Caddis flies, 455
Caecum, 384
Calapoecia, 117, **118**
Calapoecia canadensis, **118**
Calcarea, 61, 62, 68
Calcareous Coelenterata, 123
Calcareous darts, 356, **357**
Calcareous ooze, 45
Calcareous ring, **212,** 214
Calcareous shells, 29, 40
Calcareous sponge, 57, 61, **63,** 123
Calcareous sycon sponge, **63**
Calcareous test of echinoderms, 149
Calcareous worm tubes, 131, 143
Calceola, 104, 108
Calceola sandalina, **104**
Calcite as shell material, 40
Calcium carbonate in shells, 40
Calices of graptolites, 88
Calicinal budding, 76
Callograptus, **91,** 92
Callograptus compactus, **91**
Callograptus staufferi, **91**
Callus, 347, 349
Calostylus, 108
Calymene, 418, 422, **427,** 432
Calyx, of blastoid, 168, **169**
of coral, **96,** 97
of crinoid, 173, **174,** 176, 177
of cystoid, 160
definition of, 78, 158
Camarocrinus, 173
Cambrian Branchiopoda, **434**
Cambrian Protremata, **289**
Cambrian trilobites, **421**
Cambrian worms, **130**
Camera, **365, 367**
Camerata, *184*, 185, **186**
Campanularia, 83
Campeloma, **353,** 354
Campodea, 455
Campodeoidea, 455, *458*
Camptostroma, 81, 124
Canadia setigera, **130**
Canal system of sponge, **54,** 55
Candona, 437
Canu, F., 249
Caphyra, **425,** 426
Capitulum, **445**
Captacula, 362
Carapace, 407, 413, 437, **438,** 461, **467**
Cardelle, 243, **244**
Cardinal area, **270,** 272, **275, 276, 279,** 322
relation of, to plane of commissure, **272**
Cardinal margin, 263, **268**
Cardinal process, 257, **270, 276,** 277, **279, 294**
Cardinal septum, 102, **104**
Cardinal teeth, 325
Cardium, **326,** 327, 334, 335
Caribbean region, 21
Caricella, **353,** 354
Carina, **96,** 97, **104**
on barnacles, **442**
on corals, **96,** 97, **104**
Carino-lateral compartment, **442**
Carino-latus plate, **442**
Carpenter, F. M., 377
Carpoidea, 215
Carrier, **132, 162**
Caryocrinus, **162,** 163, 164
Caryocrinus ornatus, **162**
Cast, 8, **17**
Castings of organisms, 19, 137, **138,** 143, **212**
Catacline interarea, **272,** *273*
Caterpillar, 446, **450**
Caudal furca, 433
Caudal segment, **467**
Caudal shield, 422
Caudal spine, **416,** 464
Cell of graptolite, 88
Cellepora honoluluensis, **228**
Cellule, 88
Census of four square feet, 3
Centipede, 8, 406, 410, **448,** 449, 476
Central capsule, 49
Central disk, **192, 195**

Central muscle, **255, 256**
Centrechinoida, *207*, 209
Centrechinus setosus, **204**
Centrodorsal plate, 177, **178**, 181, **193, 194**
Centronella, **279**
Cephalic appendages, **414**
Cephalic region, 413
Cephalic shield, 414
Cephalic valve, **308**
Cephalon, 408, **414, 416**, 417, **432, 467**
Cephalopod shell, architecture of, **365, 368, 374, 376, 380**
  shape of, **368**
  size of, **368**
  structure of, **365**
  suture of, **372, 374, 376**
Cephalopoda, **305**, 363, **365**, 400, **402**
  anatomy of, 363
  relation of animal to shell in, **305, 365**
Cephalopods, **305, 365, 368, 372, 374, 376**
Cephalothoracic appendages, **464**
Cephalothorax, 408, **412**, 459, **464**
Cephalula, 295
Ceramoporidae, 227, 228, 233, 249
Ceratite suture, **372**, 375, 387
Ceratites, **372**, 388
Ceratites nodosus, **372**
Ceratopea calceoliformis, **348**
Ceratopsis chambersi, **438**
Ceratosa, 66, 68
Ceratospongida, 66
Ceratospyris, **49**
Ceraurus, **415**, 422, 427
Ceraurus pleurexanthemus, **415**
Cerithium, 358
Cestoda, 139
Chaetetes, **118**, 121
Chaetetidae, 117, 121, 127
Chaetoderma californica, **307**
Chaetognatha, 140
Chaetopoda, 141, 142
Chain coral, 119
Chalk, sponge remains in, 70
"Challenger" Expedition, 154, 172, 196
Chama, 340, 403
Chambered nautilus, **365**
Chamberlet, 43, 373
Chazy, 105
Cheilostomata, **223**, 229, *230*, 233, 240, 243 **244, 246**, 247, **248**, 249
Cheirurus, **427**
Chela, **412, 461**
Chelicera, 459, **461, 464, 467**
Cheliped, **412**
Chicago, fossil worms from, 133
Chilaria, **464**
Chilidial plates, 275
Chilidium, **270**, 275, **279**
Chilobolbina dentifera, **438**
Chilopoda, 449, **472**
Chitin, 29
Chitinous jaws, 131, 364, 447
Chitinous material, 47
Chitinous shells, 29, 39
Chitinous tubes, 131, 143
Chiton, 304, 306, **308**
Chloiochoanitic shell, 377
Chloromonadina, 31
Choanocytes, 53, 55, 61
Choanoflagellata, 53, 69
Chondrophore, **311, 323**
Chonetes, **268**, 292
Chordata, 8
Chronological significance of fossils, 20
Chrysomonadina, 31, 34
Cidaris, **200**, 204, 209, 210
Cidaris affinis, **204**
Cidaris tribuloides, **210**
Cidaroida, *207*, 208
Cilia, **28, 141**
  on a young bryozoan, **225**
Ciliata, 32, 50
Ciliated chambers, **54**
Ciliated groove, **169**
Circular canal, **74**
Circulation, in sponge, 55, 56
Circumesophageal vessel, **198**
Cirri, 143, **174**, 176
Cirripedia, 215, 410, 413, 440, **442, 472**, 475
Cladocera, 433–436
Clams, 301, 304, 310, **331**
Clark, A. L., 80
Clark, H. L., 206
Clark, W. B., 219
Clarke, A. H., 184, 219
Clarke, J. M., 70, 299, 404, 477
Classification, of Alcyonaria, 113, 114
  of Ammonoidea, 387
  of animals, 7, 8, **9**
  of Anthozoa, 100
  of Arachnida, 462
  of Arthropoda, 409, 410
  of Blastoidea, 172
  of Brachiopoda, 281
  of Branchiopoda, 433
  of Bryozoa, 229
  of Calcarea, 62
  of Cephalopoda, 382
  of Coelenterata, 79
  of Crinoidea, *184*
  of Cystoidea, **163**
  of Echinoderma, 157
  of Echinoidea, *207*, 208
  of Eleutherozoa, 157, 190
  of Embolobranchiata, 471
  of Foraminifera, 45
  of Gastropoda, 350
  of Graptolites, 90
  of Graptozoa, 90

Classification, of Hexacoralla, 109
of Hydrozoa, 81
of Insecta, 452
of Malacostraca, 443
of Mollusca, 304
of Myriapoda, 449
of Onychophora, 447
of Pelecypoda, 330
of Pelmatozoa, 157, *159*
of Porifera, 61
of Protozoa, 31
of Stelleroidea, 191
of Tabulata, 117
of Tetracoralla, 105
of Trepostomata, 239
of Trilobita, 423
of worms, 137
Clathrodictyon, **86**, 87
Clathrodictyon vesiculosum, **86**
Clathrodictyon vesiculosum minutum, **86**
Clathrulina, **33**
Clavate shell, 353
Clavicle, 324
Climacograptus, **93**, 94
Climacograptus modestus, **93**
Climacograptus parvus, **93**
Climate, ancient, 20, 23
Cliona, 69
Clitambonacea, 282, 291, *298*
Clitambonites, **260, 270,** 291
Cloaca, 52, 55, **62**, 343
Closed mantle, 314
Clymenia, **368**, 388
Clymeniidae, 387
Clypeaster, **200**
Cnidoblast, 73, 94, 121
"Coat-of-mail" shell, 304
Coccolith, **33**, 47
Coccolithophoridae, 34
Coccophore, **33**
Cockerell, F. D. A., 477
Cockroach, 450, 453
Cocoon, **450**
Coelenterata, 7, 72, 122, 147
budding in, **112**
evolution of, 124, 147
exoskeletal structures of, **96**
geological history of, **123**, 124
as rock builders, 125
Coelenteron, 72, 73, 97
of medusa, 75
of polyp, 73, **74, 96**
Coelom, 150
Coenenchyma, 81, **82**, 116
Coenenchymal budding, **112**
Coenosarc, 77, 85
Coenosarcal canal, **82**
Coiling in cephalopods, 366, **368**
Coleoidea, 364, 382, 383, 388, 399–401, 403
Coleoptera, 453, *458*
Coleps, 50
Collared flagellum, 2, **28**, 52, 53
Collembola, 455, *458*
Colonial corallum, 100, 106
Colonial Protozoa, 27
Color, in cephalopod shells, 400
in gastropod shells, 349
Color marking, on cephalopod shells, 371, 400
Columella, **96**, 99, **346**, 347
Columellar lobe, 373
Columellar saddle, 373
Column, 158, **169, 174,** 176, **189**
length of, 173, 176
Columnal, 158, **169**, 171, **174, 189**
Columnaria, **104**, 107, 126
Columnaria alveolata, **104**
Comastrocrinus, 174
Comatulidae, 173
Comb, **470**
Comb jellies, 121
Commensal forms of mollusks, 154, 359
Commensalism, 69, 154, 338
Commentry, France, fossils from, 459
Commissure, **263**, 276
Communication pore, **236**
Compass, **205**
Compensating sac, 243, **244**
Compensatrix, 243, **244**
Complex foraminiferal shell, **44**
Composita subtilita, **294**
Composition, of brachiopod shell, 265
of bryozoan skeleton, 224
of cephalopod shell, 366
of molluscan shell, 304
of pelecypod shell, 319
of protozoan shell, 29
of sponge skeleton, 56, 57
of worm tubes, 144
Compound corallum, 100
Compound radials, 178
Concavo-convex shells, **264**
Concentric annulations, **367**
Conch, 394
Conch shells, 341
Conchidium, **264, 270, 290,** 292, 297
Conchidium nysius, **290**
Conchiolites, 144
Conchostraca, 433, 435, 439
Condra, G. E., 249, 299
Condyle, 200, **201**
Cone-in-cone structure, 378
Conjugate pores, 202
Conjugation, 29
Conocoryphe, 418, **425**, 426
Conodonts, 133, 143
Constellaria, 229, **236**, 239
Constellaria constellata, **236**
Constricted aperture, **374**
Conularia, 355, **356**

Conularida, 355, 362
Conus, **353**, 354
Convexo-concave shell, **264**, 265
Convexo-plane shell, **264**
Convolute shell, 346, **368**, 369
Cooper, G. A., 273, 300
Copepoda, 410, 436, 440, **472**, 474
Coprolite, 19, 137
Coquina, crinoidal, 218
Coral bioherm, oldest, 126
Coral reefs, 157, 173
world distribution of, **101**
Coralline Coelenterata, 221
Coralline Crag, 221
Coralline deposits, 126
Corallines, 221
Corallite, 78, **96**, **111**, **118**
Corallum, 78, **111**
Corals, 7, **111**
Core, **17**, 18
Cornea, 420
Cornulites, **134**, 135, 144, 147
Cornulites (Ortonia) conica, **134**
Corona, 198, 199, **205**
Correlation by fossils, 22
Corrodentia, 453, *458*
Corynotrypa, 233, **234**
Corynotrypa inflata, **234**
Costate shells, **268**, 269
Costa, **268**, 269
Costal, **178**, 179
Counter septum, 102, **104**
Covering plates, 153, 159, **166**, **169**
Crabs, 406, 410, 443, 445, 474
Crania, 255, 287, **288**
Crania antiqua, **288**
Crania scabiosa, **288**
Craniacea, 282, 287, *298*
Cranidium, 418
Crassatellites, **316**, 334, **335**
Craterina bohemica, **161**
Crawfordsville, Indiana, echinoderms from, 154, 182
Crayfish, 8, 406, 410, **412**, 443, 445
Crepicephalus, **421**, 426
Crepidula, 354, **354**
Crepipora, 233, **234**
Crepipora perampla, **234**
Crest, **205**, 379
Cretaceous fossils, **321**
Crickets, 453
Crinoid, 152
Crinoid calyx, analysis of, **178**
Crinoid gardens, 172
Crinoid localities, 184
Crinoid structures, **174**
Crinoidal bioherm, 184, 218
Crinoidal coquina, 218
Crinoidal limestone, 218
Crinoidea, 149, 157, *159*, 172, *184*, 206
fossil, **186**, **187**, **189**
geologic range of, **217**
Croneis, C., 133, 219
Crown, **174**, 176
Crucibulum, **354**
Crura, **276**, 278, **279**, **294**
Crural plates, **270**, **279**
Crural process, **276**
Cruralium, **270**, 278
Crustacea, 8, 145, 406, 408–410, 473, 474
Cryptocephala, 142–144
Cryptocrinus, 160
Cryptolithidae, 424
Cryptolithus, 423, **425**, 426, 432
Cryptomonadina, 31
Cryptophragmus, **86**, 87
Cryptophragmus antiquatus, **86**
Cryptostomata, **223**, **226**, 229, *230*, 239, **240**, **242**, 245, 247, **248**, 249
Cryptozonia, 193
Ctenobranchia, 351, **402**
Ctenophora, 76, 80, 121
Ctenostomata, **223**, 229, *230*, **232**, 247, **248**
Cumacea, 444
Cumings, E. R., 87, 128, 239, 249, 299
Cup, of graptolite, 88
Cushman, J. A., 40, 45, 46, 51
Cuttlebone, 389
Cuttlefish, 8, 301, 304, 364, 365, 389, **390**
Cuvier, 22
Cyathaxonia, **104**, 105
Cyathaxonia cornu, **104**
Cyathaxonidae, 105
Cyathophyllidae, 105–107
Cyathophyllum, 107
Cyclocrinites, 68
Cyclodont dentition, **326**, 327
Cyclonema, 351, **352**, 360
Cyclonema humerosum, **352**
Cyclosphaeroma, 444, **445**
Cyclosphaeroma trilobatum, **445**
Cyclostomata, **223**, 229, *230*, **231**, 233, **234**, 245, 247, **248**
Cyclus, 463
Cylindrophyma, **64**, 65
Cypraea, **353**, 354
Cypridina messinensis, **437**
Cypris, **437**
Cypris fusca, **437**
Cyrtina hamiltonensis, **266**
Cyrtoceras, **368**, 371
Cyrtochoanites, 382, 386, 398
Cyrtocone, **368**
Cyrtodonta, 333, **335**
Cystiphyllidae, 105, 107
Cystiphyllum, **104**, 108
Cystiphyllum vesiculosum, **104**
Cystiphragm, 227, **236**
Cystoid, **152**, 156, 157, **162**

Cystoid plates, **161, 162**
Cystoid stage, 181
Cystoidea, 149, 151, 157, *159*, **162**, *163*, 206, 215
essential characters of, *163*
geological range of, **217**
Cystome, 27
Cytheropteron, 477
Cytoplasm, 27, **28**
Cytopyge, 28

D

Dactylioceras, **368**, 369
Dactyliocone, **368**, 369
Dactylopore, **82**, 83
Daddy longlegs, 471
Daedalus, 137
Dall, W. H., 404
Dalmanella, **290**, 291
Dalmanellacea, 282, 291, *298*
Dalmanites, **416, 419**, 423, 427, 432
Dalmanites hausmanni, **419**
Dalmanites myrmecophorus, 423
Dalmanitina hawlei, **432**
Dalmanitina socialis, **432**
Dana, J. D., 128
Dart sac, **357**
Darts, of *Helix*, **357**
Darwin, C., 128, 148
Davidson, C., 148
Davis, W. M., 128
Dead-men's fingers, 113
Decapoda, 382, 445, 477
Degenerate cephalopods, 371
Deltarium, 274
Delthyrial cavity, **270**, 277
Delthyrium, **270**, 274, **275, 276**
Deltidial plates, **270**, 274, **276**
Deltidium, 261, 262, **270**, 274, **279**
Deltoid cycle, 168
Deltoid plate, 168, **169**
Dendrograptus, **91**, 92
Dendrograptus hallianus, **91**
Dendrograptus ontarioensis, **91**
Dendroid graptolites, **88, 91**
Dendroidea, 90, **91**, 92
Dendrophyllia, **111**, 112
Dendrophyllia dendrophylloides, **111**
Dendrophrya, **42**, 43
Dental lamellae, **275**, 277
Dental plates, **270, 275**, 277
Dental ring, 214
Dental sockets, **270, 276**, 277, **279, 311**
Dentalium, **362**, 363
Dentalium elephantum, **362**
Denticles, 88, 142, **270**
Denticulated hinge line, 272
Denticulation, **270**
Dentition, of brachiopods, 276, 277
Dentition, formulae for pelecypods, 328
of gastropods, **303**
of mollusks, **326**
of pelecypods, 324, **326**
Derbya, 261, 320
Dermal pores, **54**, 55
Dermaptera, 453, 458
Desmons, 61
Desmospongia, 61, 65, 84
Destruction by insects, 451
Development, of a brachiopod, **262**
of a dendroid graptolite, **88**
of exoskeleton of Coelenterata, **78**
of an insect, 450
of septa in a tetracoral, **103**
of a tetracoral, **103**
Devilfish, 391, 395, 396
Dextral coiling, **345**, 347
Diagenodont dentition, **326**, 327
Diaphragm, 227, **234, 236, 238**
Diaperoecia, 233, **234**
Diaperoecia lobulata, **234**
Diaphorostoma, **352**, 354, 360
Diaphorostoma niagarensis, **352**
Diatom shells, 47, 48
Diatomaceous ooze, 48
Dibranchia (Dibranchiata), **305**, 364, 382, 388
Dibranchiate cephalopod, **305**, 364
Dichocoenia, **111**
Dicranograptus, 92, **93**
Dicranograptus nicholsoni, **93**
Dictyoclostus, **268**
Dictyonema, **88**, 91, 92
Dictyonema flabelliforme, **88**
development of, **88**
Dictyonina, 65
Dictyospongidae, 70
Dicyclic calyx, 165, **174**, 177
Diductor muscle, *256*, **257**, *258*
Diductor scar, **276**
Didymograptus, 92, **93**
Didymograptus patulus, **93**
Diet of a cephalopod, 395
Difflugia, **33**
Dikelocephalinae, 478
Dimensions, of arthropods, 406
of brachiopods, 265
of sponges, 53
of trilobites, 423
Dimorphic coelenterates, 80, 115
Dimorphism, 36
Dimyarian pelecypod, **312**, 313, 329
Dinoflagellida, 31, 34
Dinorthis, **254, 290**, 291
Dinorthis pectinella, **290**
Dinorthis (Plaesiomys) subquadrata, **254**
Diopatra ornata, **132**
Dipleurula, 215, **216**
Diplochoanitic shell, **377**

Diploglossata, 453, *458*
Diplograptus pristis, **93**
Diplopoda, 449, **472**
Diplopore, 151, 160, **161**, 165
Diploporita, *163*, 165
Diplospire, 278
Diprion, 92
Diptera, 455, *458*
Directive septum, **96**, 97, 102, 108
Discinacea, 282, 287, **298**
Discinisca, 255
Discoid tests, 43
Discolith, 34
Disease carried by protozoans, 30
Dissepiments, in an archaeocyathid, **68**
in a bryozoan, 227
in a coral, **96**, 98
in a graptolite, **88**, 90
Distichal, **178**, 179
Distillation, a mode of fossilization, 16
Distribution, of ammonoid families, 399
of Archaeocyathinae, 122, 125
of cephalopods, 394, 395
of coral reefs, **101**
of gastropods, 303, 357
of *Limulus*, 463
of mollusks, 303
of nautiloid families, 398
Divaricator muscle, *258*
Divaricator scar, **275**
Diverticulum, 151
Docoglossa, 351
Dogger Bank, pelecypods on, 337
Dolerorthis, **270**, 291
Dorsal adjustor, **257**, *258*
Dorsal fold, **365**
Dorsal furrow, 414, **416**
in a cephalopod, 369
Dorsal lobe, **262**, 373, **416**
Dorsal mantle, **253**, 295
Dorsal plates, **308**
Dorsal saddle, 373
Dorsal side, 156
of ophiuroid, **191**
Dorsal shield, 414, **415**
Dorsal valve, **253**, **257**, 261, **262**, 279
Dorsi-biconvex shell, **264**
Doryderma, 66
Doublure, **264**, **415**, 420, **432**, **467**
Dragon flies, 449, 454
Drepanellina clarki, **438**
Dresden, fossils from, 135
Dudley, England, fossils from, 183
Dunbar, C. O., 299
Dupont, E., 299
Dysodont dentition, **326**, 327

E

Ear-wigs, 453
Earthworm, 142, 145, 148
Eccyliopterus, 351, **352**
Eccyliopterus volutatus, **352**
Ecdysis, 408
Echinocaris, 444, **445**
Echinocaris socialis, **445**
Echinocystites, 211
Echinocystoida, *207*, 211
Echinoderma, 8, 149, 215
anatomy of, 150
the animal of, 147, 150
attachment of, 153
gardens of, 154
as geologic agents, 217
geologic history of, **217**
habitats of, 153
habits of, 150, 153
living position of, **152**
nature of fossil record of, 218
phylogeny of, 215
Echinoid spines, **201**, **210**
Echinoid tests, **202**, **208**, **210**
numbering of, **202**
Echinoidea, 149, **152**, 158, 190, 197, **208**, **210**, **211**
essential characters of, *207*
geologic range of, **217**
Echinosphaerites, 160, **161**
Echinosphaerites infaustus, **161**
Echinus, **198**
Echiurida, 142, 145
Echiurus, 145
Ecology, of Arthropoda, 474
of Brachiopoda, 296
of Bryozoa, 245
of Cephalopoda, 394
of Coelenterata, 77, 127
of Echinoderma, 206
of Foraminifera, 45
of Gastropoda, 357
of Mollusca, 401
of Pelecypoda, 336
of Porifera, 68
of Trilobita, 429
Ectoderm, 53, **54**, 61, 73, **74**, 131
Ectoprocta, **223**, 229
Edentulous shell, 322
Edrioaster, **166**, 167
Edrioaster bigsbyi, **166**
Edrioasteroid, **152**, 156
Edrioasteroidea, 149, 157, *159*, 166
geologic history of, **217**
Egg capsule, 344
Egg cases, 344, 436
Egg stage, 450
Eggs of trilobites, 427
Ehrenberg, C. G., 220
Eifel district, fossils from, 126
bioherms in, 126
Eldonia, 214
Eleutherozoa, 188

Elkaniidae, 286
Ellipsocephalus, **425**, 426
Embioidea, 454, *458*
Embolobranchiata, 410, 462, 469, **470**, **472**
Embryo, of a bryozoan, **222**, **225**
of a coelenterate, 77
Enalaster, 207
Encrinurus, **427**
Endobase, **415**, 423
Endoceras, 370, **376**, 377, 385, 392, 397
Endoceras subannulatum, **376**
Endocyclic echinoid, 199, **210**
Endoderm, 53, **54**, 61, 73, **74**, 75, 131
Endogastric shell, 379
Endoparasite, 139, 140
Endopodite, 411, 412, **415**
Endopunctae, 267
Endosiphon, 378
Endothyra, **42**, 46
Enemies of trilobites, 429, 430
Enrollment of trilobites, 430
Ensis, **316**, 334
Enteletes, **270**
Enteron, **141**
Entire margin, 349
Entoprocta, **223**, 229
Entovalva, 339
Environments, ancient, 10, 20
present, kinds of, **11**
Eodiscidae, 426
Eodiscus, 421, **427**
Eoharpes, 419, 421, **425**, 426
Eoscorpius, **470**, 471
Eoscorpius carbonarius, **470**
Eotomaria supracingulata, **352**
Eotrophonia, 144
Ephebic stage, 295, 394
Ephemeridae, 454, *458*
Epidermal covering of echinoid spine, **201**
Epiphysis, 205
Epistoma, 420
Epitheca, **96**, 98, 228
Epithesostoma, 145
Epoch, 26
Era, 26
Errantia, 142, 143
Eschara sulcata, **228**
Escharopora, **242**, 243
Escharopora angularis, **242**
Escutcheon, **312**, 322
Esophagus, 73, **198**, 302, **307**, 312
"Essay on Man," quoted, 396
Estheria, **434**, 436
Estheria ovata, **434**, 436
Esthonia, fossils from, 117, 126, 247, 466
Estlandia, **279**
Etheridge, R., 135
Eublastoidea, 172
Eucarida, 444
Eucidaris tribuloides, **203–205**
Eudea, 63, **64**
Eugereon, 455
Euglenoidea, 31
Eulamellibranchia, 315, **317**, 330
Eulamellibranchiate gills, 315, **317**
Eumalacostraca, 443, 444
Eunicites, **132**
Eunicites anchoralis, **132**
Eunicites mutabilis, **132**
Euonychophora, 145, 447
Eupatagus, 209, **210**
Eupatagus floridanus, **210**
Euphausia, **411**
Euphausiacea, 445
Euphoberia armigera, **448**
Euplectella, 53, 57, **63**, 65
Euprimitia sanctipauli, **438**
Eupsammidae, 112
Eurypterida, 406, 459, 461, 463, **467**, **468**, 477
Eurypterids, 406, 429, 460, **468**, 471
Eurypterus, **468**, 469
Eurypterus remipes, **468**
Euspongia, 66
Eutaxicladina, 65
Euthyneura, 350, 355
Evolute test, 43
Evolution, of Arthropoda, 471
of Brachiopoda, 295
of Bryozoa, 247
of Cephalopoda, 391
of Coelenterata, 124
of Crinoidea, 180
of Gastropoda, 357
of Mollusca, 400
of Pelecypoda, 334
of Trilobita, 427
Excrement of holothurians, **212**, 213, 215
Excremental pellets, 137
Excreta, 19
Excurrent canals, **54**
Excurrent passages, **54**, 55
Exhalant aperture, **314**
Exhalant canals, **62**
Exhalant current, 314
Exhalant pore, 55
Exhalant siphon, **305**, **307**, **312**
Exocyclic echinoid, 199, **200**
Exocycloida, **207**, 209
Exogastric shell, 379
Exogyra, 320, **321**, 322, 333, 336, 337, 340, 341, 403
Exogyra cancellata, 337
Exogyra costata, **321**
Exopodite, 411, 412, **415**
Exopunctae, 267
Exoskeleton, of Anthozoa, **96**
of Arachnida, 460
of Arthropoda, 406

Exoskeleton, of Coelenterata, 73, **74,** 77
of Crustacea, 412
of Echinoderma, **152,** 155
of Graptozoa, 87
of Trilobita, 414
Exothecal lamellae of an archaeocyathid, **68**
Exsert oculars, 203, **204**
External impressions, **17,** 18
External mold, **17,** 18
External parasitic worms, 145
External shells of cephalopods, 371
Extinction, of cephalopods, 371
of trilobites, 430, 432
Extracapsular portion of test, 48
Extrasiphonata, 387, 388
Eye facets, number of, 449
Eye spot, **141, 438**
Eye tubercle, 437
Eyes, of Arthropoda, **412**
of cephalopods, 365, 390
of eurypterids, **467**
of gastropods, **344**
of Insecta, 449
of king crab, **464**
of Mollusca, **305,** 313
of ostracod, **437**
of trilobites, **414,** 415, **416, 419, 427, 432**

F

Facets, 449
Facial suture, **414,** 415, **416,** 419
Faecal pellets, 137
False aperture, **240**
Family, definition of, 7
Families of Pelecypoda, 340
Farther India, fossils from, 79, 124
Fascioles, 200
Favosites, **118,** 119
Favosites hemisphericus, **118**
Favositidae, 117, 119
Feather star, 149, 154, 157, 172
Fenestella, **226, 242,** 243
Fenestella triserialis, **242**
Fenestellidae, 227
Fenton, C. L., 87, 127, 137, 143, 213
Fenton, M. A., 87, 127, 137, 143, 213
Ferruginous foraminiferal test, 40
Fierasfer, 154
Fiji Islands, animals from, 394
Filament, 315
Filamentous tentacles, 383
Filibranchia, 315, **317,** 330
Filibranchiate gills, 315, **317**
Filling, **17,** 18
Filose pseudopodia, 32
Finkelnburgia, **289,** 291
Finkelnburgia finkelnburgia, **289**
Finkelnburgia osceola, **289**
First glabellar lobe, 417
First laterals, **303**
First maxilla, 411
Fish, 8
Fission, 29, 56, 76, **112**
Fissurella, 351, **353**
Fistulata, 175, 182, *184*, 188
Fistulipora, 228, 233, **234**
Fistulipora foordi, **234**
Fistulose aperture, 43
Fixed brachial, 179
Fixed cheek, **414,** 415, **416,** 432
Flabelliform tests, 43
Flabellum, 110, **111**
Flagellata, 31, 32
Flagellate cells, 53
Flagellate chambers of sponges, 65
Flagellum, **28,** 53
Flat worms, 7, 129, 139
Fleas, 455
Fleshy sponge spicules, 57
Flexibilia, *184*, 185, **187**
Flies, 406, 409, 455
Float, 94
Flooring plates, **166,** 193
Florissant, Colorado, fossils from, 454, 457 477
Fly, 409
Foerste, A. F., 404
Fold, **268, 270,** 271
Food channel, **174**
Food-gathering system, of blastoid, **169**
of crinoid, **174,** 176
Food groove, 151, 153, 159, **169, 192**
Food of trilobites, 429
Foot, of an amphineuran, **308**
of a cephalopod, 363
of a gastropod, 342, **344**
of a mollusk, **302, 305, 311**
of Onychophora, 446
of pelecypods, **311,** 312, 315
Footprints, 18
Foramen, **270**
Foramina, 44
Foraminifera, 32, 35, 362
classification of, 45
ecology of, 35, 45
formation of test of, 40, 41
geologic history of, 46
nature of organism of, 35
relation of animal to test in, **30,** 35
reproduction of, 36, **37**
shells of, 35, **42, 44**
composition of, 38, 40, **42, 43**
form and architecture of, 40
ornamentation of, **42**
size of, 38, **44**
wall structure of, **44**
Foraminiferal deposits, 46, 47
Foraminiferal limestone, 46, 47
Foraminiferal tests, **30,** 38, **42, 49**

Forest soil, organisms in, 3
Forked plates, 167, 168
Form, of sponge skeleton, 58, **59**
of sponge spicules, 58, **59**
Formation of bryozoan zoarium, **226**
Fossil, definition of, **13**
Fossil animals, number of species of, 4
Fossil Cephalopoda, 399
Fossil Echinoidea, **210, 211**
Fossil excreta, 19, **138**
Fossil holothurians, **212,** 214
Fossil insects, **456,** 459
Fossil medusae, **95**
Fossil worms, **130,** 131, **132, 134,** 135, **138, 141**
Fossil record, nature of, 15
of Arthropoda, **432,** 476
of Brachiopoda, 299
of Gastropoda, 360
of Holothuroidea, 214
of Insecta, 459
of Pelecypoda, 340
of sponges, 69
of Trilobita, 432
of worms, 131
Fossils, chronological significance of, 20
kinds of, **17**
stratigraphic significance of, 20
uses of, 20, 22
Fossula, **96,** 98, 102
Free brachial, 179
Free cheek, **414,** 415, **416,** 432
Free crinoid, **152**
Free mantle, **311**
Fresh-water pelecypods, 403
Fresh-water sponges, 68
Frontal glabellar lobe, **416,** 417
Frozen mammoths of Siberia, 50
Function, of appendages, 407
of endoderm, 75
Fungia, 99, 110, **111**
Fungidae, 110
Funiculus, **222**
Funnel, **365, 390**
Fusiform shell, **353**
Fusulina, 44, 45
Fusulinid shell, **44**
Fusulinidae, 46
Fusus, **353,** 354

G

Galloway, J. J., 31, 40, 45, 51
Gardiner, S., 128
Gaskall, W. H., 462
Gastric mill, 443
Gastric pouches, 94
Gastropod borings, **361**
Gastropod trails, **361**
Gastropoda, 304, **344–346, 348, 352, 353, 356,** 363, 400
borings by, **361**
geologic history of, 357
lingual dentition of, **303**
shells of, **346, 352–354, 356**
structure of, 345, **346,** 348, 349
shells fastened to crinoid calyx, **186**
source of food for man, **359**
Gastroporella, 245, **246**
Gastroporella ventricosa, **246**
Gastropore, **82,** 83
Gastro-vascular pouch, 94
Gastrula stage, 295
Geisonoceras, 371, **376**
Geisonoceras tenuitextum, 371
Geisonoceras wauwatosense, **376**
Gelatinous tests, 39
Genal angle, 417
Genal appendages of an eurypterid, **467**
Genal spine, **416,** 417
Genital fissure of ophiuroid, **195**
Genital operculum of scorpion, **461**
Genital plates, **202,** 203, **204**
Genital pore, **162,** 164, **204**
Genital structures, **467**
Genus, definition of, 7
Geographic distribution of Archaeocyathinae, 122, 125
Geography, ancient, 23
Geologic distribution, of gastropod families, 360
of pelecypod families, 340
Geologic history, of Amphineura, 402
of Arthropoda, 471
of Blastoidea, 171, **217**
of Brachiopoda, **248,** 297
of Bryozoa, 245, 247, **248**
of Cephalopoda, 391, **402**
of Cirripedia, 441
of Coelenterata, **123,** 124, 125
of Crinoidea, **217**
of Echinoderma, **217**
of Echinoidea, **217**
of Foraminifera, 46
of Gastropoda, 357, **402**
of graptolites, 89
of Graptozoa, 89
of Hydrozoa, 81
of Insecta, 456
of Malacostraca, **443**
of Mollusca, 400
of Pelecypoda, 334
of Porifera, 69
of Scaphopoda, 363
of Stelleroidea, **217**
of Stromatoporoidea, 85
of Trilobita, 428, 429, 430
of worms, 146
Geologic range, of animal phyla, **9**

Geologic range, of Brachiopoda, *298*
of Gastropoda, 360
of Insecta, *458*
Geologic time scale, 26
Geologic time table, *24*, *25*
Geologic work of worms, 147
Gephyrea, 141, 146
Gerontic contact furrow, 369
Gerontic stage, **44**, 295, 394
Gigantella, 265
Gigantocypris, 439
Gigantostraca, 462
Gill cavity, **311**, 312, 343
Gills, 131, **305**, **311**, 315, **317**, 343, 363
of Mollusca, **305**
of pelecypods, **311**, **317**
of worms, 131, 141
Girdle, 307, **308**
Glabella, **414**, 415, **416**, 417
Glabellar furrows, **416**, 417
Glabellar lobes, **416**, 417
Gladius, 389
Glass sponge, 56, 60, 63, 70
Globigerina, **33**, **42**, 45
Globigerina ooze, 30
Glossorthis, **270**, 281, 291
Glycerites sulcatus excavatus, **132**
Glycimeris, **328**, 333, **335**, 361
Glycimeris undata, dental formula of, 328
Glyptarca, 339
Glyptosphaerites, **162**, 165
Glyptosphaerites leuchtenbergi, **162**
Gnathobase, 423
Goldius, 422, **425**
Gomphoceras deshayesi, **374**
Gonad, of an echinoid, **198**
of a medusa, **74**
Gonangium, **93**
Goniatite suture, **372**, 375, 387
Goniocidaris caniculata, **203**
Gonocyst, 227
Gonoecium, 227
Gonotheca, 80
Goose barnacle, 441
Gorgonia, **114**, 115
Gorgonia acerosa, **114**
Gorgonidae, 113, 115
Gortner, R. A., 76
Gotland, fossils from, 23, 108, 117, 126, 183
Grabau, A. W., 89, 126, 128, 404, 467
Grammysia, 328
Grand Canyon series, sponges from, 70
Graptolites, 21, 72, 81, 87, **88**, 89, **91**, **93**, 124
biologic affinities of, 90
geologic range of, 38
Graptoloidea, 90, **93**
Graptozoa, 79, 87, **91**, 124, 127
geologic history of, 89
geologic range of, **123**
Grasshopper, 409, 450, 453
Great Barrier Reef, of Australia, 127, 128
of the Michigan Basin, 126
Green River shale, 459
Greenland, fossils from, 23
Gregarious organisms, 154
Growth lines, **257**, **268**, **312**, 324, **367**
Growth stages of a dendroid graptolite, **88**
Grub, 409
Gryphaea, 320, **321**, 322, 333, 336, 340, 341
Gryphaea corrugata tucumcarii, **321**
Guard, **380**, 381
Gullet, 73, 95, **96**
Gut, 150, **212**, 216
Gymnolaemata, **223**, 229, *230*
Gyroceras, **368**
Gyrocone, **368**, **380**

H

Habitat, of animals, 10
of Anthozoa, 100
of Coelenterata, 125, 126
of Echinoderma, 183
of Eurypterida, 466
of Graptozoa, 89
of Hydrozoa, 81
Habits, of animals, 10
of Echinoderma, 150
Hadentomium, 454
Hadentomoidea, 454, *458*
Hadrophyllum, 99, **104**, 105
Hadrophyllum aplanatum, **104**
Haeckel, E., 51
Haliotis, 347, 351, **353**, 358
Hall, J., 299
Hallopora, **238**, 239
Hallopora pulchella, **238**
Halysites, **118**, 119, 120, 126
Halysites catenularia, **118**
Halysites catenularia amplitubulata, **118**
Halysitidae, 117, 120
Hamites, **368**, 370, 388
Hamulus, **134**, 144
Hamulus onyx, **134**
Handlirsch, A., 452, 477
Hanna, G. D., 34
Hapalopteroidea, 454, *458*
Haplocrinus, 182
Haptopoda, 471
Harpedidae, 426
Harrodsburg limestone, crinoids in, 218
Harvest flies, 455
Head, of brachiopod embryo, **262**, 295
of mollusk, **302**, 342
Heart, of mollusk, **302**
of ostracod, **437**
of trilobite, **415**
Heart urchin, 197, 209
Hebertella, **264**, **268**, **276**, **279**, **291**
ornamentation of, **268**

Hebertella insculpta, **276**
Hebertella occidentalis, **276**
Hebertella occidentalis sinuata, **290**
Height, measurement of, in shell, 319
Heinrich, M., 84, 127
Helicidae, 356, **357**
Helicoid coiling, 344, **353**
Helicoid spiral, 347
Heliolites, **114**, 116
Heliolites interstinctus, **114**
Heliolitidae, 75, 113, 115, 116, 125
Heliophyllum, **104**, 107
Heliopora, **114**, 115, 116
Heliopora caerulea, **114**
Helioporidae, 113, 115, 116
Heliosestrum, **49**
Heliozoa, 32, 33, 48
Helix, **353**, 356, **357**
Helminthoidichnites meeki, **138**
Helopora, **242**, 243
Helopora spiniformis, **242**
Hemiaspis, **465**, 466
Hemiaspis limuloides, 465
Hemimeridae, 453, *458*
Hemiphragma, **238**, 239
Hemiphragma irrasum, **238**
Hemipronites, **268**
Hemiptera, 455, *458*
Hemiseptum, **240**
Heptameral symmetry, 108, 109
Hermaphroditic barnacles, 441
Hermaphroditic worms, 141
Hermit crab, 445
Hesperorthis, **290**, 291
Hesperorthis tricenaria, **290**
Heterocoela, 62
Heteronema priscum, 231, **232**, 247
Heteropoda, 342, 354
Heterotomous arms, 179
Hexacoralla, 100, 103, 108, 109, 116, 125
  ancestry of, 108, 109
  geologic range of, **123**
Hexactinellid spicule, 60
Hexactinellida, 61, 65
Hexalonche, **49**
Hexameral symmetry, in corals, **96**, 108, 109
Hexameroceras, **374**
Hexameroceras byronense, **374**
Hexameroceras jolietense, **374**
Hexancistra, **49**
Hexaxial spicule, **59**, 60
Hexaxon, **59**, 60
Hickson, S. J., 128
Hinge, 324
Hinge line, 256, **262**, **270**
Hinge-line structures, of brachiopod, **270**
  of pelecypods, 322
Hinge margin, 263
Hinge plates, **276**, **279**, 323, 324, **326**
Hinge spine, 289
Hinge teeth, in brachiopods, **276**
  in pelecypods, 324, **326**
Hippurites, **316**, 320, 334, 338, 341
Hirudinea, 141, 146
Holmes, O. W., 396
Holochoanites, 382, 385, 398
Holochroal eyes, 420
Holopus, 173
Holothuria tubulosa, **212**
Holothurian castings, 143, **212**
Holothurian fossils, **212**
Holothurian plates, **212**
Holothurian skeletal elements, **212**
Holothurian tables, **212**
Holothuroid, 143, **152**
Holothuroidea, 149, 155, 158, 190, 213, 215
  fossil, **212**
  geologic range of, **217**
Homalonotus, 423, **427**
Homalonotus major, 423
Homeodeltidium, **270**, 275
Homocoela, 62
Homoptera, 455, *458*
Homotrypa, **236**, 239
Homotrypa alta, **236**
Honey-comb corals, **77**, 117
Hood, **305**, **365**, 383
Hook, **212**, 389
Hook-headed worms, 140
Hoplites, **368**, 388
Hoplocarida, 446
Hormosina, **42**, 43
Hormotoma, 351, **352**
Hormotoma trentonensis, **352**
Horny jaws, 131, **132**, 383
Horsehair worm, 139
Horseshoe crab, 463
Housefly, 450
Hudsonaster, **193**, **194**
Hudsonaster incomptus, **194**
Hutchinson, G. E., 145
Hyatt, A., 404
Hyattechinus, 199, **211**
Hyattechinus rarispinus, **211**
Hybocrinus, 182
Hybocystis, 182
Hydnoceras, 57, 64, 65, 70
Hydra, 72, 81
Hydractinia, 81, 83
Hydractinoid structure, 84
Hydrocorallinae, 81, 83
Hydropore, **162**, 180, **216**
Hydrospire, 151, 167, **169**, 170
Hydrotheca, definition of, 80, 88
  of graptolite, 80, 88, 91
  of polyp, **74**, 80
Hydrozoa, 7, 79–81, **82**, 103, 124
  geologic range of, **123**
Hydrozoans, 72
Hydrozooid structure, 84, 85, **86**

Hymenocaris, 444, **445**
Hymenocaris perfecta, **445**
Hymenoptera, 454, 458
Hyolithellus, **359**
Hyolithes, 355, **356**, 359
Hyperammina, 41, **42**, **43**
Hypercline interarea, **272**, *273*
Hypermegethes schucherti, **456**
Hyponome, 363, 379, 383, 388
Hyponomic funnel, **305**, 382
Hyponomic sinus, 379
Hypoparia, 424, 426
Hypostoma, **414**, **415**, 420, **432**
Hypothetical ancestor of Echinoderma, **216**

I

Icosaspis, **49**
Igoceras, 154, **186**, 359
Igoceras pabulocrinus, 359
Imago, **450**
Imagoal stage, **450**
Immature region, 235, **236**, 238
Immersed avicularium, **228**
Imperforate shell, 347
Imperforate wall, 29, 44
Impressed zone, 369
Impression, **17**, 18
Imprint, 18
Inadunata, 182, *184*, 185, **187**
Inarticulata, 252, **255**, 256, 282
Incipient delthyrium, 275
Incipient notothyrium, 275
Incurrent canals, **54**, 55
Indusial limestone, 455
Inferior hemiseptum, **240**, 241
Inferior-lateral lobe, 373
Inferior-lateral saddle, 373
Inferradials, 178
Inflected lip, 349
Infrabasals, **174**, 177, **178**
Inframarginal plate, **193**, **194**
Infra-median latus, **442**
Infundibuliform tabulae, **118**
Infusoria, 32
Inhalant aperture, **314**
Inhalant canal, **62**
Inhalant current, 314
Inhalant pore, 55, **62**
Inhalant siphon, **305**, **312**
Ink bag, 395
Ink gland, 364, 388
Ink sac, 388
Inner lip, **345**, 349
Inocaulis, **91**, 92
Inocaulis granti, **91**
Inoceramus, 341, 403
Insecta, 7, 406, 409, 410, 449, 460, **472**, 473, 475, 476
  geologic record of, **457**
Insects, in amber, 454, 476
  anatomy of, 449
  classification of, 8, 406, **456**
  destruction by, 451
  development of, **450**
  as enemies to man, 451
  fossil, **456**
  number of species of, 451
  of the sea, 474
Insert oculars, 203, **204**
Insertion lamina, **308**, 309
Insertion plate, **308**, 309
Integrata, **238**, 239
Interambulacral area, 150
Interambulacral plate, 177
Interambulacrum, 150, **202**
Interarea, 272
  relation to plane of commissure, **272**, *273*
Interbrachial plate, 177, 178
Intermediate teeth, **303**
Intermediate valves, **308**
Internal mold, **17**, 18
Internal parasitic worms, 145
Internal shells of cephalopods, 380
Internal structures, of brachiopod shells, **276**
  of corals, **96**
  of pelecypods, 329
Interradial pieces, **212**, 214
Interradial plates, **166**, 167, 168, **169**, 177, **178**, **193**, **194**, 214
Interray, 150
Interrupted aperture, 349
Interstitial budding, **112**
Intervallum, 122
Intestinal tract, **222**
Intestine, **212**, **222**, **253**, 302, **307**, 313
Intracapsular part of test, 48
Intrasiphonata, 387, 388
Invertebrate paleontology, definition of, 1
Involute shell, of cephalopod, **368**, 369
  of foraminifer, **42**, 43
  of gastropod, 346
Irregularia, 172
Ischadites, 66, **67**, 70
Ischadites iowensis, **67**
Isodont dentition, **326**, 327
Isopoda, 444, **445**, 474
Isoptera, 453, *458*
Isotelus, 418, 422, 423, **425**, 426
Isotelus gigas, 423, **425**
Isotomous arm, 179
Iulus maximus, **448**

J

Jackson, R. T., 206, 208, 219, 404
Japanese crab, 406
Jaws of worms, 40
Jelly, E. C., 249

Jellyfish, 72, 73, **74,** 75
composition of, 19, 76, 94
Jerea, 65
Jereica, **64,** 66
Jugal process, 278, **279**
Jugum, 278, **279**
June beetle, 409
Juresania, **270**

K

Katydids, 453
Kellett, B., 477
Keokuk, Iowa, fossils from, 182
Kidney, of brachiopod, **253,** 255
of mollusk, **302,** 365
of trochophore, **141**
King crab, 459, 462, **464**
Kionoceras, 371, **376,** 386
Kionoceras angulatum, 371
Kionoceras strix, **376**
Kirk, E., 183
Kloedenella obliqua, **438**
Knight, J. B., 405
Koninckinidae, 293
Krausella inaequalis, **438**
Kudo, R. R., 31, 51
Kustarachnida, 471
Kutorgina, **283,** 284
Kutorgina cingulata, **283**
Kutorginacea, 282, 284, 289, *298*

L

Labrador, flies in, 452
Labrum, 414
Lacewing flies, 454
Lagena, 40, **42, 43**
Lagoon, **11**
Lagynidae, 38
Lamarck, 22
Lamellibranchia, 309
Laminated layer, 265, **266, 311,** 319
Lamottia, 126
Lamp shells, 8, 251
Lancet plate, 168, **169**
Land habitat, **11**
Land snails, 356, **358**
Lankester, E. R., 392
Laotira, 95
Larva, 450
of arthropods, 450
of brachiopods, 295
Larval case, 476
Larval stage, **411, 450**
Larviformia, 182, *184*, 188
Lateral eye, 437
Lateral lobe, 373
Lateral muscle, *256*
Lateral plates, **270**
Lateral saddle, 373
Lateral shield, **191**
Lateral teeth, 325
Leech, 146
Left-handed coiling, **345,** 347
Left mantle lobe, **311**
Legs, on Onychophora, 446
Length, measurement of, in shells, 262, 319
Lenticulina, 41, **42**
Lepadidae, 441
Leperditella inflata, **438**
Leperditia fabulites, **438**
Leperditiidae, 439
Lepidesthes, 199, **203, 211**
Lepidesthes colletti, **203, 211**
Lepidoptera, 455, *458*
Leptaena, **268,** 292
Leptolinae, 81
Leptostraca, 443, 444
Leptosynapta, **212,** 213
castings of, **212,** 213
Leucones, 62
LeVene, C. M., 84, 252, 282
Lever-fulcrum principle, 257
Lichas, **425,** 426
Lid on coral, 107
Life of mollusks, 303, 403
Life habitats, 10
Life zones of the ocean, **12, 42**
Ligament, **311,** 313, 322
Ligamental grooves, **312,** 322
Limifossor talpoideus, **307**
Limpet, 345
Limulava, 463, 469
Limulus, 459, 460, 462, 463, **464,** 466, 476
Limulus polyphemus, **464**
Lingual dentition of a gastropod, **303**
Lingula, 251, 252, **255,** 259, **260, 266, 285,** 286, 297
Lingula aequalis, **285**
Lingula anatina, **255, 260, 266**
Lingula? lesueri, **285**
Lingulacea, 282, 286, *298*
Lingulasma, 281
Lingulella, **266, 268, 285,** 286
Lingulella acutangula, **266**
Lingulella ampla, **285**
Linoporella, **270,** 271
Liospira angustata, **346**
Listrium, 276
Lithistida, 61, 65
Lithobius forificatus, 448
Lithodesma, 324
Lithostrotion, **104,** 107
Lithostrotion canadense, **104**
Littoral zone, 11, **12**
Littorina, 358
Lituites, **368,** 386
Liver, of a gastropod, **307**
of a mollusk, **302**

Liver fluke, 139
Living chamber, of a cephalopod shell, **365,** 366, 376
Living position, of brachiopods, **260**
of echinoderms, **152**
of sponges, **63**
Lobes, **372,** 373
Lobocrinus pyriformis, **186**
Lobose pseudopodia, **28**
Lobster, 443, 445, 474
Lobworm, 148
Locomotory structures of Protozoa, **28**
Locust, 451, 453
Loligo, **390,** 394
Longitudinal ridge, **367**
Longley, W. H., 69
Loop, **257, 276,** 278, **279**
Lophomenia spiralis, **307**
Lophophore, **223,** 250, **253,** 258
Lophophyllum, 102, **104,** 106
Lophophyllum eruca, **104**
Lophospira, 348, 351, **352**
Loricula, **442,** 444
Loricula darwini, **442**
Lottia, **352, 353**
Louisville, Kentucky, corals from, 23, 106
reef at, 126
Loven, S., system of numbering rays of echinoid, 201, **202**
Lovenechinus missouriensis, **203**
Lower Greensand, sponges in, 70
Lower lip, 349
Lucina occidentalis ventricosa, 340
Luidia clathrata, 153
Lumbricaria, **138,** 143, 213
Lumbriconereites basalis, **132**
Lunarium, 228, **234**
Lung, 343
Lung cavity, 343
Lunule, **312,** 322
Lyssacina, 65

M

McAtee, W. L., 4
McCormack, J., 219
Maccoya burlingtonensis, **203**
Machaeridia, 215
McIntosh, W. C., 135
Mackenzia, 80, 125
Maclurites, 351, **352**
Maclurites bigsbyi, **352**
Macrocystella, **162,** 165
Macrocystella mariae, **162**
Macula, 229, **234, 236,** 237, **238**
Madrepora, **111,** 112
Madreporaria, 109, 110, **111**
Madreporite, **151,** 175, 191, **192–194,** 197, **198, 202, 204**
Magellania, **253,** 256, **257, 263, 266, 276, 279,** 295
Magellania australis, **266**
Magellania flavescens, **257, 263, 266, 276**
Magellania lenticularis, **253**
Maggot, 409, 450
Magnolias, ancient, 23
Malacostraca, 410, **411,** 443, **445, 472,** 475
Mallophaga, 453, *458*
Malocystites, 164
Mammal, 8
Mammoths, frozen in Siberia, 15
Mandaloceras, **374,** 379, 386, 397
Mandaloceras hawthornensis, **374**
Mandibles, 342, **411,** 436, 470
in cephalopods, **305**
of a nauplius, **411**
Mandibular appendage, **437**
Mansfield, W. C., 405
Mantle, **253,** 254, **305,** 310, **311,** 313, 342, 363, **365,** 383
Mantle cavity, **305**
Mantoidea, 453, *458*
Marginal doublure, **467**
Marginal furrow, **416**
Marginal pore, 170
Marine arachnids, 469
Marine gastropods, 403
Marine pelecypods, 403
Marine worms, 142
Marr, J. E., 89
Marsipella, 40
Marsupium, 227
Mastigophora, 31, 32, 47, 61
Mature region, 235, **236, 238**
Maxilla, **411,** 436
of a nauplius, **411**
of an ostracod, **437**
in worms, **132**
Maxilliped, **412**
May flies, 409, 454
Mazon Creek, Illinois, fossils from, 457
Meadow soil, organisms in, 3
Median eye, 437
Median ocelli, 462
Median septum, **270, 279**
Medinan, 137
Medusa, 72, 73, **74,** 75, 94
composition of, 19, 76, 94
Medusaegraptus, **91**
Medusaegraptus mirabilis, **91**
Medusoid stage, 80
Megalopore, **308**
Megaloptera, 454, *458*
Megalospheric shell, 36
Megamorina, 66
Megasecoptera, 455, *458*
Melania, 358
Mellita, 154
Melonechinus, 154, **203,** 207, 211

Melonechinus multiporus, **203**
Meridional rows of plates, 199
Meristellidae, 293
Meristina, 293, **294**
Meristina maria, **294**
Merostomata, 410, 462, 463, 466, **469, 472, 476**
Merostome, **285**
Mesentery, **96**
in a coelenterate, 75, 95, 97
in a holothurian, **212**
Mesoderm, 131
Mesogloea, 53, **54,** 61, 73, **74**
function of, 75
spicules in, 57
Mesopore, 227, **234, 236, 238**
Mesosoma, 460, **461**
Metacephalopoda, 382
Metamere, 141
Metamorphosis, 409, **450**
Metasoma, 460, **461, 467**
Metasomatic segments, **461**
Metastoma, **414,** 420, **467**
Metazoa, 27, 52, 61
Metroperiella, 245, **246**
Metroperiella biplanata, **246**
Metroperiella latipora, **246**
Michigan Basin, 23, 117
Micraster cor-anguineum, **203**
Micromitra (*Paterina*), 270, **283**, 284
Micromitra (*Paterina*) *bella*, **283**
Micromitra (*Paterina*) *phillipsi*, **283**
Micropore, 309
Microspheric shell, 36, **37**
Middle lateral muscle, 91
Miliary granule, **212,** 214
Miliolina, **42**
Millepora, 81, **82,** 83
Milleporoid structure, 84
Millipede, 406, 410, **448,** 449, 476
Mimoceras, **368,** 369
Mimocone, **368,** 369
Miskoa, 143, 144
Mites, 459, 460, 469, 471, 476
Mixochoanites, 382, 385, 398
Mixotermatoidea, 453, *458*
Mold, **17,** 18
Mollia granifera, **225**
Mollusca, 8, 147, 301, 440
geologic range of, **402**
relation of animal to shell in, **305**
Molluscoidea, 250
Mollusks, ancestral, **302**
dimensions of organism, 301
life of, 401
habitat of, 401
nature of animal, 301, **305**
number of species of, **301**
Molting, 408
Monactinellida, 66
Monaxon, 58
Monochoanitic shell, 377
Monocyclic calyx, **174,** 177
Monograptus, **93,** 94
Monograptus flexilis, **93**
Monomyarian shell, 313
Monoprion, 92
Monothalamous shell, 40
Monotrypa, **238,** 239
Monotrypa magna, **238**
Monticule, 229, 237
Monticulipora, **236,** 239
Monticulipora molesta, **236**
Monticuliporoid, 221, **236,** 239
Mosquito, 409, 451, 452
Moss animals, 8, 220
"Mother-of-pearl" layer, 319, 384
Moths, 455
Mouth, of an amphineuran, **308**
of an arthropod, **412, 415**
of an asteroid, **192**
of a blastoid, **169**
of a brachiopod, **253**
of a bryozoan, **222, 223, 225**
of a cephalopod, **390**
of a crinoid, **174**
of a cuttlefish, **390**
of a cystoid, **162**
of *Dipleurula*, **216**
of an echinoderm, **152**
of an echinoid, **198, 200**
of an edrioasteroid, **166**
of an eurypterid, **467**
of a gastropod, **307**
of a holothuroid, **212**
of a king crab, **464**
of a medusa, **74**
of a mollusk, **302, 305, 307,** 312
of a polyp, 73, **74**
of a trochophore, **141**
of a worm, **136**
Mouth shield, 195
Mucoid material, 47
Mucro, 389
Mud-dwelling brachiopods, 251
Mud fillings, 214
Multilocular test, 40, **42, 43**
Multivincular ligament, 323
Mural pore, 77, 116, 117, **118**
Murex, **353,** 354, 359
Muscle mark, 280
Muscle scar, **255,** 256, **257, 270,** 276, **279,** 280, 329
Muscle track, 280
Muscles, in Aristotle's lantern, **205**
in a brachiopod, **255,** *256*, **257,** *258*, 280
in a bryozoan, 222, **244**
in an echinoid spine, **201**
in an echinoid test, **205**
in a mollusk, **305**

Muscular system, in barnacles, **442**
in brachiopods, 255
in pelecypods, 313
Mussel, 301, 304
Mya, 251, **311,** 313, **316, 323,** 327, 334, 338
Mya arenaria, 251, **323**
Myalina, 333, **335**
Myalina subquadrata, **335**
Mycetozoa, 32, 35
Myophore, **323,** 324
Myriapod, 449, 476
Myriapoda, 406, 409, 410, 447, **448,** 473
Mysidacea, 444
Mytilus, **316, 326,** 327, 333, 336
Mytilus edulis, 336
Myxospongida, 66
Myzostomida, 142, 145

N

Natantia, 445
Natica, 342, **353,** 354, 359
Natica alderi, 359
Natland, M., 46
Natural cast, **17,** 18
Natural mold, **17,** 18
Natural replica, **17,** 18
Nature of fossil record, 15
of trilobites, **432**
Nauplius stage, **411,** 427, 440
Nautilicone, **368,** 369
Nautiloid suture, **372,** 375
Nautiloidea, 364, 368, 373, 382, 387, 399, 401, 403
geologic range of, 398, **402**
Nautilus, 304, 363, 364, **365,** 366, **368,** 371, **372, 374,** 375, 380, 383, 384, 386, 389, 390–396, 398
Nautilus pompilius, **365, 374**
Nautilus undulatus, **372**
Neanic stage, 394
Nebalia, 444
Nebaliacea, 444
Neck lobe, 417
Nekton, **12,** 13
Nektonic organisms, 73
Nema, 87, **88, 93**
Nemacaulus, 87
Nemathelminthes. 7, 129, 139
Nematoda, 140
Nematocyst, 73, **74**
Nematodes, 140, 155
Nemertinea, 139
Neobolidae, 286
Neolenus, 422, **425,** 426
Neolimulus, **465,** 466
Neolimulus falcatus, **465**
Neometra, **174,** 176, 188
Neospiridia, 32
Neotremata, **248,** 252, 259, **264,** 269, 275, 286, **288**
Nephridia, **253,** 255
Nepionic stage, 295, 394
Nereis, **132,** 143
Nereis cultrifera, **132**
Neritic life zone, 11, **12**
Neritina, 358
Nerve commissure, 351
Nervous system, of arthropods, 407
of mollusks, **302**
Neuroptera, 454, *458*
Neusina, 38
Nevadia, 420
New Brunswick, fossils from, 466
New South Wales, fossils from, 459
Nicholson, H. A., 84, 127
Nickles, J. M., 249
Nidulites, 68
Niobrara chalk, 183
Nipponites, 397
Node, 229, 271
Nodosaria, 40, **42, 43**
Northumberland, castings on coast of, 148
Nothoceras, 377
Notostraca, 433, 435
Notothyrial cavity, **270,** 277, **279**
Notothyrium, **270,** 275, 277
Nucleus, 27, **28**
Nucula, **316,** 333
Nudibranchia, 355
Nudibranchs, 350
Number of species, of cephalopods, 394
of Nautiloidea, 383
of Pelecypoda, 341
Number of teeth in radula, 342
Numbering of echinoid test, **202**
Nummulites, 45, 47
Nummulitic limestone, 47
Nummuloidal siphuncle, 386

O

Obconical shell, **353**
Obelia, **74,** 81
Obolacea, 282, 284, *298*
Obolidae, 284
Obolus, **232, 285,** 286
Obolus johni, **285**
Obovate shell, **353**
Obverse side, 242
Occipital furrow, 417
Occipital lobe, 417
Occipital segment, 416
Ocellus, 424, **465, 467**
O'Connell, M., 89, 467, 477
Octameral symmetry, 108, 109
Octocoralla, 100, 112, 125
Octopod, 364, **391**
Octopoda, 364, 382, 388, **391, 402**

Octopus, 8, 301, 304, 364, 365, **391**, 393, 396, 401
Octopus vulgaris, **391**
Ocular plate, 192, **202**, **204**
Oculogenital system, 198, **200**, 203, 204
Odonata, 454, 458
Odontophore, 303, 342, 364
Oeningen, 459
Oenonites tacitus, **132**
Oesia, 146
Ogygopsis, 418, **425**
Oldest coral bioherm, 125
Olenellus, 418, **421**, 422, 426, 466
Oligochaeta, 142, 145
Oligoporus danae, **203**
Oliva, **353**, 354
Olocyst, **246**
Oncoceras, **376**, 386
Oncoceras pandion, **376**
Oncoceratidae, 379
One-rayed spicule, 58
Ontogeny, of Anthozoa, 99
of Blastoidea, 171
of Brachiopoda, 295
of Cephalopoda, 391
of Crinoidea, 179, 180
of Echinoidea, 206
of Gastropoda, 357
of Pelecypoda, 334
of Trilobita, 427
Onychophora, 145, 406, 409, 410, 446, 447, **472**, 473
Onychophoroid, 447
Ooecium, **222**, 227
Opabina, 435
Operculum, of an arachnid, 460
in bryozoans, 226, **244**
in corals, **104**, 107
of an eurypterid, 467
in gastropods, **344**, **348**, 350
of *Hyolithes*, **356**
of a king crab, **464**
of a scorpion, **461**
in worm tubes, **134**, 144
Ophiocone, **368**, 369
Ophioglypha, **195**, **197**
Ophioglypha lacertosa, **195**
Ophiura, **196**
Ophiura decheni, **196**
Ophiuroid, **152**, 154
Ophiuroidea, 149, **191**, 194, **195**, **196**
arm structure of, **191**, **195**
Opisthobranchia, 355, **402**
Opisthodetic ligament, 313, 323
Opisthogoneata, 410, 448, 449
Opisthogyre shell, 322
Opisthoparia, 424, **425**, 426
Opisthoparian trilobite, 419
Oral disk, 73
Oral opening of polyp, 73
Oral papilla, 446
Oral plates, **162**
Oral side, 155, **200**
Orbiculoidea, **270**, 287, **288**
Orbiculoidea nitida, **288**
Order, definition of, 7
Organ-pipe coral, 113, 120
Organic evolution, 21
Organic world, 2
Orientation of pelecypod shell, 318
Orifice, 225
Oriostoma, **348**
Ornamentation, on brachiopod shells, **268**
on cephalopod shells, 371
Orthacea, 282, 291, *298*
Orthis, **254**, 291
Orthis rotundata, pallial markings on, **254**
Orthoceras, **365**, **368**, **374**, 375, **376**, 377, 381, 386
Orthoceras whitfieldi, **376**
Orthoceras wilmingtonense, **376**
Orthoceratite, **367**
Orthoceratite suture, 372, 375
Orthochoanites, 382, 386, 398
Orthocline interarea, **272**, *273*
Orthocone, **367**, **368**
Orthodonticus, 327
Orthogyre shell, 322
Orthoidea, 291
Orthoptera, 453, 458
Ortonia, 144
Osceolinae, 478
Osculum, 52, **54**, **62**
Ostracoda, 407, 410, 413, 435, 436, **437**, **438**, 440, **472**, 474
Ostracoderm, 429, 431
Ostrea, 313, **316**, 320, 322, **332**, 333, 338, 340, 403
Ostrea percrassa, **332**
Oswego limestone, 126
Ottoia, 146
Outer laterals, **303**
Outer lip, **345**, 349
Outer side plates, 170
Outside lateral muscle, **255**
Ovarian sinus, **276**
Ovary, **222**
Ovicell, 227, **244**, **246**
Oysters, 301, 304, 310, **332**

P

Pachydiscus septemradensis, 370, 399
Paedumias robsonensis, 421
Palaeacis, 108
Palaeechinus elegans, **203**
Palaeocaris typus, **445**
Palaeocyclidae, 105

Palaeodictyoptera, 452, 453, 455, **456,** 457, *458*
Palaeodiscus, 211
Palaeohemiptera, 455, *458*
Palaeophonus, 460, **461,** 471
Palaeophonus caledonicus, **461**
Palaeophonus nuntius, **461**
Palaeopsylla, 455
Palaeotremata, **248,** 252, 259, 261, 265, 282, **283,** 284, 289, *298*
Paleobotany, 1
Paleoconcha, 328, 330
Paleoecology, 20
Paleofavosites, 117, **118,** 126
Paleofavosites prolificus, **118**
Paleogeography, 20, 23
Paleontology, definition of, 1
Paleozoic bioherms, 117
Paleozoic reefs, 117
Paleozoology, definition of, 1
Pali, **96,** 99
Palintrope, 272
Palinura, 445
Pallial line, 254, **311, 312, 326,** 329
Pallial markings, **254,** 280
Pallial sinus, **253,** 280, **312,** 315, **326,** 330
Pallium, 254
Palmars, **178,** 179
Palms, ancient, 23
Palpebral lobe, **416,** 418, 419, **432**
Palpigradi, 471
Panartus, **49**
Panicium, **49**
Panopaea, **314,** 334
Panopaea norvegica, **314**
Panorpatae, 455, *458*
Pantodont dentition, 327
Pantostomitidia, 31
Papilla, 446
Paradoxides, **421,** 423, 426, 432
Paradoxides harlani, 423
Parafusulina, 38
Paragastric cavity, 52, **54, 62**
Parapodium, 129, 131, 141
Parasitic protozoans, 28
Parasitic worms, 139, 155
Paravincular ligament, 323
Paries, **442**
Parks, W. A., 84, 127
Pasceolus, 68
Patella, 345
Patellate shell, **353**
Paterina (see *Micromitra*)
Paterinacea, 282, 284, *298*
Paterinidae, 284
Patina, 181
Patten, W., 462
Pauropoda, 449
Pavement cells, 53
Pearls, formation of, 319, 339
Pearse, A. S., 69
Pecten, **311,** 314, **316,** 322, **326,** 327, **331,** 333
Pectin, 460, **461**
Pectinate rhomb, 160
Pedal disk, 73
Pedal muscles, 329
Pedicellaria, 192, **198, 201**
Pedicle, 252, **253, 257, 262, 285**
Pedicle adjustors, 256
Pedicle opening, 274, **276**
Pedicle valve, 261
Pedipalp, 459, **461**
Pedipalpida, 471
Peduncle, 252, **442**
Pedunculate avicularium, **228**
Pelecypod and brachiopod compared, 318
Pelecypoda, 304, **305,** 309, **311, 312, 314, 321, 331, 332, 335,** 342, 400
  adaptations among, **316**
  dispersion of, 337
  as food, 339
  geological distribution of families of, 498, 499
  gills of, **317**
  number of species of, 310
  relation of animal to shell in, **305**
  shells of, in the arts, 339
    composition of, 311
    dentition of, **326**
    height of, 319
    length of, 319
    shape of, **312**
    structure of, **311, 326**
  stratigraphic range of, 339
Pelmatozoa, 157, 158, 163, 164
  essential characters of, *159*, 166
  hypothetical ancestor of, **216**
Pen, **305,** 389, **390**
Pennatulidae, 113, 115
Pentacrinus, 153, 188, **189**
Pentacrinus astericus, **189**
Pentacrinus maclearanus, **189**
Pentacrinus stage, 181
Pentameracea, 282, 291, 292, *298*
Pentameral symmetry, 108, 109
Pentameroidea, 291
Pentamerous symmetry, 156, 292
Pentamerus, 9, 10, 16, **270,** 297
Pentamerus oblongus, 16
Pentamerus oblongus cylindricus, 9, 10
Pentremital limestone, 171
Pentremites, 168, **169,** 171, 172
Pentremites pyriformis, **169**
Peracarida, 444
Perforata, 110
Perforate protozoan tests, 29, 42, 44
Perforate shell, 347
Periderm, 87
Perigastrella, 245, **246**
Perigastrella oscitans, **246**

Perignathic girdle, 156, **198**, 206
Period, 26
Periostracum, 265, **311**, 319, **331**, 347
Peripatidae, 447
Peripatus, 145, 446
Peripodium, 202
Periproct, 197, 198, 199, **202**, **204**
Perischoechinoida, *207*, 211
Peristome, 159, **200**, **205**, **246**
 of an echinoderm, 197, 198, **205**
 of a mollusk, 349
 of a polyp, 73
Peristomella, 245, **246**
Peristomella falcifera, **246**
Peristomice, **246**
Perlaria, 454, *458*
Permineralization, 16
Perner, J., 405
Persistent dorsal furrow, 369
Petrunkevitch, A., 471, 477
Peytoia, 95
Phacops, **427**, 432
Phalangida, 471
Phalangiotarbi, 471
Phanerocephala, 142, 143
Phanerozonia, 193
Pharetrones, 62, 63
Phasmoidea, 453, *458*
Phillipsia, **425**, 426
Pholas, 327, 338
Phoronid burrows, 137
Phragmoceras, **374**, 379, 386, 397
Phragmoceras rex, **374**
Phragmoceratidae, 379
Phragmocone, **380**, 381
Phyla, geologic range of, **9**
Phylactolaemata, **223**, 229
Phyllocarida, 413, 444
Phyllograptus, 92, **93**
Phyllograptus angustifolius, **93**
Phyllograptus ilicifolius, **93**
Phyllopod, 410
Phyllopoda, 434
Phylogeny, of the Cephalopoda, 393
 of the Echinoderma, 215
Phylum, definition of, **7**
Phytomonadina, 31
Pierre shale, fossils in, 340
Pikaia, 146
Pill bug, 406, 444
Piloceras, 370, **376**, 385
Piloceras amplum, **376**
Pilsbry, H. A., 405
Pilulina, **42**
Pinna, 320, 322, 323
Pinnulate arms, **174**, 179
Pinnule, 156, 167, **174**
Pisocrinus, 182
Pit, 436, 439
Placenticeras, 370, **372**, 388, 393, 394, 397
Placenticeras lenticularis, **372**
Placenticeras placenta, **372**
Planaria, 139
Plane of commissure, relation of interareas
 to, **272**, *273*
Plane of symmetry, 191, 201, 250, **263**
Plankton, **12**, 13
Plano-convex shell, **264**
Planolites corrugatus, **136**
Planorbis, **353**, 356, 358
Planospiral shells, 344, 345
Planospiral tests of Foraminifera, 41, 42
Plant kingdom, 2
Plant lice, 455
Plants and animals, relations of, **2**
Planula, 76
Plate, 214
 of echinoid test, **201**
Platelet, 47
Plates of cystoids, **161**
Plates of holothuroids, **212**
Platform, 281
Platyceras, **352**, 354
Platyceras paxillifer, **352**
Platycrinus, 185, **186**
Platycrinus hemisphericus, **186**
Platycrinus subspinosus, **186**
Platyhelminthes, **7**, 129, 139
Platypoda, 354
Platystrophia, **268**, 291
Plectoptera, 454, *458*
Plectorthis, 291
Plectronoceras, 386, 397, 398
Plesiocidaroida, *207*, 209
Plesiosiro, 471
Pleura, 416
Pleural lobes, **414**, **416**
Pleural segments, **416**
Pleurocystis, **162**, 163, 165
Pleurocystis filitextus, **162**
Pleurotomaria, 351
Pleurotomaridae, 349
Plica, 271
Plicate shells, 269
Plication, 269
Plicatula, 322
Plumose tentacles, 112
Pneumatophore, 83
Podium, **132**, 151, **191**, **192**, **198**
Podocyrtis, **49**
Podogonida, 471
Poetry, cephalopods in, 396
Polyaxial spicules, **59**, 61
Polyaxon, **59**, 61
Polychaeta, **132**, 142, 145, 146
Polychera punctulata, **470**
Polygordiidae, 146
Polygordius, **141**, 146
Polygordius neapolitanus, **141**, 146
Polymastigidia, 31

Polymorphic hydrozoan, 80
Polyp, 73, **74**
Polyp stage, 76, 80
Polypary, 88
Polypide, 223, **225**, 244
Polyplacophora, 306, 307, 309
Polypora, **242**, 243
Polypora varsoviensis, **242**
Polyserial arrangement of plates, 202
Polythalamous test, 40, **42, 43**
Polyzoa, 220
Pompeii, fossil at, 14
Pope, A., 396
Pore rhomb, 151, 160, **161, 162**
Pores, in blastoid calyx, **169**
in echinoid test, 202
in food grooves of edrioasteroid test, **166**
Porifera, 7, 52, **54, 63, 64, 67,** 122
body wall of, 53
canal system of, 55
character of animal of, 52
geologic range of, **123**
shape of animal of, 53
Pork worm, 140
Port Byron, Illinois, crinoids from, 182
Position of sutures, 377
Postabdominal region, 461
Posterior adductors, **312, 326,** 329
Posterior position, 263
Posterolateral teeth, 327
Postpalmars, **178**, 179
Potato beetles, 451
Poterioceras, 370
Poterioceratidae, 379
Powell, J. W., 1
Powers, S., 360
Prasopora, **236**, 239
Prasopora conoidea, **236**
Prasopora simulatrix, **236**
Pratt, H. S., 4
Praying insects, 453
Pre-Cambrian fossils, 22, 46, **136**
Precious coral, 113, 115
Pre-oral lobe, **216**
Prestwichia rotundata, **464**
Primary cycle of septa, 97
Primary disk, **88**
Primary lamella, 278, **279**
Primary plates of calyx, 167
Primary septa, 97, 99
Primary spines of echinoid, **201**
Primibrach, **178**, 179
Primitive mollusk, **302**
Primitive septa, 293
Principal diductor, 256, *258*
Prionodesmacea, 330, 333, **402**
Prismatic layer, 265, **311**, 319
Prismatophyllum, **104, 260**
Prismatophyllum davidsoni, 93, **104, 260**
Prismodictya, 57, **64**, 70
Procline interarea, **272**, *273*
Prodeltidium, 261, **262**, 274
Prodissoconch, 334
Prodryas persephone, **456**
Productid shell, **268**
Productidae, 261
Productus, 265, 292, 297
Productus (Gigantella) giganteus, 265
Proetus, 432
Progoneata, 410, 448, 449
Prolimulus, 463
Proloculum, 36, **44**
Proostracum, **380**, 381
Proparia, 419, 424, 426, **427**
Proparian trilobite, 419
Proscorpius, 471
Prosiphon, 378, **380**
Prosiphonate septum, 377
Prosodetic ligament, 313, 322
Prosogyre shell, 322
Prosoma, 460, **461, 467**
Protaspis, 427, **428**
Protaspis stage, **428**
Protegulum, 261, 269, 274
Proteomyxa, 31, 35
Protephemeroidea, 454, *458*
Protoblastoidea, 172
Protoblattoidea, 453, *458*
Protobranchia, 315, 330
Protobranchiate gill, 315
Protocardium, 341
Protocaris marshi, **434**
Protocephalopoda, 382
Protoconch, 344, 357, 366, 377, **380**, 384, 393
Protodonta, 454, *458*
Protoecium, 224, **226**
Protohemiptera, 455, *458*
Protomonadina, 31
Protonychophora, 145, 447
Protopodite, 411
Protorthoptera, 453, **456**, *458*
Protoscolex, **130**, 133, 144
Protoscolex batheri, **130**
Protospongia, 57, **64**, 65, 70
Protozoa, 7, 27
Protozoa, 7, 27
locomotory structures of, **28**
relations of, to disease, 30
shells of, composition of, 29
formation of, 29, **30**
structure of, 29
Protractor muscles, *256*, **257**, *258*
Protractor scar, **257, 276,** 329
Protremata, **248**, 252, 259, 274, 277, 281, 284, 287, **289, 290**
Protura, 456, *458*
Psammosphaera, 40, **42, 43**
Psammosphaera fusca, 40
Psammosphaera parva, 40
Pseudocardinal area, 272

Pseudocardinal teeth, 325
Pseudocaudina, 214
Pseudoceratite suture, 375
Pseudochilidium, 275
Pseudochitinous material, 47
Pseudocolumella, **96,** 99
Pseudodeltidium, **270,** 274, **275**
Pseudointerarea, 272
Pseudolamellibranchiate gill, 315, 330
Pseudoniscus, 466
Pseudopodium, **28**
Pseudoscorpionida, 471
Pseudoseptum, **96,** 98, 113, 115, 116, 373
Pseudospondylium, **270,** 281
Pseudoresupinate, **264,** 265
Pterocera, **354**
Pteropod ooze, 355, 403
Pteropoda, 342, 355, 362
Pterygogenea, 410, 452, *458*
Pterygotus, 466, **468,** 469
Pterygotus buffaloensis, **468**
Ptilopora, **242,** 243
Ptilopora cylindracea, **242**
Ptiograptus, **91,** 92
Ptiograptus percorrugatus, **91**
Pulmonata, 355, **402**
Pulmonate gastropods, 355, 358, **402,** 403
Punctae, **266,** 267
Punctate shell, 267
Pupa, **450**
Pupal case, **450,** 459
Pupal stage, **450**
Purpura, 342, **361**
Purpura lapillus, **361**
Pygidial appendages, **414**
Pygidial region, 413
Pygidium, 413, **414, 416,** 422, **432**
Pyramids, of echinoids, **205**
 of Gizeh, 47
Pyriform sponge, 53
Pyriform tests and shells, 43, **353**

Q

Quadrant shale, 133
Quadriserial arrangement of hydrothecae, 88
Quahog, **312, 316**
Queensland, fossils from, 459
Quenstedt, F. A., 173
Quinqueloculina, 43

R

Raasch, G. O., 466
Rachidian teeth, **303**
Racine, Wisconsin, fossils from, 182
Radial canals, **54,** 151, **212**
 of holothuroid, **212**
 of medusa, **74**
Radial chambers, **54,** 55
Radial pieces, **212**
Radial pillars, **86**
Radial plate, **169, 178, 193, 194,** 214
Radial plates, 167, 169, 177, 178, **193, 194,** 214
Radial shields, 195
Radial symmetry, 108
Radial vessels, **151, 191**
Radials, **174, 178, 189**
Radianal plate, **178,** 179
Radiolaria, 32, 48, **49**
 geologic record of, 50
 skeletons of, **49**
  structure of, **49**
Radiolarian ooze, 30, 48
Radiolites, 320, 338, 341
Radius, **442**
Radula, **303, 307,** 342, 362, 383
Rafinesquina, **134, 260, 264, 268, 288, 290,** 292, 297, **361**
Rafinesquina alternata, **260, 290**
 bryozoans on, **234**
Raphididoidea, 454, *458*
Raphiophoridae, 426
Raphistoma, 359
Rathburn, M. J., 477
Ray, 150
Raymond, P. E., 66, 126, 477
Receptaculites, 66, **67,** 70
Receptaculites oweni, **67**
Recula, 453
Reculoidea, 453, *458*
Reed, F. R. C., 478
Reef-building corals, 77, 100, 108, 109, 112, 126
Reef corals, **101,** 107, 126
Reefs, ancient, 126, 218
Reeside, J. B., 405
Reflected lip, 349
Regularia, 172
Rejuvenescence, 76
Relation of animal to hard parts, in brachiopods, 252
 in mollusks, **305,** 310
 in ostracods, **437**
 in polyps, **74,** 97
Relations of animals and plants, **2**
Reophax, **42**
Replacement, 16
Replacing substances, 16
Replica, **17**
Reproduction, in Anthozoa, 99
 in Arachnida, 460
 in Bryozoa, 224
 in Coelenterata, 76
 in Foraminifera, 36, **37**
 in Gastropoda, 343
 in Insecta, 451, 460
 in Mollusca, 303
 in Porifera, 56

Reproduction, in Protozoa, 28
Reptantia, 445
Reptile, 8
Reservoir, **151**
Resilifer, **311,** 313, 323, **326**
Resilium, **311,** 313, 322
Respiratory tree of holothuroid, **212**
Resser, C. E., 478
Resupinate shell, **264**
Retepora phoenicea, **226**
Reticulate sponges, 70
Reticulose pseudopodium, **28**
Retiograptus, **93,** 94
Retiograptus geinitzianus, **93**
Retiolitidae, 94
Retractor muscle, *256*
Retractor scar, 329
Retrosiphonate septum, 377
Rhabdammina, 41, **42, 43**
Rhabdolith, **33**
Rhabdosome, **88**
Rhagon sponge, **54,** 55
Rhinidictya, **240, 242,** 243
Rhinidictya fidelis, **240**
Rhinidictya grandis, **240, 242**
Rhipidoglossa, 351
Rhizomorina, 66
Rhombifera, *163*, 164
Rhombopora, **242,** 243
Rhombopora lepidodendroides, **242**
Rhopalonaria, 231, **232**
Rhopalonaria venosa, **232**
Rhynchonellacea, 282, 293, *298*
Rhynchospirinidae, 293
Rhynchotrema capax, 293, **294**
Ribbon worms, 139
Richthofenia, **260,** 292, 320
Richthofenia lawrenciana, **260**
Richthofenidae, 261
Ricinulei, 471
Right-handed coiling, **345,** 347
Right mantle lobe, **311**
Ring canal, **151,** 175
Ringerike district, Norway, fossils from, 106
Robinson, W. J., 105, 108, 109
Rock builders, coelenterates as, **82**
Rock units, 26
Rocket locomotion, 395
Roofing plates, 193
Root system, **169, 174,** 176
Rootlets, 176
Rosen, Baron von, 84
Rosettes, 214
Rostral-latus, **442**
Rostro-lateral compartment, **442**
Rostrospiracea, 282, 293, *298*
Rostrum, **442**
Rotifers, 140
Roundworm, 139
Rudistids, 322, 340, 403
Ruedemann, R., 81, 83, 89, 90, 124, 127, 128, 133, 144, 405, 477
Rugosa, 67, 100
Rustella, 260, 275, **283,** 284
Rustella edsoni, **283**
Rustellacea, 282, 284, 286, *298*

S

Saarbrucken, Germany, fossils from, 459
Sabellaria, 135
Saccamina, **42**
Saccosomus, 145
Saddle, **372,** 373, **376**
Sagenella, **42**
Sagittate aperture, **374**
St. Lawrence, Gulf of, 21
St. Louis, Missouri, fossils from, 154, 207
Salem limestone, bryozoans in, 241
Salpingostoma, 351, **352,** 357
Salpingostoma buelli, **352**
Saluda, 104
Sand dollars, 8, 158, 197
Sand fleas, 444
Sand hoppers, 444
Sandworm, 143
Sao hirsuta, **428**
Sarcode, 27
Sarcodina, 31, 34
Sarcophyton, **114**
Sarle, C. J., 137
Saukiinae, 478
Saville-Kent, W., 127, 128
Scalpellum fossulum, 441, **442**
Scaphites, **368,** 369, 370, **374,** 388
Scaphites refractus, **374**
Scaphopoda, 304, 305, 360, **362,** 400, 403
distribution of, **402**
Scavengers, 11
Scenella, 351, **352,** 357, 359
Scenella affinis, **352**
Schistochoanites, 382, 385, 398
Schizochroal eyes, 420
Schizocrania, **260,** 287
Schizocrania filosa, **260**
Schizodont dentition, 325, **326**
Schizophoria, **290,** 291
Schizophoria tulliensis, **290**
Schuchert, C., 219, 252, 273, 282, 300
Sclerites, 110
Sclerobasis, 113
Scleroblast, 57
Sclerodermite, **113**
Scofield, W. H., 405
Scolecodont, **132,** 133, 142, 143
Scolithus, **136,** 137, 146
Scorpion, 406, 459, 460, **461,** 469–471, 476
Scorpion flies, 455
Scorpionida, 471
Scott, H. W., 133

Scudder, S. H., 478
Sculda, 446
Scutum, 441, 442
Scyphocrinus, 173
Scyphozoa, 79, 94, 128
  geologic range of, **123**
Sea anemone, 72, 109
Sea chestnut, 197
Sea cucumber, 149, 158, 213, 217
Sea fan, 113, 115
Sea lily, 8, 149, 157, 172
Sea mice, 304, 306, **308**
Sea moss, 8
Sea mouse, 304, 306, 307, **308**
Sea pen, 113
Sea porcupine, 197, **210**
Sea urchin, 8, 149, 158, 197, **210**
Sea weeds, 220
Second glabellar lobe, 417
Second maxilla, 411
Secondary radial plate, 193, 194
Secondary septum, **96**
Secondary spine, **201**
Secundibrach, **178,** 179
Sedentaria, 142, 143
Segmented worms, 8, 129, **136**
Segments, **136**
Sepia, 394
Sepioidea, 364, 382, 388, 389, 399, **402**
Sepion, 389
Septal budding, **112**
Septal fluting, **44**
Septal neck, 366, **367,** 377
Septal perforation, **367**
Septal plate, **270**
Septal pore, **44**
Septal spine, **118**
Septibranchia, 315, **317,** 330
Septibranchiate gill, 315, **317**
Septopora, **242,** 243
Septopora biserialis nervata, **242**
Septopora quadrans, **242**
Septula, 243, **244**
Septum, in an archaeocyathid, **68**
  in brachiopods, **279**
  in cephalopods, **365,** 366, **367,** 371, 377, **380**
  in corals, 75, 95, 96
  definition of, 75, 95, 371, 377
  development of, in a tetracoral, **103**
  in foraminiferal tests, **44**
Serial budding, 87
Series, 26
Serpent star, 195
Serpula, **134,** 144
Serpula atoll, 135, 144
Serpula contortuplicata, **134**
Serpuliten-kalk, 135
Serpuliten sandstein, 135
Serpulites, 133, **134**
Serpulites intermedius, **134**
Sertularia, 81
Sessile avicularium, **228**
Sessile benthos, 13, 153
Sessile organisms, 73, 150, 153
Seta, **130, 136,** 141, **253,** 269
Sexual reproduction, 29, 56, 76
Shaft, 200, **201**
Shape, of brachiopod shell, 263
  of cephalopod shell, 370
  of gastropod shell, 349
  of pelecypod shell, 320
  of sponge skeleton, 58
  of zooecia, 225
Shell, of Brachiopoda, 261, **264, 276**
  of Cephalopoda, **305, 365, 367, 368,** 370
  of Gastropoda, **305,** 345
  of Mollusca, **302,** 304, **305**
  of *Nautilus*, 384
  of Ostracoda, 437
  of Pelecypoda, 318
  of Protozoa, 29
  relation of, to animal, in mollusks, **302, 305**
  structure of, **266**
Shell structure in Pelecypoda, **311,** 319
Shipworm, **316,** 338, 339
Shrimp, 443
Shrock, R. R., 87
Shumardia, **427**
Shumardiidae, 426
Sicula, 87, **88, 93**
Side mouth shields, 195
Side plates, **169,** 170
Sidneyia, **469**
Sidneyia inexpectans, **469**
Sieve plate, of echinoderms, 151
  of sponge, **63**
Sigmoid body, **212**
Siliceous shells, 29, 40
Siliceous sponge, **63**
Silicoflagellidae, 31, **33,** 34
Silk moth, **450**
Silkworm, 450
Simple corallum, 100, 102
Sinistral shell, **345,** 347
Sinus, **268,** 271, 379
Siphon, **305, 314,** 343, **344–346,** 349, **365,** 378, 383, **391**
Siphonal lobe, 373
Siphonal saddle, 373
Siphonated shell, **345, 346**
Siphonophora, 81, 83, 89
Siphonopore, 113, **114**
Siphonotreta, 287, **288**
Siphonotreta unguiculata, **288**
Siphonotretacea, 282, 287, *298*
Siphonozooid, **114**
Siphuncle, **305, 365,** 366, **367, 374, 376, 380**
Siphuncular funnel, 377

Siphuncular perforation, 377
Siphuncular tube, 366, 377
Siphunculata, 453, *458*
Sipunculoidea, 141, 146
Size of shell, of brachiopod, 263
of cephalopod, 370
of pelecypod, 319
Skeletal elements, in Alcyonaria, **113**
in Coelenterata, 75, 78
Skeletal structures, of brachiopods, 276
of echinoderms, 192
of sponges, 57
Skeleton, of Bryozoa, 224
of Coelenterata, 77
of Crinoidea, 176
of Porifera, 56
of Stelleroidea, 192
Slider muscles, *256*
Slit band, 349, **352**
Slug, 301, 304, 358
Smith, J. P., 405
Smith, W., 22
Smoke screen, 389, 395
Snail, 8, 301, 304, 341
Snake flies, **454**
Socket plates, 278
Sockets, dental, 277, **312**, 322, **326**
Solariidae, 350
Solenopsis, 328
Solitary corals, 78, 100
Solitary polyp, 102
Solnhofen, Bavaria, fossils from, 95, 143, 443, 457
Solpugida, 471
Somite, 136, 141
Soothsayer insects, 453
Spaniodera ambulans, **456**
Species, definition of, 4, 7
naming of, 4
number of, 8
Spermatidia, **222**
Sphaeroma, 444, **445**
Sphaeroma gigas, **445**
Spicules, 32, **54**, 56, **59, 114, 307**
Spicular skeletal elements, 155, 214
Spider, 8, 406, 459, 460, 469, 471, 476
Spines, of a brachiopod shell, **260**, 271
of a bryozoan, 229
of an echinoid, **198, 201**
Spinose tests of Foraminifera, **42**
Spiracle, **169**, 170
Spiral ornamentation, 350
Spiralium, 278, **279**
Spire, 214, 278, **345**, 346
Spirifer, **268, 270, 279**, 293
Spiriferacea, 282, 293, *298*
Spiriferoid spiralium, **276**, 278
Spiropora, 233, **234**
Spiropora majuscula, **234**
Spirorbis, **134**, 135, 144, 147
Spirorbis arkonensis, **134**
Spirorbis communis, **134**
Spirotheca, **44**
Spirula, 364, 365, **380**, 381, 388–390, 399, 401
Spirula australis, **380**
Spirula peronii, **380**
Spirulirostra, 389
Spissula elliptica, 359
Spitz, **68**
Spitzbergen, 23
Spondylium, **270**, 281
Spondylium duplex, 281
Spondylus, 322, 327
Sponge, 7, **54, 63, 64, 67**
fossil, **63, 64, 67**
living, **54, 63**
shape of, **54, 63**
spicules of, **54, 59, 64**
Spongilla, **54**, 66
Spongillidae, 68
Spongin material, 56, 57
Spore, 50
Sporozoa, 32, 50
Spring tails, 455
Springer, F., 184, 219
Squids, 304, 364, 365, 389, 391, 394, 396
Stalk, 176
Stalked echinoderms, 182
Stalked eyes, 419, **427**, 434
Starfish, 8, 149, **151**, 153, 158, 190, **192, 193**, 339
Steinmann, G., 328
Stellate macula, **234, 236**
Stellate test, 43
Stelleroidea, 149, 158, 190, 206
arm structure of, **191**
geologic range of, **217**
Stem, 153, 158, 171, 176, 231
Stemmed echinoderms, 176
Stenidia, 365
Stenochisma formosa, **294**
Stenodictya, 452
Stephanoceras braikenridgii, **374**
Stephenson, L. W., 337
Stereoplasm, 107
Sternal plate, 461
Sternite, **467**
Sternum, 460, **461**
Stigmata, 461
Stigmatella, **236**, 239
Stigmatella incrustans, **236**
Sting, **461**
Stinging cell, 72
Stock, 88
Stockdale, P. B., 183
Stolon, 231, **232**
Stolonal budding, 76, **112**
Stomach, of a brachiopod, **253**
of a bryozoan, **222, 244**

Stomach, of a coral, 72
of an echinoid, **198**
of a gastropod, **307**
of a mollusk, 302, 312
of an ostracod, **437**
Stomatopoda, 446
Stomatopora, **226**, 233, **234**
Stomatopora contracta, **234**
Stomatopora parvipora, **226**
Stone canal, **151**, 198
Stone lily, 172
Stony corals, 72, 97, 109
Strabops, 467, **468**
Strabops thatcheri, **468**
Straparollus, 351, **352**
Straparollus spergenensis, **352**
Stratigraphic range, of Arthropoda, 475
of Cephalopoda, 397
of Coelenterata, 124
of Crinoidea, 182
of Echinoderma, 157, 206
of Echinoidea, 206
of Gastropoda, 359
of Mollusca, 401
of Ostracoda, 439
of Pelecypoda, 339
of Trilobita, 431
Streptelasma, **104**, 106
Streptelasma corniculum, **104**
Streptoneura, 350, 351, 401
Strepula concentrica, **438**
Striations, **268**, 269
Stromatocerium, 126
Stromatopora, 85, **86**, 87
Stromatopora antiqua, **86**
Stromatoporidae, 84
Stromatoporidea, 8, 79, 83, **86**, 124, 125, 127
geologic range of, **123**
skeleton of, 84
Stromatoporoids, 72, 81, 84, 126
Strongylocentrotus, **203–205**, 209, **210**
Strongylocentrotus dröbachiensis, **203–205**
Strontium sulphate, in Radiolaria, 32, 49
Strophalosia radicans, **260**
Stropheodonta, 270
Strophomena, **232**, 261, **264**, **266**, **290**, 292, 297
Strophomena aculeata, **266**
Strophomena neglecta, **290**
Strophomena septata, bryozoan on, **232**
Strophomenacea, 282, 292, *298*
Structure, of brachiopod shell, 265
of cardinal margin, 271
Styliform columella, 107
Stylommatophora, 356
Stylonurus, 466, **468**, 469
Stylonurus excelsior, **468**
Subcarina, **442**
Subdermal cavities in sponge, **54**
Subrostrum (plate), **442**
Subtegminal mouth, 159
Subulites, **352**, 354
Subulites regularis, **352**
Subumbonal teeth, 325
Sucker, of squid, 389, **390**
Suctoria, 32, 50, 455, **458**
Sulcus, 271, **438**
Sunflower coral, 66, **67**
Superior hemiseptum, **240**, 241
Superior-lateral lobe, 374
Superior-lateral saddle, 373
Superradial, 178
Supporting rods, **212**, 214
Supramarginal plate, **193**, **194**
Surface ornamentation, of brachiopod shells, 267, **268**
of cephalopod shells, **367**
of foraminiferal tests, **42**, 44
of gastropod shells, 349
of pelecypod shells, 324
Sutural lamina, **308**, 309
Suture, in cephalopod shells, 366, **367**, **372**, 373, 375
facial, **414**, **416**
in gastropod shells, **345**
Swabian Alps, sponge bioherms in, 70
Swarmer, 36, **37**
Swimmeret, **412**, 469
Swimming legs, 467
Switzerland, fossils from, 459
Sycon sponge, **54**, **55**
Sycon gelatinosum, **54**
Sycones, 62
Symmetry, of echinoderms, 150
Symphala, 449
Synapticula, in an archaeocyathid, **68**, 122
in a coral, **96**, 97
Syncarida, 444
Synrhabdosome, 88, **93**
Syntrophia, **290**, 292
Syntrophia orthia, **290**
Syntrophiacea, 282, 291, 292, *298*
Synxiphosura, 463, 465, 466
Sypharoptera, 454
Sypharopteroidea, 454, *458*
Syringopora, **118**, 120, 121
Syringoporidae, 117, 120, 121
Syringothyris, **275**
Syrinx, **275**
System, definition of, 26

T

Table, 214
Tabula, of an archaeocyathid, **68**
of a bryozoan, 227
of a coral, 37, **96**, 98
of a millepore, **82**
Tabular budding, **112**

Tabulata, 100, 108, 109, 116, 124, 125, 221
geologic range of, **123**
Tabulate corals, 117
Tabulated corallite, **96**
Tactile appendages, 411
Tagelus, **316**
Tail, 461
Tanaidacea, 444
Tapeworm, 139
Tar pits of California, 14
Taxocrinus, 185, **187**
Taxocrinus praestans, **187**
Taxodont dentition, 325, **326**
Taylor, T. G., 67, 71, 128
Tectibranchia, 355
Teeth, 156, 276, **311**, 322, 326
Tegmen, 159, 173, **174**, 177, 180
Tegmentum, **308**
Tegula, 351, **353**
Teichert, C., 404
Teleodesmacea, 330, 334, **402**
Teleodont dentition, 325, **326**
Telephidae, 478
Teletremata, 356
Tellina interrupta, dentition formula of, 328
Telospiridia, 32
Telotremata, **248**, 252, **257**, 261, 274, 275, 277, 278, 281, 289, 292, **294**
Telson, **412**, 415, 463, **464**, **467**
Telson region, 408, **412**
Tentacles, of a bryozoan, **222**, **244**
of a cephalopod, 363, **390**
of a coelenterate, 95
of a dibranchiate cephalopod, **390**, **391**
of a holothuroid, **212**
of a medusa, **74**
of a mollusk, **305**
of a polyp, 73, **74**, **96**
Tentacular lobe, 364
Tentaculites, 355, **356**, 362
Tepee buttes, 340
Terataspis, 413, 419, 423
Terataspis grandis, 423
Terebra, **353**, 354
Terebratalia, **260**
Terebratulacea, 282, 293, *298*
Terebratuloid, 293
Teredo, **316**, 334, 338
Tergite, **467**
Tergum, 441, **445**, 460, **461**
Terminal plate, **193**
Termites, 453
Terrestrial arachnids, 460
Terrestrial environments, **11**
Tertiary septum, **96**
Tertiary sponges, 70
Tertibrach, **178**, 179
Test, of Asteroidea, **193**
of Echinoidea, **198**, **205**
of Echinoderma, 149, 155
Test, of Protozoa, 40, **42**, **43**
of Radiolaria, **49**
Testacea, 32, 47, **64**
Tethys sea, 47
Tetrabranchia, **305**, 382
Tetrabranchiata, 382
Tetrabranchiate cephalopod, **305**, 364
Tetracidaris, 199, 208
Tetracladina, 65
Tetracoralla, 67, 75, 100, 102, 103, **104**, 108, 110, 115, 124, 125
geologic range of, **123**
Tetractinellida, 65
Tetragraptus, 92, **93**
Tetragraptus fruticosus, **93**
Tetragraptus pendens, **93**
Tetrameral symmetry, **96**
Tetraxial spicule, **59**, 60
Tetraxon, **59**, 60
Textularia, 41, **42**
Textularian arrangement of chambers, 41, **42**
Thalassophila, 356
Thanatocoenose, 22
Theca, in corals, **96**
in graptolites, **88**, **91**, **93**
Thecamoeba, 47
Thecidium (Lacazella) mediterraneum, **262**
Thecosmilia, 110, **111**
Thecosmilia annularis, **111**
Thecospiridae, 293
Theocapsa, **49**
Thickness of shell, measurement of, 263, 319
Thilipsura v-scripta discreta, **438**
Third glabellar lobe, 417
Thompson, J. B., 220
Thoracic appendages, **414**
Thoracic region, 413
Thoracic segment, **432**
Thorax, 408, 413, **414**, **416**, 420, **432**
Threadworms, 7, 129, 139
Thyone briarcus, **212**
Thysanoptera, 453, *458*
Thysanura, 455, *458*
Tiarechinus, 209
Ticks, 459, 460, 469, 471, 476
Tidal zone, 11, **12**
Tillyard, R. J., 478
Time scale, 26
Time units, 26
Timor, 183
Tirol, fossils from, 209
Tolmachoff, I. P., 15
Tooth, of echinoid, **205**
of pelecypod shell, **311**
Torticone, **368**, 369
Trachea, 449, 461, 470
Trachyceras, **368**, 388
Trachylinae, 83
Tracks, 18, 459

Trails, 18, **138,** 143
Transitional siphuncle, 377
Transmedian muscle, **255,** *256*
Transverse ornamentation, 350
Tree of animal life, **6**
Trematoda, 139, 155
Trepostomata, **223,** 229, *230*, 235, **236, 238,** 240, 247, **248,** 249
Triarthrus, **414,** 422, 426
Triarthrus beckii, **414**
Triaxial spicule, **59,** 60
Triaxon, **59,** 60
Trichina, 140
Trichoptera, 455, 458
Tridacna, 301, 319, 324, 327, 335
Tridictyopus, **49**
Trigonia, 313, **321,** 327, 333
Trigonia eufalensis, **321**
Trigonosemus, **268, 270, 294,** 295
Trigonosemus palissa, **294**
Trilobita, 406, 410, 413, **414–416, 419, 421, 425,** 466, **472,** 473, 475
  burial of, 431
  dimensions of, 423
  eggs of, 433
  enemies of, 429
  enrolling of, 430
  evolution shown by, **428**
  extinction of, 430
  eyes of, **419**
  as food, 429
  food of, 429
  naked forms of, 433
  parts of, **416**
  as scavengers, 429
  trails of, 433
Trilobites, 8, 406
Triloculina, 43
Triloculine test, **42**
Trimerella, 281, **285,** 286
Trimerella grandis, **285**
Trimerellacea, 282, 286, *298*
Trimerellidae, 286
Trimeroceratidae, 379
Trimorphism, 36
Trinucleidae, 426
Triplosoba, 454
Triradiate spicule, 58, **59,** 60
Triserial arrangement, of chambers, 41, **42**
Trivium, 191, **200,** 201
Trochelminthes, 8, 129, 140
Trochoceras, **368,** 369
Trochocone, **368,** 369
Trochoid test, 41
Trochophore, 140, **141,** 146, 224, 247, 400
Trochophore larva, **141,** 180, 357
Trochophore stage, **141,** 295, 303, 400
Trochosphere, 140, **141,** 180
Trochospheric stage, 140
Trochus, 348, 358
True aperture, of a bryozoan, **240**
True stromatoporoids, 84
Tube feet, **151, 198, 212**
Tubercle, **198, 201,** 436, 439
Tubes, 19, **134**
Tubicola, 142, 143
Tubicolar worms, **134**
Tubiporidae, 113, 115, 120
Tubularia, 81
Turbellaria, 139
Turbinate shell, **353**
Turbinolia, 110, **111**
Turbinolia sulcata, **111**
Turbinolidae, 110
Turbo, 351, **353**
Turreted shell, **353**
Turrilites, **368,** 369, 388
Turriliticone, **368,** 369
Turritella, **353,** 354
Tusk shells, 304, **362**
Twenhofel, W. H., 148
Twitchell, G. B., 84, 127, 219
Tyrian purple, use of gastropods for, 359

U

Uintacrinus, 177, 183
Ulrich, E. O., 90, 128, 133, 144, 249, 405, 478
Umbilical perforation, **368,** 384, 387
Umbilicus, **346,** 347, **368,** 370
Umbo, 269, **312,** 313, 318, **326**
Umbonal muscle, **255, 256**
Unaltered remains, 15
Uncites, 293, **294**
Uncites gryphus, **294**
Uncitidae, 293
Under lancet plate, 168, **169**
Ungulite sandstone, 247
Uniaxial spicule, 58, **59**
Unilocular shell, 40, **42, 43**
Unio, **326,** 327, **331,** 333, 337
Uniserial arm, **174,** 179
Uniserial arrangement, of chambers, 41, **42, 43**
Uniserial hydrothecae, 88
Uniserial plates, 163, 202
Upper Cambrian brachiopods, **289**
Upper latus, **442**
Upper lip, 349
Upper Rundle limestone, 218
Uropod, **412**

V

Vagrant benthos, 13
Vagrant echinoderms, 153
Valcourea, **264,** 265
Vallacerta hortoni, **33**
Valve, 252, 308, 310
Valvular pyramid, **162,** 166

Vanuxemia, 333, **335**
Vascular markings, **254, 276**
Vaughan, T. W., 128
Vegetative reproduction, 29, 56
Veliger, 303
Velum, **74,** 76, 80, 94
Vent, 164
Venter side, 373
Ventral adjustor, **257,** *258*
Ventral hypostoma, 420, **432**
Ventral lobe, **262,** 373
Ventral mantle, **253**
Ventral mantle lobe, 295
Ventral membrane, of trilobite, 414, **415**
Ventral saddle, 373
Ventral shield, **191**
Ventral side, 155
  of trilobite, **414,** 422
Ventral valve, **253, 257,** 261, **262, 279**
Ventriculites, **64,** 65
Venus, **311, 312, 316,** 322, 325, **326,** 328, 334, 335
Venus mercenaria, **312,** 328, 335
  dentition formula of, 328
Vermicularia, 347, **353,** 354
Verneuiliana, 41, **42**
Verrill, A. E., 378
Vertebral ossicle, **191,** 194, 195
Vesicle, 461
Vesicular structure, 98
Vesiculose structure, **68, 104**
Vestibulum, 239, **240**
Vibraculum, 227, **228**
Vinella, 80, 231, **232**
Vinella repens, **232**
Virgula, 88, **93**
Viscera, 312
Visceral cavity, 224, 254, **255**
Visceral mass, 302
Visceral sac, 342
Volborthella, 385, 397, 398

W

Wachsmuth, C., 184, 219
Walcott, C. D., 71, 80, 128, 131, 140, 144–146, 219, 300, 435, 478
Walcottella, **434,** 436
Walcottella breviuscula, **434**
Walcottella leperditoides, **434**
Walking legs, **461, 467**
Walking stick insects, 453
Wall structure, of foraminiferal tests, 44
Wandering amoeboid cells, 56
Wanneria, 420
Waptia, **434,** 435
Waptia fieldensis, **434**
Wasps, 454
Water-breathing arachnids, 462
Water content, of medusae, 19, 76, 94
Water fleas, 434, 436
Water pore, 164, **166**
Water-vascular system, 150, **151, 175,** 194, **198**
Wax bugs, 455
Weller, S., 133
Westonia, **285,** 286
Westonia aurora, **285**
Westphalia, cephalopods from, 399
Wheel, of holothuroid, **212**
Wheel animalcules, 8, 129, 140
Wheel worms, 8, 129, 140
White ants, 453
Whorl, 345
Width of shell, measurement of, 262
Wings, 449
Wood, E., 219
Wood-Jones, F., 128
Worm castings, **138,** 147
Worm jaws, **132,** 133, 142
Worm trails, **138,** 139
Worm tubes, 131, **134,** 135, 144
Worms, 8, 129, **130, 136**
  anatomy of, 129
  burrows of, **136,** 139
  fossil record of, 131, 147

X

Xiphosura, 463, **464, 465**

Y

Yohoia, **434,** 435
Yohoia tenuis, **434**
Yonge, C. M., 127, 128

Z

Zaphrentidae, 105, 106
Zaphrentis, **104,** 106
Zittel, K. von, 117, 458
Zittelella, **64**
Zoarium, 225, **234,** 237, **238**
Zooecial aperture, **242**
Zooecium, **222,** 223, 224, **234, 238, 240, 244, 246**
Zooid, **222,** 223, **244**
Zooidal tube, **82,** 84
Zoology, definition of, 1
Zoophytes, 220
Zoospores, 36, **37**
Zygobeyrichia ventripunctata, **438**
Zygosella macra, **438**
Zygosella vallata, **438**
Zygote, 36, **37**